INTRODUCTION TO
NUCLEAR THEORY

INTRODUCTION TO
NUCLEAR THEORY

I. E. McCarthy

*Department of Physics
and Institute of Theoretical Science
University of Oregon*

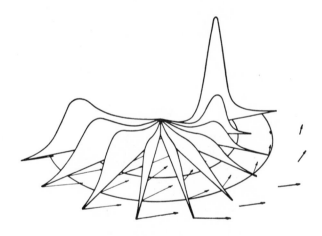

John Wiley & Sons, Inc.   New York · London · Sydney · Toronto

PREFACE

Nuclear physics has now entered its quantitative phase. Theoretical techniques have been developed to such an extent that it is becoming possible to predict numbers derived from accurate experiments by starting from basic nuclear forces. Much progress has been made in analyzing experiments to obtain consistent and meaningful numbers. This book introduces experimentalists and beginning theorists to the techniques used for understanding simpler nuclei and reactions.

The book developed from courses that I have taught at the first- and second-year graduate level, during the past six years, at the Universities of Adelaide, California (Davis), and Oregon. The level of much of the work, taken in isolation, is that of a second-year graduate course for a student with a good knowledge of quantum mechanics. The application of quantum mechanics that is often not familiar to first-year graduate students is scattering theory. It is treated in such a way that a first-year graduate student may acquire the necessary familiarity with it by reading the book from the beginning. Potential scattering is dealt with in great detail, and formal scattering theory and its applications in nuclear physics are introduced by way of progressively less familiar examples. For a course involving simpler mathematics, much of Chapter 3C and D, Chapter 4, Chapter 6, Chapter 8B and C, Chapter 9B, Chapter 10A, B, C, and E, and Chapter 12D could be omitted with little loss of continuity. A knowledge of elementary quantum mechanics, relativistic kinematics, and some atomic theory is assumed, but no previous knowledge of nuclear physics is necessary.

The central theme is the understanding and calculation of the motion and correlations of nucleons in large aggregates and the discovery of the various modes of motion by means of reaction experiments. A particular branch of the theory is generally treated in four steps which attempt to answer the following questions:

1. How is the theory related to the central theme?
2. What is done in the calculation?
3. How is the calculation done?
4. What are some typical results, and what do they tell us about nuclei and reactions?

The answer to question 2 lies in the exposition of the formal structure of the theory. It is essential for the experimentalist (as well as the student of theory) to understand this, since he must form a critical judgment of approximations and a feeling for the experiments that are necessary to distinguish between theoretical models or to obtain new information that is not yet encompassed by a theoretical picture. Since the basis of our understanding of nuclei is two-body scattering, the formal theory usually involves some form of two-body scattering theory in the t-matrix formulation. This avoids the difficulties associated with strong nucleon-nucleon forces in low orders of perturbation theory.

Great attention has been devoted to developing the formal aspects of the theory in each case, since these aspects are not generally familiar to students. At the same time, the formal theory is related wherever necessary to the more familiar potential scattering problem, and the analogies between formal theories for different aspects of nuclear physics are pointed out.

Certain specialized calculations (such as the two-nucleon problem, the three-nucleon problem, and nuclear matter) are of basic interest, rather than of continuing interest in the interpretation of new experiments. In describing these I have omitted step 3 and have given only a formal introduction to the theory, with simple examples to illustrate the ideas involved and a comparison of the results with experiment.

For the purpose of detailed discussion in this book, nuclei are described by the shell model involving particles in a single configuration, the elementary vibrational model, or the elementary rotational model, or they are considered to be inert. For configuration-mixing and for particle-hole calculations of the states of closed-shell nuclei, examples of results are given to show their relevance. For a treatment at this level of more sophisticated approaches to nuclear structure theory, the reader is referred to the book by M. K. Pal to be published by John Wiley. In the cases of elementary nuclear-structure theory mentioned, for elastic scattering and for direct reactions involving the simple shell or collective models, step 3 is carried out until the only remaining step is to write the computer program. To avoid overcomplication, spin-orbit coupling is omitted from reaction theories other than elastic scattering.

The style of this book attempts to expand certain key parts of the literature rather than to survey the literature or to serve as an encyclopedia of nuclear physics. The selection of key parts reflects my own prejudices and point of view: those of a person interested in the use of nuclear reactions in order to understand nuclear structure.

The subject matter is restricted to the interaction of nucleons either in bound states (nuclear-structure theory) or in states with enough energy for one or more nucleons to separate (reaction theory). Occasionally I have quoted the results of electron-scattering experiments and the theory of electromagnetic transitions where they illuminate nuclear structure uniquely. I have also described, qualitatively, the meson-exchange theory of nuclear forces. Otherwise I have not discussed the interaction of nucleons with particles such as photons, electrons, neutrinos, mesons, and strange particles.

The question of notation is one that cannot be satisfactorily resolved. On the one hand, it is essential to make a book self-contained and coherent by using consistent notation. However, it is equally essential that the reader should be stimulated to read the original literature in which considerable variation of notation occurs, even within a specialized subject. Often I have compromised by using a notation that will enable the reader to read one of the key papers in the original, without the annoyance of translating too much notation. Where this is necessary, and where the compromise has required notation changes from one part of the book to another, I have tried to indicate how the translation is to be made.

Another dilemma that I encountered was the question of whether to interrupt the flow of ideas by including details of mathematical derivations. I adopted the following compromise. Whenever I introduced new ideas that are not found in standard treatments of elementary quantum mechanics, I gave the step-by-step derivation in full. If the extension of a physical idea involved mere algebraic substitution, the equation numbers were given and the appropriate substitutions were stated. Details of Coulomb wave functions and the main ideas of angular momentum algebra are collected in appendices.

Problems are given at the end of each chapter. Some of these are stated vaguely as physical questions, the answers to which are of interest. It is the student's job to formulate the question just as in a real research problem. Often there is no unique correct answer.

This book was written concurrently with my research program at the University of Oregon, which was sponsored by the Air Force Office of Scientific Research, Office of Aerospace Research, United States Air Force. Both the book and the research program made vital contributions to each other. I am grateful for this support.

I thank my many colleagues for their help in reading and criticizing the manuscript, in explaining points, in allowing me to use prepublication versions of their work, and for permission to reproduce published tables and figures. I am especially grateful to Professor M. K. Pal for his help and guidance with the first seven chapters and to Professor R. M. Eisberg for very detailed criticism of the manuscript. I also express my appreciation to Mrs. Kay Knighten and Mrs. Melinda Piluso for their patience and accuracy in the typing.

I. E. McCarthy

EUGENE, OREGON
MAY, 1968

CONTENTS

1

QUALITATIVE INTRODUCTION

The nucleus was discovered in 1911 by Rutherford (11). The next twenty years saw great activity in England, France, and Germany, inspired largely by Rutherford. The sizes of nuclei were inferred; atomic masses were measured; and transmutations of certain nuclei into others (together with the accompanying energy changes) were observed. By 1932, enough information had been obtained and correctly interpreted to serve as a starting point for an understanding of nuclei.

For a long time it was thought that the nucleus consisted of protons and electrons, although simple arguments based on the uncertainty principle showed that an electron of sufficiently low energy could not exist inside a nucleus. The neutron, whose existence had been conjectured in 1920 by Rutherford, was discovered in 1932 by Chadwick (32a), who correctly interpreted experiments of Curie-Joliot and Joliot (32) and checked them with his own experiment. He discovered that the mass of the neutron is almost that of the proton. Because of the statistics of the ^{14}N nucleus, Heisenberg (32) interpreted the neutron as a fermion of spin $\frac{1}{2}$.

The accurate measurements of atomic masses in the 1920's, by Aston (27) and others, enabled the relationship between mass and energy to be confirmed, and led to an understanding of the energy relationships between nuclei which could be observed by transmuting one nucleus into another. By 1932, nuclei were known to consist of neutrons and protons whose masses are almost identical, whose spins are each $\frac{1}{2}$, and which differ seriously only in their charges. (Later it was discovered that their magnetic moments are also different.) The approximate sizes of nuclei were known, as were certain excited energy levels.

Most of the information, except the direct measurement of masses, came from nuclear reactions. A nuclear reaction occurs when a nuclear particle strikes a nucleus and is either elastically scattered or excites the nucleus with

1

the emission of a new particle or a γ-ray or both. Up to 1932, reactions were studied by means of collimated beams of α-particles from radioactive sources (often polonium). These beams are monoenergetic with energies of a few million electron volts (MeV).

For a reaction it is essential to know the momenta of the incident and outgoing particles. Information about the distribution of nuclear matter in space comes from measurements of momentum transfer. We shall show, for example, how the size of nuclei can be determined by measuring the distribution of momentum transfers in elastic scattering. Such measurements were made very early by Rutherford and interpreted by classical mechanics. More detailed information is obtained by calculating momentum-transfer distributions by means of quantum mechanics, starting with mathematical models for the space characteristics of a system. The main theme of this book is the interpretation of nuclear reactions to obtain information about nuclear structure.

In 1932, once again, a new dimension was introduced into nuclear studies by Cockcroft and Walton (32) who accelerated a beam of protons in a machine up to energies of 0.6 and 0.8 MeV. The first reaction studied in this way was ^{7}Li (p, α) ^{4}He.

Reactions are written as $T(p_i, p_f)R$, where T is the target nucleus, R is the residual nucleus and p_i and p_f are the initial and final particles whose momenta are measured. The mass number A of a nucleus is written as a left superscript. The nuclear system consisting of $T + p_i$ or, equivalently, $p_f + R$ is called the compound nucleus. We shall use this term even if the compound system lasts only for the time it takes the incident particle to cross the nuclear volume. The idea of the formation of a compound nucleus that lasts much longer than this has played a vital part in the understanding of nuclear reactions.

From early reaction studies, it was known that compound nuclei are formed with greatest probability at particular incident energies. At such an energy the system is said to be in resonance. It was also known that nuclei exist in different energy levels from which they decay by emitting particles or γ-rays. An early example was the reaction ^{27}Al (α, p) ^{30}Si (Chadwick, 32b). α-particles are captured by Al in four resonance levels between about 4 and 5.3 MeV. The resonances have widths of about 0.25 MeV. Protons are emitted in groups of different energies, each group being based on one resonance energy of the compound nucleus (^{27}Al + ^{4}He) or ^{31}P.

The study of the energy levels of nuclei and their spins, parities, and other static properties is known as nuclear spectroscopy. For many years, reactions were used merely to excite nuclei to certain levels so that the properties of the levels could be determined. Another very useful method of producing nuclei in excited states is β-decay from a neighboring nucleus. Methods for determining spins and parities have been very valuable to the experimentalist. They are still being developed. Analysis of the angular correlation of γ-rays emitted in successive decays is one very powerful method. Measurements of momentum transfers in reactions can also yield information about spins and parities of nuclear states.

In the early chapters of this book, models for nuclear structure, which predict the properties of energy levels, are developed. In Chapter 1*B*, we shall observe how even simple considerations about nuclear sizes and masses lead to qualitatively correct ideas of the way protons and neutrons interact to form nuclei.

In the late 1940's, the energy of experimental beams was increased to the point where the modern study of nuclear reactions could begin. Particles which enter or leave a nucleus fast enough can be thought of to a good approximation as feeling only the presence of a potential. Modern nuclear reaction theory interprets many reactions in this way. They are called direct interactions. If a sufficient understanding of the reaction mechanism is available, the reaction can be used as a dynamic check on nuclear structure models based on spectroscopic data. It can also be used to improve the models and to obtain spectroscopic data. In the later chapters we shall discuss the conditions under which potential models of reactions are valid. Then we shall develop the formal theory in order to illustrate the principles behind reaction models. Finally, we shall consider the approximations that are made for specific classes of reactions and the use of the reactions in obtaining nuclear structure information.

Today we have a quantitative understanding of many aspects of nuclear structure in terms of a description of the forces which bind the neutrons and protons together. We have a qualitative understanding in terms of nuclear forces of nearly all phenomena, although some are too complicated to compute without the use of collective descriptions which treat a large fraction of the particles in a nucleus as a collective entity with only a few degrees of freedom. Descriptions of nuclear reactions have not kept pace with those of the static properties of nuclei, possibly because of computing difficulties, but also because they are conceptually more difficult. An elementary treatment of nuclear theory will thus be closer to the forefront in reaction theory than in the theory of nuclear structure. The theory of some of the conceptually simplest reactions is now on a quantitative basis, and they have proved to be critical in the understanding of the structure of the nuclei involved.

A.   RUTHERFORD SCATTERING AND NUCLEAR RADII

Scattering of charged particles by the electrostatic field outside a nucleus is an extremely useful study as an introduction to nuclear theory. Historically, it is the way the nucleus was discovered and its size first estimated. Pedagogically, it provides a very easily understood pictorial introduction to the idea of potential scattering, which underlies the modern study of direct interactions. Since it is a reaction that provides information from which a qualitative understanding of nuclei can be obtained, it is an ideal example of the use of a reaction in understanding nuclear structure. It also illustrates the use of mathematical models in nuclear physics.

Rutherford's group used a monoenergetic beam of α-particles. They measured the number dN of particles scattered per second into an elementary solid angle $d\Omega$ making an angle (θ, ϕ) with the incident beam. For a single scattering center, dN is given by

$$dN = I \frac{d\sigma(\theta, \phi)}{d\Omega} d\Omega, \tag{1.1}$$

where I is the incident intensity (number per unit area per second). The quantity $d\sigma(\theta, \phi)/d\Omega$ is the differential cross section. It is independent of the beam intensity in the particular experiment, and serves to characterize the reaction. It is essentially the probability that a beam particle will be scattered in a certain way.

Since probabilities are the quantities calculated by quantum mechanics, the differential cross section is a very useful way to characterize a reaction. Rutherford used classical mechanics, which gives the same answer as quantum mechanics for this problem. Because of its pictorial value, we shall use classical mechanics.

To describe the reaction, we make a mathematical model which contains enough degrees of freedom for the required description. The model contains one or more parameters whose values are adjusted to fit the experiment. If several different experiments yield related values of the parameters we say that, to this extent, the model represents underlying reality. Nuclear physics involves testing a model until it fails to predict a certain experiment accurately. It must then be modified by adding more degrees of freedom or, sometimes, even radically changed.

Rutherford's model considered the nucleus as a point mass M with electric charge Ze. The α-particle has mass m and charge $Z'e$. The scattering process was assumed to be the deflection of particles by the Coulomb field.

The potential is

$$V = \frac{k}{r}, \tag{1.2}$$

where r is the separation distance of the centers of mass of the incident particle and the target and

$$k = ZZ'e^2. \tag{1.3}$$

Since we have axial symmetry,

$$d\Omega = 2\pi \sin\theta \, d\theta. \tag{1.4}$$

The classical assumption is that particles travel on well-defined orbits, one for each scattering angle θ. The orbit is also uniquely related to the impact parameter s, which is the asymptotic distance from the scattering axis. s is related to the angular momentum l by

$$l = s(2\mu E)^{1/2}, \tag{1.5}$$

where

$$\mu = \frac{mM}{m + M}. \tag{1.6}$$

μ is the reduced mass. Here we are using the fact, well-known in classical mechanics, that a two-body problem is equivalent to the motion of a single particle in a fixed potential in the center of mass system, where the single particle has the reduced mass.

Consider a beam of particles of mass μ, incident momentum p, energy E, and impact parameter s in the range $(s, s + ds)$. The extreme orbits a, b are asymptotic to the lines A and B through the scattering center C at angles θ, $\theta + d\theta$ (Fig. 1.1).

The equation of motion of a particle is

$$\frac{1}{r} = \frac{k\mu}{l^2} (\epsilon \sin\theta' - 1), \tag{1.7}$$

where the z axis for the polar coordinates r, θ' bisects the scattering angle θ. This equation is derived, for example, by Becker (54). For very large r, Equation (1.7) gives for the parameter ϵ

$$\epsilon = \left[1 + \left(\frac{2Es}{k}\right)^2\right]^{1/2} = \operatorname{cosec}\frac{\theta}{2}. \tag{1.8}$$

The number of particles in the angular range $(\theta, \theta + d\theta)$ is equal to the number of particles in the impact parameter range $(s, s + ds)$. If the incident intensity is I particles per unit area,

$$2\pi I s \, ds = -2\pi \frac{d\sigma(\theta)}{d\Omega} I \sin\theta \, d\theta. \tag{1.9}$$

Using equations (1.5, 7, 8, 9), we find that

$$\frac{d\sigma(\theta)}{d\Omega} = \frac{1}{4}\left(\frac{k}{2E}\right)^2 \operatorname{cosec}^4\frac{\theta}{2}. \tag{1.10}$$

Note that the momentum-transfer P is $2p \sin \theta/2$, so that

$$\frac{d\sigma(\theta)}{d\Omega} = 4\mu^2 k^2 P^{-4}. \tag{1.11}$$

Equation (1.10) is the Rutherford scattering formula. It depends on only one parameter, k^2, which must be adjusted to fit experimental results. The experiment, once the formula is verified, can be considered as a method of measuring the charge parameter k^2. It is not a free parameter since its value

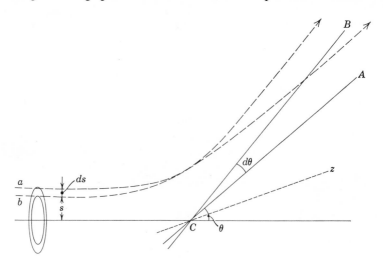

FIG. 1.1   Geometry of the Rutherford scattering experiment.

is, of course, known from independent experiments. Note that only the magnitude of the nuclear charge can be measured by this experiment, not its sign. In Fig. 1.1 we could have drawn the orbits the other side of the scattering center without altering the result.

Geiger (10) and Geiger and Marsden (09) scattered α-particles from Ag and Au and verified the Rutherford scattering formula over a range of angles for which $\operatorname{cosec}^4 \theta$ varied by a factor of 250,000, while the velocity-dependent factor was varied by a factor of 10. Thus it was established that α-particles are scattered by a center of force, not by a screened potential of atomic dimensions.

It was of course suspected by Rutherford that the scattering law is not a complete theory, but that it is valid only under certain conditions. It was verified for different nuclei and for certain energies and angles, but of course the nucleus is not really a point. The obvious refinement of the point model is to extend it to a uniform charged sphere of radius R. For energies and angles where the impact parameter s is less than R, the law will break down because the potential is no longer the pure Coulomb potential for the corresponding trajectory. The range of the specifically nuclear force is measured by R. Large angles correspond to small impact parameters. The angle at which the Rutherford law breaks down will give us a measure of the nuclear radius. This angle is smaller for higher energies or smaller Z.

Rutherford's group were able to find energies and angles at which the law breaks down and thus were able to obtain an order-of-magnitude estimate of the radius for nuclei whose charge was sufficiently small for α-particles to penetrate to the nuclear force region. Nuclei up to about ^{27}Al could be investigated with available energies. The calculation gives a good introduction to the units and orders of magnitude involved in nuclear physics. If θ_0 is the angle of breakdown corresponding to an impact parameter s_0, we have from Equation (1.8),

$$R = s_0 = \frac{k}{2E} \cot \frac{\theta_0}{2}. \tag{1.12}$$

For example, suppose that the angle of breakdown for the scattering of 4.4 MeV α-particles on ^{40}Ca is 90°. From atomic considerations we know that the charge of ^{40}Ca is 20 and the charge of the α-particle is 2. Equation (1.12) becomes

$$R = \frac{ZZ'e^2}{2E} (\cot 45°)$$

$$= \frac{40}{2} \frac{1}{(4.4 \, MeV)} \frac{e^2}{mc^2} mc^2. \tag{1.13}$$

Rather than use, for example, cgs units, which are awkward for nuclei, we have expressed the formula for the radius in terms of well-known quantities whose values are known in terms of MeV for energies and fermis for distances. One fermi is 10^{-13} cm. Values of well-known quantities that are useful for nuclear calculations are given in Appendix 1. Equation (1.13) has been artificially constructed to yield the value

$$R = 6.4 \, fm,$$

which might be obtained with more modern experiments and methods of analysis.

In fact the quantum nature of the collision results in fluctuations of the differential cross section in either energy or angle about the Rutherford value, which become more pronounced as the angle and energy increase. These fluctuations may be considered as a diffraction pattern caused by the deflection or removal of the α-particle from the incident beam by the nucleus. It is difficult to give a precise definition for the energy and angle where the

Rutherford law breaks down. Reliable radius estimates can only be obtained from a quantum theory of scattering.

As a result of early estimates, it became clear that nuclear radii are given to a first approximation by

$$R = r_0 A^{\frac{1}{3}}, \tag{1.14}$$

where A is the mass number of the nucleus. The value of r_0 depends on the projectile, which may itself have a finite radius.

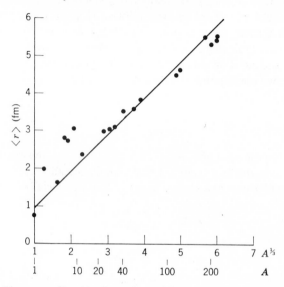

FIG. 1.2   The rms radius $\langle r \rangle$ of certain nuclei as determined from high-energy electron scattering plotted against $A^{\frac{1}{3}}$. The straight line represents $r_0 = 0.97$ fm (Hofstadter, 56).

As scattering experiments using different projectiles have become more refined, the meaning of r_0 has become clarified by describing the shape of the nuclear matter distribution by further parameters. High energy electron scattering (Herman and Hofstadter, 60), for example, is well described by a model which includes a diffuse nuclear surface. Electrons measure the charge density, since they are not affected by specifically nuclear forces. The radius for which the density has half its maximum value is given approximately by

$$r_0 = 1.1 \text{ fm}.$$

The root mean square (rms) radius is a useful concept for the case of a diffuse surface. Values obtained from electron scattering are given in Fig. 1.2.

From studying the analysis of Rutherford, we have seen how a nuclear model is made and used to obtain values of a parameter—in this case, Z^2. We believe the model because Z is not a free parameter. Its value can be obtained independently by atomic methods. We have also seen how the model is tested, how it is refined when it breaks down, and how the refinement is used to estimate another parameter, R. Later we shall study some independent determinations of R. We have also been introduced to a very important principle—the use of momentum-transfer measurements to obtain information about the space characteristics of a small system. There is one other important point to be learnt from the analysis of Rutherford. In the crudest sense, the momentum-transfer distribution depends on the radius of the α-particle as well as that of the nucleus. The "measured" R is $R_N + R_\alpha$. R_α can be considered as a property of the reaction or the measuring process. It is impossible to separate them in a single experiment, although an independent experiment such as α-α scattering could give us a value of R_α. Another method of obtaining R_α would be to analyse a series of radius measurements on different nuclei by fitting the equation

$$R = R_\alpha + r_0 A^{1/3}$$

to them.

Nearly all nuclear structure information is obtained from reactions. It is necessary to have a thorough understanding of the reaction, in order to be sure of the information that we gain about nuclear structure. This information is always inextricably mixed up with information about the reaction in any given experiment, so that several independent experiments are needed for a unique determination.

B. SIMPLE UNDERSTANDING OF NUCLEAR MATTER

From the information that was available in 1932, it is possible to obtain a semiquantitative understanding of nuclei and to anticipate the effects that are now known after many years of detailed study. In this section we will introduce many of the ideas that form the basis of nuclear theory.

The fact that protons exist in close proximity to each other in nuclei indicates the existence of nuclear forces which are much stronger than electrostatic forces. Their range is of the order of fermis, since α-particles obey electrostatic laws beyond a few fermis. One of the energy relationships revealed by mass measurements on neighboring nuclei is that the energy required to remove a proton is about the same as that required to remove a neutron, 8 MeV on the average. Thus nuclear forces are of this order of magnitude and are roughly independent of the charge of the particle.

An extremely important fact is obtained from the radius, mass number relationship (1.14). The density of nuclei is approximately constant. This, with the charge independence of nuclear forces, leads to the concept of nuclear matter formed of particles which exert similar forces on each other.

The particles are called nucleons. Four different types of nucleons are distinguishable experimentally. They are neutrons with spin up or down and protons with spin up or down. Because the nucleons obey Fermi-Dirac statistics, the nuclear forces act differently between particles, depending on their quantum states. The concept of charge independence can be formulated within these restrictions. This will be done in Chapter 3.

Coulomb forces between two protons of course violate the idea of charge independence. It is interesting to obtain an order-of-magnitude estimate of their effect. The volume of a nucleus Ω is given by

$$\Omega = \tfrac{4}{3}\pi(1.1)^3 A \text{ fm}^3$$
$$= 5.6A \text{ fm}^3.$$

The average distance of two nucleons from center to center is about 1.8 fm. The Coulomb potential between two protons at this distance is

$$V_C = \frac{e^2}{1.8 \text{ fm}}$$

$$= \frac{e^2}{mc^2} mc^2 \frac{1}{1.8 \text{ fm}}$$

$$= 0.8 \text{ MeV}.$$

Unless stated otherwise, the symbol m represents the mass of the electron. Since the Coulomb repulsion is an order of magnitude less than the nuclear force, it is a reasonable approximation to neglect it in detailed considerations of the forces in nuclear matter. However, its long range enables it to build up over the whole nucleus as the number of protons increases, so that nuclei do not exist in nature with more than 92 protons. Up to this proton number the Coulomb repulsion can be countered in nuclei by increased attractive forces due to the presence of neutrons. In nuclei with $A > 40$ there are more neutrons than protons.

If the Coulomb force is neglected entirely, nucleons can form infinite nuclear matter which is similar to the matter inside a large nucleus. Infinite nuclear matter is a concept which greatly aids our understanding of the behavior of nucleons in bulk.

[i]   THE INDEPENDENT PARTICLE MODEL FOR NUCLEAR MATTER

Nuclear phenomena are understood by setting up mathematical models with enough degrees of freedom to describe the phenomena. The first requirement of a model is that it should be self-consistent, that is, that it should reproduce a nucleus with the properties which are assumed as the basis of the model.

The simplest nuclear model is the independent particle model in which the motion of a nucleon is assumed to be independent of the presence of other nucleons, except that they exert an average force which binds the nucleon. In infinite nuclear matter the presence of the average force merely alters the zero value for the potential energy, so that it is not observable.

The independent particle assumption is equivalent to the assumption that nucleon-nucleon forces do not act strongly in nuclear matter. Superficially, there is much evidence against this. For example, one effect of the forces is that they bind nucleons together in tightly packed aggregates. Some energies associated with nuclear forces are the average energy required to separate a nucleon from a nucleus, about 8 MeV, and the binding energy of the deuteron, 2.2 MeV. This value of the deuteron binding energy shows that nuclear forces between free particles are at least much stronger than Coulomb forces.

The collective or liquid drop model treats the nuclear forces as if they are strong. The unbalanced forces at the surface are responsible for a strong surface tension which causes the nucleus to act like a drop. We might expect that some of the lower-energy levels would be described in terms of vibrations of the surface or rotations of a nucleus with a nonspherical surface. This is, in fact, confirmed for many nuclei, although the vibration frequencies and moments of inertia are not well-described by simple hydrodynamic models.

We shall first consider the independent particle model because the collective model essentially ignores the problem of understanding nuclear phenomena in terms of nucleons, while the independent particle model at least describes the nucleons. We shall find that the independent particle model is self-consistent up to a point. The reason why the forces do not act strongly in nuclear matter, whereas they do act strongly between free nucleons, is the Pauli exclusion principle.

For infinite nuclear matter, the independent particle model is the *Fermi gas model*. Nuclear matter consists of four gases of identical spin $\frac{1}{2}$ particles which obey Fermi statistics. We have protons and neutrons, each with spin up or spin down. For nuclei in the ground state, all the lowest energy single-particle states are occupied. The Fermi gas is degenerate. We shall first consider some of the properties of this model. A degenerate Fermi gas is very different from a classical gas.

Suppose two particles come close together, so that they would interact if they were in free space. Interaction means a transfer of momentum and energy from one particle to another. This cannot happen because there are no unoccupied energy states below a certain level, the Fermi energy. The mean free path of a nucleon in such a gas is very long.

Thus the first prediction of the model is consistent with the independent particle assumption. The motion of a particle is largely independent of the motion of other particles. It is also independent of the strength of the nuclear forces, unless they are strong enough to give a particle more energy than the Fermi energy in a two-body collision. This collision process does not conserve energy, since the nucleus cannot change spontaneously into a state of higher energy. It is a virtual process. Virtual processes are detected by their effects on the energy levels and other spectroscopic properties of nuclei. They are responsible for departures from the independent particle model or *correlations*. They occur most readily for particles near the top of the Fermi sea, that is, those with energies near the Fermi energy.

If particles are so near the Fermi energy that the nuclear forces that act at the average separation distance of nucleons (a few MeV), can produce virtual excitations, the resulting correlations are said to be weak. Weak correlations *must* occur because there are at least some particles near the Fermi energy.

If, however, nucleons come very close together, the forces are very strong, of the order of 100 MeV. We shall see this in Chapter 3. We must calculate the Fermi energy in order to estimate the likelihood of nuclear forces causing correlations which invalidate the independent particle model.

[ii]   PROPERTIES OF A FERMI GAS OF NUCLEONS

In order to normalize wave functions, it is necessary to consider a quantum mechanical system as being enclosed in a finite box with perfectly reflecting walls. This means that the Hamiltonian has countable eigenvalues rather than the continuous set for free particles. The volume of the box will be expanded to infinity at an appropriate point in the calculation. This technique is very important whenever unbound particles are considered, and it will be used later in scattering theory.

The wave equation for each particle is

$$-\nabla^2 u = k^2 u = (k_x^2 + k_y^2 + k_z^2)u, \tag{1.15}$$

where

$$k^2 = \frac{2m_p E}{\hbar^2}. \tag{1.16}$$

The mass of the proton is m_p and k_x, k_y, and k_z are the x, y and z components of the propagation vector $\mathbf{k}$.

If the box is a cube of side L the wave function u must vanish for $x = y = z = 0$ or L.

$$u = A \sin k_x x \cdot \sin k_y y \cdot \sin k_z z, \tag{1.17}$$

where

$$k_x = \frac{n_x \pi}{L}, \qquad k_y = \frac{n_y \pi}{L}, \qquad k_z = \frac{n_z \pi}{L}. \tag{1.18}$$

n_x, n_y, n_z are positive integers. States with wave number $k < K$ are given by

$$k_x^2 + k_y^2 + k_z^2 < K^2, \tag{1.19}$$

that is,

$$n_x^2 + n_y^2 + n_z^2 < \frac{K^2 L^2}{\pi^2}. \tag{1.20}$$

The number N' of different combinations (n_x, n_y, n_z) which satisfy this inequality is the number of lattice points in a cubic lattice of unit interval in one octant of a sphere of radius KL/π. This is the volume of the octant.

$$N' = \frac{\tfrac{1}{8}\tfrac{4}{3}\pi K^3 L^3}{\pi^3}. \tag{1.21}$$

Since there are four particles in each state, the total number N of particles with wave number less than K is

$$N = \frac{2\pi}{3} L^3 \left(\frac{K}{\pi}\right)^3. \tag{1.22}$$

In a degenerate gas all states up to a certain one are filled. Hence $N = A$. K is the wave number of a particle with the Fermi energy. L^3 is the volume of the box. In the nuclear case the box is a nucleus whose volume is $(\tfrac{4}{3})\pi$ $(1.1)^3 A$ fm³. Therefore

$$K = \pi \left(\frac{3}{2\pi}\frac{A}{\tfrac{4}{3}\pi/(1.1)^3 A}\right)^{\!\!\tfrac{1}{3}} \text{fm}^{-1}$$

$$\simeq 1.4 \text{ fm}^{-1}.$$

This corresponds to a proton energy of 40 MeV. The average nucleon kinetic energy is about 25 MeV. Hence, for the independent particle model to break down completely, the strength of the forces at the average inter-nucleon distance (1.8 fm) must be about 40 MeV. This can be compared with the deuteron binding energy, 2.2 MeV, although a better comparison will be obtained by studying the nuclear force in more detail in Chapter 3.

[iii] CORRELATIONS IN NUCLEAR MATTER

We have seen that the independent particle model is self consistent for particles whose energy is significantly less than the Fermi energy. It predicts a Fermi energy which is significantly larger than the forces causing virtual excitations or correlations. These forces are roughly the internucleon forces at the average distance. Of course it is possible for particles to come much closer than the average distance, in which cases the forces are much stronger and result in strong correlations.

A pictorial idea of strong correlations is to consider that when particles are very close together they are capable of having very high kinetic energies or momenta.

A very useful idea, which is connected with the presence of strong correlations, is therefore the concept of the momentum distribution of nucleons in nuclei. If strong correlations are important, there will be present a larger proportion of high momentum components in the momentum distribution than there would be for the independent particle model. The nucleon momentum distribution is formally the square of the momentum wave function of all the nucleons which, in turn, is the Fourier transform of the total nuclear space wave function.

A very interesting nuclear reaction would be one which gives us some idea of the momentum distribution. We shall see that there are such reactions, but that the information about the nuclear momentum distribution is hard to distinguish from the properties of the reaction mechanism.

[iv] FINITE NUCLEI

Thus far we have considered the independent particle model for infinite nuclear matter in which the collective potential, which acts on all the nucleons, is undefined. For a finite nucleus, it is defined with respect to the potential in free space, which is taken to be zero. The average energy needed to lift the top particle out of the collective potential is 8 MeV. The top particle has a kinetic energy of 40 MeV. Hence the collective potential has an average depth of about 50 MeV.

The independent particle model for finite nuclei is the *shell model*. It was developed from experimental considerations rather than the ones of this chapter. In the chapter devoted to this model, we shall see that the present considerations are valid, even to the rough numerical value of the single-particle potential.

So far we have a general theoretical picture of nuclei in terms of the motion and interaction of the nucleons. Many details of the picture have to be filled in; for example, we have not yet found a detailed model for the nuclear forces, and we have not considered the details of the independent particle model for finite nuclei. Even with all the details filled in, we would only have a plausible picture, not a theory. We must find critical points in the picture that can be tested by experiments and work out the theory of the experiments. We must also think of experiments that will tell us the nature of the correlations which *must* occur because nuclear forces are strong enough to cause virtual excitations, at least for particles whose energy is near the Fermi energy.

FURTHER READING

1. E. Rutherford, *Proc. Roy. Soc. (London)*, **A123**, 373 (1929).
   The opening address of a discussion on the structure of nuclei. Early size determinations are discussed.

2. F. W. Aston, *Proc. Roy. Soc. (London)*, **A115**, 487 (1927).
   Experimental determination of atomic masses.

3. J. Chadwick, *Proc. Roy. Soc. (London)*, **A136**, 692 (1932).
   The discovery of the neutron.

4. N. Bohr, *Nature*, **137**, 344 (1936).
   R. Serber, *Phys. Rev.*, **72**, 1114 (1947).
   Qualitative discussions of nuclear reaction mechanisms.

5. J. H. D. Jensen, "Progress in the Theory of Nuclear Structure," *Proceedings of the Robert A. Welch Foundation Conference on Chemical Research*, Vol. I, edited by W. O. Milligan, Rice University, Houston, 1958, p. 95.
   Qualitative discussion of correlations in nuclei.

6. Conference on Nuclear Sizes, Stanford, 1957, *Rev. Mod. Phys.*, **30**, 412 (1958).
   L. R. B. Elton, *Nuclear Sizes*, Oxford University Press, London, 1961.
   R. Hofstadter, *Rev. Mod. Phys.*, **28**, 214 (1956).
   Determination of nuclear sizes and density distributions.

PROBLEMS

1. The atom is neutral. Explain how an α-particle can be scattered according to the Rutherford law in the presence of the electrons. Give numerical estimates of the modification of the law due to electrons.

2. Under what conditions would it be a good approximation to consider an electron beam as being scattered by interaction with nuclei rather than with the electrons in the target?

3. Compare the validity of the independent particle model for electrons in an atom, for electrons in a metal, and for nucleons in a nucleus.

4. Find an expression for the total energy of a nucleus of mass number A, density ρ, assuming the Fermi gas model.

5. Chadwick interpreted the uncharged radiation from the reaction $^9\text{Be}(\alpha, n)^{12}\text{C}$ as neutrons rather than γ-rays because it caused protons from hydrogen gas to be knocked on with a maximum velocity of 3.3×10^9 cm/sec. The α-particle

energy was 5 MeV. Reproduce the reasoning. Use the table of mass defects (Appendix 2) to deduce the mass of the neutron from the masses of ^{9}Be, ^{4}He, and ^{12}C and the kinetic energies of the α-particle and knocked-on protons. Chadwick found that the value is between 1.005 and 1.008 times the proton mass.

6. Devise an experiment which would give a rough measurement of the momentum distribution of nucleons in nuclei.

2

ELASTIC SCATTERING
IN QUANTUM MECHANICS

We have seen how Rutherford scattering can yield information which gives a theoretical picture of nuclei. This picture provides us with a central theme for our study of nuclear physics. The first step in filling in the details of the picture is to study the nature of the nuclear forces which cause the breakdown of the Rutherford scattering theory at small distances.

In this chapter we shall develop the theory of two-body elastic scattering. We shall solve the Schrödinger equation for the problem, using plausible physical arguments for the boundary conditions, and we shall examine the connection of the theory with classical mechanics. In a later chapter we shall formulate nuclear scattering theory from first principles in a general way. The present chapter will provide a useful concrete example which will help in understanding the rather formal mathematics of the more general theory.

A. THE DIFFERENTIAL EQUATION FOR POTENTIAL SCATTERING

For Rutherford scattering we postulated a potential, the Coulomb potential, worked out the differential cross section, and found that it fitted a wide range of data. We shall do the same thing for nuclear elastic scattering. We postulate a potential $V(\mathbf{r}_1, \mathbf{r}_2)$ that acts between the two bodies whose coordinates are $\mathbf{r}_1$ and $\mathbf{r}_2$ in the laboratory system. The total energy of the system is E.

Just as in classical mechanics, the two-body problem can be reduced to a one-body problem in the center of mass system.

The coordinate of the center of mass $\mathbf{R}$ is given by

$$(m_1 + m_2)\mathbf{R} = m_1\mathbf{r}_1 + m_2\mathbf{r}_2, \tag{2.1}$$

where m_1 and m_2 are the masses of the bodies. The coordinate of 1 relative to 2 is $\mathbf{r}$, where

$$\mathbf{r} = \mathbf{r}_1 - \mathbf{r}_2. \tag{2.2}$$

The Schrödinger equation is

$$\left[\frac{\hbar^2}{2m_1}\nabla_1^2 + \frac{\hbar^2}{2m_2}\nabla_2^2 - V(\mathbf{r}_1, \mathbf{r}_2)\right]\Psi(\mathbf{r}_1, \mathbf{r}_2) = -E\Psi(\mathbf{r}_1, \mathbf{r}_2). \tag{2.3}$$

We transform to the $\mathbf{R}, \mathbf{r}$ coordinate system.

$$
\begin{aligned}
\nabla_1^2 &= \left(\frac{m_1}{m_1 + m_2}\right)^2\nabla_R^2 + \frac{2m_1}{m_1 + m_2}\nabla_R \cdot \nabla_r + \nabla_r^2 \\
\nabla_2^2 &= \left(\frac{m_2}{m_1 + m_2}\right)^2\nabla_R^2 - \frac{2m_2}{m_1 + m_2}\nabla_R \cdot \nabla_r + \nabla_r^2.
\end{aligned}
\tag{2.4}
$$

Hence

$$\frac{1}{m_1}\nabla_1^2 + \frac{1}{m_2}\nabla_2^2 = \frac{1}{m_1 + m_2}\nabla_R^2 + \frac{m_1 + m_2}{m_1 m_2}\nabla_r^2. \tag{2.5}$$

The potential is a function of the relative coordinate. We shall write it $V(\mathbf{r})$. The transformed Schrödinger equation is

$$\left[\frac{1}{m_1 + m_2}\nabla_R^2 + \frac{1}{\mu}\nabla_r^2 - \frac{2}{\hbar^2}V(\mathbf{r})\right]\Phi(\mathbf{r}, \mathbf{R}) = -\frac{2}{\hbar^2}E\Phi(\mathbf{r}, \mathbf{R}), \tag{2.6}$$

where μ is the reduced mass. This equation is separable. We write

$$\Phi(\mathbf{r}, \mathbf{R}) = \psi(\mathbf{r})\phi(\mathbf{R}). \tag{2.7}$$

The constant of separation is E_i. The separated equations are

$$\nabla_R^2\phi(\mathbf{R}) + \frac{2(m_1 + m_2)}{\hbar^2}(E - E_i)\phi(\mathbf{R}) = 0, \tag{2.8}$$

$$\nabla_r^2\psi(\mathbf{r}) + \frac{2\mu}{\hbar^2}(E_i - V)\psi(\mathbf{r}) = 0. \tag{2.9}$$

Equation (2.8) describes the motion of the center of mass. In the center of mass (C.M.) system $E - E_i = 0$. Therefore E_i is the total energy of the two particles in the C.M. system. In this system the second term of (2.8) vanishes. The solution of (2.8) is $\phi(\mathbf{R}) = 1$, describing a motionless point. The wave function of the two-body system is $\psi(\mathbf{r})$.

We shall consider the simple case where V is local and central. In the general form (2.3) or (2.9) of the Schrödinger equation, V could be an integral operator, called a nonlocal potential, for which the Schrödinger equation is written

$$(\nabla^2 + k^2)\psi(\mathbf{r}) = \int d^3r' V(\mathbf{r}, \mathbf{r}')\psi(\mathbf{r}'). \tag{2.10}$$

A local central potential is defined by

$$V(\mathbf{r}, \mathbf{r}') = V(r)\delta(\mathbf{r} - \mathbf{r}'). \tag{2.11}$$

In (2.10) we have used the notation

$$k^2 = \frac{2\mu E}{\hbar^2}, \tag{2.12}$$

which makes the equation look formally more like a wave equation. For $V = 0$ (free propagation), the solution is

$$\psi(\mathbf{r}) = e^{i\mathbf{k}\cdot\mathbf{r}}, \tag{2.13}$$

where $\mathbf{k}$ is the wave vector or propagation vector. Its magnitude, k, is the wave number. For the central potential the problem is axially symmetric about the incident direction $\hat{\mathbf{k}}$. A spherical outgoing wave interferes with the incident plane wave. At large distances we expect the wave function to be given by

$$\psi(\mathbf{r}) \sim e^{i\mathbf{k}\cdot\mathbf{r}} + \frac{f(\theta)e^{ikr}}{r}. \tag{2.14}$$

$f(\theta)$ is the scattering amplitude for the scattering angle θ.

Consider an element of area dS perpendicular to the radius vector and subtending a solid angle $d\Omega$. The number of scattered particles crossing this area in unit time is

$$vr^{-2}|f(\theta)|^2\, dS = v\,|f(\theta)|^2\, d\Omega. \tag{2.15}$$

The plane wave $e^{i\mathbf{k}\cdot\mathbf{r}}$ has probability flux $\hbar k/\mu = v$, where v is the velocity of the particle relative to the scattering center, so we can see from (1.1) that

$$\frac{d\sigma(\theta)}{d\Omega} = |f(\theta)|^2. \tag{2.16}$$

The Schrödinger equation for a central potential is separable in spherical polar coordinates. If the $\mathbf{k}$ direction is Ω_k and the angular coordinates of $\mathbf{r}$ are Ω_r, the solution is

$$\psi(\mathbf{r}) = 4\pi(kr)^{-1}\sum_{l=0}^{\infty}\sum_{m=-l}^{l} i^l u_l(k, r) Y_l^m(\Omega_r) Y_l^{m*}(\Omega_k). \tag{2.17}$$

To normalize the wave function to unit incident flux, it must be multiplied by

$v^{-\frac{1}{2}}$. This factor is most easily derived for the plane wave exp $(i\mathbf{k} \cdot \mathbf{r})$, whose probability flux is v. The indices l and m come from separating the equation in spherical harmonics in a way familiar from the elementary theory of the hydrogen atom. l is the orbital angular momentum quantum number. m is its projection in the z direction.

$Y_l^m(\Omega_r)$ is the solution of the angular equation. It is called a spherical harmonic.

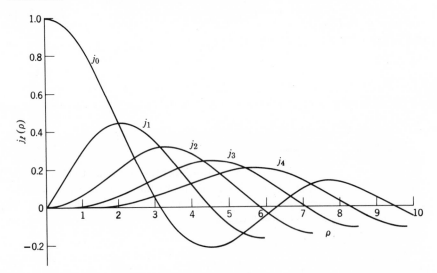

FIG. 2.1   Spherical Bessel functions $j_l(\rho)$ as a function of ρ. Only the first peaks are shown for $l > 0$ so as not to confuse the picture. It must be remembered that $j_l(\rho)$ usually occurs with an angular momentum factor, for example $(2l + 1)i^l$ in a plane wave, so that contributions from different values of l do not necessarily decrease as l increases.

The wave function $u_l(k, r)$ is the solution of the radial equation

$$\frac{d^2}{dr^2} u_l + \left[k^2 - \frac{2\mu}{\hbar^2} V(r) - \frac{l(l + 1)}{r^2} \right] u_l = 0. \qquad (2.18)$$

The radial equation for a free particle $(V = 0)$ is used so much that its solutions are standard functions in scattering theory. They are discussed more fully in Appendix 3.

For $V(r) = 0$,

$$u_l(k, r) = krj_l(kr) = U_l(kr), \qquad (2.19)$$

where $j_l(kr)$ is a spherical Bessel function, $U_l(kr)$ is a Riccatti-Bessel function (Fig. 2.1).

The radial equation (2.18) is a second-order equation which has two independent solutions. For $V = 0$ they may be taken as $krj_l(kr)$ and $krn_l(kr)$.

$j_l(kr)$ is regular at the origin. $n_l(kr)$ is irregular at the origin. It is a spherical Neumann function. The corresponding Riccatti-Bessel function is

$$V_l(kr) = -krn_l(kr). \tag{2.20}$$

The solution must be regular at the origin, but it is a linear combination of j_l and n_l outside the potential. We write

$$u_l(k, r) = kr\{j_l(kr) + C_l[-n_l(kr) + ij_l(kr)]\}. \tag{2.21}$$

We need to know the asymptotic expressions for j_l and n_l for large kr.

$$\rho j_l(\rho) \sim \cos\left[\rho - \frac{(l + 1)\pi}{2}\right],$$
$$\rho n_l(\rho) \sim \sin\left[\rho - \frac{(l + 1)\pi}{2}\right]. \tag{2.22}$$

For convenience we have used the abbreviated notation

$$\rho = kr. \tag{2.23}$$

It is convenient also to define spherical Hankel functions

$$h_l^{(1)}(\rho) = j_l(\rho) + in_l(\rho) \sim \rho^{-1}e^{i[\rho - (l+1)\pi/2]},$$
$$h_l^{(2)}(\rho) = j_l(\rho) - in_l(\rho) \sim \rho^{-1}e^{-i[\rho - (l+1)\pi/2]}. \tag{2.24}$$

$h_l^{(1)}$ represents an outgoing wave at infinity and $h_l^{(2)}$ represents an ingoing wave at infinity.

Equation (2.21) for the wave function may be rewritten

$$u_l(k, r) = \tfrac{1}{2}\rho[h_l^{(2)}(\rho) + \eta_l h_l^{(1)}(\rho)], \tag{2.25}$$

where

$$\eta_l = 2iC_l + 1. \tag{2.26}$$

η_l is the reflection coefficient. It gives the amplitude of the outgoing wave for unit ingoing wave.

The radial equation (2.18) is solved numerically by integrating it from the origin up to a cutoff distance r_0, beyond which the potential is negligible. There is such a distance if

$$rV(r) \to 0 \text{ as } r \to \infty. \tag{2.27}$$

This condition is satisfied by "short range" forces, but not by the Coulomb potential. The Coulomb potential distorts the wave function at infinity.

The inner solution $u_l(k, r)$ is matched to the outer solution given by (2.21) or (2.25) at the cutoff radius r_0. The matching condition determines C_l or η_l.

If we are interested in charged-particle scattering, we must match the inner solution to the solution of (2.18) for a Coulomb potential. r_0 is then the radius where the specifically nuclear potential is negligible. The Coulomb potential is never negligible. The Coulomb radial equation is also sufficiently well-used for its solutions to be standard functions in scattering theory.

The Coulomb functions G_l and F_l are related to the Riccatti-Bessel functions by the fact that for zero charge

$$F_l(\rho) = U_l(\rho),$$
$$G_l(\rho) = V_l(\rho). \tag{2.28}$$

They are described in detail in Appendix 3. Ingoing and outgoing Coulomb functions are defined by analogy with (2.24).

If we write the ingoing and outgoing wave functions in the exterior region as $u_l^{(-)}$ and $u_l^{(+)}$, we can write the wave function as

$$u_l = x_l u_l^{(+)} + y_l u_l^{(-)}. \tag{2.29}$$

The matching condition for $u_l(k, r)$ to be continuous at r_0 is

$$u_l(k, r_0) = x_l u_l^{(+)}(k, r_0) + y_l u_l^{(-)}(k, r_0),$$
$$u_l'(k, r_0) = x_l u_l^{(+)\prime}(k, r_0) + y_l u_l^{(-)\prime}(k, r_0). \tag{2.30}$$

The functions $u_l^{(\pm)}$ appear only in the Wronskian combination

$$W(f, g) = fg' - f'g, \tag{2.31}$$

where the prime denotes differentiation with respect to r. A well-known property of Hankel functions is that

$$W(u_l^{(+)}, u_l^{(-)}) = -2ik. \tag{2.32}$$

From the matching conditions (2.30), we have

$$x_l = -\frac{1}{2ik} W[u_l(k, r_0), u_l^{(+)}(k, r_0)]$$

$$y_l = \frac{1}{2ik} W[u_l(k, r_0), u_l^{(-)}(k, r_0)], \tag{2.33}$$

$$\eta_l = \frac{x_l}{y_l}. \tag{2.34}$$

Note that η_l does not depend on the normalization of u_l. η_l is often called the partial scattering amplitude because it tells us how much of the incident wave for a certain l is scattered. It is also called the S-matrix element for this problem. u_l is called a partial wave, and the expansion (2.17) a partial wave expansion.

Substituting (2.25) into the partial wave expansion (2.17) of (2.14) gives

$$f(\theta) = \frac{4\pi}{2ik} \sum_{lm} (\eta_l - 1) Y_l^m(\Omega_r) Y_l^{m*}(\Omega_k). \qquad (2.35)$$

We choose the z-axis for the coordinates r, Ω_r to be the symmetry axis $\hat{k}$. We choose the detector to have the azimuthal coordinate $\phi = 0$. Making use of the fact that

$$Y_l^m(\theta, 0) = Y_l^0(\theta, 0) = \left(\frac{2l + 1}{4\pi}\right)^{1/2} P_l(\cos \theta), \qquad (2.36)$$

where $P_l(\cos \theta)$ is a Legendre polynomial, we have

$$f(\theta) = \frac{1}{2ik} \sum_l (2l + 1)(\eta_l - 1) P_l(\cos \theta). \qquad (2.37)$$

The parameters η_l determine the cross section.

Sometimes we express the cross section in terms of phase shifts δ_l where

$$\eta_l = e^{2i\delta_l}. \qquad (2.38)$$

If we have a scattering problem where only a few partial waves contribute to the sum, i.e., only a few have $\eta_l \neq 1$ or $\delta_l \neq 0$, we can sometimes find the η_l or δ_l by curve-fitting procedures with experimental data. Such a procedure is called a phase-shift analysis. There is no theory involved in this. We are finding empirical values of the δ_l, not deducing them from a theory. The usefulness of a phase-shift analysis is that it is a convenient reduction of the data to a smaller set of parameters than the set of experimental cross sections.

From Equation (2.37) it is seen that the differential cross section is an oscillatory function of angle if the phase shifts are sensibly zero for values of l higher than a maximum value l_0. In the next section it will be seen physically that there is such a cutoff. A phase-shift analysis consists in postulating numbers δ_l, which are real for real potentials, so that Equations (2.16), (2.37), and (2.38) describe the angular distribution of the differential cross section for a particular energy. For higher energies more phase shifts are required. Each phase shift is, in general, a function of energy. Phase shifts must be found by trial and error or by curve-fitting techniques which choose them so as to minimize the deviation of the computed angular distribution from the experimental one. Since only a finite set of phase shifts can be determined from experiments in a limited energy range, this procedure sometimes leads to ambiguous sets. Further experiments must be done to resolve the ambiguities. For example, a measurement of the total cross section (which is finite only for uncharged particles) gives an independent check on the phase shifts.

As an introduction to the units and dimensions of scattering theory, we shall compute a differential cross section and a total cross section from a set of phase shifts. Suppose we have a neutron-scattering experiment at 5 MeV in the C.M. system. We want to fit the data as well as possible with a set of three phase shifts, assuming that the ones beyond the third are insignificantly small. At present we shall ignore the neutron spin. Postulating the values

$$\delta_0 = 50°, \qquad \delta_1 = 20°, \qquad \delta_2 = 5°,$$

we shall compute cross sections.

From Equation (2.37) and the functional forms of the Legendre polynomials

$$P_0(x) = 1, \; P_1(x) = x, \; P_2(x) = \tfrac{1}{2}(3x^2 - 1),$$

we have for the scattering amplitude

$$f(\theta) = \frac{1}{2i}\left(\frac{20.7}{5}\right)^{\frac{1}{2}} \{(\cos 100° - 1 + i\sin 100°)$$

$$+ 3(\cos 40° - 1 + i\sin 40°)\cos\theta$$

$$+ 5(\cos 10° - 1 + i\sin 10°)\tfrac{1}{2}(3\cos^2\theta - 1)\} \text{ fm}.$$

The value of $f(\theta)$ is, at 90° for example,

$$f(90°) = i(1.94 - 0.26i)\,\text{fm}.$$

The differential cross section is

$$\frac{d\sigma(90°)}{d\Omega} = 3.8 \text{ fm}^2/\text{sr}$$

$$= 38 \text{ mb/sr}.$$

Differential cross sections are usually expressed in millibarns (mb) per sterradian (sr) where

$$1 \text{ mb} = 10^{-1} \text{ fm}^2.$$

Using the orthogonality property of the spherical harmonics, it is easy to integrate $|f(\theta)|^2$ over angles to obtain the total cross section. The relationship (2.36) between the Legendre polynomials and the spherical harmonics gives for (2.37)

$$f(\theta) = \frac{(4\pi)^{\frac{1}{2}}}{2ik} \sum_l (2l + 1)^{\frac{1}{2}}(\eta_l - 1)Y_l^0(\theta, 0). \tag{2.39}$$

Squaring and integrating over θ and ϕ, we have

$$\int |f(\theta)|^2 \, d\Omega = \frac{4\pi}{4k^2} \sum_{ll'} (2l + 1)^{\frac{1}{2}} (2l' + 1)^{\frac{1}{2}} (\eta_l - 1)(\eta_{l'}^* - 1)$$

$$\times \int d\Omega \, Y_l^0(\Omega) Y_{l'}^0{}^*(\Omega)$$

$$= \frac{\pi}{k^2} \sum_l (2l + 1) |\eta_l - 1|^2. \tag{2.40}$$

The total cross section in our example is 700 mb or 0.7 barns. Nuclear total cross sections are of the order of barns. Using the value $r_0 = 1.1$ fm we find that the geometrical cross section (πR^2) of a nucleus of $A = 80$ is about 0.7 barns.

A theory of scattering, which essentially involves postulating a form for $V(\mathbf{r})$, can be tested by seeing how well it predicts phase shifts. To compute the η_l or δ_l for a given potential, we compute the internal solution and its derivative by numerical integration. The functions $u_l^{(\pm)}$ and their derivatives are computed at r_0 by recursion formulas that have been obtained for the differential equation for scattering in a Coulomb field. The values are substituted into (2.33).

The physical wave functions $u_l(k, r)$ can be computed knowing the x_l and y_l. There is only one complication for the charged case, namely, each partial wave is multiplied by $e^{i\sigma_l}$ where σ_l is the Coulomb phase shift. It also is computed from recursion formulas. The details are described in Appendix 3.

B. INTUITIVE PICTURE OF THE SCATTERING WAVE FUNCTION

The functions of the quantum scattering theory seem to be far removed from the easily visualized orbits of the classical theory which was discussed for Rutherford scattering. In fact the quantum picture is easily related to the classical picture. The relationship is an extremely valuable one to study because it leads to a physical idea of the scattering process, which is applicable to many nuclear reactions, even those much more complicated than elastic scattering.

[i] THE WKB APPROXIMATION

The relationship of quantum to classical ideas is accomplished by means of the WKB approximation. This is an expansion of the wave function in powers of $\hbar$. If $\hbar$ is small in comparison with other quantities in the theory, the system is near the classical limit.

The partial wave $u_l(r)$ is written in the form

$$u_l(r) = A_l \exp [(i/\hbar)s_l(r)]. \tag{2.41}$$

Substitution of (2.41) in the radial wave equation (2.18) gives

$$i\hbar \frac{d^2 s_l}{dr^2} - \left(\frac{ds_l}{dr}\right)^2 + \hbar^2 k_l^2 = 0, \tag{2.42}$$

where

$$k_l^2(r) = \frac{2\mu}{\hbar^2} [E - V(r)] - \frac{l(l+1)}{r^2}. \tag{2.43}$$

We now expand $s_l(r)$ in powers of $\hbar$, remembering that k_l^2 is of order $\hbar^{-2}$. It is helpful to remember that $l\hbar$ has dimensions of angular momentum. The second term of (2.43) may be written $l\hbar(l+1)\hbar/\hbar^2 r^2$.

$$s_l(r) = s_l^{(0)}(r) + \hbar s_l^{(1)}(r) + \cdots. \tag{2.44}$$

Comparing coefficients of powers of $\hbar$ in (2.42), we have for the first two orders

$$-[s_l^{(0)\prime}]^2 + \hbar^2 k_l^2 = 0, \tag{2.45a}$$

$$is_l^{(0)\prime\prime} - 2s_l^{(0)\prime}s_l^{(1)\prime} = 0. \tag{2.45b}$$

Integrating (2.45), we have

$$s_l^{(0)}(r) = \hbar \int^r k_l(x)\, dx, \tag{2.46a}$$

$$s_l^{(1)}(r) = \tfrac{1}{2}i \ln k_l(r). \tag{2.46b}$$

Approximating $s_l(r)$ by the first two terms of (2.44) we have, using the values (2.46), the first order WKB approximation to $u_l(r)$.

$$u_l^{(1)}(r) = A_l[k_l(r)]^{-\frac{1}{2}} \exp \left[i \int^r k_l(x)\, dx \right]. \tag{2.47}$$

The condition for $u_l^{(1)}$ to be a good approximation to u_l is that s_l'' can be omitted from the Schrödinger equation (2.42), since $u_l^{(1)}$ is the exact solution of (2.42) if $s_l'' = 0$. This means that

$$i\hbar \frac{d^2 s_l}{dr^2} \ll \left(\frac{ds_l}{dr}\right)^2, \tag{2.48}$$

which is equivalent to

$$\frac{d}{dr}\frac{1}{k_l(r)} \equiv \frac{d}{dr} \lambda_l(r) \ll 1. \tag{2.49}$$

$\lambda_l(r)$ is the local de Broglie wave length, that is the de Broglie wave length of a plane wave in a uniform potential for which k_l^2 is given by (2.43) with the local value of r. The WKB approximation is good when the potential changes slowly relative to the local de Broglie wavelength, that is, for high energies or smooth potentials.

The connection with classical mechanics is made through (2.45a). This equation is formally equivalent to the Hamilton-Jacobi equation which expresses the principle of least action. The principle defines the classical trajectory. $s_l^{(0)}$ corresponds to the action variable. The values of $s_l^{(0)}$ relevant to the problem are those on the classical trajectory. The integral in (2.46a) and (2.47) is taken over the classical trajectory. Equation (2.45b) corresponds to the classical conservation of particle flux.

The WKB approximation relates each partial wave to a classical trajectory for orbital angular momentum l. In other words, it associates a partial wave with an impact parameter t_l. We can think of a partial wave as being localized in space with impact parameter

$$t_l \cong \frac{l}{k_l}. \tag{2.50}$$

This picture leads immediately to a physical understanding of an important fact. The partial wave expansion (2.37) of the scattering amplitude $f(\theta)$ cuts off at some angular momentum quantum number l_0. Large values of l are associated with large impact parameters, so that the classical trajectory misses the potential. The phase shift is therefore negligible.

The phase shift is given in the WKB approximation by the difference, for a point r outside the potential, between the phase values for the potential $V(r)$ and for zero potential where $k_l(r) = k_l^{(0)}(r)$.

$$\delta_l = \int^r [k_l(x) - k_l^{(0)}(x)] \, dx. \tag{2.51}$$

In practice the condition (2.49) means that the classical trajectory may be approximated by a straight line. The form (2.51) assumes this. Note that the phase shift is positive for attractive potentials and negative for repulsive potentials.

The quantum statement of the fact that the partial wave expansion cuts off is understood by examining the curves for $j_l(kr)$ in Fig. 2.1. It is most easily understood for the example of a square well potential. The internal value of $u_l(k, r)$ is $j_l(k'r)$, where k' is the internal wave number. For large l this is negligible inside the potential, so it matches smoothly to $j_l(kr)$ with no phase shift.

It is interesting that the probability density for the partial waves of a plane wave is concentrated at values of r near the classical impact parameter. In Fig. 2.1 it is seen that the first maximum of $j_l(kr)$ occurs roughly at $kr = l + 1$. This is the quantum way of associating a partial wave with an impact parameter.

A very good feeling for the relevance of the WKB approximation to nuclear physics will be obtained by working problems 3 and 4 at the end of the chapter. It is a good approximation for proton energies greater than about 100 MeV.

[ii] Picture of the Wave Function

An interesting fact which gives us a picture of the wave function is that the classical trajectories focus somewhere near the back of the nucleus, particularly at energies too low for the WKB approximation to be valid. The focusing property is due to the fact that the principle of least action requires the trajectory of a particle to bend towards a region in which the potential becomes more attractive. In wave language the nucleus acts like a lens. The shorter internal wavelength results in the particles being refracted toward the scattering axis. We would expect the wave function to be extremely large in the focal region for low energies.

We shall not be content with the classical picture, but we shall show how the wave function can actually be seen to conform to the picture. This exercise will help us greatly in the future where quite complicated expressions will arise involving scattering wave functions, which can be easily understood qualitatively with our pictures.

The actual wave function $\psi(\mathbf{r})$ is a linear combination of partial waves $u_l(r)$. Each $u_l(r)$ is a complex number which has a magnitude $|u_l(r)|$ and phase $\phi_l(r)$. In quantum mechanics we add complex numbers coherently so that the phases result in interference effects.

The potentials used in nuclear physics are normally flat in the middle, that is, they have zero derivative at the origin. The solution to the radial Schrödinger equation at the origin is a spherical Bessel function in the internal potential except for a phase factor ϕ_l. This is the most general form for a wave function which, near the origin, is a solution of the radial Schrödinger equation with a constant potential. The regular solution must of course be used, but it is still regular if it is multiplied by a phase factor, which plays the role of a complex normalizing factor. The value of the phase $\phi_l(0)$ at the origin will be determined.

$$u_l(k, r) = j_l(\rho') \exp i\phi_l, \tag{2.52}$$

where

$$\phi_l \equiv \phi_l(0), \tag{2.53}$$

$$\rho' = k'r, \tag{2.54}$$

$$k'^2 = \frac{2\mu}{\hbar^2} [E - V(r)]. \tag{2.55}$$

The matching conditions (2.33) for η_l give for δ_l, from the definition (2.38),

$$\tan \delta_l = -\frac{B}{A},\tag{2.56}$$

where A and B are the following Wronskians.

$$\begin{aligned}A &= W(G_l, u_l)\\ B &= W(F_l, u_l).\end{aligned}\tag{2.57}$$

The functions F_l and G_l are the regular and irregular Coulomb functions which are related to $u_l^{(\pm)}$ by the Coulomb analogue of (2.21).

The normalization $e^{i\phi_l}$ of the radial wave function is given by matching internal and external solutions at ρ_0.

$$\exp i\phi_l = \frac{F_l(\rho_0) + C_l[G_l(\rho_0) + iF_l(\rho_0)]}{u_l(k, r_0)}.\tag{2.58}$$

Equations (2.26) and (2.34) give for C_l

$$C_l = -\frac{B}{A + iB}.\tag{2.59}$$

Using Equations (2.57), (2.58), and (2.59), we obtain

$$\tan \phi_l = -\frac{B}{A}.\tag{2.60}$$

Comparing (2.56) and (2.60) we see that the phase of the wave function at the origin is equal to the phase shift. For a square well or for a potential which is fairly flat in the middle, the phase does not change much with r until the surface R, so the phase of the wave function for $r < R$ is roughly δ_l.

The magnitude of the wave function $j_l(k'r)$ is greatest where $k'r \simeq l + 1$. Thus if we are only interested in adding the partial waves for the first peaks in spherical Bessel functions, which are much larger than the subsequent peaks, we can say that the phase of the lth partial wave is δ_l. This is in addition to the $\pi l/2$ coming from the factor i^l in (2.17).

The variation of δ_l and l can be understood from the WKB approximation (2.51). The phase of the partial wave is shifted from that of a plane wave when $k_l(x)$ is different from k_l for a significant part of the trajectory. The phase shifts are obviously small for $l > kR$, large and roughly constant for $l < kR$, and intermediate for two or three values of l near kR.

Let us now consider the wave function on the z axis (the $\hat{\mathbf{k}}$ direction) for $\theta = 0$. The angular factor in the partial wave is $(2l + 1)/4\pi$. According to

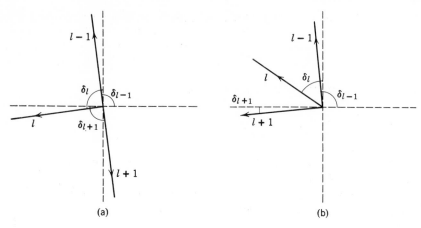

FIG. 2.2 (*a*) The partial waves which contribute most to the wave function for $l \ll kR$, plotted as vectors on an Argand diagram. (*b*) The corresponding plot for $l \simeq kR$.

our knowledge of the position of the first maximum in $j_l(kr)$, we know that only the few partial waves with $l \simeq kr$ will contribute significantly to the sum. Consider $l \simeq kr - 1$, kr, and $kr + 1$. For $r < R$, the complex numbers u_l will appear on an Argand diagram as in Fig. 2.2*a* each shifted from its position for $V = 0$ by a phase angle δ_l, all of which are roughly equal to δ_0. The wave function on the axis for $r < R$ is like the plane wave $e^{i\mathbf{k}'\cdot\mathbf{r}}$ except that its phase is changed by roughly δ_0.

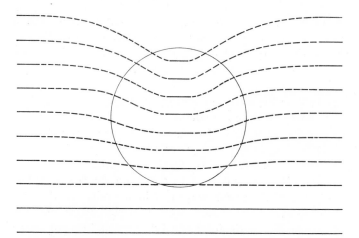

FIG. 2.3 Schematic diagram showing lines of equal phase in an elastic scattering wave function in a fairly high-energy case where the WKB approximation is reasonable. Reflections and consequent standing waves are less important at high energy.

For $r \simeq R$, we have the situation in Fig. 2.2b where the phase shifts decrease rapidly with increasing l, resulting in constructive interference. This interference produces a large value of $\psi(\mathbf{r})$ for $\theta = 0$ and $r = R$ at energies such that δ_0 is within 20° or 30° of 90°. This is the quantum analogue of the focus.

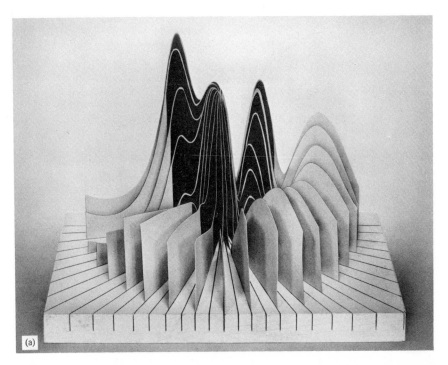

(a)

FIG. 2.4   The magnitude (a) and phase (b) of the wave function for the scattering of 10 MeV protons from a real potential that approximately represents the ¹⁹F nucleus. The central depth of the potential is 40 MeV. In (a) the protons are incident from the right; in (b) the protons are incident from the bottom. The dark area in (a) represents the surface where $V(r)$ is between 90 per cent and 10 per cent of its central value. (Reproduced by kind permission—Amos, 64.)

We can complete our picture of an elastic scattering wave function by considering the form of the wave function inside the potential and at large distances. Inside the potential we know from Equation (2.52) and Fig. 2.2a that the wave function looks just like a plane wave with increased wave number and an overall change in phase. At large distances, it looks like the incident plane wave. The solid lines in Fig. 2.3 illustrate these conditions. The wave is incident from the bottom of the picture.

Lines of equal phase must be continuous. The dotted lines join them up. The focusing effect is obvious. We have illustrated a high-energy case where the WKB approximation is good and reflections are unimportant. The effect of reflections is to cause standing waves which modify the picture considerably at lower energies.

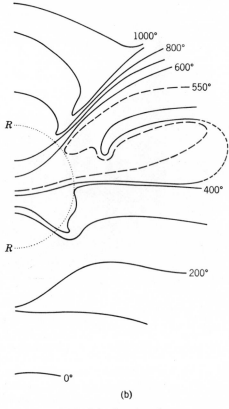

(b)

FIG. 2.4   (*continued*)

The magnitude and phase of the scattering wave function for a real potential at a lower energy are illustrated in Fig. 2.4. The main focus is very prominent. In addition, there are subsidiary maxima due to standing waves.

We shall see later that complex potentials are very useful in nuclear physics as approximations for calculating particle wave functions near a nucleus. The imaginary part of the potential causes attenuation of the wave function and damps out reflections. This picture is much better at lower energies for complex potentials than for real potentials.

Figure 2.5 illustrates the magnitude and phase of the scattering wave function for a complex potential. The standing wave effects are considerably reduced, but the main focus is still the most prominent feature of the wave function.

We have now developed a picture of potential scattering and learnt a lot about the properties of the functions used in the theory and their significance.

FIG. 2.5   The magnitude (*a*) and phase (*b*) of the wave function for the scattering of 24 MeV neutrons from a complex potential that approximately describes the scattering from the ^{118}Sn nucleus. The central depth of the potential is $(40 + 11i)$ MeV. In (*a*) the neutrons are incident from the right; in (*b*) the neutrons are incident from the bottom. The dark area in (*a*) represents the surface where $V(r)$ is between 90 per cent and 10 per cent of its central value. (Reproduced by kind permission—Amos, 66.)

C.   THE INTEGRAL EQUATION FOR POTENTIAL SCATTERING

It is helpful at this stage to consider the integral equation for the potential scattering process. Much of the subsequent theory will involve integral equations. These equations are much less familiar to students than differential equations. This section will illustrate the usefulness of integral equations in scattering phenomena, show by an example how they are related to the corresponding differential equations, and say something about solving them.

In general, an integral equation is equivalent to a differential equation with the boundary conditions built in. It gives a complete description of the process in one equation. It is thus conceptually much easier, and is useful for formulating new theories whose physical content is rendered more obvious by the fact that it is all in the one equation. Why students do not study integral equations much is because it is hard to find analytic solutions to

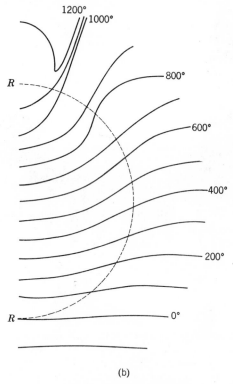

(b)

FIG. 2.5 (*continued*)

them. They require numerical computing. The easiest method is often to go back and solve the original differential equation and put in the boundary conditions, as was done in Section *A* of this chapter for the Schrödinger equation.

[i]   THE INTEGRAL EQUATION

We shall first derive an integral equation from the Schrödinger equation for scattering from a short-range local central potential.

$$(\nabla^2 + k^2)\psi(\mathbf{r}) = \frac{2\mu}{\hbar^2} V(r)\psi(\mathbf{r}) \equiv F(\mathbf{r}). \tag{2.61}$$

We define a Green's functions $G_0(E; \mathbf{r}, \mathbf{r}')$ for an energy $E = \hbar^2 k^2 / 2\mu$ by

$$(\nabla^2 + k^2)G_0(E; \mathbf{r}, \mathbf{r}') = -4\pi\delta(\mathbf{r} - \mathbf{r}'). \tag{2.62}$$

The purpose of the Green's function is simply to enable us to write a formal integral equation. We expand (2.61) as

$$(\nabla^2 + k^2)\psi(\mathbf{r}) = \int d^3r' F(\mathbf{r}')\delta(\mathbf{r} - \mathbf{r}')$$

$$= -\frac{1}{4\pi}\int d^3r' F(\mathbf{r}')(\nabla^2 + k^2)G_0(E; \mathbf{r}, \mathbf{r}'). \tag{2.63}$$

Since ∇^2 operates on $\mathbf{r}$, it can be taken outside the integral. The Schrödinger equation becomes

$$(\nabla^2 + k^2)\psi(\mathbf{r}) = -(\nabla^2 + k^2)\frac{1}{4\pi}\int d^3r' F(\mathbf{r}')G_0(E; \mathbf{r}, \mathbf{r}'). \tag{2.64}$$

A particular solution of the Schrödinger equation (2.64) is

$$\psi_{\text{part}}(\mathbf{r}) = -\frac{1}{4\pi}\int d^3r' F(\mathbf{r}')G_0(E; \mathbf{r}, \mathbf{r}'). \tag{2.65}$$

The general solution is the sum of a particular solution and the solution of the homogeneous equation,

$$(\nabla^2 + k^2)\phi(\mathbf{r}) = 0. \tag{2.66}$$

The general solution gives us an integral equation for $\psi(\mathbf{r})$,

$$\psi(\mathbf{r}) = \phi(\mathbf{r}) - \frac{1}{4\pi}\int d^3r' G_0(E; \mathbf{r}, \mathbf{r}')\frac{2\mu}{\hbar^2}V(r')\psi(\mathbf{r}'). \tag{2.67}$$

We must now include the boundary conditions. This is done by an appropriate definition of $G_0(E; \mathbf{r}, \mathbf{r}')$.

The solutions ϕ of the homogeneous equation are plane waves.

$$\phi(\mathbf{r}) = A \exp(i\mathbf{k} \cdot \mathbf{r}) + B \exp(-i\mathbf{k} \cdot \mathbf{r}). \tag{2.68}$$

They form a complete orthonormal set which may be used to expand $\psi_{\text{part}}(\mathbf{r})$.

$$\psi_{\text{part}}(\mathbf{r}) = \int d^3k' A(\mathbf{k}') \exp(i\mathbf{k}' \cdot \mathbf{r}). \tag{2.69}$$

Operating on (2.69) by $(\nabla^2 + k^2)$ gives from the Schrödinger equation (2.61), using the fact that k^2 is an eigenvalue of ∇^2,

$$F(\mathbf{r}) = (\nabla^2 + k^2)\int d^3k' A(\mathbf{k}') \exp(i\mathbf{k}' \cdot \mathbf{r})$$

$$= \int d^3k'(-k'^2 + k^2)A(\mathbf{k}') \exp(i\mathbf{k}' \cdot \mathbf{r}). \tag{2.70}$$

Multiply by $\exp(-i\mathbf{k}'' \cdot \mathbf{r})$ and integrate on $\mathbf{r}$.

$$\int d^3r F(\mathbf{r}) \exp(-i\mathbf{k}'' \cdot \mathbf{r})$$

$$= \int d^3k'(-k'^2 + k^2)A(\mathbf{k}') \int d^3r \exp[i(\mathbf{k}' - \mathbf{k}'') \cdot \mathbf{r}]$$

$$= \int d^3k'(-k'^2 + k^2)A(\mathbf{k}')(2\pi)^3 \delta(\mathbf{k}' - \mathbf{k}'')$$

$$= (2\pi)^3(k^2 - k''^2)A(\mathbf{k}''). \tag{2.71}$$

We have thus found the Fourier coefficients $A(\mathbf{k}')$ of $\psi_{\mathrm{part}}(\mathbf{r})$.

$$A(\mathbf{k}') = \frac{1}{(2\pi)^3(k^2 - k'^2)} \int d^3r F(\mathbf{r}) \exp(-i\mathbf{k}' \cdot \mathbf{r}). \tag{2.72}$$

The expansion (2.69) of $\psi_{\mathrm{part}}(\mathbf{r})$ may be written, using (2.72), as

$$\psi_{\mathrm{part}}(\mathbf{r}) = (2\pi)^{-3} \int \frac{d^3k'}{k^2 - k'^2} \int d^3r' \left(\frac{2\mu}{\hbar^2}\right) V(r')\psi(\mathbf{r}') \exp[i\mathbf{k}' \cdot (\mathbf{r} - \mathbf{r}')]. \tag{2.73}$$

The form of the Green's function comes from identifying (2.73) with (2.65).

$$G_0(E; \mathbf{r}, \mathbf{r}') = -\frac{4\pi}{(2\pi)^3} \int \frac{d^3k'}{k^2 - k'^2} \exp[i\mathbf{k}' \cdot (\mathbf{r} - \mathbf{r}')]. \tag{2.74}$$

Thus far we have simply converted the differential equation into an integral equation and manipulated the mathematics. Equations (2.67) and (2.74) are equivalent to the original Schrödinger equation. The boundary conditions representing an ingoing plane wave and outgoing spherical wave are put in by considering the $\mathbf{k}$ integration.

Take spherical polar coordinates with the z axis in the direction $\boldsymbol{\rho}$, where

$$\boldsymbol{\rho} = \mathbf{r} - \mathbf{r}'. \tag{2.75}$$

$$G_0(E; \mathbf{r}, \mathbf{r}') = -\frac{4\pi}{(2\pi)^3} \int_0^\infty k'^2 \, dk' \int_0^\pi d(\cos\theta) \int_0^{2\pi} d\phi \, \frac{\exp(ik'\rho \cos\theta)}{k^2 - k'^2}. \tag{2.76}$$

Performing the (θ, ϕ) integrations, we have

$$(4\pi)^{-1} G_0(E; \mathbf{r}, \mathbf{r}') = -(2\pi^2\rho)^{-1} \int_0^\infty \frac{\sin k'\rho}{k^2 - k'^2} k' \, dk'$$

$$= (4\pi^2\rho)^{-1} \int_{-\infty}^\infty \frac{\kappa \sin \kappa}{\kappa^2 - \sigma^2} d\kappa, \tag{2.77}$$

where

$$\sigma = k\rho = k\,|\mathbf{r} - \mathbf{r}'| > 0. \tag{2.78}$$

There are singularities in the integrand at $\kappa = \pm\sigma$. At this stage we use the fact that at large distances

$$\psi(\mathbf{r}) \sim \exp(i\mathbf{k} \cdot \mathbf{r}) + r^{-1}f(\theta)\exp(ikr).$$

From (2.67) we can see that the integral in (2.77) must be evaluated so that it approaches $e^{i\sigma}$ when σ is large. $\psi_{\text{part}}(\mathbf{r})$ must represent a superposition of

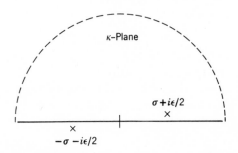

FIG. 2.6   The complex κ-plane for the evaluation of the Green's function integral in Equation 2.77, illustrated for the case of ingoing boundary conditions (outgoing spherical waves) where ϵ has the same sign as σ^2.

outgoing spherical waves from a distribution of points $\mathbf{r}'$ which looks like a single scattering center from far enough away. This is Huygens' principle.

$$\psi_{\text{part}}(\mathbf{r}) \sim \frac{1}{4\pi} \int d^3r' \, \frac{e^{ik|\mathbf{r}-\mathbf{r}'|}}{|\mathbf{r} - \mathbf{r}'|} \frac{2\mu}{\hbar^2} V(r')\psi(\mathbf{r}'). \tag{2.79}$$

The contribution to the integral from the neighborhood of $\kappa = \pm\sigma$ can be seen by regarding it as a contour integral in the complex κ plane (Fig. 2.6). The main path of integration is the real axis. We can make this avoid the singularities if we add to the denominator $\pm i\epsilon$. ϵ will be allowed to tend to zero at the end of the calculation.

We want to evaluate

$$\begin{aligned}
I &= \int \frac{\kappa \sin \kappa \, d\kappa}{\kappa^2 - \sigma^2 \pm i\epsilon} \\
&= (2i)^{-1} \int \frac{\kappa e^{i\kappa} \, d\kappa}{(\kappa - \sigma \pm i\epsilon/2)(\kappa + \sigma \mp i\epsilon/2)} \\
&\quad - (2i)^{-1} \int \frac{\kappa e^{-i\kappa} \, d\kappa}{(\kappa - \sigma \pm i\epsilon/2)(\kappa + \sigma \mp i\epsilon/2)} \\
&= (2i)^{-1}(I_1 + I_2). \tag{2.80}
\end{aligned}$$

For I_1, we close the contour by an infinite semicircle in the upper half plane since the integrand vanishes for large real and large positive imaginary values of κ. I_1 is $2\pi i$ times the residue at $\kappa = \sigma$. The residue is the coefficient of $1/(\kappa - \sigma)$ in the integrand.

For the $-i\epsilon$ case, allowing $\epsilon \to 0 +$,

$$I_1 = \pi i e^{i\sigma}. \tag{2.81}$$

Closing the contour in the lower half plane gives

$$I_2 = \pi i e^{i\sigma}. \tag{2.82}$$

Thus the integral (2.80) is

$$I = \pi e^{i\sigma}. \tag{2.83}$$

This is the solution we want. It corresponds to outgoing spherical waves in (2.79). The $+i\epsilon$ solution corresponds to ingoing spherical waves. It is said to be the time-reversed solution. An expression for the Green's function, which is of very general significance because we can explicitly show whether we have ingoing or outgoing boundary conditions, is

$$G_0^{(\pm)}(E; \mathbf{r}, \mathbf{r}') = (\pi\rho)^{-1} \lim_{\epsilon \to 0+} \int \frac{\kappa \sin \kappa \, d\kappa}{\kappa^2 - \sigma^2 \mp i\epsilon}, \tag{2.84}$$

where

$$\boldsymbol{\rho} = \mathbf{r} - \mathbf{r}', \qquad \sigma = k\rho, \qquad E = \frac{\hbar^2 \sigma^2}{2\mu\rho^2}. \tag{2.85}$$

The Green's function for ingoing or outgoing boundary conditions $G_0^{(\pm)}(E; \mathbf{r}, \mathbf{r}')$ is obtained from solving the Schrödinger equation at an energy $E \pm i\eta$, where $\eta = (\hbar^2/2\mu\rho^2)\epsilon$. The small positive energy η is allowed to tend to zero. The notation $G_0^{(\pm)}$ will be used frequently. It is related to the original notation by

$$G_0^{(\pm)}(E; \mathbf{r}, \mathbf{r}') \equiv G_0(E \pm i\eta; \mathbf{r}, \mathbf{r}'). \tag{2.86}$$

A more useful form for our immediate purpose is obtained from (2.77) and (2.83). It incorporates the ingoing boundary conditions.

$$G_0^{(+)}(E; \mathbf{r}, \mathbf{r}') = \frac{e^{ik|\mathbf{r}-\mathbf{r}'|}}{|\mathbf{r} - \mathbf{r}'|}. \tag{2.87}$$

The integral equation (2.67) for the scattering problem becomes

$$\psi(\mathbf{r}) = e^{i\mathbf{k}\cdot\mathbf{r}} - \frac{\mu}{2\pi\hbar^2} \int d^3r' \frac{e^{ik|\mathbf{r}-\mathbf{r}'|}}{|\mathbf{r} - \mathbf{r}'|} V(r')\psi(\mathbf{r}'). \tag{2.88}$$

This equation expresses Huygens' principle. The second term is a superposition of spherical wavelets scattered from all points $\mathbf{r}'$ with amplitudes proportional to the incident amplitude at $\mathbf{r}'$ and the potential causing the scattering at $\mathbf{r}'$. It provides a very good mental picture of the scattering process.

We shall examine the asymptotic form of (2.88) in order to find the scattering amplitude. We assume that $V(r')$ falls off so rapidly with increasing r' that there is an asymptotic region where r is much larger than any r' for which $V(r')$ is significant.

$$|\mathbf{r} - \mathbf{r}'| \sim r - wr',$$

$$w = \mathbf{r} \cdot \mathbf{r}'/rr', \qquad (2.89)$$

$$|\mathbf{r} - \mathbf{r}'|^{-1} \sim \frac{1}{r} + \frac{wr'}{r^2}.$$

$$\psi(\mathbf{r}) \sim e^{i\mathbf{k}\cdot\mathbf{r}} + \frac{\mu}{2\pi\hbar^2} \frac{e^{ikr}}{r} \int d^3r' e^{ikwr'} V(r')\psi(\mathbf{r}')$$

$$= e^{i\mathbf{k}\cdot\mathbf{r}} + f(\theta) \frac{e^{ikr}}{r}. \qquad (2.90)$$

The scattering amplitude is given by

$$f(\theta) = \frac{\mu}{2\pi\hbar^2} \int d^3r' e^{-i\mathbf{k}'\cdot\mathbf{r}'} V(r')\psi(\mathbf{r}'). \qquad (2.91)$$

where $\mathbf{k}'$ is the propagation vector in the direction of $\mathbf{r}$. A knowledge of $\psi(\mathbf{r}')$ implies a knowledge of the scattering amplitude. However, a knowledge of $f(\theta)$ does not imply a knowledge of $\psi(\mathbf{r})$, only of its form outside the potential.

We thus have two methods of computing the scattering amplitude and the wave function. The differential equation method requires a partial wave expansion and is laborious but straightforward. It leads through the WKB approximation to a pictorial understanding of the scattering in terms of classical orbits. The integral equation method is much more direct. It leads to an immediate recognition of the underlying significance of scattering theory in terms of waves—Huygens' principle—but not to a picture of the wave function, since we have not used it to compute the solution. This is much more difficult than for the differential equation, even though the whole scattering process is expressed by one equation.

[ii] BORN APPROXIMATION AND SCATTERING DIAGRAMS

The solution of the integral equation requires considerable computing techniques. The simplest approximation is again one for $V \ll E$. (This condition was not so strictly required for the WKB approximation, where it was sufficient that $rdV/dr \ll E$.) It is known as the Born approximation.

If $V(r')$ is very small in (2.88), the inhomogeneous term $\exp(i\mathbf{k} \cdot \mathbf{r})$ is a close approximation to $\psi(\mathbf{r})$. We can substitute this for $\psi(\mathbf{r}')$ inside the integral. This process can be repeated for the improved solution so obtained. It is called iteration. It generates the Born series.

$$\psi(\mathbf{r}) = \exp(i\mathbf{k} \cdot \mathbf{r})$$

$$- \frac{\mu}{2\pi\hbar^2} \int d^3r' G_0^{(+)}(E; \mathbf{r}, \mathbf{r}') V(r') \exp(i\mathbf{k} \cdot \mathbf{r}')$$

$$+ \left(\frac{\mu}{2\pi\hbar^2}\right)^2 \int d^3r' \int d^3r'' G_0^{(+)}(E; \mathbf{r}, \mathbf{r}'') V(r'') G_0^{(+)}(E; \mathbf{r}'', \mathbf{r}') V(r')$$

$$\times \exp(i\mathbf{k} \cdot \mathbf{r}') - \cdots. \tag{2.92}$$

The first term in the series is generally called the Born approximation. It converges only for small enough values of $V(r)/E$. There is a theorem which says that there must be an energy above which the Born approximation converges.

The scattering amplitude in the Born approximation is obtained by substituting $\exp(i\mathbf{k} \cdot \mathbf{r})$ for $\psi(\mathbf{r})$ in (2.91). It is

$$f(\theta) = \frac{\mu}{2\pi\hbar^2} \int d^3r \exp(i\mathbf{K} \cdot \mathbf{r}) V(r), \tag{2.93}$$

where

$$\mathbf{K} = \mathbf{k} - \mathbf{k}'. \tag{2.94}$$

$\hbar\mathbf{K}$ is the momentum transfer. The Born approximation gives us an immediate way of converting a momentum-transfer distribution to a distribution in space of the potential causing the scattering.

The Born series for the scattering amplitude can be understood quite easily in terms of a diagrammatic representation, first used by Feynman (49) for relativistic scattering, which we might call scattering diagrams in the nonrelativistic case. It is a sum of integrals of products of terms which involve Green's functions and potentials. The potentials represent the elementary scattering centers or sources of spherical waves at each point $\mathbf{r}', \mathbf{r}'', \ldots$, etc. The Green's functions represent the spherical waves describing the propagation of the particles from the points $\mathbf{r}', \mathbf{r}'', \ldots$, etc. They are called propagators.

The scattering amplitude is written

$$f(\mathbf{k}_f, \mathbf{k}_i) = \frac{\mu}{2\pi\hbar^2} \int d^3r' \exp(-i\mathbf{k}_f \cdot \mathbf{r}') V(r') \exp(i\mathbf{k}_i \cdot \mathbf{r}')$$

$$- \left(\frac{\mu}{2\pi\hbar^2}\right)^2 \int d^3r' \int d^3r'' \exp(-i\mathbf{k}_f \cdot \mathbf{r}') V(r') G_0^{(+)}(E; \mathbf{r}', \mathbf{r}'') V(r'')$$

$$\times \exp(i\mathbf{k}_i \cdot \mathbf{r}'') + \cdots. \tag{2.95}$$

We represent the propagators by solid lines and the potentials by wavy lines. The scattering amplitude (2.95) is written as in Fig. 2.7.

Each wavy line from the origin to the point $\mathbf{r}'$ corresponds to a factor $(\mu/2\pi\hbar^2)V(r')$; each internal line corresponds to a propagator $G_0^{(\pm)}(E; \mathbf{r}', \mathbf{r}'')$; and each external line corresponds to a plane wave. Each diagram represents the probability amplitude for scattering involving a certain number of vertices. There is an infinite number of vertices that could take part; hence the sum is infinite. All points $\mathbf{r}'$ could be the elementary scattering centers; hence the integrations over the vertex positions.

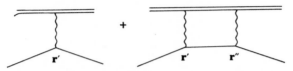

FIG. 2.7   Scattering diagrams representing the first two terms (2.95) of the Born series for the scattering amplitude. The origin or two-body center of mass is represented by a double line.

The diagrams are a good illustration of the superposition principle which is the fundamental principle of quantum mechanics. Probability amplitudes are linear superpositions of other probability amplitudes formed according to the following rules:

Probability amplitude of event *A or* event *B* occurring is (probability amplitude of *A*) + (probability amplitude of *B*).

Probability amplitude of event *A and* event *B* occurring is (probability amplitude of *A*) × (probability amplitude of *B*).

In subsequent chapters we shall consider the scattering amplitudes for more complicated processes. They can always be expanded in a Born series whose terms are integrals of products of two-body $G_0^{(\pm)}$ propagators and potentials $(\mu/2\pi\hbar^2)V$. The series may be represented by diagrams using the same correspondence between external lines, internal lines, and vertices as has been used here for the two-body case. In nuclear physics V is large and the Born series is not meaningful. This is circumvented by defining operators describing two-body scattering which is a finite process, even if the Born series is divergent.

[iii]   INTEGRAL OPERATORS AND THE *t*-MATRIX

The last term on the right-hand side of the integral equation (2.88) could be considered as the result of operating on ψ with a nonlocal potential or an integral operator, as defined in (2.10). It is convenient to incorporate the factor $(\mu/2\pi\hbar^2)$ into the definition of the potential V. The integral equation

(2.88) is rewritten in operator notation

$$\psi^{(+)} = \phi - G_0^{(+)}V\psi^{(+)}, \tag{2.96}$$

where the plane wave is denoted by ϕ. We have also used the superscript $(\pm)$ notation on the wave function ψ to indicate ingoing or outgoing boundary conditions, that is, outgoing or ingoing spherical waves, respectively.

A concept which will be extremely useful in later work is that of a distortion operator $\Omega^{(\pm)}$ which operates on the free-particle wave function ϕ to give the actual wave function, or distorted wave, ψ.

$$\psi^{(\pm)} = \Omega^{(\pm)}\phi. \tag{2.97}$$

We may rewrite (2.96) and its analogue for outgoing boundary conditions as

$$\psi^{(\pm)} = (1 + G_0^{(\pm)}V)^{-1}\phi. \tag{2.98}$$

Expanding (2.98) by means of the binomial theorem we have (under the conditions that it is convergent)

$$\psi^{(\pm)} = (1 - G_0^{(\pm)}V + G_0^{(\pm)}VG_0^{(\pm)}V - G_0^{(\pm)}VG_0^{(\pm)}VG_0^{(\pm)}V + \cdots)\phi, \tag{2.99}$$

which is just the Born series (2.92) for $\psi^{(\pm)}$.

We define the complete Green's function $G^{(\pm)}$ for the problem by

$$G^{(\pm)} = G_0^{(\pm)} - G_0^{(\pm)}VG_0^{(\pm)} + G_0^{(\pm)}VG_0^{(\pm)}VG_0^{(\pm)} - \cdots, \tag{2.100}$$

so that (2.99) may be written

$$\psi^{(\pm)} = (1 - G^{(\pm)}V)\phi. \tag{2.101}$$

The distortion operator $\Omega^{(\pm)}$ of (2.97) is now seen to be given by

$$\Omega^{(\pm)} = 1 - G^{(\pm)}V. \tag{2.102}$$

It is often convenient to consider undistorted wave functions in formal discussions of problems in quantum mechanics. The two-body scattering amplitude (2.91) is written in Dirac bracket notation

$$f = \langle \mathbf{k}'| V |\psi^{(+)}(\mathbf{k})\rangle, \tag{2.103}$$

where the plane wave is denoted by

$$|\exp (i\mathbf{k}' \cdot \mathbf{r})\rangle \equiv |\phi(\mathbf{k}')\rangle \equiv |\mathbf{k}'\rangle. \tag{2.104}$$

We may use (2.97) to rewrite (2.103) in terms of plane waves.

$$f = \langle \mathbf{k}'| V\Omega^{(+)} |\mathbf{k}\rangle = \langle \mathbf{k}'| T(E) |\mathbf{k}\rangle, \tag{2.105}$$

where the t-matrix T is defined by

$$\begin{aligned} T(E) &= V\Omega^{(+)}(E) \\ &= V - VG^{(+)}(E)V \\ &= V - VG_0^{(+)}(E)T(E). \end{aligned} \tag{2.106}$$

The t-matrix is an extremely important operator, in fact it is the operator whose matrix elements are computed approximately in all actual nuclear physics problems, either bound state or reaction problems. In nuclear physics we are interested in the t-matrix for nucleon-nucleon scattering. It may be computed from a phenomenological form for the potential or from a phenomenological fit to scattering cross sections using (2.105) directly. In (2.105) and (2.106) we have shown explicitly that the t-matrix is a function of E. It is derived by solving the two-body Schrödinger equation with energy E. For two-body scattering amplitudes we have

$$\frac{\hbar^2 k'^2}{2\mu} = E = \frac{\hbar^2 k^2}{2\mu} \, . \tag{2.107}$$

For more complicated problems we need matrix elements of $T(E)$ where one or both of these relationships no longer hold. They are called matrix elements off the energy shell. They cannot be measured in a two-body experiment, where energy is conserved, but can be deduced from the potential. In experiments involving more than two bodies, energy and momentum are not necessarily conserved in internal two-body collisions because momentum can be absorbed by the other bodies. Virtual processes, which were first discussed in Chapter 1B[i], are described by off-shell t-matrix elements.

Thus, although elastic scattering cross sections can be deduced from a potential, we cannot uniquely deduce a potential from cross sections. Different potentials may have t-matrices whose elements are the same on the energy shell but different off the energy shell.

Matrix elements of $T(E)$ are finite even if individual terms of the Born series are infinite, as they are for a hard core potential whose value is $+\infty$ for radii less than a core radius c. Such a potential is often used to represent the nucleon-nucleon force.

FURTHER READING

1. N. F. Mott and H. S. W. Massey, *The Theory of Atomic Collisions* (third edition), Oxford University Press, London, 1965.

R. G. Newton, *Scattering Theory of Waves and Particles*, McGraw-Hill Book Co., New York, 1966.

Comprehensive reviews of scattering theory.

2. K. A. Amos, *Nucl. Phys.* **77**, 225 (1966).

N. Austern, *Ann. Phys.* (*N.Y.*), **15**, 299 (1961).

I. E. McCarthy, *Nucl. Phys.*, **10**, 583 (1959); **11**, 574 (1959).

R. M. Eisberg, I. E. McCarthy, and R. A. Spurrier, *Nucl. Phys.* **10**, 571 (1959).

Wave functions and probability flux for scattering by complex potentials.

PROBLEMS

1. Show that a nonlocal potential $V(\mathbf{r}, \mathbf{r}')$ for a two-body problem is equivalent to a potential $V(\mathbf{k}, \mathbf{r})$ which is velocity-dependent.

2. Make a partial wave expansion of the wave function

$$\psi(\mathbf{r}) = \exp\,[i(k + i\gamma)\hat{\mathbf{k}} \cdot \mathbf{r}].$$

   This is a plane wave with decreasing amplitude. What are the phase shifts?

3. Calculate η_0 and δ_0 for neutrons of 50 MeV and 100 MeV incident on a square well potential of depth 50 MeV and radius 5 fm.

4. Calculate η_0 and δ_0 in Problem 3 using the WKB approximation.

5. Find an expression for the phase shift in the Born approximation. Calculate η_0 and δ_0 in Problem 3 using the Born approximation.

6. Plot the angular distribution of neutrons for the 5 MeV neutron example in the text where

$$\delta_0 = 50°, \ \delta_1 = 20°, \ \delta_2 = 5°.$$

7. Calculate the real and imaginary parts of the normalized wave function for the first case of Problem 3 at $\rho = 1$. Verify that the phase of the wave function ϕ_0 is equal to δ_0.

8. Show that the Born series for the t-matrix is

$$T = V - VG_0^{(+)}V + VG_0^{(+)}VG_0^{(+)}V - \cdots.$$

3

NUCLEON-NUCLEON FORCES

The starting point of nuclear physics is a knowledge of the forces which act between two nucleons. The knowledge is based on a study of two-body scattering experiments and bound states. In fact, since there is only one bound state, the ground state of the deuteron, most information comes from scattering experiments. We observed in the previous chapter that a study of scattering experiments is not enough for a knowledge of the forces off the energy shell. Such knowledge is essential for problems involving more than two bodies, at least in principle. It can only be obtained from a study of systems with more than two bodies. The situation is complicated still further by the possibility of many-body forces. Not only is it possible that off-shell matrix elements of the t-matrix may be important, it is possible that the t-matrix itself may be altered by the presence of other bodies. A simple macroscopic example of three-body forces is the interaction of three charged conducting spheres.

The assumption is generally made that three-body and higher-order forces are negligible. So far we have not been able to think of an experiment for which the theory is so well understood that we can distinguish between the predictions of theories involving reasonable two-body or three-body forces. Experiments are known for which the result is sensitive to off-shell matrix elements of the two-body t-matrix. These experiments enable us in principle to prefer certain phenomenological two-body potentials to others which fit elastic scattering almost equally well.

The problems of nuclear forces are severe because we are still in the stage of describing them phenomenologically. There is no satisfactory underlying theory of nuclear forces at energies relevant to nuclei as there is for atomic forces at energies relevant to atoms.

A. QUALITATIVE PREDICTIONS FROM SIMPLE FIELD THEORIES

To obtain an idea why nuclear forces are very difficult to describe, let alone understand, we shall look briefly and qualitatively at the theory of the interaction of particles. Electrons interact by exchanging virtual photons. The photon exchange potential is the Coulomb potential.

The existence of virtual particles can be understood in terms of the uncertainty principle. Two particles interact by means of a force of a certain range. In other words, their interaction is confined to a certain region of configuration space, which means that there are corresponding momentum uncertainties. Another way of looking at the interaction is to consider that the particles remain within range of each other for a certain time, so that there are corresponding energy uncertainties. It is possible for energy to exist as mass in the form of particles. The possibility that a certain amount of energy might exist during the interaction time is equivalent to the possibility that a certain particle might exist with a certain momentum during this time. If there is not enough total energy in the collision, this particle cannot be observed at infinity as a final product of the collision. It is a virtual particle. If there is enough energy in the collision, there is a finite probability that some of it may be changed into mass by creating a particle with conservation of energy and momentum. The study of the interactions of particles has shown that, in addition to the conservation of energy and momentum, the creation of particles must obey certain selection rules. For example, bosons with spin zero can be created singly, but fermions are created only in fermion-antifermion pairs. Conservation of charge and angular momentum are also among the rules which must be satisfied. The same rules apply to virtual particles except that their creation does not obey the conservation of energy or momentum, so that they cannot be directly observed.

Very small energy uncertainties are required to produce photons, so electromagnetic interactions have a long range. We shall first examine the theory of the electromagnetic or photon field.

Maxwell's equations can be written

$$\nabla^2 \mathbf{A} - \frac{1}{c^2} \frac{\partial^2 \mathbf{A}}{\partial t^2} = -\frac{4\pi}{c} \mathbf{j},$$

$$\nabla^2 \phi - \frac{1}{c^2} \frac{\partial^2 \phi}{\partial t^2} = -4\pi\rho. \tag{3.1}$$

$\mathbf{A}$, ϕ are the vector and scalar potentials, which have some arbitrariness. We have chosen them to satisfy the Lorentz condition (usually called the

Lorentz gauge)

$$\nabla \cdot \mathbf{A} + \frac{1}{c}\frac{\partial \phi}{\partial t} = 0. \tag{3.2}$$

$\mathbf{j}$, ρ are the current and charge density. It is usual to employ convariant notation. We write 4-vectors instead of 3-vectors.

$$x_\mu = (\mathbf{r}, ict),$$
$$A_\mu = (\mathbf{A}, i\phi),$$
$$j_\mu = (\mathbf{j}, ic\rho), \tag{3.3}$$
$$p_\mu = \left(\mathbf{p}, \frac{iE}{c}\right); \qquad \mu = 1, \ldots, 4.$$

Maxwell's equations become

$$\left[\sum_\nu \frac{\partial^2}{\partial x_\nu^2}\right] A_\mu = -\left(\frac{4\pi}{c}\right) j_\mu. \tag{3.4}$$

For free photons in the absence of charges, $j_\mu = 0$, the solution is a plane wave

$$A_\mu = A_\mu{}^0 \exp(ik_\mu \cdot x_\mu). \tag{3.5}$$

The notation $k_\mu \cdot x_\mu$ for the scalar product of 4-vectors implies a sum over the repeated indices μ. Substituting (3.5) in (3.4) with $j_\mu = 0$, we have

$$k_\mu \cdot k_\mu = \hbar^{-2}\left(p^2 - \frac{E^2}{c^2}\right) = \hbar^{-2}m^2c^2 = 0. \tag{3.6}$$

Thus photons have no mass.

The electrostatic solution is interesting. We cannot write this covariantly because we are interested in the frame in which the charges are stationary, $\mathbf{j} = 0$. If the charges ρ are constant in time, $\partial\rho/\partial t = 0$, Equation (3.4) reduces to

$$\nabla^2\phi = -4\pi\rho(\mathbf{r}). \tag{3.7}$$

The most general solution of (3.7) that vanishes at infinity is

$$\phi(\mathbf{r}) = \int d^3\mathbf{r}' \frac{\rho(\mathbf{r}')}{|\mathbf{r} - \mathbf{r}'|}. \tag{3.8}$$

If the field is due to a point charge e at $\mathbf{r}_0$, we can replace the integral over the small volume Ω_0 near $\mathbf{r}_0$ by an integral for a constant charge in Ω_0, and ignore the variation in $(\mathbf{r} - \mathbf{r}_0)$.

$$\phi(\mathbf{r}) = \frac{1}{|\mathbf{r} - \mathbf{r}_0|} \int_{\Omega_0} d^3r' \rho(\mathbf{r}') = \frac{e}{|\mathbf{r} - \mathbf{r}_0|}. \tag{3.9}$$

The scalar potential $\phi(\mathbf{r})$ is the Coulomb potential.

We would suspect that nuclear forces are also due to the creation and exchange of virtual bosons. (Fermions must be created in pairs.) The next lightest boson to the photon is the π-meson, so we would expect nucleon-nucleon forces at large distances to be due to the creation and exchange of π-mesons as well as photons. The π-meson mass is about 139 MeV. At shorter distances (larger incident energies), it would be possible to create more than one virtual π-meson with high probability and even to create ρ or ω mesons, whose masses are about 763 MeV and 783 MeV, or a nucleon-antinucleon pair. We would expect nucleon-nucleon forces to be very complicated at very short distances, to have a strong resemblance to the one-pion exchange force for not-so-short distances (or small interaction energies) and to be Coulomb forces at very large distances.

We may think of uncreated pions as being in a potential well 139 MeV below the zero-energy level. If we give a pion a momentum such that its kinetic energy is 139 MeV, it will be able to jump out of the well; that is, it can be created. At a range of 1 fm, the momentum uncertainty is about $1 \text{ fm}^{-1} \simeq 200 \text{ MeV}/c$. The kinetic energy of a 200 MeV/c pion is about 100 MeV which is just about enough to create it. According to this prescription, the range of the force due to exchange of a particle of mass m is about $113/mc^2$ in MeV-fermi units.

$$\Delta r = \frac{\hbar}{\Delta p} = \frac{\hbar c}{(E^2 - m^2 c^4)^{1/2}}$$

For creation of a particle of mass m, $E = 2mc^2$. Thus

$$\Delta r = \frac{\hbar c}{\sqrt{3} mc^2} \simeq \frac{113}{mc^2} \text{ fm}$$

if mc^2 is measured in MeV.

To create two pions we need about 500 MeV/c. The corresponding radial uncertainty is 0.4 fm. We can say that the two-pion exchange force range is 0.4 fm. At about this distance we can expect the actual nucleon-nucleon potential to depart from the one-pion exchange form. The range for a ρ-meson exchange force is 0.15 fm, corresponding to a momentum of 1300 MeV/c and a ρ-meson kinetic energy of about 750 MeV.

By contrast with these considerations for particles with mass, a photon does not need any kinetic energy to be created. Thus the corresponding momentum uncertainty is zero and the range of the photon exchange force is infinite.

We shall examine the pion field in the same way that we examined the photon field. The field variable A_μ was a 4-vector in electrodynamics. We shall see what happens if we make the simplest assumption for our field variable, namely, that it is a scalar, ϕ. This assumption was made by Yukawa (35) when he first worked out a meson field theory.

The plane-wave solution must describe particles with mass $\hbar\mu/c$, rather than zero. The analogy with (3.6) is

$$\phi = \phi_0 \exp (ik_\mu \cdot x_\mu); \qquad k_\mu \cdot k_\mu = -\mu^2. \tag{3.10}$$

Therefore the field equation must have the form

$$\left[\sum_\nu \frac{\partial^2}{\partial x_\nu{}^2}\right]\phi(x_\mu) - \mu^2\phi(x_\mu) = 4\pi\eta(x_\mu). \tag{3.11}$$

η measures the strength of the sources of the field by analogy with the current-charge 4-vector j_μ.

The equation for a static source distribution is

$$\nabla^2\phi - \mu^2\phi = 4\pi\eta(\mathbf{r}). \tag{3.12}$$

The solution which vanishes at infinity is

$$\phi(\mathbf{r}) = -\int d^3r' \frac{\exp (-\mu |\mathbf{r} - \mathbf{r}'|)}{|\mathbf{r} - \mathbf{r}'|}\eta(\mathbf{r}'). \tag{3.13}$$

If the point source strength is g rather than e, we obtain for a point source at $\mathbf{r}_0$ by an argument analogous to the electrostatic argument

$$\phi(\mathbf{r}) = -g \exp (-\mu |\mathbf{r} - \mathbf{r}_0|)/|\mathbf{r} - \mathbf{r}_0|. \tag{3.14}$$

The source is a nucleon, the potential is the Yukawa potential. For the one-pion interaction $\mu = 0.71 \text{ fm}^{-1}$.

The interaction energy between two sources whose relative coordinate is $\mathbf{r}$ is

$$V(\mathbf{r}) = -g^2 \frac{\exp (-\mu r)}{r}. \tag{3.15}$$

Note that the potential is local and central. It is more usually written in the form of a potential multiplied by a dimensionless form factor.

$$V(r) = -V_0 \frac{\exp (-\mu r)}{\mu r}. \tag{3.16}$$

The range μ^{-1} of this potential is $197/mc^2$ in MeV-fermi units for exchange of a particle of mass m. This value is quite close to the one obtained by our previous uncertainty argument.

We shall see that certain aspects of scattering experiments at low energies are fairly well described by (3.16). They enable us to find a value for $g^2/\hbar c$. This may be taken as confirmation of Yukawa's scalar meson theory. However, the interaction of π-mesons with other particles has been studied separately and it has been shown that conservation of angular momentum requires that ϕ be a pseudoscalar rather than a scalar.

$$\phi(-x_\mu) = -\phi(x_\mu). \tag{3.17}$$

Although the radial dependence of the strength of the pseudoscalar meson potential has the Yukawa form, the potential depends on the spins of the nucleons in a way that will be discussed further on. There is no scalar central potential part. Attempts by Bryan and Scott (64) to fit two-nucleon scattering

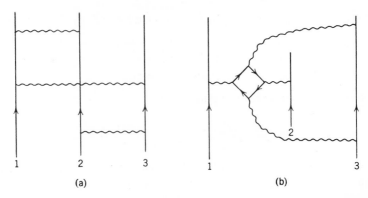

FIG. 3.1 Low-order Feynman diagrams for one meson exchange terms in the interaction of three nucleons: (*a*) two-body forces, (*b*) three-body forces.

data with potentials derived from meson exchange theories require scalar mesons of masses not much greater than the π-meson mass. Such particles have not yet been found.

The pion exchange theory of nuclear forces can help us to understand the reason in principle why we would expect many-body forces. We have seen that the potentials in scattering theory are due largely to π-mesons and can be represented by wavy lines in a diagram. These diagrams, called Feynman diagrams, can also be drawn to represent scattering amplitudes in a properly antisymmetrized, covariant theory describing the interaction of pions and nucleons. We shall consider the diagrams without giving the mathematical theory that they represent. An understanding of the scattering diagrams of Chapter 2C[ii] and the derivation of the photon and meson field theoretical potentials will give us sufficient understanding of the Feynman diagrams. The wavy lines represent pions. The two-body forces are represented by the pion lines in Fig. 3.1*a*.

With two-body forces the presence of the third body interferes with the motion of the other two, but the force law between them is still the same.

Three-body forces are represented in Fig. 3.1*b*. Here the force between particles 1 and 2 is changed by the presence of particle 3. The π-meson is scattered in flight by another π-meson from particle 3. The scattering involves the creation and annihilation of virtual nucleon-antinucleon pairs. The potential strength, which is a factor for each vertex in the integrand of the scattering amplitude, is proportional to $g^2/\hbar c$ [Equation (3.15)]. For electrodynamics, each vertex involves a factor $e^2/\hbar c$ which is 1/137, so that the four vertices introduce an extremely small factor in the probability amplitude for photon-photon scattering.

The nucleon-nucleon potential is much stronger, so that $g^2/\hbar c$ is larger. We cannot expect these diagrams to give such a small contribution to the cross sections for problems involving nucleons. We must study the two-nucleon problem experimentally to get an idea of the magnitude of $g^2/\hbar c$, to see how well the Yukawa potential describes experiments, and to see how it must be modified at high interaction energies.

B. THE DEUTERON

The deuteron has one bound state at $E = -2.226$ MeV whose total angular momentum is given by $j = 1$. Its magnetic moment is $\mu_d = 0.857393$ nuclear magnetons, where the nuclear magneton is the magnetic moment of a charge e with orbital angular momentum $l = 1$. This is almost equal to the sum of the proton and neutron magnetic moments which are $\mu_p = 2.79270$ and $\mu_n = -1.91316$. (Their sum is 0.87954.) This indicates that, to a good approximation, the relative orbital angular momentum l of neutron and proton is zero and that the spins are in the same direction. It is almost a triplet s-state. However, the difference in μ_d and $(\mu_p + \mu_n)$ is evidence that a small amount of the wave function is due to values of $l > 0$.

Eigenstates of a central potential can be written

$$\Psi_l^m(\mathbf{r}) = R_l(r) Y_l^m(\theta, \phi). \tag{3.18}$$

l must be a good quantum number for a purely central force. For a noncentral force we must expand the wave function in spherical harmonics

$$\Psi(\mathbf{r}) = \sum_{lm} R_l^m(r) Y_l^m(\theta, \phi). \tag{3.19}$$

Admixtures of higher angular momenta result from noncentral forces. Further evidence for noncentral forces is the small but finite electric quadrupole moment, $Q = 0.273$ fm^2, which means that the deuteron is not spherically symmetric. Thus it cannot be in a pure s-state.

Since total angular momentum is conserved, the spin $j = 1$ is a good quantum number. Parity is also conserved. Since the deuteron is predominantly an s-state, we know that its parity is even. The parity of $Y_l^m(\Omega)$ is $(-1)^l$, so the admixture can only include even values of l. Conservation of angular momentum and parity require the deuteron to be a mixture of triplet s- and triplet d-states.

Since there are no bound states of $j = 0$, but there is a bound state for $j = 1$, we know that the n-p force is spin-dependent. It is different in singlet and triplet states.

Assuming the one pion range, $\mu = 0.71$ fm^{-1}, for the triplet state, we can work out the Yukawa strength parameter V_0 required to give a binding energy of 2.226 MeV. Using approximate numerical methods we obtain

$$V_0 = 49 \text{ MeV.}$$

From Equations (3.15) and (3.16), we obtain a value for $g^2/\hbar c$ assuming a scalar meson potential. This value is not numerically correct, but it will serve for comparison with $e^2/\hbar c$ which is $1/137$.

$$\frac{g^2}{\hbar c} = \frac{V_0}{\mu} \frac{e^2}{\hbar c} \frac{mc^2}{e^2} \frac{1}{mc^2}$$

$$= \frac{49 \text{ MeV}}{0.73 \text{ fm}^{-1}} \frac{1}{137} \frac{1}{2.8 \text{ fm}} \frac{1}{0.511 \text{ MeV}}$$

$$= 0.34.$$

Clearly this is so large that we cannot expect the Born approximation for the meson theory of nuclear forces to converge or the many-body forces to be necessarily small.

It is thus very surprising, and as yet unexplained, that a theory of nuclear forces involving the exchange of different single bosons (Bryan and Scott, 64) represents the nuclear force very well and that strong evidence from bound nucleus calculations suggests that the two-nucleon t-matrix is sufficient to describe many-body phenomena.

The shape of the two-body potential required to give a binding energy of 2.226 MeV is obviously very ambiguous. However, we can get some information about the wave function, assuming only that the potential is of short range and that we have an s-state. The radial wave function in the external region is the solution of the radial Schrödinger equation (2.18) for negative $k^2 = -2\mu E/\hbar^2$ and $l = 0$ which vanishes at infinity.

$$R_0(r) \sim \exp\left[-\left(\frac{-2\mu E}{\hbar^2}\right)^{\frac{1}{2}} r\right] = \exp(-\alpha r). \tag{3.20}$$

For the deuteron $\mu = M/2$, $\alpha = 0.232$ fm^{-1}. We can take $1/\alpha$ to measure the size of the deuteron.

$$\frac{1}{\alpha} = 4.31 \text{ fm.}$$

Thus the deuteron is a very large and loosely bound system. Its nucleons are separated by more than twice the separation distance of nucleons in nuclear matter. Its binding energy is much less than the average binding energy of a nucleon in nuclear matter.

C. SPIN AND ISOSPIN CONSERVATION AND THE PAULI PRINCIPLE

[i] SPIN WAVE FUNCTIONS AND OPERATORS

Thus far we have discussed the state of a two-body system with respect to coordinate space degrees of freedom. Nucleons have additional degrees of freedom called spin, represented by the coordinate σ. Each nucleon has an intrinsic angular momentum $\frac{1}{2}\hbar$. Its wave function is expressed as the product of a space wave function $\psi(\mathbf{r})$ and a spin wave function $\chi_{\frac{1}{2}}^{\mu}(\sigma)$. The notation for the quantum numbers associated with the spin wave function corresponds to that for other angular momentum wave functions, for example $Y_l^m(\Omega)$. The total angular momentum j is written as a subscript and its projection on the z axis as a superscript. The eigenvalue of j^2 is $j(j + 1)$.

The spin wave functions of two nucleons may be written with the use of a Clebsch-Gordan coefficient which represents the coupling of two angular momenta (see Appendix 4).

$$\chi_S{}^M(\sigma_1, \sigma_2) = \sum_{\mu\mu'} C_{\frac{1}{2}\frac{1}{2}S}^{\mu\mu'M} \chi_{\frac{1}{2}}^{\mu}(\sigma_1)\chi_{\frac{1}{2}}^{\mu'}(\sigma_2). \tag{3.21}$$

Equation (3.21) states that the spin of particle 1 (represented by the quantum numbers $\frac{1}{2}$, μ) and the spin of particle 2 (represented by the quantum numbers $\frac{1}{2}$, μ') add to form a two-body system with total spin and projection represented by the quantum numbers S, M.

The two-body system may have spin 0 (singlet state) or 1 (triplet state). Using the numerical values of the Clebsch-Gordan coefficients we may write the wave functions for four different states of spin and spin projection. Singlet state:

$$\chi_0{}^0 = 2^{-\frac{1}{2}}[\alpha(1)\beta(2) - \beta(1)\alpha(2)], \tag{3.22}$$

Triplet states:

$$\chi_1{}^1 = \alpha(1)\alpha(2)$$
$$\chi_1{}^0 = 2^{-\frac{1}{2}}[\alpha(1)\beta(2) + \beta(1)\alpha(2)] \tag{3.23}$$
$$\chi_1{}^{-1} = \beta(1)\beta(2).$$

In Equation (3.22) we have used the abbreviated notation

$$\chi_{\frac{1}{2}}^{\frac{1}{2}}(\sigma_i) = \alpha(i), \qquad \chi_{\frac{1}{2}}^{-\frac{1}{2}}(\sigma_i) = \beta(i). \tag{3.24}$$

The Pauli exclusion principle states that the wave function of a two-fermion system must be antisymmetric (odd) with respect to the exchange of any co-ordinate. The spin wave functions (3.22, 3.23) have the following properties: triplet states are even under spin exchange, singlet states are odd under spin exchange.

It is convenient to represent the operation of exchanging spins mathematically by a spin-exchange operator P^σ, which can be written in terms of the Pauli spin operators. The Pauli spin operators σ_1, σ_2, σ_3 are operators in two-dimensional spin space whose eigenvalues give the possible values of the spin of a particle in a particular direction in configuration space. The x, y, and z components of the spin $\boldsymbol{\sigma}$ are σ_1, σ_2, and σ_3.

Properties of the spin operators are

$$\sigma_1{}^2 = \sigma_2{}^2 = \sigma_3{}^2 = 1,$$

$$\sigma_1\sigma_2 = i\sigma_3, \qquad \sigma_2\sigma_3 = i\sigma_1, \qquad \sigma_3\sigma_1 = i\sigma_2. \tag{3.25}$$

The spin S of a two-nucleon system is quantized in the z direction. Its z-component is given by

$$M = S_3 = s_3(1) + s_3(2) = \tfrac{1}{2}\sigma_3(1) + \tfrac{1}{2}\sigma_3(2). \tag{3.26}$$

The fact that spin operators for different particles commute, together with (3.25) gives

$$S^2 = \tfrac{1}{2}[3 + \boldsymbol{\sigma}(1) \cdot \boldsymbol{\sigma}(2)]. \tag{3.27}$$

A second application of (3.25) gives

$$S^2(S^2 - 2) = 0, \tag{3.28}$$

so that S^2 has only two eigenvalues, 0 and 2. The corresponding eigenstates are $\chi_0{}^0$ and $\chi_1{}^M$ respectively. From (3.27) we see that

$$\boldsymbol{\sigma}(1) \cdot \boldsymbol{\sigma}(2) \text{ has eigenvalues} \quad \begin{array}{l} -3 \text{ in singlet states} \\ +1 \text{ in triplet states.} \end{array} \tag{3.29}$$

The operator

$$P^\sigma = \tfrac{1}{2}[1 + \boldsymbol{\sigma}(1) \cdot \boldsymbol{\sigma}(2)] \tag{3.30}$$

has eigenvalues -1 for singlet states, $+1$ for triplet states. It is the spin-exchange operator. We shall see in the next section that the two-nucleon Hamiltonian may contain a term dependent on this operator.

[ii] CONSEQUENCES OF CONSERVATION LAWS

We have already seen from the deuteron that spin-dependent forces and noncentral forces are necessary to describe the nucleon-nucleon interaction. We shall use the conservation laws and an argument due to Wigner and Eisenbud (41) to find the most general velocity-independent Hamiltonian that can represent two-nucleon forces.

The Hamiltonian must be a scalar in configuration and spin space in order to conserve angular momentum. It depends on $r(1)$, $r(2)$, $\sigma(1)$, and $\sigma(2)$. We shall show that only certain scalar expressions can be formed from vector addition and multiplication of these quantities.

The number of independent expressions containing $\sigma(1)$ and $\sigma(2)$ is finite. Two particles of spin ½ have four different spin states. Any expression involving their spins is a 4 × 4 matrix in spin space. There are 16 independent 4 × 4 matrices.

(a) 1 scalar matrix

$$1,$$

(b) 1 scalar matrix

$$\tfrac{1}{2}[1 + \sigma(1) \cdot \sigma(2)],$$

(c) 3 components of the pseudovector matrix

$$\sigma(1) + \sigma(2),$$

(d) 3 components of the pseudovector matrix

$$\sigma(1) - \sigma(2),$$

(e) 3 components of the pseudovector matrix

$$\sigma(1) \times \sigma(2),$$

(f) 5 components of the symmetric tensor matrix with zero trace

$$T_{ij} = \tfrac{1}{2}[\sigma_i(1)\sigma_j(2) + \sigma_j(1)\sigma_i(2)] - \tfrac{1}{3}\delta_{ij}\sigma(1) \cdot \sigma(2). \qquad (3.31)$$

The terms scalar, pseudovector, and tensor refer to x, y, and z space. The term matrix refers to spin space. Clearly some of the 9 components of $\sigma_i(1)\sigma_j(2)$ are related to tensors already taken into account. There are three relations with $\sigma(1) \times \sigma(2)$ and one with $\sigma(1) \cdot \sigma(2)$. Thus there are only 5 independent components listed under (f).

In order to conserve momentum, the vectors $r(1)$ and $r(2)$ must appear only in the combination $r = r(1) - r(2)$. We can form the following expressions:

(a) Scalar functions $f(r)$

(b) 1 vector r (3.32)

(c) 1 tensor $r_i r_j$

The Hamiltonian must be composed of products of expressions (3.31, 3.32). There are only three types of scalar expression: scalar functions $f(r)$ multiplied by 1, scalar functions $f(r)$ multiplied by $\tfrac{1}{2}[1 + \sigma(1) \cdot \sigma(2)]$, and tensors (3.31f) dotted with tensors (3.32c) and multipled by a scalar function.

We have for the interaction Hamiltonian

$$V_W(r) + V_B(r)P^\sigma + V_T(r)S_{12}, \tag{3.33}$$

where

$$S_{12} = 3[\sigma(1)\cdot r][\sigma(2)\cdot r] - \sigma(1)\cdot\sigma(2). \tag{3.34}$$

$V_W(r)$ is called a Wigner force, $V_B(r)$ is a Bartlett or spin-exchange force. $V_T(r)S_{12}$ is a tensor force, which is noncentral.

It is possible that the forces are velocity-dependent, that is, they may depend on $p(1)$ and $p(2)$. The discussion up to now has assumed that they are not velocity-dependent. Only $p = p(1) - p(2)$ can appear. We shall consider only terms up to second order in p. We can form three scalars from p and r,

$$p^2, r^2, p\cdot r.$$

The function $f(r)$ in (3.32) can be replaced by

$$f(p^2, r^2, p\cdot r). \tag{3.35}$$

f must be an even function of $p\cdot r$ for time-reversal invariance. The scalar product of the pseudovector $r \times p$ with any of the pseudovectors of (3.31c, d, e) can be formed to give a scalar, time-reversal-invariant quantity. From (3.31c) we obtain

$$V_S(r)\tfrac{1}{2}[\sigma(1) + \sigma(2)]\cdot(r \times p) = V_S(r)S\cdot l, \tag{3.36}$$

where $l = r \times p$ is the orbital angular momentum. This is the spin-orbit coupling term.

Another restriction is that nuclear forces are charge-independent. The interaction must be symmetric with respect to interchange of nucleons. The terms obtained from (3.31d, e) change sign with interchange of nucleons. Thus the spin-orbit term is the only legitimate term in the first power of p. The term "velocity-dependent potentials" usually describes potentials that depend on p^2. We shall discuss them later.

[iii] CHARGE INDEPENDENCE AND ISOSPIN CONSERVATION

We have already used the concept of charge independence of nuclear forces in Chapter 1B. It is of course violated by the Coulomb force, but at internucleon distances this is relatively weak. Empirical evidence from many-body systems for charge independence will be discussed in Chapter 7A. We describe the two charge states of the nucleon by isospin operators in analogy with the two spin states.

The isospin matrices τ_1, τ_2, τ_3 operate in isospin space in exactly the same way that the spin matrices operate in spin space. Only the third component is measurable, by analogy with spin. The magnitude of the isospin provides a classification of two-nucleon states, which has measurable consequences. The use of this classification will be discussed in this section. The values assigned to τ_3 are

$$\tau_3 = +1 \text{ for proton},$$
$$\tau_3 = -1 \text{ for neutron}. \tag{3.37}$$

We can replace the eigenfunctions of σ_3, namely α and β by eigenfunctions of τ_3, namely p and n.

The isospin-exchange operator P^τ for a two-nucleon system is

$$P^\tau = \tfrac{1}{2}[1 + \boldsymbol{\tau}(1) \cdot \boldsymbol{\tau}(2)]. \tag{3.38}$$

It has eigenvalue -1 operating on the isospin-singlet state

$$\tau_0{}^0 = 2^{-\frac{1}{2}}[p(1)n(2) - n(1)p(2)],$$

and $+1$ operating on the isospin-triplet states

$$\tau_1{}^1 = p(1)p(2)$$
$$\tau_1{}^0 = 2^{-\frac{1}{2}}[p(1)n(2) + n(1)p(2)] \tag{3.39}$$
$$\tau_1{}^{-1} = n(1)n(2),$$

again in complete analogy with the spin-exchange operator.

Charge independence is described in isospin language by saying that the Hamiltonian is independent of the orientation of the total isospin vector $\mathbf{T}$. By analogy with angular momentum, this means that isospin $\mathbf{T}$ is conserved. The conservation of isospin is an approximate conservation law which is violated by Coulomb forces.

By analogy with our spin discussion, the most general velocity-independent, charge-independent nuclear force is

$$V_W(r) + V_B(r)P^\sigma + V_T(r)S_{12} + P^\tau[V_W{}'(r) + V_B{}'(r)P^\sigma + V_T{}'(r)S_{12}]. \tag{3.40}$$

The Pauli exclusion principle requires that the wave function be antisymmetric with respect to exchange of any of the coordinates, space, spin, or isospin.

Operating on an antisymmetric wave function,

$$P^r P^\sigma P^\tau = -1. \tag{3.41}$$

P^r is the space-exchange operator. It is often convenient to express the two-nucleon force in terms of P^r and P^σ by using antisymmetrized wave functions and the relation (3.41). The space-exchange force V_M is named after Majorana, the space-spin (or isospin) exchange force is named after Heisenberg who first thought of exchange forces by analogy with the hydrogen molecule.

In many applications, particularly in reaction theories where the theoretical principles are just becoming well enough understood for the character of the nuclear force to matter in calculations, the ease of computation of matrix elements is a relevant factor in deciding how much detail is required in representing the nuclear force.

The tensor force is very hard to manipulate in matrix elements. It is convenient for many applications to omit it and rewrite (3.40) in terms of central forces with exchange. The omission of the tensor force is of course partially compensated by appropriate changes in the central force.

[iv] STATES ALLOWED BY THE PAULI PRINCIPLE

Although all nucleons are treated as equal and the forces are considered to be charge-independent in most nuclear problems, the actual difference between spin-up and spin-down particles and between protons and neutrons means that more states of nonidentical particles can occur than states of identical particles. States of identical particles are more restricted by the Pauli exclusion principle.

The spin, isospin formalism automatically takes care of these facts. The Pauli principle requires that a state be antisymmetric with respect to the interchange of space, spin, or isospin coordinates. The symmetry of states with respect to different coordinates is as follows.

Space: States with even l are even, states with odd l are odd.
Spin: Singlet states are odd, triplet states are even.
Isospin: Singlet states are odd, triplet states are even.

The states of the two-nucleon system allowed by the Pauli principle are

$$T = 1, \quad S = 0, \quad l \text{ even,}$$
$$T = 1, \quad S = 1, \quad l \text{ odd,}$$
$$T = 0, \quad S = 0, \quad l \text{ odd,}$$
$$T = 0, \quad S = 1, \quad l \text{ even.}$$

Two protons or two neutrons are in a $T = 1$ state. The neutron-proton system may be in either a $T = 1$ or a $T = 0$ state.

D.   THE NUCLEON-NUCLEON SCHRÖDINGER EQUATION

In order to find a potential which fits nucleon-nucleon scattering data one must choose a trial potential, solve the Schrödinger equation for it, and see how well the data are fitted, making adjustments to the potential parameters to improve the fit. If the data are reduced to phase shifts for particular states of angular momentum and isospin, one may fit the phase shifts by considering the Schrödinger equation for one state (or in the case of tensor forces two states) at a time.

One must start with a potential of the form (3.40). In fact it has been found that more velocity dependence is necessary. Both spin-orbit terms $(\mathbf{S} \cdot \mathbf{l})$ and quadratic spin-orbit terms, for example

$$L_{12} = [\boldsymbol{\sigma}(1) \cdot \boldsymbol{\sigma}(2)]l^2 - \tfrac{1}{2}\{[\boldsymbol{\sigma}(1) \cdot \mathbf{l}][\boldsymbol{\sigma}(2) \cdot \mathbf{l}] + [\boldsymbol{\sigma}(2) \cdot \mathbf{l}][\boldsymbol{\sigma}(1) \cdot \mathbf{l}]\}, \quad (3.42)$$

result in significantly improved phase shifts.

The radial form factors may not be as smooth as the ones discussed in Chapter 2. In fact, a force which is strongly repulsive (hard core) at small distances is demanded by experiment if a local potential is to be used for the description. The reason for this will be seen when we examine the energy dependence of the phase shifts. In some cases, radial form factors which are functions of p^2 are used.

Whether one or more states of total angular momentum $\mathbf{j}$, orbital angular momentum $\mathbf{l}$, and spin $\mathbf{S}$ (which determine the isospin through the Pauli principle) can be treated separately depends on whether l is a good quantum number. For central forces, where l is a good quantum number, the wave function may be represented by the product of a radial wave function and a spin-angle-isospin wave function.

$$\psi_{lSjmT_3}(\mathbf{r}) = (kr)^{-1}u_{lj}(r) \mid lSjmT_3\rangle. \quad (3.43)$$

The projection quantum number for the total angular momentum $\mathbf{j}$ is m. The states are labeled by an abbreviated notation. The orbital angular momentum quantum number l is represented by a letter of the old spectroscopic notation, the total angular momentum quantum number j is represented by a subscript, and the spin multiplicity $2S + 1$ (which, with the other two quantum numbers, determines the isospin) is represented by a left superscript. Thus the principal state of the deuteron, the triplet s-state, is represented by $^3S_1$.

We have seen that for the deuteron this wave function is insufficient. A wave function having the same total angular momentum and parity as the triplet s-state $^3S_1$ is the triplet d-state $^3D_1$. Thus the deuteron state is represented by a linear combination $(^3S_1 + {}^3D_1)$. This indicates that the tensor force is important in the description of these states.

Even with tensor forces the singlet states cannot be combined with another because $l = j$ is the only possible value of l which has the same parity. The possible states of low angular momentum, with possible combined states bracketed, are listed according to the total isospin T.

$$T = 1. \quad {}^1S_0, \, {}^1D_2, \, {}^1G_4, \, {}^3P_0, \, {}^3P_1, \, ({}^3P_3 + {}^3F_2), \, {}^3F_3, \ldots ;$$
$$T = 0. \quad {}^1P_1, \, {}^1F_3, \, ({}^3S_1 + {}^3D_1), \, {}^3D_2, \, ({}^3D_3 + {}^3G_3), \, {}^3G_4, \ldots . \quad (3.44)$$

The p-p and n-n systems exist only in $T = 1$ states, the n-p system exists in all the possible states.

The radial wave functions are the only parts of the wave functions (3.43) that depend on the shape of the potential. Hence the spin-angle-isospin parts will be eliminated by multiplying on the left by their Hermitian conjugates, integrating over angles, and summing over spin and isospin. Taking the most general case where we have a superposition of two wave functions with l differing by 2, we have

$$\left(\frac{d^2}{dr^2} - \frac{l^2}{r^2} - U(r) + k^2\right)[u_{lj}(r)\,|lSjmT_3\rangle + u_{(l+2)j}(r)\,|(l+2)SjmT_3\rangle] = 0,$$

$$(3.45)$$

where

$$U = \frac{MV}{\hbar^2}. \qquad (3.46)$$

This equation is analogous to the radial equation (2.18) for the spinless case. The inclusion of spin wave functions does not affect the separation of radial and angular variables. An explicit discussion of the spin-angle-isospin wave functions will be left until Chapter 7. The operator l^2 has the eigenvalue $l(l + 1)$ when it acts on $|lSjmT_3\rangle$.

We multiply (3.45) on the left, first by $\langle lSjmT_3|$ and second by

$$\langle(l + 2)SjmT_3|.$$

On performing the integrations and sums using the orthonormality of the spin-angle-isospin functions, we have two coupled equations.

$$\left(\frac{d^2}{dr^2} - \frac{l(l + 1)}{r^2} + k^2\right)u_{lj} - \langle lSjmT_3|\,U\,|lSjmT_3\rangle u_{lj}$$

$$- \langle lSjmT_3|\,U\,|(l+2)SjmT_3\rangle u_{(l+2)j} = 0, \qquad (3.47a)$$

$$\left(\frac{d^2}{dr^2} - \frac{(l + 2)(l + 3)}{r^2} + k^2\right)u_{(l+2)j} - \langle(l+2)SjmT_3|\,U\,|lSjmT_3\rangle u_{lj}$$

$$- \langle(l+2)SjmT_3|\,U\,|(l+2)SjmT_3\rangle u_{(l+2)j} = 0. \qquad (3.47b)$$

If U is a central force, the matrix elements of U are zero unless all the quantum numbers in the bra vector are the same as those in the ket vector. In this case the coupling terms disappear and we have uncoupled equations for u_{lj} and $u_{(l+2)j}$. The same is true for the spin-orbit potential.

For singlet states we can only have $l = j$, and for certain other states the spin-angle-isospin wave functions cannot be nonzero for both l and $l + 2$. These states are unpaired in the table (3.44). Again the equations are uncoupled, since one of the radial wave functions, say $u_{(l+2)j}$, does not exist.

For tensor forces, all the matrix elements in (3.47) are finite and the equations are coupled. We shall illustrate the way in which coupled equations are handled by the example of the $^3S_1$ and $^3D_1$ states. For these states the coupled equations (3.47) are

$$\left(\frac{d^2}{dr^2} + k^2\right)u_{01} - U_C(r)u_{01} = \sqrt{8}U_T(r)u_{21}, \qquad (3.48a)$$

$$\left(\frac{d^2}{dr^2} + k^2 - \frac{6}{r^2}\right)u_{21} - [U_C(r) - 2U_T(r)]u_{21} = \sqrt{8}U_T(r)u_{01}. \qquad (3.48b)$$

If an ingoing wave is pure $^3S_1$, the outgoing wave is a mixture of $^3S_1$ and $^3D_1$. The same is true for an ingoing $^3D_1$ wave. It is better to use waves that have the same $^3D_1$, $^3S_1$ superposition before and after the scattering. They are called eigenstates of the scattering.

One eigenstate, the α wave, is mainly $^3S_1$. The other eigenstate, the β wave, is mainly $^3D_1$. The asymptotic form of the eigenstate is

$$\begin{aligned} u_{01} &\sim a \sin (kr + \delta) \\ u_{21} &\sim b \sin (kr - \pi + \delta). \end{aligned} \qquad (3.49)$$

It is an eigenstate if δ is the same for both u_{01} and u_{21}. There are two solutions satisfying this condition, the α and β solutions, with different phase shifts δ_α and δ_β, and different ratios of amplitudes. In fact

$$\frac{b_\alpha}{a_\alpha} = -\frac{a_\beta}{b_\beta} \equiv \tan \epsilon, \qquad (3.50)$$

so that the condition that the α wave is mainly $^3S_1$ automatically ensures that the β wave is mainly $^3D_1$.

The scattering in coupled states is characterized by δ_α, δ_β, and ϵ. δ_α and δ_β are often called the $^3S_1$ and $^3D_1$ phase shifts. The parameter ϵ characterizes the amount of coupling.

The matrix elements for the different potential operators other than the tensor operator are numbers. Denoting the matrix element of the operator P by $\langle P \rangle$, we have

$$\begin{aligned} \langle P^r \rangle &= (-1)^l \\ \langle P^\sigma \rangle &= (-1)^{S+1} \\ \langle P^\tau \rangle &= (-1)^{T+1} \\ \langle \mathbf{S} \cdot \mathbf{l} \rangle &= \tfrac{1}{2}[j(j+1) - l(l+1) - S(S+1)]. \end{aligned} \qquad (3.51)$$

The last of these relations is derived in Appendix 4. The others follow immediately from the definitions of the exchange operators.

The problem of solving the uncoupled radial equations is identical to the one discussed in Chapter 2A as far as the external boundary conditions are concerned. The internal boundary conditions are similar, namely $u_{lj}(r)$ is regular at the origin, unless there is a hard core potential. The wave function cannot exist inside the hard core so it must be zero at the core radius. The derivative of the wave function is nonzero at the core radius.

E. PHENOMENOLOGICAL NUCLEAR FORCES

The problem of describing nuclear forces consists in finding values of a set of parameters that fit all the scattering and bound-state data. It is a huge phenomenological problem. If the data cannot be fitted by any set of the six potentials of (3.40), we must modify the model by including velocity-dependent forces, first of all a spin-orbit force, then higher ones if necessary.

In such a large phenomenological problem it would not be surprising if different possible parametrizations of the force were found. For example, it might be possible to fit the data equally well with a static force in which the radial form factors depend only on r and a velocity-dependent force where they depend also on p^2. Such forces would give the same scattering cross sections for a two-body experiment, which involves matrix elements $\langle \mathbf{k}_f | T | \mathbf{k}_i \rangle$ between states which conserve momentum and energy. We shall discuss different parametrizations in this section.

We need to know matrix elements of the two-body interaction off the energy shell. This is equivalent to knowing the potential or the wave function in the internal region. Thus, even if three-body forces are negligible we can get, in principle, more information about two-body forces from many-body experiments than from two-body experiments although the information is much easier to obtain in the two-body case.

An important branch of nuclear physics consists in trying to fit the density and volume energy of infinite nuclear matter assuming realistic two-body forces. This is really a many-body scattering problem because the zero potential is irrelevant for nuclear matter. It provides constraints which otherwise-acceptable two-body forces must satisfy if we are going to keep the philosophy of exhausting the hypothesis of two-body forces before trying many-body forces.

The theory of finite nuclei has now reached the stage where it is capable of distinguishing between different forces which are acceptable on the energy shell. At present we shall be interested in information about the nucleon-nucleon force obtained from nucleon-nucleon scattering experiments.

The experimental data on nucleon-nucleon scattering are made up of p-p and n-p angular distribution and polarization data at different energies. There are some systematic trends in the data that are worth noticing.

1. p-p angular distributions are nearly isotropic up to about 400 MeV except for a Coulomb peak at small angles. They are symmetric about 90° because of the Pauli principle.

2. n-p angular distributions are roughly symmetric about 90° although this is not required by any selection rules. The anisotropy increases as the energy increases.

3. Both p-p and n-p cross sections decrease rapidly with increasing energy up to about 100 MeV and then decrease very slowly up to and above 300 MeV. The 90° p-p differential cross section at 300 MeV is about 4 mb/sr, giving a total cross section of $16\pi = 50$ mb or 5 fm², corresponding to a geometrical radius of about 1.2 fm. At 600 MeV the 90° p-p differential cross section is about 2.5 mb/sr.

4. The polarization is defined as $[\sigma(\alpha) - \sigma(\beta)]/[\sigma(\alpha) + \sigma(\beta)]$, where $\sigma(\alpha)$, $\sigma(\beta)$ are the differential cross sections for particles with spin up and spin down. Because of the Pauli principle p-p polarization at 90° is zero. At 90° in the C.M. system, the scattering is symmetric in the laboratory system. The wave function is symmetric under space exchange. Therefore it must be antisymmetric under spin exchange. Isospin is of course fixed for two protons. p-p scattering at 90° occurs in singlet states. p-p polarization is largest at about 45°. It increases with increasing energy from 0.015 at 50 MeV to 0.12 at 100 MeV and 0.22 at 160 MeV.

5. Phase shift analysis of scattering data indicates that the singlet *s*-state phase shift becomes negative for energies greater than about 240 MeV. The phase shifts, which fully characterize the data, will be discussed in Part [ii] of this section.

The number of parameters used in a phenomenological calculation of nuclear forces depends on the degree of refinement that we are interested in for the calculation. We shall mainly be interested in using two-body forces to predict the results of three- and more-body reactions where approximations other than the one for the two-nucleon force are made. These approximations are often quite crude, justified by the limited range of data we are trying to fit in the more complicated experiment. In these cases we are justified in using equally crude two-nucleon models. For example, in a many-nucleon scattering experiment where polarizations are not measured, but only momentum transfers are to be calculated, we would expect not to have to use tensor or spin-orbit forces in the effective two-nucleon potential. Often it is convenient to use a simplified two-nucleon model to fit a limited range of two-nucleon data that are relevant to the problem we are interested in.

We shall consider phenomenological representations of nuclear forces according to the subsets of scattering data that they are designed to fit. Phenomenological representations fall into two classes. In the first class are phenomenological potentials. For these the data are reduced first to phase shifts which can be computed easily from a Schrödinger equation into which one substitutes the potential. At very low energies, where only s-state inter-actions are important, the variation of the phase shift with energy may be parametrized simply. This is done by means of the effective range approxima-tion which will be treated in the following section.

The second class of representations is useful when one is primarily interested in nucleon-nucleon t-matrix elements. One attempts to parametrize the scattering amplitude directly by using a phenomenological t-matrix. Attempts in this direction have not been very detailed. The most accurate phenomeno-logical representations are potentials from which the t-matrix can be cal-culated. However, this is extremely difficult, and the more direct method has proved very useful. A representation of the t-matrix which is local in con-figuration space is called a pseudopotential. It is obviously not sufficiently general to represent the off-shell matrix elements correctly, but it does give a representation off the energy shell which has provided much information about the validity of certain reaction approximations and which even provides a good enough description of certain reactions to enable them to be used as spectroscopic tools. The pseudopotential is equal to the potential if the Born approximation is valid.

[i] Effective Range Theory

At very low energies only the wave function for s-waves is nontrivial. For p-p scattering the low-energy effects are due to the Coulomb potential. The nuclear forces at low energy are studied in the n-p system. Outside the poten-tial, the zero-energy limit of the wave function is a straight line given by $d^2\psi_0/dr^2 = 0$.

$$\psi_0 = c(r - a). \tag{3.52}$$

The s-wave scattering amplitude is

$$f_0 = k^{-1} \exp(i\delta_0) \sin \delta_0. \tag{3.53}$$

The differential cross section, neglecting $l > 0$, is

$$\frac{d\sigma}{d\Omega} = k^{-2} \sin^2 \delta_0. \tag{3.54}$$

The wave function outside the potential is

$$A \sin(kr + \delta_0) \cong c(r - a) \cong A(kr + \delta_0), \tag{3.55}$$

which gives

$$kA = c, \qquad A\delta_0 = -ca, \qquad \delta_0 = -ka. \tag{3.56}$$

The total cross section is, from (3.54),

$$\sigma = 4\pi a^2 = 4\pi \lambda^2 \sin^2 \delta_0. \tag{3.57}$$

The r-intercept a is the scattering length. The magnitude of a is determined by the cross section, and the sign of a is determined by the phase shift. For singlet scattering, a turns out to be large and negative.

Figure 3.2 illustrates the singlet wave function at very low energy.

If the slope of the line were slightly negative rather than slightly positive, the wave function would be that of a bound state. We have a virtual bound state at almost zero energy. The cross section at zero energy is large.

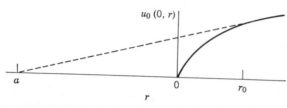

FIG. 3.2   Schematic diagram of the singlet n-p wave function at zero energy.

We can evaluate the scattering length for the triplet state knowing the binding energy of the deuteron. The external wave function is $e^{-\alpha r} \cong 1 - \alpha r$. Hence

$$a_t \cong \frac{1}{\alpha} = 4.31 \text{ fm}$$

$$\sigma_t = 2.80 \text{ barns}.$$

The singlet scattering length is evaluated by knowing the cross section for an unpolarized beam in the low-energy limit.

$$\sigma = \tfrac{3}{4}\sigma_t + \tfrac{1}{4}\sigma_s \cong 20.36 \text{ barns}$$

$$\sigma_s \cong 73 \text{ barns}$$

$$|a_s| \cong 24 \text{ fm}.$$

The sign of a_s could be determined by scattering a polarized beam of neutrons from hydrogen, but this is unnecessary since we can use a para-hydrogen target in which the spins of the two protons in the hydrogen molecule are opposed. For the n-p system, when there is a definite relationship between singlet and triplet states (coherent scattering),

$$a = \tfrac{1}{4}(3a_t + a_s) + (a_t - a_s)(\mathbf{s}_n \cdot \mathbf{s}_p).$$

Here we are using the more common notation of denoting the particle by a subscript on the spin operator, since we are not interested in spin directions. For the hydrogen molecule,

$$a_H = a_{p_1} + a_{p_2} = \tfrac{1}{2}(3a_t + a_s) + (a_t - a_s)[\mathbf{s}_n \cdot (\mathbf{s}_{p_1} + \mathbf{s}_{p_2})].$$

For para-hydrogen,

$$a_{\text{para-}H} = \tfrac{1}{2}(3a_t + a_s),$$

$$\sigma_{\text{para-}H} = \frac{(\mu')^2}{\mu} 4\pi(a_{\text{para-}H})^2 \simeq 22a^2_{\text{para-}H} \text{ barns},$$

where μ and μ' are the reduced masses for the n-p and n-H systems.
For $a_t = 4.31$ fm we have:

$$\text{for } a_s = +24 \text{ fm}, \quad \sigma_{\text{para-}H} = 80 \text{ barns},$$
$$\text{for } a_s = -24 \text{ fm}, \quad \sigma_{\text{para-}H} = 5.5 \text{ barns}.$$

The experimental value is 3.9 barns, indicating that the sign of a_s is negative.

In addition to the scattering length, another parameter called the effective range is used to describe low-energy scattering. It enables us to correct our formula (3.56) for the phase shift by including a description of the range of the potential without describing the exact shape of the potential.

For energy E the wave equation is, putting $\psi_0 = u$,

$$\frac{d^2}{dr^2} u + k^2 u - \frac{2\mu V}{\hbar^2} u = 0. \tag{3.58}$$

For zero energy it is

$$\frac{d^2}{dr^2} u_0 - \frac{2\mu V}{\hbar^2} u_0 = 0. \tag{3.59}$$

Multiplying (3.58) by $u_0(r)$ and (3.59) by $u(r)$, and subtracting, enables us to eliminate $V(r)$.

$$\frac{d}{dr}(uu_0' - u_0u') = k^2 uu_0. \tag{3.60}$$

With convenient normalization the corresponding asymptotic solutions are

$$v(r) = \frac{\sin(kr + \delta_0)}{\sin \delta_0}$$

$$v_0(r) = 1 - \frac{r}{a}. \tag{3.61}$$

They satisfy an equation similar to (3.60).

$$\frac{d}{dr}(vv_0' - v_0v') = k^2 vv_0. \tag{3.62}$$

Subtract (3.62) from (3.60) and integrate over r. Using $u(0) = 0$ and values for v, v_0, and their derivatives at zero obtained from (3.61), we have

$$k \cot \delta_0 = -a^{-1} + k^2 \int_0^\infty (vv_0 - uu_0) \, dr. \tag{3.63}$$

This equation is exact. In order to use it as the basis of an approximation method, we observe that the significant contributions to the integral come from the interior where u, u_0 differ appreciably from v, v_0. Here the potential is much larger than the total energy E, so the local wave number is almost independent of E. It is a good approximation to replace u and v by their zero energy forms u_0 and v_0. We obtain the shape-independent approximation.

$$k \cot \delta_0 = -a^{-1} + \tfrac{1}{2} r_0 k^2,$$

$$r_0 = 2 \int_0^\infty (v_0^2 - u_0^2) \, dr. \tag{3.64}$$

r_0 is the effective range. For a square well it is the radius. It depends on $V(r)$ and not on k^2. Using this approximation for δ_0 in (3.54) and (3.57), we can determine the singlet and triplet effective ranges as well as the scattering lengths from the low-energy experiments discussed in this section. We must know the low-energy dependence of the cross sections, not just their zero-energy limits. Good values of the low-energy n-p parameters are

$$a_t = 5.39 \text{ fm}, \ r_{0t} = 1.70 \text{ fm}, \ a_s = -23.7 \text{ fm}, \ r_{0s} = 2.7 \text{ fm}.$$

[ii] PHASE SHIFTS

The results of extensive searches for phase shifts are summed up in the papers of Breit, Hull, Lassila, and Pyatt (60) and Hull, Lassila, Ruppel, McDonald, and Breit (61). The first paper describes p-p scattering, the second describes n-p. The phase shifts for some of the lower partial waves as functions of energy are shown in Figs. 3.3 and 3.4 in order to give an idea of the strength of the nucleon-nucleon force in different states. These phase shifts are known as the YLAM phase shifts for $T = 1$ and YLAN3M phase shifts for $T = 0$, from the computer terminology of the group which determined them.

In addition to the phase shifts the asymptotic scattering for coupled states is characterized by a coupling parameter ϵ_j that indicates the strength of the tensor force. The function $\sin 2\epsilon_1$ for the $^3S_1$ and $^3D_1$ states for example goes from approximately zero at low energies to 0.25 at 300 MeV.

The phase shifts of Figs. 3.3, and 3.4 serve to characterize the nucleon-nucleon scattering data fairly completely. Phase shifts and coupling parameters for higher partial waves are quite small. For a complete representation of the data up to 300 MeV, it has been necessary to include states up to $l = 4$.

Some outstanding features of the phase shifts are as follows.

1. The charge-independence hypothesis is verified by the fact that both n-p and p-p scattering data are fitted by the same $T = 1$ phase shifts.

2. At energies below 100 MeV the largest phase shifts are the s-wave and some of the p-wave phase shifts. Both $^1S_0$ and $^3S_1$ phase shifts are positive,

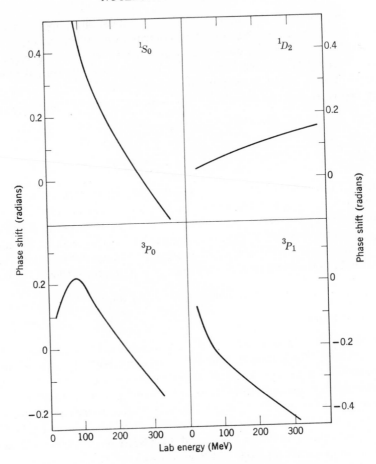

FIG. 3.3   Nucleon-nucleon phase shifts for $T = 1$ states.

while the $^1P_1$ and $^3P_1$ phase shifts are negative. Negative phase shifts indicate a repulsive potential. A rough generalization is that the forces are attractive in even states, repulsive in odd states.

3. For p-p scattering below 100 MeV the $^1S_0$ (singlet-even) phase shift is several times larger than the $^3P_0$ and $^3P_1$ (triplet-odd) phase shifts, indicating a relatively small contribution to p-p scattering from triplet-odd states.

4. The $^1S_0$ and $^3P_0$ phase shifts change from positive to negative at about 200 MeV. In terms of a local potential we can use the correspondence between partial waves and classical impact parameters to interpret this. It means that the potential becomes strongly repulsive if the impact parameter becomes small enough. Most local potential models use a hard core to represent the change

in sign of the phase shifts. Various types of nonlocal potential are capable of representing this change without the use of infinite or very large strengths.

The use of a hard core in the local potential was suggested by Jastrow (51). We will give his argument in the simplest case of p-p scattering in singlet-even states. At energies of roughly 300 MeV the p-p differential cross section is very nearly isotropic, while below 100 MeV it is greater at smaller angles. The $^1S_0$ and $^1D_2$ states give the only significant contributions to the scattering amplitude (2.37). The absolute square of the scattering amplitude contains two positive-definite terms for the absolute squares of the $^1S_0$ and $^1D_2$ amplitudes and an interference term proportional to

$$\sin \delta_0 \sin \delta_2 \, P_0(\cos \theta) P_2(\cos \theta).$$

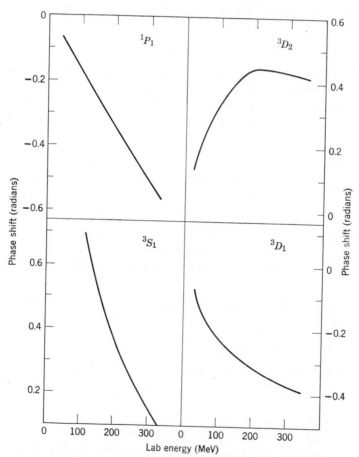

FIG. 3.4   Nucleon-nucleon phase shifts for $T = 0$ states.

Both P_0 and P_2 are positive at $0°$ but P_2 is negative at $90°$, so that the interference is constructive at $0°$ and destructive at $90°$ provided both phase shifts are positive. Since Legendre polynomials for $l > 0$ are maximum at $0°$, the trend of the cross section, apart from the interference term, is to be large at forward angles and decrease towards $90°$. In order to obtain an isotropic cross section, the sign of the interference term must be changed so that the interference is destructive at $0°$ and constructive at $90°$. This will happen if one of the phase shifts is negative and the other positive.

Negative phase shifts correspond to repulsive potentials [see Equation (2.51)]. A potential with a short-range repulsive core satisfies the above requirements. At high energies the s-waves feel the repulsive core while the d-waves do not. The $^1S_0$ phase shift is negative. At lower energies the attractive part of the potential has the predominant effect and the $^1S_0$ phase shift is positive.

[iii] LOCAL POTENTIALS

The most detailed fits to nuclear phase shifts have been obtained with local potentials. Gammel and Thaler (57) found that spin-orbit coupling terms were necessary to fit p-p scattering data up to 310 MeV. Hard cores of radius $c^\pm$ were used in the radial dependence. Outside the core the potential had

$c^+ = 0.4$ fm,		
$V_C{}^+ = -425.5$ MeV,	$\mu_C{}^+ = 1.45$ fm^{-1}.	
$c^- = 0.4125$ fm,		
$V_C{}^- = 0$,		
$V_T{}^- = +22$ MeV,	$\mu_T{}^- = 0.8$ fm^{-1},	
$V_S{}^- = -7317.5$ MeV,	$\mu_S{}^- = 3.7$ fm^{-1}.	

TABLE 3.1. The parameters of the Gammel-Thaler potential for $T = 1$.

the Yukawa shape $Y(\mu^\pm r)$ with range parameter $\mu^\pm$. The plus and minus refer to states of even and odd parity, respectively.

$$V(r) = +\infty, \qquad r < c^\pm,$$
$$= V_C{}^\pm Y(\mu_C{}^\pm r) + S_{12} V_T{}^\pm Y(\mu_T{}^\pm r) + \mathbf{S} \cdot \mathbf{l} V_S{}^\pm Y(\mu_S{}^\pm r), \qquad r > c^\pm,$$
$$Y(\mu r) = \frac{e^{-\mu r}}{\mu r}. \tag{3.65}$$

The values of the parameters are given in Table 3.1.

The Gammel-Thaler potential is interesting from the historical point of view because it was found necessary to modify it when off-shell information was needed, in this case for nuclear matter calculations. This will be discussed in Chapter 6.

The main feature of the potential is that the singlet-even potential is dominant and very straightforward. It is a strongly attractive force of rather short range compared to the one-pion force whose range parameter μ_π is 0.71 fm^{-1}. The triplet-odd force has no central part. The tensor part is weak but of very long range, and the spin-orbit force is extremely strong and of extremely short range.

This potential was obtained from purely phenomenological considerations. More recent potentials are those of Hamada and Johnston (62) and the Yale potential (Lassila, Hull, Ruppel, McDonald, and Breit, 62. The potential is given explicitly by Brueckner and Masterson, 62). These potentials are parametrized with the restriction that they tend to the one-pion exchange potential at large distances.

The Hamada-Johnston potential fits scattering data very well. It is given by

$$V = V_C + S_{12}V_T + \mathbf{S} \cdot \mathbf{l}V_S + L_{12}V_{SS},\tag{3.66}$$

where L_{12} is the spin-orbit squared operator (3.42).

$$V_C = 0.08(\tfrac{1}{3}\mu_\pi)(\boldsymbol{\tau}_1 \cdot \boldsymbol{\tau}_2)(\boldsymbol{\sigma}_1 \cdot \boldsymbol{\sigma}_2) Y(x)[1 + a_C Y(x) + b_C Y^2(x)]$$
$$V_T = 0.08(\tfrac{1}{3}\mu_\pi)(\boldsymbol{\tau}_1 \cdot \boldsymbol{\tau}_2)Z(x)[1 + a_T Y(x) + b_T Y^2(x)]$$
$$V_S = \mu_\pi G_S Y^2(x)[1 + b_S Y(x)]$$
$$V_{SS} = \mu_\pi G_{SS}x^{-2}Z(x)[1 + a_{SS} Y(x) + b_{SS} Y^2(x)],\tag{3.67}$$

$$Z(x) = \left(1 + \frac{3}{x} + \frac{3}{x^2}\right) Y(x),$$

$$x = \mu_\pi r.\tag{3.68}$$

The units of V in (3.67) are $(\mu_\pi{}^2/\hbar^2)$ MeV. The same hard core is used in all states. Its radius is

$$c = 0.485 \text{ fm.}$$

The numerical values of the potential parameters are given in Table 3.2.

It is useful to consider some qualitative aspects of the potential. At distances greater than the one-pion radius (1.4 fm) the singlet-even potential is dominated by the attractive central term. The triplet-odd potential is dominated by the tensor force, which is of longer range than the central force but is weaker on the average by a factor of about 2. These facts characterize the p-p force. The additional terms for the n-p force are singlet-odd and triplet-even. The singlet-odd force is small at large distances but dominated by the central term. The triplet-even force, which is responsible for the binding of the deuteron, is dominated by the tensor force, which is larger than the central

State	a_C	b_C	a_T	b_T	G_S	b_S	G_{SS}
Singlet even	+8.7	+10.6					−0.000891
Triplet odd	−9.07	+3.48	−1.29	+0.55	+0.1961	−7.12	−0.000891
Triplet even	+6.0	−1.0	−0.5	+0.2	+0.0743	−0.1	+0.00267
Singlet odd	−8.0	+12.0					−0.00267

a_{SS}	b_{SS}
+0.2	−0.2
−7.26	+6.92
+1.8	−0.4
+2.0	+6.0

TABLE 3.2. The parameters of the Hamada-Johnston potential.

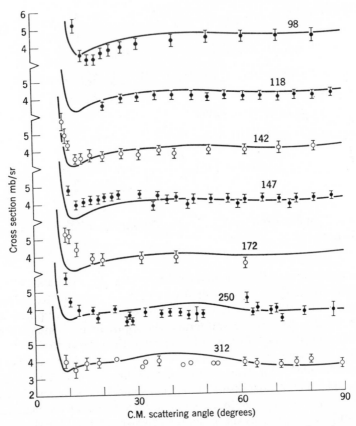

FIG. 3.5 The p-p differential cross sections at various energies (indicated on the figure in MeV) fitted by the Hamada-Johnston potential. (Adapted from Hamada and Johnston, 62.)

force by about a factor of 2. The quality of the fit to p-p scattering data given by the Hamada-Johnston potential is illustrated in Fig. 3.5.

A good idea of the strengths of the dominant forces is given by considering their values at 1.4 fm and at 1.8 fm, the average separation distance in nuclear matter. They are shown in Table 3.3.

		V(1.4 fm)(MeV)	V(1.8 fm)(MeV)
Singlet even	V_C	−45	−18
Triplet odd	V_T	+11	+8
	V_C	−4	−2
	V_S	−12	−2
Triplet even	V_T	−52	−24
	V_C	−25	−11
Singlet odd		Small	Small

TABLE 3.3. Values of the strength of the dominant terms in the Hamada-Johnston potential in different states at the one-pion radius (1.4 fm) and at the average separation distance in nuclear matter (1.8 fm).

Both local potentials illustrated here have similar characteristics at large and small distances. The hard core of course introduces strong correlations into nuclear wave functions for the reasons noted in Chapter 1B[iii].

[iv] SEPARABLE POTENTIALS

A separable potential is a form of nonlocal potential for which it is particularly easy to compute phase shifts. It is defined for the relative coordinate **r** in the situation where there are two possibly coupled wave functions with orbital quantum numbers l, l' as

$$V(\mathbf{r}, \mathbf{r}') = (\hbar^2/M)\sum_{\alpha ll'} |lSjmT_3\rangle[-\tilde{g}_{\alpha l}(r)\tilde{g}_{\alpha l'}(r') + \tilde{h}_{\alpha l}(r)\tilde{h}_{\alpha l'}(r')]$$
$$\times \langle l'SjmT_3|. \qquad (3.69)$$

The spin-angle-isospin function refers to the angular coordinate of **r**′ or **r**, depending on whether it has a prime outside the bracket. The quantum numbers $SjmT_3$ are represented by α.

We are interested in separable potentials because they provide an example of a potential which can be chosen to fit scattering data as well as a local potential (if enough parameters are used) but which has extremely different t-matrix elements off the energy shell. The use of such a potential in problems involving more than two bodies would enable us to design experiments to distinguish between potentials whose off-shell t-matrix elements are different although they are similar on the energy shell.

A set of separable potentials which fit nucleon-nucleon phase shifts quite well has been given by Tabakin (64). These potentials are smooth and do not have extremely large values at small distances which result in strong correlations and a large proportion of high-momentum components in nuclear wave functions.

One mathematical property which makes separable potentials particularly easy to handle is that the Schrödinger equation can easily be expressed in momentum space. In configuration space the Schrödinger equation is, for incident energy $\hbar^2 k_0^2/M$,

$$(\hbar^2/M)(\nabla^2 + k_0^2)\psi(\mathbf{r}) = \int d^3r' V(\mathbf{r}, \mathbf{r}')\psi(\mathbf{r}'). \tag{3.70}$$

The momentum-space representation of (3.70) is

$$(\hbar^2/M)(k_0^2 - k^2)\psi(\mathbf{k}) = \int d^3k' V(\mathbf{k}, \mathbf{k}')\psi(\mathbf{k}'), \tag{3.71}$$

where

$$\psi(\mathbf{k}) = (2\pi)^{-3/2} \int d^3r e^{-i\mathbf{k}\cdot\mathbf{r}}\psi(\mathbf{r}). \tag{3.72}$$

The form of the potential in momentum space is

$$V(\mathbf{k}, \mathbf{k}') = (2\hbar^2/\pi M) \sum_{all'} |lSjmT_3\rangle f_{ll'}^{\alpha}(k, k')\langle l'SjmT_3|', \tag{3.73}$$

where

$$f_{ll'}^{\alpha}(k, k') = i^{l'-l}[-g_{\alpha l}(k)g_{\alpha l'}(k') + h_{\alpha l}(k)h_{\alpha l'}(k')],$$

$$g_{\alpha l}(k) = \int r^2 dr j_l(kr)\tilde{g}_{\alpha l}(r), \tag{3.74}$$

$$h_{\alpha l}(k) = \int r^2 dr j_l(kr)\tilde{h}_{\alpha l}(r).$$

The spin-angle-isospin functions in (3.73) refer to the angular coordinates of $\mathbf{k}$, $\mathbf{k}'$.

A potential which is separable in configuration space is also separable in momentum space.

The integral equation corresponding to (3.71) is, for ingoing boundary conditions,

$$\psi^{(+)}(\mathbf{k}) = \delta(\mathbf{k}_0 - \mathbf{k})\chi_S^{Ms}\chi_T^{T_3}$$
$$- \frac{1}{(\hbar^2/M)(k^2 - k_0^2 - i\epsilon)} \int d^3k' V(\mathbf{k}, \mathbf{k}')\psi^{(+)}(\mathbf{k}'). \tag{3.75}$$

The inhomogeneous term of (3.75) is the Fourier transform of the plane wave $\exp(i\mathbf{k}_0 \cdot \mathbf{r})$ multiplied by the appropriate spin and isospin wave functions.

The scattering amplitude and phase shifts are found by applying the same spin-isospin generalization of the integral equation scattering theory of Chapter 2 as we applied in Chapter 3D to the differential equation for nucleon-nucleon scattering. A partial wave decomposition of the wave function, which is not essentially complicated by the presence of spin-isospin wave functions, leads to integral equations for the radial wave function, which are coupled if $l' \neq l$ and further coupled if more than one separable potential is used, as is the case in (3.69).

The essential mathematical simplification introduced by separable potentials is that the integral equations reduce to algebraic equations, which can be solved by matrix inversion.

In order to illustrate the potential we shall consider only the $^1S_0$ state, the dominant state for p-p scattering. In this state the essential problem of the change of sign of the phase shift, which necessitates a hard core in the local potential, is very prominent.

Tabakin managed to fit the $^1S_0$ phase shift very well with a smoothly varying combination of attractive and repulsive potentials given by

$$g_0(k) = \gamma(k^2 + a^2)^{-1}$$

$$h_0(k) = \beta k^2[(k - d)^2 + b^2]^{-1}[(k + d)^2 + b^2]^{-1}. \qquad (3.76)$$

Defining the equivalent strengths of the attractive and repulsive terms by

$$V_\gamma = \frac{\hbar^2}{M}\frac{\gamma^2}{a}$$

$$V_\beta = \frac{\hbar^2}{M}\frac{\beta^2}{b}, \qquad (3.77)$$

the parameters which fit the $^1S_0$ phase shift are

$$V_\gamma = 115.9 \text{ MeV}, \qquad a^{-1} = 0.834 \text{ fm},$$

$$V_\beta = 235.6 \text{ MeV}, \qquad b^{-1} = 0.801 \text{ fm},$$

$$d^{-1} = 0.694 \text{ fm}.$$

The quantities a and b are equivalent Yukawa range parameters and d is a correlation parameter. The fact that strong short-range correlations are absent in the wave function is seen in Fig. 3.6 where the zero-energy wave function is compared with the wave function for a hard-core potential and for a velocity-dependent potential, which will be discussed in the next section.

Potentials V, V' which are equivalent on the energy shell have the same scattering amplitude.

$$\int d^3r \int d^3r' e^{-i\mathbf{k}_f \cdot \mathbf{r}} V(\mathbf{r}, \mathbf{r}')\psi(\mathbf{k}_i, \mathbf{r}') = \int d^3r \int d^3r' e^{-i\mathbf{k}_f \cdot \mathbf{r}} V'(\mathbf{r}, \mathbf{r}')\psi'(\mathbf{k}_i, \mathbf{r}'). \quad (3.78)$$

Since V and V' are different, the wave functions ψ, ψ' must be different in the internal region where V, V' are nonzero. ψ and ψ' are identical in the exterior region since the scattering amplitude is determined from their asymptotic form. Differences in off-shell t-matrix elements are thus indicated by differences in the internal wave functions.

An extremely important fact about local and separable potentials which are equivalent on the energy shell may be understood from Fig. 3.6. The wave function $u_l(k, r)$ for a separable potential is greater than that for a local potential at small values of r and less than that for a local potential at larger values of r. Outside the potential they of course coincide. Off-shell t-matrix elements are integrals of products of $u_l(k, r)$, V and $U_l(k', r')$. The difference between the wave functions for local and nonlocal potentials tends to average out when the integration is performed, so that the corresponding off-shell t-matrix elements are not necessarily very different. This effect occurs when k and k' do not differ greatly. The difference is zero when $k = k'$. For very large k', it is of course possible to have the opposite effect.

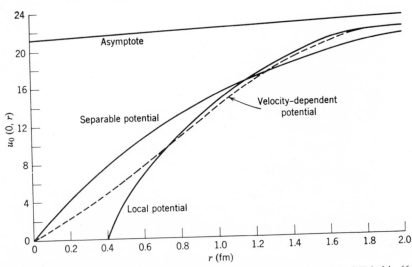

FIG. 3.6 The zero energy $^1S_0$ wave function for the separable potential of Tabakin (64) compared with the wave functions for a local potential with a hard core and for the velocity-dependent potential of Green (63). (Adapted from Tabakin, 64.)

Any nonlocal potential is equivalent to a velocity-dependent potential. This can be seen by expanding $\psi(\mathbf{r}')$ in a Taylor series about $\mathbf{r}' = \mathbf{r}$.

$$\int d^3 r' V(\mathbf{r}, \mathbf{r}') \psi(\mathbf{r}') = \left[\int d^3 r' V(\mathbf{r}, \mathbf{r}') e^{i(\mathbf{r}'-\mathbf{r}) \cdot \mathbf{p}/\hbar} \right] \psi(\mathbf{r}), \tag{3.79}$$

where

$$\mathbf{p} = -i\hbar \, \boldsymbol{\nabla}. \tag{3.80}$$

The equivalent velocity-dependent potential is

$$V(\mathbf{r}, \mathbf{p}) = \int d^3 r' V(\mathbf{r}, \mathbf{r}') e^{i(\mathbf{r}'-\mathbf{r}) \cdot \mathbf{p}/\hbar}. \tag{3.81}$$

For low momenta we can define an equivalent static potential, which is the first term of the following expansion of (3.81).

$$V(\mathbf{r}, \mathbf{p}) = \int d^3 r' V(\mathbf{r}, \mathbf{r}') + 0(\mathbf{p}) + \cdots \tag{3.82}$$

Consideration of the equivalent static potential enables us to understand how the Tabakin potential introduces repulsion at high energies while it allows attraction at low energies. At high energies the term $h_0(k)$ of (3.76) is positive definite and purely repulsive. It is of order k^{-2}, which is the same order as the attractive term $g_0(k)$. The static potential equivalent to $h_0(k)$ is

$$V(r, p = 0) = [\cos dr + (2bd)^{-1}(d^2 - b^2) \sin dr] V_\beta \frac{e^{-br}}{br}. \tag{3.83}$$

It is a Yukawa form* with a modulation whose period is determined by d. It alternates in sign, so that its effect on the low-energy scattering amplitude averages out.

The definition of the equivalent static potentials serves to clarify the meaning of the equivalent strength and Yukawa range parameters.

[v] VELOCITY-DEPENDENT POTENTIALS

The first few terms of the series (3.81), with suitable parametrization, have been used to fit phase shifts by Green (63). The potential has a static part with central, tensor, and spin-oribt character and a part dependent on p^2. The radial dependence for all types of static force is

$$V(r) = -A \exp\left[-(0.677 a\mu r)^2\right] - B \exp\left(-\mu r\right)]1 - \exp\left(-\alpha\mu r\right)]/\mu r. \tag{3.84}$$

* The details of the evaluation of the Fourier transform of the Yukawa potential are given in (3.87).

The velocity-dependent part is

$$\frac{p^2}{M}\,\omega(r) + \omega(r)\,\frac{p^2}{M}$$

$$\omega(r) = C \exp\left[-(0.6772\,c\mu r)^2\right]$$ (3.85)

$$\mu = 0.7082 \text{ fm}^{-1}.$$

The values of the parameters for p-p scattering are given in Table 3.4.

State	A_C	B_C	α_C	a_C	C_C	c_C	A_T	B_T	α_T
Singlet even	1.185	0.266	6	1.645	1.14	3	0	0	0
Triplet odd	0	−0.089	6	0	0	0	0	−0.35	6
	A_S	B_S	a_S						
Singlet even	0	0	0						
Triplet odd	2.0	0	2						

TABLE 3.4. Parameters of Green's velocity-dependent potential for $T = 1$ scattering.

The zero-energy $^1S_0$ wave function for this potential is shown in Fig. 3.6. It resembles the wave function for the separable potential at very small distances but, outside the core radius, it is much more like the wave function of the static potential.

[vi] PSEUDOPOTENTIALS

The most important properties of nuclear forces which must be represented for a first-order description of problems involving more than two bodies are their spin and isospin dependence and their radial dependence, from which an estimate of momentum-transfer amplitude distributions can be made. The simplest parametrization of these properties is a local, central pseudo-potential with exchange operators.

$$T(\sigma, \tau, r) = (W + BP^\sigma + MP^r + HP^\sigma P^r)t(r).$$ (3.86)

This force does not describe polarization. The radial form of $t(r)$ is generally parametrized by a linear combination of Yukawa form factors mainly because their Fourier transform is easily evaluated to give the scattering amplitude.

We shall evaluate the Fourier transform of the Yukawa form factor. The details will be useful as an introduction to the technique of handling three-dimensional integrals.

$$\int d^3r \, \frac{e^{i\mathbf{K}\cdot\mathbf{r}}\,e^{-\mu r}}{\mu r} = \sum_{lm} \int r^2 \, dr \int d\Omega \, \frac{4\pi i^l j_l(Kr) Y_l^{m*}(\Omega_K) Y_l^m(\Omega) e^{-\mu r}}{\mu r}$$

$$= \sum_{lm} 4\pi i^l Y_l^{m*}(\Omega_K) \int d\Omega \, Y_l^m(\Omega) Y_0^{0*}(\Omega)(4\pi)^{1/2}$$

$$\times \int r^2 \, dr \, \frac{j_l(Kr)e^{-\mu r}}{\mu r}$$

$$= 4\pi \int r^2 \, dr \, \frac{\sin Kr e^{-\mu r}}{K\mu r^2}$$

$$= \frac{4\pi}{\mu(K^2 + \mu^2)} \, . \tag{3.87}$$

We have used the orthogonality of the spherical harmonics to eliminate the angular momentum sums.

Clearly the differential cross section for a scattering amplitude calculated with a single Yukawa factor is large for small momentum transfers K and decreases towards 180°.

$$\mathbf{K} = \mathbf{k}_f - \mathbf{k}_i, \tag{3.88}$$

where $\mathbf{k}_f$ and $\mathbf{k}_i$ are the final and initial momenta of the projectile in the center of mass system. This is not good enough to fit fact 2 about n-p angular distributions although it does fit fact 3 about n-p and p-p energy distributions for fairly low energy.

The space-exchange parameter P^r changes $e^{i\mathbf{k}_i\cdot\mathbf{r}}$ into $e^{-i\mathbf{k}_i\cdot\mathbf{r}}$ in the matrix element. The scattering amplitude for a space-exchange force with a single Yukawa factor is

$$T_M = M \int d^3r e^{-i\mathbf{k}_f\cdot\mathbf{r}} \, \frac{e^{-\mu r}}{\mu r} \, P^r e^{i\mathbf{k}_i\cdot\mathbf{r}}$$

$$= \frac{M4\pi}{\mu} \, (Q^2 + \mu^2), \tag{3.89}$$

where

$$\mathbf{Q} = \mathbf{k}_f + \mathbf{k}_i. \tag{3.90}$$

The cross section calculated from this matrix element is evidently large for 180° scattering and small for 0° scattering.

A superposition of roughly equal values of Wigner and Majorana forces will fit the symmetry criterion quite well. For n-p scattering Serber (47) recommended the force

$$T(r) = -g^2 \frac{e^{-\mu r}}{r} \frac{1 + P^r}{2},$$ (3.91)

where

$$\frac{g^2}{\hbar c} = 0.405 \quad \text{for triplet scattering,}$$

$$= 0.280 \quad \text{for singlet scattering,}$$

$$\mu = 0.83 \text{ fm}^{-1}.$$

Since the calculation was based on 90 MeV n-p scattering, it is not unreasonable to make the Born approximation connection between the pseudopotential and the potential. The values of the parameters in (3.91) may be considered as estimates of the one-meson coupling constant and mass parameter.

To illustrate the use of exchange forces with antisymmetrized wave functions to describe spin dependence, we shall consider p-p scattering in some detail. First we shall treat the problem with a central potential $V(r)$. We can easily make the appropriate changes for a pseudopotential $T(r)$. The wave function of a free proton may be written as

$$= \exp (i\mathbf{k} \cdot \mathbf{r})(a_+\alpha + a_-\beta),$$ (3.92)

where, in a scattering experiment, the z-axis for the spin coordinates is given by the incident direction. The probability amplitudes for finding the proton with spin up or down are $a_\pm$.

If we ignore terms in the scattering potential which do not commute with spin, spin-up and spin-down particles can be considered as identifiable particles which scatter independently. Protons which start in a singlet state finish in a singlet state, and protons which start in a triplet state finish in a triplet state. We can consider singlet and triplet scattering as separate experiments because we can in principle make completely polarized beams and targets.

Two-particle wave functions must be totally antisymmetric with respect to space and spin. Denote the space wave functions for the scattering problem for spin-up and spin-down particles by X, Y. The total scattering wave function with asymptotic states X, Y, for example, will be written XY for triplet scattering and $\overline{XY}$ for singlet scattering. The corresponding final asymptotic states will be denoted by X', Y'. The subscripts L and R will denote the left and right particles in the scattering experiment. For the total scattering wave functions X, Y, L denotes the projectile, R denotes the struck particle. In principle we can distinguish six types of experiment by knowing the spins. The six matrix elements, given by a slight extension of (2.103), are written schematically as

$$
\begin{aligned}
T_1 &= \langle X_L{}', X_R{}' |V| X_L, X_R \rangle, \\
T_2 &= \langle X_L{}', Y_R{}' |V| X_L, Y_R \rangle, \\
T_3 &= \langle Y_L{}', X_R{}' |V| Y_L, X_R \rangle, \\
T_4 &= \langle X_L{}', Y_R{}' |V| Y_L, X_R \rangle, \\
T_5 &= \langle Y_L{}', X_R{}' |V| X_L, Y_R \rangle, \\
T_6 &= \langle Y_L{}', Y_R{}' |V| Y_L, Y_R \rangle.
\end{aligned}
\tag{3.93}
$$

The antisymmetric wave functions for final or total states, depending on whether they are written with or without primes, are

$$
\begin{aligned}
& 2^{-\frac{1}{2}}(X_L X_R - X_R X_L)\alpha_1\alpha_2, \\
& 2^{-\frac{3}{2}}[(X_L Y_R - Y_R X_L)(\alpha_1\beta_2 + \beta_1\alpha_2) + (\overline{X_L Y_R} + \overline{Y_R X_L})(\alpha_1\beta_2 - \beta_1\alpha_2)], \\
& 2^{-\frac{3}{2}}[(Y_L X_R - X_R Y_L)(\alpha_1\beta_2 + \beta_1\alpha_2) - (\overline{Y_L X_R} + \overline{X_R Y_L})(\alpha_1\beta_2 - \beta_1\alpha_2)], \\
& 2^{-\frac{1}{2}}(Y_L Y_R - Y_R Y_L)\beta_1\beta_2.
\end{aligned}
$$

In this notation the wave function for coordinates $\mathbf{r}_1$, $\boldsymbol{\sigma}_1$ is written on the left, and for $\mathbf{r}_2$, $\boldsymbol{\sigma}_2$ it is written on the right.

The central potential $V_{TS}(r)$ is given by

$$
V_{TS}(r) = (W + BP^\sigma + MP^r + HP^rP^\sigma)V(r).
\tag{3.94}
$$

The evaluation of the matrix elements will be illustrated by using T_2 as an example.

$$
\begin{aligned}
T_2 = \tfrac{1}{8}\langle &(X_L{}'Y_R{}' - Y_R{}'X_L{}')(\alpha_1\beta_2 + \beta_1\alpha_2) \\
&+ (X_L{}'Y_R{}' + Y_R{}'X_L{}')(\alpha_1\beta_2 - \beta_1\alpha_2)| \\
&\times V(r)(W + BP^\sigma + MP^r + HP^rP^\sigma) \\
&\times |(X_L Y_R - Y_R X_L)(\alpha_1\beta_2 + \beta_1\alpha_2) + (\overline{X_L Y_R} + \overline{Y_R X_L})(\alpha_1\beta_2 - \beta_1\alpha_2)\rangle.
\end{aligned}
\tag{3.95}
$$

This matrix element is evaluated by using the fact that the wave functions are eigenfunctions of the exchange operators. We have

$$
\begin{aligned}
T_2 = \tfrac{1}{8}\langle (X_L{}'Y_R{}' &- Y_R{}'X_L{}')(\alpha_1\beta_2 + \beta_1\alpha_2) \\
&+ (X_L{}'Y_R{}' + Y_R{}'X_L{}')(\alpha_1\beta_2 - \beta_1\alpha_2)| \\
\times V(r)\,|W[(X_L Y_R &- Y_R X_L)(\alpha_1\beta_2 + \beta_1\alpha_2) \\
&+ (\overline{X_L Y_R} + \overline{Y_R X_L})(\alpha_1\beta_2 - \beta_1\alpha_2)] \\
+ B[(X_L Y_R - Y_R X_L)(\alpha_1\beta_2 &+ \beta_1\alpha_2) \\
&- (\overline{X_L Y_R} + \overline{Y_R X_L})(\alpha_1\beta_2 - \beta_1\alpha_2)] \\
+ M[-(X_L Y_R - Y_R X_L)(\alpha_1\beta_2 &+ \beta_1\alpha_2) \\
&+ (\overline{X_L Y_R} + \overline{Y_R X_L})(\alpha_1\beta_2 - \beta_1\alpha_2)] \\
+ H[-(X_L Y_R - Y_R X_L)(\alpha_1\beta_2 &+ \beta_1\alpha_2) \\
&- (\overline{X_L Y_R} + \overline{Y_R X_L})(\alpha_1\beta_2 - \beta_1\alpha_2)]\rangle.
\end{aligned}
\tag{3.96}
$$

The right-hand state vector in this matrix element can be written

$$|(W + B - M - H)(X_L Y_R - Y_R X_L)(\alpha_1 \beta_2 + \beta_1 \alpha_2)$$
$$+ (W - B + M - H)(\overline{X_L Y_R} + \overline{Y_R X_L})(\alpha_1 \beta_2 - \beta_1 \alpha_2)\rangle.$$

Using the orthonormality of the spin wave functions α and β, the matrix element becomes

$$T_2 = \tfrac{1}{4}[(W + B - M - H)\langle X_L' Y_R'| V(r) |X_L Y_R - Y_R X_L\rangle$$
$$+ (W - B + M - H)\langle X_L' Y_R'| V(r) |\overline{X_L Y_R} + \overline{Y_R X_L}\rangle$$
$$- (W + B - M - H)\langle Y_R' X_L'| V(r) |X_L Y_R - Y_R X_L\rangle$$
$$+ (W - B + M - H)\langle Y_R' X_L'| V(r) |\overline{X_L Y_R} + \overline{Y_R X_L}\rangle] \tag{3.97}$$

Interchanging coordinates 1 and 2 in the last two terms of (3.97) gives

$$T_2 = \tfrac{1}{2}(W - B + M - H)\langle X_L' Y_R'| V(r) |\overline{X_L Y_R} + \overline{Y_R X_L}\rangle$$
$$+ \tfrac{1}{2}(W + B - M - H)\langle X_L' Y_R'| V(r) |X_L Y_R - Y_R X_L\rangle. \tag{3.98}$$

The first matrix element of (3.98) is space-symmetric. It represents scattering in a spin-antisymmetric or singlet state. The second matrix element of (3.98) is space-antisymmetric. It represents scattering in a triplet state, which can be experimentally distinguished from singlet scattering.

We can perform similar reductions of all six matrix elements (3.93). T_1 and T_6 reduce to single matrix elements. The others give pairs like T_2. All these 10 matrix elements represent distinguishable experiments, so the total cross section is obtained by adding the squares of each.

We shall use the following notation for the exchange parameters.

$$A_{01} = W + B + M + H = 1$$
$$A_{00} = W - B - M + H$$
$$A_{10} = W - B + M - H \tag{3.99}$$
$$A_{11} = W + B - M - H.$$

A_{TS} represents scattering in isospin-state T, spin-state S. For two protons the isospin is 1. A_{10} is the singlet parameter, A_{11} is the triplet parameter. We have freedom to choose a value for one. We choose $A_{01} = 1$.

The total cross section for p-p scattering is

$$
\frac{d\sigma}{d\Omega} = \left(\frac{\mu}{2\pi\hbar^2}\right)^2 \Big\{ A_{11}{}^2 \, |\langle X_L' X_R'| \, V(r) \, |X_L X_R - X_R X_L\rangle|^2
$$

$$
+ A_{11}{}^2 \, |\langle Y_L' Y_R'| \, V(r) \, |Y_L Y_R - Y_R Y_L\rangle|^2
$$

$$
+ \tfrac{1}{4}A_{11}{}^2 \, |\langle X_L' Y_R'| \, V(r) \, |X_L Y_R - Y_R X_L\rangle|^2
$$

$$
+ \tfrac{1}{4}A_{11}{}^2 \, |\langle X_L' Y_R'| \, V(r) \, |Y_L X_R - X_R Y_L\rangle|^2
$$

$$
+ \tfrac{1}{4}A_{11}{}^2 \, |\langle Y_L' X_R'| \, V(r) \, |X_L Y_R - Y_R X_L\rangle|^2
$$

$$
+ \tfrac{1}{4}A_{11}{}^2 \, |\langle Y_L' X_R'| \, V(r) \, |Y_L X_R - X_R Y_L\rangle|^2
$$

$$
+ \tfrac{1}{4}A_{10}{}^2 \, |\langle X_L' Y_R'| \, V(r) \, |\overline{X_L Y_R} + \overline{Y_R X_L}\rangle|^2
$$

$$
+ \tfrac{1}{4}A_{10}{}^2 \, |\langle X_L' Y_R'| \, V(r) \, |\overline{Y_L X_R} + \overline{X_R Y_L}\rangle|^2
$$

$$
+ \tfrac{1}{4}A_{10}{}^2 \, |\langle Y_L' X_R'| \, V(r) \, |\overline{Y_L X_R} + \overline{X_R Y_L}\rangle|^2
$$

$$
+ \tfrac{1}{4}A_{10}{}^2 \, |\langle Y_L' X_R'| \, V(r) \, |\overline{X_L Y_R} + \overline{Y_R X_L}\rangle|^2 \Big\}. \tag{3.100}
$$

The notation X and Y for the asymptotic space wave functions has of course only been used for convenience in identifying particles. In the absence of spin dependence other than $\boldsymbol{\sigma}(1)\cdot\boldsymbol{\sigma}(2)$, the space wave functions are all identical for a given spin state.

$$
\frac{d\sigma}{d\Omega} = \left(\frac{\mu}{2\pi\hbar^2}\right)^2 \left(3A_{11}{}^2 \frac{d\sigma_t}{d\Omega} + A_{10}{}^2 \frac{d\sigma_s}{d\Omega}\right), \tag{3.101}
$$

where σ_s and σ_t are cross sections for singlet and triplet scattering.

The first 6 terms denote triplet scattering. For a Wigner force they have a statistical weight 3. The last 4 terms denote singlet scattering. For a Wigner force they have a statistical weight 1. For a Serber force ($W = M, H = B = 0$), $A_{11} = 0$; protons can only scatter in singlet states.

Proton-proton scattering at 90° in the C.M. system can only depend on the Serber part of the force because triplet scattering is excluded by the Pauli principle. The energy dependence of 90° p-p scattering gives us a model for the radial shape of the singlet-even nuclear force in the exchange mixture model.

This particular situation is ideally suited to the representation of the force by a central pseudopotential, since the singlet-even force is mainly central. In the foregoing analysis the potential $V(r)$ is replaced by $T(r)$ and the total scattering wave function is replaced by a product of two plane waves. The final asymptotic (Coulomb) wave function is replaced by a plane wave. The effects of the Coulomb force are now included in $T(r)$, which is chosen to fit 90° p-p scattering up to 300 MeV.

A function which fits quite well was chosen by Lim and McCarthy (64a).

$$T(r) = V_0 \left(\frac{e^{-\mu_1 r}}{\mu_1 r} + \alpha_2 \frac{e^{-\mu_2 r}}{\mu_2 r} + \alpha_3 \frac{e^{-\mu_3 r}}{\mu_3 r} \right). \qquad (3.102)$$

The parameter values are (Fig. 3.7):

$$\mu_1 = 0.73 \text{ fm}^{-1}, \qquad \mu_2 = 1.5 \text{ fm}^{-1}, \qquad \mu_3 = 3.0 \text{ fm}^{-1},$$

$$V_0 = -83 \text{ MeV}, \qquad \alpha_2 = -5, \qquad \alpha_3 = 20.$$

At angles away from 90° this function does not fit so well. It gives too much anisotropy. However, it has proved extremely useful for representing the t-matrix in reaction theories where, until recently, the problem has been to find a good approximation in principle to the reaction amplitude. The pseudopotential approximation has enabled reaction theories to be successfully compared to experiments, thereby checking the reaction approximations. The use of a more accurate representation of the t-matrix has not yet proved necessary for reaction calculations.

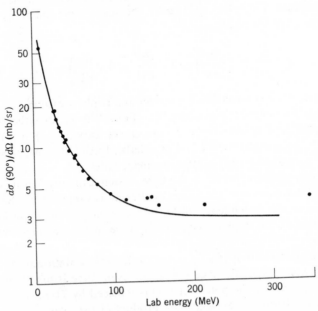

FIG. 3.7   The p-p differential cross section at 90° fitted by the pseudopotential (3.102).

F. SUMMARY

In this chapter we have first given a semiquantitative description of nucleon-nucleon forces based on general principles of quantum mechanics. We have given rough values for the strength of the forces based on the deuteron. We have then seen what effect on our mathematical description is caused by general symmetry principles and the Pauli exclusion principle, and we have observed some phenomenological approximations to the forces that are used for different purposes.

We may sum up our basic understanding of the nuclear force by saying that meson theories give essentially divergent scattering amplitudes in the Born approximation because the first Born approximation predicts a large value for $g^2/\hbar c$. There is no basic theory of nuclear forces that is as satisfactory as quantum electrodynamics is for atomic forces. However, the Born approximation, including the exchange of bosons whose properties correspond largely to those of known bosons, predicts scattering very well. The reason for this is not known.

At nonrelativistic energies ($v^2/c^2 = 0.1$ for 40 MeV protons), we can describe nuclear forces by a potential model. The forces are spin-dependent and very nearly charge-independent. Charge independence is confirmed by studying simple many-nucleon rather than two-nucleon problems, although the same $T = 1$ phase shifts fit both n-p and p-p scattering. The simplest force is the singlet-even force which applies to p-p scattering at 90°. For bound-state problems and other scattering problems there are tensor and spin-orbit forces whose effects are only moderately small compared to the effects of the central forces.

To give a good semiquantitative idea of the effects of two-body forces in nuclear reactions, we shall generally use only central forces in our work.

We must remember that only limited information about two-body forces is obtained from two-body scattering experiments. Scattering amplitudes do not determine the potential uniquely. Many-body experiments depend on the potential, not the two-body scattering amplitudes. We sometimes express this by saying that we need two-body scattering information off the energy shell. Examples have been given of local, separable, and velocity-dependent potentials which fit two-body scattering data. They have very different internal wave functions, hence very different off-shell t-matrix elements.

Many-body experiments are interpreted on the basis of two-body forces as a working hypothesis. There is a priori evidence that many-body forces are not negligible. There is no reason to expect effective nuclear forces in nuclear matter to be exactly the same as effective two-body forces for two-body experiments. Reactions and many-body bound states will be studied with a view to obtaining more information about this point.

FURTHER READING

1. D. M. Brink, *Nuclear Forces*, Pergamon Press, London, 1965.
   Historical account of the development of the study of nuclear forces.

2. L. Hulthen and M. Sugawara, *Encyclopedia of Physics*, Vol. XXXIX, Berlin: Springer-Verlag, 1957.
   M. J. Moravcsik, *The Two-Nucleon Interaction*, Oxford University Press, London, 1963.
   R. Wilson, *The Nucleon-Nucleon Interaction*, Interscience Publishers, New York, 1963.
   Comprehensive reviews.

3. W. Heisenberg, *Z. phys.*, **77**, 1 (1932).
   E. Majorana, *Z. Phys.*, **82**, 137 (1933).
   E. P. Wigner, *Phys. Rev.* **43**, 252; *Z. Phys.*, **83**, 253 (1933).
   Original papers on exchange forces.

4. H. A. Bethe and R. F. Bacher, *Rev. Mod. Phys.*, **8**, 82 (1936).
   Early review of nuclear forces with detail on the deuteron.

5. R. Jastrow, *Phys. Rev.*, **81**, 165 (1951).
   The repulsive core for local potentials.

6. H. Yukawa, *Proc. Math. Soc. Japan*, **17**, 48 (1935).
   Original paper on the meson field.

7. R. A. Bryan and B. L. Scott, *Phys. Rev.*, **135**, B434 (1964).
   Fits to phenomenological potentials and phase shifts using different one-boson exchange potentials.

8. L. M. Delves and J. M. Blatt, *Nucl. Phys.*, **A98**, 503 (1967) (and references therein).
   R. Aaron, R. D. Amado, and Y. Y. Yam, *Phys. Rev.*, **136**, B650 (1964); **140**, B1291 (1965); *Rev. Mod. Phys.*, **37**, 516 (1965).
   Two-nucleon forces in three-nucleon problems.

PROBLEMS

1. Using experimental information, derive the order of magnitude of the strength of the nucleon-nucleon potential by an uncertainty principle argument.

2. Write out four-dimensional matrix representations of the spin-exchange operator P^σ and the three components of the pseudovector matrix $\sigma(1) \times \sigma(2)$.

3. What is the depth of a square well of radius 1.7 fm which gives a binding energy of 2.226 MeV for the deuteron?

4. Using the well of Problem 3 check the Born approximation for the *s*-wave phase shift against the exact value at 10 MeV, 50 MeV and 100 MeV.

5. In a p-p scattering experiment the final-state protons are counted in coincidence. One counter is kept at an angle of 45° to the incident direction. What is the angular distribution of the particles in the other counter? How is this result reconciled with the uncertainty principle?

6. Calculate the well depth and effective range for a potential with an infinitely repulsive core at $r = c$ followed by a square well, used to represent the singlet n-p force.

$$V(r) = \infty, \quad r < c,$$
$$= -V, \quad c < r < b + c,$$
$$= 0, \quad r > b + c.$$

7. Plot the angular distribution for p-p scattering at a laboratory energy of 60 MeV using the pseudopotential (3.102).

4

NUCLEAR FORCES
IN NUCLEAR MATTER

In the qualitative discussion of nuclear matter in Chapter 1B, it was shown that there is some validity in the independent particle description because the Pauli principle prevents the strong nucleon-nucleon forces from causing virtual scattering of two nucleons into occupied states. Really short-range collisions will give the particles virtual momenta that are outside of the Fermi sphere. Hence there are strong short-range correlations resulting in high-momentum components in the wave functions. For nucleons whose energy is near the Fermi energy, long-range collisions can be important because only small virtual momentum transfers are necessary to put the particles into unoccupied states. Such virtual collisions lead to weak or long-range correlations.

The object of this chapter is first to formulate the concept of virtual collisions and momentum transfers in the language of quantum mechanics. These ideas are basic to nuclear theory and it is convenient to introduce them in the context of nuclear matter. We will then discuss the formulation of the fact that the Pauli principle allows certain virtual collisions and not others. The equation that is formulated is the Brueckner-Bethe-Goldstone (BBG) equation (Brueckner and Gammel, 58; Bethe and Goldstone, 56. A summary of the earlier work of Brueckner and collaborators is given by Bethe, 56). The equation describes the relative motion of two nucleons in nuclear matter. From the wave functions which are the solutions of this equation we shall develop quantitative ideas about the importance of strong and weak correlations, using a simplified local nuclear force which contains the essential elements of exchange and repulsion. The approach is largely that of Gomes, Walecka, and Weisskopf (58. See also Walecka and Gomes, 67).

A. THE INDEPENDENT PAIR MODEL

The independent particle model, by definition, excludes a description of the forces between nucleons. The first approximation which includes such a description is the independent pair model. The interaction of any pair of particles is treated according to an assumption about the nuclear force, but we neglect the interaction of all other particles among themselves and with the pair.

The general expression for the expectation value of the energy of a system of A particles is

$$E = \langle \Psi | \sum_{i=1}^{A} \left(-\frac{\hbar^2}{2M} \nabla_i^2 \right) + \frac{1}{2} \sum_{i=1}^{A} \sum_{k=1}^{A} v_{ik} | \Psi \rangle, \qquad (4.1)$$

where v_{ik} is the potential energy operator for the ik pair. We shall study the ground-state wave function Ψ in some detail. The approximate validity of the independent particle model encourages us to describe the system basically in terms of single-particle states labelled by $\alpha, \beta, \ldots$.

[i] THE EFFECTIVE MASS APPROXIMATION

In the independent particle model the A particles occupy the A single-particle states that lie lowest in energy. Each particle feels the same collective potential W due to the combined effect of all the other particles. In infinite nuclear matter our considerations are not affected by the single-particle potential if it depends only on the position of the particle. Since there is no physically distinguished point from which to determine the position, the zero of potential energy is not defined. We may set the velocity-independent part of the single-particle potential as zero.

If, however, the single-particle force W is velocity-dependent, the total energy of the independent particle model is given by

$$E_{IPM} = E_0 + \frac{1}{2} \sum_{\alpha} W(p_\alpha), \qquad (4.2)$$

where p_α is the momentum of the particle in the single-particle state α.

Considering only the p^2 terms, we express $W(p)$ as

$$W(p) = W_0 + \frac{1}{2} \frac{M - M^*}{MM^*} p^2. \qquad (4.3)$$

The single-particle Schrödinger equation for the state α is, using $p^2 = -\hbar^2\nabla^2$,

$$\frac{p^2}{2M} + W_0 + \frac{M - M^*}{2MM^*} p^2 - \epsilon_\alpha = \frac{p^2}{2M}\left(1 + \frac{M - M^*}{M^*}\right) + W_0 - \epsilon_\alpha$$

$$= \frac{p^2}{2M^*} + W_0 - \epsilon_\alpha$$

$$= 0.$$

We then have for the energy of the level α

$$\epsilon_\alpha = \frac{p^2}{2M^*} + W_0. \tag{4.4}$$

M^* is the effective mass of a nucleon. The approximation in which only terms up to order p^2 are considered is the effective mass approximation. In this approximation, nuclear matter is like a Fermi gas of particles with mass different from M. The Fermi momentum is

$$k_F = (3\pi^2 \rho/2)^{1/3}. \tag{4.5}$$

The energy of the degenerate state is

$$E_0 = \sum_\alpha \frac{\hbar^2}{2M} \frac{1}{2}\left(1 + \frac{M}{M^*}\right) k_\alpha^2$$

$$= A \frac{3}{10} \frac{\hbar^2}{2M}\left(1 + \frac{M}{M^*}\right) k_F^2. \tag{4.6}$$

In the independent pair model we shall include possible velocity dependence of the single-particle force in the effective mass approximation. The effective mass can be determined self-consistently from the independent pair model, as will be seen.

The energy of the system in this model is written

$$E = E_0 + \tfrac{1}{2} \sum_{\alpha\beta} U_{\alpha\beta}, \tag{4.7}$$

where α, β are occupied states and $U_{\alpha\beta}$ is the energy correction coming from the pair interaction. The assumption of the model is that the interaction is zero for any pair not in states α or β.

The states can be identified by the asymptotic behavior of the wave function for large distances at which they correspond to two states of well-defined momentum $e^{ik_\alpha \cdot r_1}$ and $e^{ik_\beta \cdot r_2}$. The subscripts 1 and 2 label the particles.

For a particle in state α, the interaction energy with all other particles is $\sum_\beta U_{\alpha\beta}$. Hence

$$W(p_\alpha) = \sum_\beta U_{\alpha\beta}. \tag{4.8}$$

Self-consistent determination of W means that the $U_{\alpha\beta}$ resulting from the motion of particles in a momentum-dependent single-particle potential reproduces the original choice (4.8) of W.

[ii] VIRTUAL COLLISIONS

Since the pair of particles under consideration is in a Fermi gas, there are restrictions on the way it can scatter under the potential law. In free space an observable collision could occur in which the initial momenta are k_α,

$\mathbf{k}_\beta$ and the final momenta are $\mathbf{k}_\gamma$, $\mathbf{k}_\delta$. In nuclear matter this cannot happen. The energy of the system cannot change spontaneously as it would have to do if the pair could be lifted into unoccupied states γ and δ. At large distances the particles must always have the momenta $\mathbf{k}_\alpha$ and $\mathbf{k}_\beta$.

The scattering problem in nuclear matter thus differs from the scattering problem in free space by the fact that the boundary conditions are different. No scattering is observable at large distances, however, the interaction can distort the wave function at small distances. This distortion corresponds to virtual excitations. The system is never observed at small distances.

The mathematical formulation of the problem has been given by Bethe and Goldstone (56). The wave equation for a free pair is

$$\left[\frac{\hbar^2}{2M}(\nabla_1^2 + \nabla_2^2) + \epsilon_{\alpha\beta}\right]\Psi_{\alpha\beta}(\mathbf{r}_1, \mathbf{r}_2) = v(\mathbf{r}_1, \mathbf{r}_2)\Psi_{\alpha\beta}(\mathbf{r}_1, \mathbf{r}_2), \qquad (4.9)$$

where

$$\epsilon_{\alpha\beta} = \frac{\hbar^2}{2M}(k_\alpha^2 + k_\beta^2). \qquad (4.10)$$

It is convenient to express (5.9) in terms of the relative coordinate

$$\mathbf{r} = \mathbf{r}_1 - \mathbf{r}_2, \qquad (4.11)$$

as was done in Chapter 2.

The scattering amplitude for initial states α, β, and final states γ, δ is given by

$$f(\mathbf{k}', \mathbf{k}) = \frac{\mu}{2\pi\hbar^2} \int d^3r\, e^{-i\mathbf{k}'\cdot\mathbf{r}} v(r)\psi_\alpha(\mathbf{k}, \mathbf{r}) \qquad (4.12)$$

where $\hbar\mathbf{k}'$ is the momentum of particle 1 in the center-of-mass system defined by $\mathbf{k}_\gamma = -\mathbf{k}_\delta$, and $\hbar\mathbf{k}$ is the momentum of particle 1 in the center-of-mass system defined by $\mathbf{k}_\alpha = -\mathbf{k}_\beta$. ψ_α is the wave function of relative motion for an initial situation defined by α.

For elastic scattering or, in other words, for an observable collision, the amplitude f is *on the energy shell*. This means $\mathbf{k}_\gamma + \mathbf{k}_\delta = \mathbf{k}_\alpha + \mathbf{k}_\beta$, or $k = k'$. Equation (4.12), however, still defines a function $f(\mathbf{k}', \mathbf{k})$ for the case $k \neq k'$. This is called a *scattering amplitude off the energy shell*. It is irrelevant for elastic scattering. The scattering amplitude off the energy shell is the t-matrix element for which the C.M. energy of the incident particle, but not the final state particle, is the same as the energy eigenvalue for which the Schrödinger equation is solved.

It is a general feature of many-body problems that the presence of more than two bodies introduces into the theory matrix elements representing two-body interactions off the energy shell. These may be called *virtual transition amplitudes* because such a two-body transition cannot be observed in isolation. The case of nuclear matter provides our first example of this situation. Virtual transition amplitudes describe the shape of the two-body wave function, since they are the Fourier components of $v\psi_\alpha$.

Since the pair is embedded in a Fermi distribution, we must exclude scattering into occupied states. We replace (4.9) with the Brueckner-Bethe-Goldstone equation.

$$\left[\frac{\hbar^2}{2M^*}(\nabla_1{}^2 + \nabla_2{}^2) + \epsilon_{\alpha\beta}\right]\Psi_{\alpha\beta}(\mathbf{r}_1, \mathbf{r}_2) = Q_{\alpha\beta}{}^F v(\mathbf{r}_1, \mathbf{r}_2)\Psi_{\alpha\beta}(\mathbf{r}_1, \mathbf{r}_2). \quad (4.13)$$

$\epsilon_{\alpha\beta}$ is the eigenvalue and $Q_{\alpha\beta}{}^F$ is a projection operator which rejects all matrix elements $f(\mathbf{k}', \mathbf{k})$ for scattering to states that are not outside the Fermi distribution.

In order to find the form of $Q_{\alpha\beta}{}^F$ it is again convenient to transform (4.13) to the system of center-of-mass coordinate $\mathbf{R}$ and relative coordinate $\mathbf{r}$. The free scattering equation (4.9) becomes, in terms of the motion of the particle in state α,

$$\left[\frac{\hbar^2}{2\mu^*}\nabla^2 + \epsilon\right]\psi_\alpha(\mathbf{r}) = v(\mathbf{r})\psi_\alpha(\mathbf{r}). \quad (4.14)$$

The right-hand side can be expanded using the Fourier expansion of $\delta(\mathbf{r} - \mathbf{s})$.

$$v(\mathbf{r})\psi_\alpha(\mathbf{r}) = \int d^3s v(\mathbf{s})\psi_\alpha(\mathbf{s})\delta(\mathbf{r} - \mathbf{s})$$

$$= (2\pi)^{-3}\int d^3s v(\mathbf{s})\psi_\alpha(\mathbf{s})\int d^3k e^{i\mathbf{k}\cdot(\mathbf{r}-\mathbf{s})}. \quad (4.15)$$

The right-hand side of the BBG equation contains only Fourier components of $v\psi_\alpha$ outside the Fermi sphere or, in other words, amplitudes for virtual transitions to states outside the Fermi sphere. It may be written similarly.

$$Q_\alpha{}^F v(\mathbf{r})\psi_\alpha(\mathbf{r}) = \int d^3s v(\mathbf{s})\psi_\alpha(\mathbf{s})\,\Delta(\mathbf{r} - \mathbf{s})$$

$$= (2\pi)^{-3}\int d^3s v(\mathbf{s})\psi_\alpha(\mathbf{s})\int_{k_F} d^3k e^{i\mathbf{k}\cdot(\mathbf{r}-\mathbf{s})}. \quad (4.16)$$

We can break up the $\mathbf{k}$ integral into the integral for all space minus the integral for excluded states:

$$Q_\alpha{}^F v(\mathbf{r})\psi_\alpha(\mathbf{r}) = v(\mathbf{r})\psi_\alpha(\mathbf{r}) - \int d^3s v(\mathbf{s})G(\mathbf{r} - \mathbf{s})\psi_\alpha(\mathbf{s}), \quad (4.17)$$

where

$$G(\mathbf{r} - \mathbf{s}) = (2\pi)^{-3}\int_0^{k_F} d^3k e^{i\mathbf{k}\cdot(\mathbf{r}-\mathbf{s})}. \quad (4.18)$$

The operator Q_α^F turns v into a nonlocal potential operator $V(\mathbf{r}, \mathbf{s})$ given by

$$V(\mathbf{r}, \mathbf{s}) = v(\mathbf{s})[\delta(\mathbf{r} - \mathbf{s}) - G(\mathbf{r} - \mathbf{s})]. \qquad (4.19)$$

In the case where the center of mass of the two nucleons in states α, β is at rest relative to the average motion of the Fermi distribution,

$$G(r) = \frac{\sin k_F r - k_F r \cos k_F r}{2\pi^2 r^3}. \qquad (4.20)$$

In other cases the Fermi distribution is not isotropic with respect to the center of mass.

If we change the order of integration in (4.16), we can see how the operator Q_α^F selects off-energy-shell scattering amplitudes. The scattering amplitudes (4.12) are Fourier components of $v(\mathbf{r})\psi_\alpha(\mathbf{r})$ with respect to $\mathbf{k}'$. Equation (4.16) is rewritten as

$$Q_\alpha^F v(\mathbf{r})\psi_\alpha(\mathbf{k}, \mathbf{r}) = (2\pi)^{-3} \int_{k_F} d^3k' e^{i\mathbf{k}'\cdot\mathbf{r}} \int d^3s e^{-i\mathbf{k}'\cdot\mathbf{s}} v(\mathbf{s})\psi_\alpha(\mathbf{k}, \mathbf{s}). \qquad (4.16')$$

The $\mathbf{s}$ integral of (4.16') is a scattering amplitude for a virtual collision, since values of $\mathbf{k}'$ which do not conserve momentum are allowed. If all values of $\mathbf{k}'$ are allowed, we can see from (4.15) that the scattering amplitude is on the energy shell because the $\mathbf{k}'$ integral is $\delta(\mathbf{r} - \mathbf{s})$. However, the many-body nature of the problem, which requires the cutoff k_F in the $\mathbf{k}'$ integration, introduces virtual scattering amplitudes. In fact all real scattering amplitudes (except that for forward scattering, $\gamma = \alpha$, $\delta = \beta$) are zero.

B. THE SOLUTION OF THE BRUECKNER-BETHE-GOLDSTONE EQUATION

The single-particle wave functions, denoted by $\phi_\alpha(\mathbf{r})$, are given by plane waves normalized in a volume Ω.

$$\phi_\alpha(\mathbf{r}) = \Omega^{-1/2} e^{i\mathbf{k}_\alpha \cdot \mathbf{r}}. \qquad (4.21)$$

The boundary conditions on the solution $\Psi_{\alpha\beta}(\mathbf{r}_1, \mathbf{r}_2)$ of (4.13) are

$$\Psi_{\alpha\beta}(\mathbf{r}_1, \mathbf{r}_2) \sim \phi_\alpha(\mathbf{r}_1)\phi_\beta(\mathbf{r}_2), \qquad \alpha,\beta \text{ not identical}$$

$$\sim 2^{-1/2}[\phi_\alpha(\mathbf{r}_1)\phi_\beta(\mathbf{r}_2) - \phi_\beta(\mathbf{r}_1)\phi_\alpha(\mathbf{r}_2)], \qquad \alpha,\beta \text{ identical.} \qquad (4.22)$$

For very small distances where $|\mathbf{r}_1 - \mathbf{r}_2| \ll 1/k_F$, $\Psi_{\alpha\beta}$ is equal to the solution of the free-scattering problem, since the exclusion of Fourier components for $k < k_F$ has a very small effect on the wave function where its Fourier components are mostly for high momenta.

The first step in the discussion of the solution of (4.13) is the self-consistent determination of the effective mass M^*. The eigenvalue $\epsilon_{\alpha\beta}$ becomes

$$\epsilon_{\alpha\beta} = \langle \Psi_{\alpha\beta} | - \frac{\hbar^2}{2M^*} (\nabla_1^2 + \nabla_2^2) + v | \Psi_{\alpha\beta} \rangle. \qquad (4.23)$$

Here we have used the fact that $\Psi_{\alpha\beta}$ has no Fourier components except k_α, k_β in the Fermi distribution. Hence

$$Q_{\alpha\beta}{}^F \Psi_{\alpha\beta} = \Psi_{\alpha\beta}. \qquad (4.24)$$

The energy correction $U_{\alpha\beta}$ caused by the interaction is the difference between $\epsilon_{\alpha\beta}$ and the value for $v = 0$.

$$U_{\alpha\beta} = \langle \Psi_{\alpha\beta} | - \frac{\hbar^2}{2M^*} (\nabla_1^2 + \nabla_2^2 + k_\alpha^2 + k_\beta^2) + v | \Psi_{\alpha\beta} \rangle$$

$$= \epsilon_{\alpha\beta} - W(p_\alpha) - W(p_\beta) - \frac{\hbar^2}{2M} (k_\alpha^2 + k_\beta^2). \qquad (4.25)$$

Thus we can determine the one-particle potential $W'(p_\alpha)$ which would result from this calculation.

$$W'(p_\alpha) = \sum_\beta U_{\alpha\beta}. \qquad (4.26)$$

To be self-consistent we choose $W(p)$ so that the resulting $W'(p)$ is as close to it as possible. In general $W'(M^*, p)$ is not a quadratic function of p. We approximate $W'(M^*, p)$ by the best parabola and then equate M^* with the value one would get from the parabola. This leads to the following equation for M^*.

$$\frac{1}{p^*} \left[\frac{\partial W'(M^*, p)}{\partial p} \right]_{p=p^*} = \frac{1}{M^*} - \frac{1}{M}. \qquad (4.27)$$

If W' is a quadratic function of p, the left-hand side is independent of p. We must choose a suitable value of p^* for determining M^*. Since the deviation of $\Psi_{\alpha\beta}$ from the unperturbed form comes from Fourier components just above p_F, we shall choose $p^* = p_F$. Together with equations (4.26) and (4.27), this enables us to choose M^* self-consistently. The value of M^* is approximately 0.6 M.

We are now in a position to discuss the solution of the BBG equation in detail. This will be done by the method of Gomes, Walecka, and Weisskopf (58). We introduce the difference

$$g(\mathbf{r}_1, \mathbf{r}_2) = \Psi_{\alpha\beta} - \phi_\alpha(\mathbf{r}_1)\phi_\beta(\mathbf{r}_2), \qquad \alpha, \beta \text{ not identical}$$

$$= \Psi_{\alpha\beta} - 2^{-\frac{1}{2}}[\phi_\alpha(\mathbf{r}_1)\phi_\beta(\mathbf{r}_2) - \phi_\beta(\mathbf{r}_1)\phi_\alpha(\mathbf{r}_2)], \qquad \alpha, \beta \text{ identical.} \quad (4.28)$$

The distance beyond which g becomes negligible is the healing distance.

The interaction causes a distortion of the unperturbed wave function at short distances which must heal at larger distances, since there is no phase shift. For the isolated pair the distortion has a permanent effect, a phase shift. The healing distance is of the order $1/k_F$, since collisions at much larger distances would result in at least one of the particles having a momentum less than k_F.

The solution of the Brueckner-Bethe-Goldstone equation is more difficult than that of the free-scattering equation. The term $Q_{\alpha\beta}{}^F(v\Psi)$ contains a nonlocal potential operator V which depends on the C.M. momentum $\mathbf{P} = \mathbf{k}_\alpha + \mathbf{k}_\beta$ of the pair. For $\mathbf{P} \neq 0$, the Fermi distribution is not isotropic in momentum space in the two-body C.M. system. Thus the relative angular momentum is not a constant of the motion and the problem does not decompose into separate substates with definite angular momentum.

We shall restrict the discussion to $\mathbf{P} = 0$. We express (4.13) in the relative coordinate $\mathbf{r}$.

$$\left(\frac{\hbar^2}{M^*}\nabla^2 + \epsilon\right)\psi_\alpha(\mathbf{r}) = Q_\alpha{}^F v(r)\psi_\alpha(\mathbf{r}). \tag{4.29}$$

We are allowing for momentum dependence of the single-particle potential by the effective mass approximation. G is now given by (4.20).

$Q_\alpha{}^F$ removes from $v(r)\psi_\alpha(\mathbf{r})$ those Fourier components whose wave numbers are less than k_F and not equal to $\mathbf{k}_\alpha$ or $-\mathbf{k}_\alpha$. Equation (4.29) can be separated according to the relative angular momentum quantum number L. We shall consider only the $L = 0$ part. We are thus excluding pairs of identical particles which do not have a relative s-wave because of antisymmetry. The s-wave equation is

$$\left(\frac{\hbar^2}{M^*}\frac{d^2}{dr^2} + \epsilon\right)u(r) = Q^F v(r)u(r). \tag{4.30}$$

Here $u(r)/r$ is the $L = 0$ component of $\psi_\alpha(\mathbf{r})$ and the corresponding projection operator is Q^F.

$$u(r) \sim \left(\frac{2}{R}\right)^{\frac{1}{2}} \sin kr. \tag{4.31}$$

k is the relative momentum of the pair. The square integral of the wave function is unity in a large sphere of radius R.

For the s-state, it is convenient to define dimensionless variables

$$\mathbf{x} = k_F\mathbf{r},$$

$$\mathbf{y} = k_F\mathbf{s}, \tag{4.32}$$

$$\varkappa = \mathbf{k}/k_F.$$

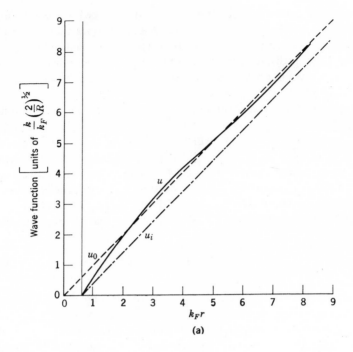

(a)

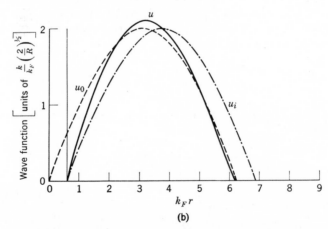

(b)

FIG. 4.1   The radial wave function for two nucleons in a relative *s*-state for $k = 0$ (*a*) and $k = 0.5k_F$ (*b*), showing the cases of no interaction [$u_o(r)$], the repulsive core interaction for an isolated pair [$u_i(r)$], and for a pair embedded in a Fermi distribution with $k_F = 1.48\text{fm}^{-1}[u(r)]$. (Adapted from Gomes, Walecka, and Weisskopf, 58.)

The right-hand side of the s-state BBG equation (4.30) becomes

$$k_F^{-2} v(x) u(x) - k_F^{-2} x \int \frac{d^3 y}{k_F^3} \frac{v(y) u(y)}{y} G(\mathbf{x} - \mathbf{y}).$$ (4.33)

Using the substitution

$$|\mathbf{x} - \mathbf{y}| = z, \qquad d^3 y = \frac{2\pi y\, dy\, z\, dz}{x}, $$ (4.34)

and integrating over z using (4.20) for G, we have for the integral in (4.33)

$$x \int \frac{d^3 y}{k_F^3} \frac{u(y) v(y)}{y} G(\mathbf{x} - \mathbf{y}) = \int dy\, u(y)\, v(y)\, f(x, y),$$ (4.35)

where

$$f(x, y) = \pi^{-1} \int_0^1 d\kappa [\cos \kappa(x - y) - \cos \kappa(x + y)]$$

$$= \pi^{-1} \left[\frac{\sin |x - y|}{|x - y|} - \frac{\sin |x + y|}{x + y} \right].$$ (4.36)

We have thus derived an integro-differential equation for the s-state in terms of functions of single variables, which can be solved on a computer. The equation may be written out in terms of x and y.

$$\left(\frac{\hbar^2}{M^*} \frac{d^2}{dx^2} + \frac{\epsilon}{k_F^2} \right) u(x) = \frac{v(x) u(x)}{k_F^2} - \frac{1}{k_F^2} \int_0^\infty dy\, u(y) v(y) f(x, y),$$ (4.37)

where $f(x, y)$ is given by (4.36).

The solutions for several characteristic potentials will now be discussed. First, a hard core by itself at $r = 0.4$ fm.

In Fig. 4.1 the s-state solutions $u(r)$ are plotted for $k = 0$ and $k = 0.5\, k_F$. We have used $k_F = 1.48$ fm^{-1}. For comparison we have plotted the free-particle wave function $u_0(r)$ which is the solution of (4.37) for $v = 0$,

$$u_0(r) = \left(\frac{2}{R} \right)^{\frac{1}{2}} \sin kr,$$ (4.38)

and the solution $u_i(r)$ for the corresponding scattering problem of an isolated pair, which is the solution of (4.37) without the integral term that restricts the Fourier components to those outside the Fermi sphere. For the hard core potential.

$$u_i(r) = \left(\frac{2}{R} \right)^{\frac{1}{2}} \sin k(r - c).$$ (4.39)

On the basis of our virtual transition argument, we expect $u(r)$ to be different from $u_0(r)$ only by virtual transitions to states outside the Fermi sphere. These transitions will affect the short-range part of the wave function, $r \lesssim k_F^{-1}$. In fact, for very small r, $u(r)$ will approach the scattering solution $u_i(r)$. The long-range part of the wave function, $r \gg k_F^{-1}$ will have no Fourier components except the one for k. That is, it will be the same as $u_0(r)$.

It can be seen from the figures that the healing distance is a few times k_F^{-1}. For the isolated pair the perturbation of the wave function due to the hard core is carried out to infinity resulting in a phase shift.

The actual nuclear force has an attractive part outside the repulsive core. We shall use a simplified potential chosen to fit the singlet effective range.

The potential is chosen first to have the Serber exchange property. That is, it does not act in states of odd relative angular momentum. Thus p-state forces are excluded and, as a first approximation, we can reduce the discussion to s-state forces. The potential will consist of a central part which is spin-independent. Tensor forces will be neglected for further simplicity.

The central force is a square well with a repulsive core.

$$
\begin{aligned}
V(r) &= +\infty, && r < c, \\
&= -V, && c \leq r \leq b + c, \\
&= 0, && r > b + c.
\end{aligned}
\tag{4.40}
$$

The singlet force gives rise to a stationary state of zero binding energy. We must therefore have for the singlet effective range and well depth

$$
\begin{aligned}
2c + b &= r_{0s} = 2.7 \text{ fm}, \\
V_0 &= \hbar^2 \pi^2 / 4Mb^2.
\end{aligned}
\tag{4.41}
$$

High-energy scattering data indicate a repulsive core of

$$
c = 0.4 \text{ fm.}
$$

We therefore choose

$$
b = 1.9 \text{ fm.}
$$

Figure 4.2 shows the healing of the wave function for the nuclear potential (4.40) which fits the singlet effective range. Here we have used $k = 0.3k_F$, $k_F = 1.48 \text{ fm}^{-1}$.

Comparison of Figs. 4.1 and 4.2 is very interesting. The attractive part of the potential has a very small effect on the shape of $u(r)$. This can be understood in the virtual transition picture. The scattering wave function for an isolated pair in the attractive well of (4.40) would contain mostly Fourier components with wave numbers less than k_F. The internal wave number K is given by

$$
\left(\frac{K}{k_F}\right)^2 = 0.18 + \left(\frac{k}{k_F}\right)^2.
$$

Hence $K < k_F$ for $k < 0.9k_F$. The long-range correlations caused by the attraction in this case are expected to be important only for values of k in the top 10 per cent of the Fermi distribution.

We thus have a numerical estimate of the effects discussed in Chapter 1 B. Departures of the wave function $u(r)$ from the independent particle wave function $u_0(r)$ can be called correlations between the nucleons. The hard core causes short-range or strong correlations which correspond to Fourier

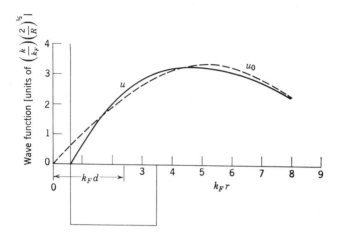

FIG. 4.2 The radial wave function for two nucleons in a relative *s*-state for $k = 0.3k_F$ for the cases of no interaction $[u_0(r)]$ and a pair embedded in a Fermi distribution $k_F = 1.48$ fm^{-1}, with the indicated nuclear potential $[u(r)]$. The average internucleon distance d is also indicated. (Adapted from Gomes, Walecka, and Weisskopf, 58.)

components or virtual transitions with $k > k_F$. The range of these correlations is such that $u(r)$ is a reasonably good approximation to $u_0(r)$ outside the average internucleon distance. Strong correlations are important for all particles, but do not affect the wave functions much at the average internucleon distance. Hence they only cause appreciable departures from the predictions of the independent particle model for experiments which depend on the high-momentum components of the nuclear wave function.

The attractive long-range part of the potential causes weak correlations. They are important for, roughly, the top ten per cent of particles in the nucleus. They can cause departures from the predictions of the independent particle model in experiments which depend on the low-momentum components of the nuclear wave function.

The most obvious correlation caused by the attractive forces is the clumping together of nucleons into approximately spherical nuclei. A large part of the effect on the nucleon wave functions can be expected to be given by the fact that they are restricted to depend on a spherical one-particle potential rather than to approach plane waves at large internucleon distances.

That the independent pair model is approximately self-consistent can be seen from the fact that when one of the partners of the pair makes a close encounter with a third particle the average distance between the pair is d. The pair wave function is already well-healed. Since it looks like the free-particle wave function, the collision with the third particle usually takes place under conditions as if the original pair had no interaction at all.

C. THE ENERGY PER PARTICLE OF NUCLEAR MATTER

We have now accomplished our main objective which is to understand the effect of nuclear forces on the wave functions of nucleons in nuclear matter. The wave function can be tested by calculating the energy per particle according to Equation (4.1).

The experimental value of the energy per particle comes from a study of the mass defects of nuclei. It is given by the volume term of the semiempirical mass formula (Chapter 7C).

$$\epsilon_{\text{EXP}} = -15 \text{ MeV}.$$

For the independent particle model the energy per particle is given by Equation (4.6).

$$\epsilon_{\text{IPM}} = \frac{E_0}{A} = +27.3 \text{ MeV}.$$

The result of the calculation using the oversimplified potential (4.40) in s and d states is shown in Fig. 4.3. This potential predicts an energy per particle which has the right sign, but which is not as much as the experimental energy -15 MeV. The minimum in the curve A of Fig. 4.3 is at $k_F = 1.33 \text{ fm}^{-1}$. Its value is -6.8 MeV. The value of E/A for $k_F = 1.48 \text{ fm}^{-1}$, which corresponds to the observed density of nuclear matter, is about -6.5 MeV. In this calculation $M^* = 0.68$ M.

Curve B of Fig. 4.3 is calculated with corrections for tensor forces and includes a p-state force with a hard core at 0.45 fm (Walecka and Gomes, 67). The minimum occurs at -14.3 MeV with $k_F = 1.55 \text{ fm}^{-1}$ and $M^* = 0.62$ M.

This is quite a good result, considering that a very simplified form was used for the nuclear force, and that we have omitted clusters of order greater than 2. It gives us no reason to include many-body forces in the theory. Calculations made with more refined potentials may get close to the experimental value of the energy per particle. For example, the value obtained by Brueckner and Gammel (58) using the Gammel-Thaler (57) potential is

-15.2 MeV with $k_F = 1.55$ fm^{-1} and $M^* = 0.73$ M. However the question of the prediction of saturation properties of nuclear matter from the most accurate two-body potentials is by no means closed. The Hamada-Johnston, and other potentials that fit two-body data as accurately, predict a value several MeV too low for E/A (Bethe, 67).

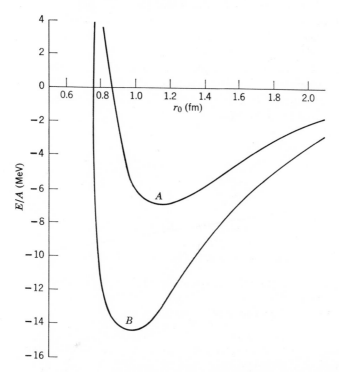

FIG. 4.3   Total energy per particle as a function of $r_0 = (9\pi/8)^{1/3}k_F^{-1}$ calculated by the theory of Gomes, Walecka, and Weisskopf. (Adapted from Walecka and Gomes, 67.)

It is very interesting to consider the results obtained for nuclear matter using the separable potential of Tabakin, which was designed to fit two-body scattering data fairly well while having a very different form off the energy shell from the local potential. In particular, strong correlations are much less important for the Tabakin potential than they are for local potentials with hard cores. Tabakin (64) computed the saturation curve for nuclear matter. The values obtained for saturation were $E/A = -14.1$ MeV, $k_F = 1.8$ fm^{-1} and $M^* = 0.6$ M. Although the fit to two-body scattering is not precise for the Tabakin potential, these results give a strong indication that short-range strong correlations do not play a significant part in determining the saturation of nuclear matter. Far more subtle experiments are necessary to determine the presence or absence of strong correlations in nuclear matter. The numerical reason for this was discussed for free particles in connection with Fig. 3.6. Differences between the wave functions computed in equivalent local and separable potentials tend to average out in the integral (4.16'), where k and k' never differ by more than k_F.

The success of the independent pair model for predicting saturation properties suggests that three-body correlations are unimportant. The contribution of three-body correlations (with two-body forces) to the energy of nuclear matter has been estimated by Bethe (65) and Moszkowski (65). Using a pseudopotential approximation to the Faddeev (60) equations for the three-body problem (see Chapter 10E), Moszkowski obtains a three-body contribution to E/A of 0.6 MeV.

FURTHER READING

1. K. A. Brueckner and J. L. Gammel, *Phys. Rev.*, **109**, 1023 (1958) (and references therein).
   K. A. Brueckner in *The Many-body Problem*, edited by C. DeWitt, John Wiley and Sons, New York, 1959.
   Early work of Brueckner and collaborators.

2. H. A. Bethe, *Phys. Rev.*, **103**, 1353 (1956).
   H. A. Bethe and J. Goldstone, *Proc. Roy. Soc. (London)*, **A238**, 551 (1956).
   H. A. Bethe, B. H. Brandow, and A. G. Petschek, *Phys. Rev.*, **129**, 225 (1963).
   B. D. Day, *Rev. Mod. Phys.*, **39**, 719 (1967).
   B. H. Brandow, *Rev. Mod. Phys.*, **39**, 771 (1967).
   Reviews, clarifications, and developments.

3. L. C. Gomes, J. D. Walecka, and V. F. Weisskopf, *Ann. Phys. (N.Y.)*, **3**, 241 (1958).
   J. D. Walecka and L. C. Gomes, *Anais da Academia Brasileira de Ciencas*, 1967.
   B. L. Scott and S. A. Moszkowski, *Ann. Phys. (N.Y.)*, **11**, 65 (1960); **14**, 107 (1961); *Nucl. Phys.*, **29**, 665 (1962).
   Simplified and lucid treatments.

4. H. A. Bethe, *Phys. Rev.*, **138**, B804 (1965).
   S. A. Moszkowski, *Phys. Rev.*, **140**, B283 (1965).
   Three-body correlations in nuclear matter.

5. H. S. Köhler, *Nucl. Phys.*, **88**, 529 (1966).
   Nucleon holes in nuclear matter.

PROBLEMS

1. Assuming nuclear matter is a Fermi gas in a momentum-dependent potential given by the effective mass approximation, what is the effective mass which gives the correct energy per particle? What conclusions do you draw from the answer?

2. Assume that long-range correlations cause the single-particle wave function to look like the wave function for an s-state particle bound in an infinite square potential well of radius π/K where K is the internal wave number. Estimate the virtual transition amplitudes to states with $k = 2K$, $k = 10K$. Use the value for the effective mass $M^* = 0.5\ M$.

3. Summarize the reasons for believing the independent particle model to be a reasonable first approximation for nuclei.

4. Why are the saturation properties of nuclear matter insensitive to the character of the interaction off the energy shell, provided it gives the correct free two-body scattering?

5. Would you expect experiments which depend mainly on the shape of single particle wave functions to yield information about the role of strong correlations in nuclei? Suggest experiments which might yield the required information.

5

THE SINGLE-PARTICLE SHELL
MODEL FOR FINITE NUCLEI

We shall now study real nuclei individually, instead of nuclear matter in bulk. As in the case of nuclear matter, we shall first consider the independent particle model. The knowledge of the effect of the Pauli exclusion principle, which we have built up, makes us expect that the independent particle model will have some validity as a first approximation to a description of nuclei.

The independent particle model for finite nuclei is called the single-particle shell model. The single-particle force acting on a nucleon in state α is described in terms of the independent pair model as

$$V = \sum_\beta U_{\alpha\beta}. \tag{5.1}$$

For a finite nucleus the momentum-independent part V is not irrelevant because there is a boundary separating the internal region, where a particle feels a potential V, from the external region where it feels no nuclear potential.

The single-particle model treats each nucleon as if it moves independently in a finite potential well given by V. The nuclear wave function in this model is an antisymmetrized product of single-particle wave functions, which can be written as a determinant.

$$\Psi(x_1, \ldots, x_A) = \det \phi_i(x_j), \tag{5.2}$$

where the coordinate x_i includes the spin and isospin of the particle as well as its position coordinates. The eigenstates ϕ_i of V replace the plane wave eigenstates of nuclear matter. Nucleons will fill up these states, just as electrons do in an atom, until there is one nucleon in each state up to a certain level, with unfilled states above this level. The simplest assumption about V is that it is central. In this case the angular momentum l is a good quantum number. The eigenstates also depend on the principal quantum number n, the spin s, and the charge of the particle.

As more and more particles are put into the nucleus, they fill states which are higher and higher in energy. If there are states separated by energy gaps large enough to inhibit virtual transitions significantly, nuclei with all states filled below the gap are expected to have special properties. They are called closed-shell nuclei. They are expected to be more tightly bound than nuclei with one or two particles outside a closed shell.

Evidence of shell structure is found in the periodic table. Nuclei which are particularly (or surprisingly) stable are, for example,

$$_2^4\text{He},\ _6^{12}\text{C},\ _8^{16}\text{O},\ _{20}^{40}\text{Ca},\ _{20}^{48}\text{Ca},\ _{82}^{208}\text{Pb}.$$

In this notation the mass number A is written as a left superscript, and the proton number Z is written as a left subscript. Evidence for shell structure includes the binding energy of the nucleus, the binding energy of the last nucleon, and the frequency of occurrence of stable nuclei with a particular proton number Z or neutron number N. For example, there is an anomalously large number of stable nuclei with $N = 50$.

The magic numbers for both protons and neutrons which indicate shell structure are [Elsasser (34)],

$$2, (6), 8, (14), 20, 28, 50, 82, 126.$$

Numbers with less-pronounced magic properties are bracketed. Other notable features of the periodic table are that nuclei with even numbers of neutrons or protons are much more stable than ones with odd numbers, and that the ground-state spins of even nuclei are invariably zero.

For many years, knowledge of the strength of the nuclear forces prevented people from taking the single-particle model seriously, although the evidence for shell structure was accumulating. A strong inhibiting factor was the failure of the model in detail. A local potential could not be found whose energy eigenvalues predicted shell closing at the correct magic numbers. Also binding energies per particle were badly underestimated by the model. In 1948 the experimental evidence was convincingly correlated independently by Mayer (48, 49) and by Haxel, Jensen, and Suess (49). The inclusion of a spin-orbit term in the potential enabled shell closing at the correct magic numbers to be obtained.

Before going into the details of the eigenstates of single-particle potentials, we shall consider some general properties of nuclei which indicate how the single-particle levels are filled as nucleons are added to a nucleus. We shall suppose that the addition of a few particles does not greatly alter the shape of the potential or the positions of the single-particle levels; that is to say, we shall not allow the potential to change self-consistently.

The Coulomb potential has a very long range and may be regarded as constant over a nucleus to a first approximation. The proton and neutron potentials, assuming charge independence of the nuclear force, are similar in this approximation except that the proton potential is V_C MeV higher, where V_C is the average Coulomb potential.

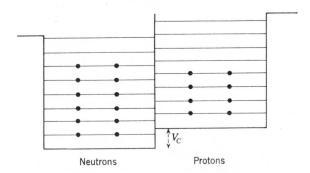

Neutrons   Protons

FIG. 5.1   Schematic diagram of the single-particle levels for neutrons and protons in a nucleus, where the Coulomb potential V_c is approximately constant over the dimensions of the nucleus.

Figure 5.1 indicates the difference between neutron and proton single-particle models. It gives a qualitative explanation of the fact that neutrons are more numerous than protons in most nuclei. The nucleus is in a state of lowest energy if the neutron and proton states are filled to approximately the same level. Since the neutron potential well is lower in energy, there will be more states for neutrons than protons.

With spin-orbit coupling, the total angular momentum j is a good quantum number. The spin s may have two directions for each j, so that there are two nucleons of a particular kind in each level. The diagram also offers a partial explanation of why protons and neutrons tend to be added in pairs of opposite spin.

To the nucleus of Fig. 5.1 it is easiest to add a proton. The next particle must also be a proton of opposite spin if the lowest energy state is to be achieved. Of the three nuclei involved in this process, only one has an unpaired nucleon, and none have both odd N and odd Z.

In fact, the nucleons experience pairing forces, that is, nucleon-nucleon forces which exist over and above the single-particle force V. These forces are mainly attractive, so that there is a pairing energy which increases the binding energy of the nucleus when N or Z becomes even. The odd nucleon and the added nucleon both experience an attractive force which lowers the potential felt by each.

For indicating whether N or Z are even or odd in a nucleus we shall employ the following convention.

If N and Z are both even we have an even nucleus.

If N or Z is odd we have an odd-N or odd-Z nucleus, respectively. If we do not want to specify which of N or Z is odd, it will be called an odd-A nucleus.

If both N and Z are odd we have an odd nucleus.

In order to predict the positions of the large energy gaps that are responsible for shell structure, we must solve the Schrödinger equation for plausible single-particle potentials.

A. SHELL CLOSING

The Schrödinger equation with spin-orbit coupling is

$$\left[-\frac{\hbar^2}{2\mu} \nabla^2 + V_C(r) + V_S(r) \; \mathbf{l} \cdot \mathbf{s} \right] \psi(\mathbf{r}) = E\psi(\mathbf{r}). \tag{5.3}$$

For a purely central potential in which the spin wave function of the nucleon is included in the formalism, the space-spin wave function is

$$\psi(\mathbf{r})\chi_{\frac{1}{2}}^{\mu} = r^{-1} R_{nl}(r) Y_l^m(\Omega) \chi_{\frac{1}{2}}^{\mu}. \tag{5.4}$$

The product functions $Y_l^m(\Omega)\chi_{\frac{1}{2}}^{\mu}$ are simultaneous eigenfunctions of the operators l^2, l_3, s^2, s_3 but not of the operator $\mathbf{l} \cdot \mathbf{s}$. This may be remedied by introducing functions $\mathscr{Y}_{jls}^{m_j}$ which are simultaneous eigenfunctions of l^2, s^2, j^2, and j_3 and thus also of $\mathbf{l} \cdot \mathbf{s}$. The total angular momentum $\mathbf{j}$ is given by

$$\mathbf{j} = \mathbf{l} + \mathbf{s}.$$

Since $s = \frac{1}{2}$, the possible values of j are $l \pm \frac{1}{2}$. The corresponding eigenfunctions are

$$\mathscr{Y}_{jls}^{m_j} = \sum_{\mu} C_{l\;s\;j}^{m\mu m_j} Y_l^m(\Omega) \chi_s^{\mu}. \tag{5.5}$$

The eigenfunctions for $j = l \pm \frac{1}{2}$ may be written more explicitly using the notation α and β for spin wave functions.

$$\mathscr{Y}_{l+\frac{1}{2},l,s}^{m_j} = \left(\frac{l + m_j + \frac{1}{2}}{2l+1} \right)^{\frac{1}{2}} Y_l^{m_j - \frac{1}{2}} \alpha + \left(\frac{l - m_j + \frac{1}{2}}{2l+1} \right)^{\frac{1}{2}} Y_l^{m_j + \frac{1}{2}} \beta,$$

$$\mathscr{Y}_{l-\frac{1}{2},l,s}^{m_j} = -\left(\frac{l - m_j + \frac{1}{2}}{2l+1} \right)^{\frac{1}{2}} Y_l^{m_j - \frac{1}{2}} \alpha + \left(\frac{l + m_j + \frac{1}{2}}{2l+1} \right)^{\frac{1}{2}} Y_l^{m_j + \frac{1}{2}} \beta. \tag{5.6}$$

The radial wave equation splits into two uncoupled equations. Different j states have different potentials. States with $j = l \pm \frac{1}{2}$ are denoted, respectively, by $R_{nl}{}^{\pm}$. The matrix elements of $\mathbf{l} \cdot \mathbf{s}$ follow from (A4.57) when $s = \frac{1}{2}$.

$$\frac{d^2 R_{nl}{}^{\pm}}{dr^2} + \left\{ k^2 - \frac{2\mu}{\hbar^2}\left[V_C + \frac{\hbar^2}{2}\binom{l \ \text{or}}{-l-1} V_S \right] - \frac{l(l+1)}{r^2} \right\} R_{nl}{}^{\pm} = 0 \quad (5.7)$$

where

$$k^2 = -\beta^2 = \frac{2\mu E}{\hbar^2}. \quad (5.8)$$

Thus each j state has a different eigenvalue given by the solution of (5.7). Nucleons with the same j are in a subshell. The number of nucleons of a given charge in a subshell is the number of degenerate magnetic substates. It is $2j + 1$. Levels with larger l are split more by V_S than levels with smaller l. The parity of $\mathscr{Y}_{jls}^{m_j}$ is still $(-1)^l$. States are labeled by the quantum number $n + 1$, a letter from the old spectroscopic notation indicating the value of l, and the value of j. For example, if $n = 1$, $l = 1$ and $j = \frac{3}{2}$, we have a $2p_{3/2}$ state.

It is convenient to define a local wave number K^2 by

$$K^2 = k^2 + \frac{2\mu}{\hbar^2}\left[V_C(r) + \frac{\hbar^2}{2}\binom{l \ \text{or}}{-l-1} V_S(r) \right]. \quad (5.9)$$

For an attractive potential and negative energy E, the solution of (5.7) is an eigenvalue problem. The boundary conditions are as follows.

1. The wave function and its derivative must be everywhere finite and continuous.

2. The wave function must vanish at infinity.

For the internal solution, K^2 is positive and the solution is obtained by numerical integration of (5.7) in the same way as was discussed for the scattering problem (2.18). In particular, for a square well potential, it is a spherical Bessel function $j_l(Kr)$.

The external solution, however, has a negative value of K^2 because E is negative. Setting $K^2 = -\beta^2$, we can see from Equation (2.24) that the appropriate linear combination of regular and irregular solutions of (5.7), which vanishes at infinity, is the spherical Hankel function $h_l^{(1)}(i\beta r)$.

The exterior part or tail of the bound-state wave function therefore depends only on the binding energy. In the present section we shall be more interested in the interior part of the wave function, which can be quite well represented by a simple infinite potential such as a square well or a harmonic oscillator. The relative positions of energy levels can be obtained from such a model, but not of course the absolute single-particle binding energy.

The harmonic oscillator potential is an extremely useful one because of its special mathematical properties. The energy levels are very simple.

$$E = 2n + l + \frac{3}{2}\,\hbar\omega, \tag{5.10}$$

where ω is the oscillator frequency and n is the number of nodes in the radial wave function, not counting the one at the origin or the one at infinity. The most useful property of this model is that the product wave function for two particles in terms of the coordinates $\mathbf{r}_1$, $\mathbf{r}_2$ of each particle can be transformed into a product function of $\mathbf{R}$ and $\mathbf{r}$, the C.M. and relative coordinates of the pair. This property is invaluable when we consider the effect of pairing forces, as we shall in Chapters 6 and 7. Plane waves are the only other wave functions with this property.

The normalized radial harmonic oscillator wave functions are

$$R_{nl}(\rho) = \left\{ \frac{2\Gamma(n + l + \tfrac{3}{2})}{n!} \right\}^{\tfrac{1}{2}} e^{-\tfrac{1}{2}\rho^2} \rho^{l+1} \sum_{K=0}^{n} C_{nl}(K)\rho^{2K}, \tag{5.11}$$

where

$$\rho = \left(\frac{M\omega}{\hbar} \right)^{\tfrac{1}{2}} r,$$

$$C_{nl}(K) = (-1)^K \binom{n}{K} \Gamma^{-1}(K + l + \tfrac{3}{2}), \tag{5.12}$$

and $\binom{n}{K}$ is a binomial coefficient. The oscillator constant $(M\omega/\hbar)^{\tfrac{1}{2}}$ has been treated as a scale factor in (5.11).

For more realistic potentials the eigenvalue problem must be solved numerically. Given a radial shape factor for the potential in a particular eigenstate of j, either the binding energy or the potential depth is determined if the other is given.

This is done by searching numerically until the eigenvalue or potential depth that causes the logarithmic derivatives of interior and exterior solutions to match at the boundary is found. For a square well the matching conditions can be derived explicitly. Putting $\zeta = KR$, $\eta = \beta R$, the trigonometric forms for $j_l(Kr)$ and $h_l^{(1)}(i\beta r)$ may be used to show, for example, that the matching conditions for s- and p-states are

$$l = 0; \quad \zeta \cot \zeta = -\eta,$$
$$l = 1; \quad \frac{\cot \zeta}{\zeta} - \frac{1}{\zeta^2} = \frac{1}{\eta} + \frac{1}{\eta^2}. \tag{5.13}$$

Using the identity

$$\zeta^2 + \eta^2 = \frac{2\mu V R^2}{\hbar^2},$$ (5.14)

we can solve the transcendental equations graphically to find one of E, R, V, given the other two.

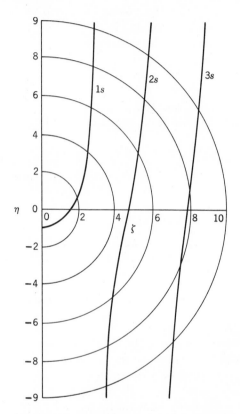

FIG. 5.2   Solutions of Equations (5.13, 14) for $l = 0$.

For the s-state this is illustrated in Fig. 5.2. The circles represent Equation (5.14), the other curves represent Equation (5.13) for $l = 0$. For a given value of VR^2 the solution is on a particular circle. The intersection of the circle with the curves for Equation (5.13) then enables us to determine, for example, E for a given R, V or R for a given E, V. Only the upper half of the diagram is physical.

For large enough VR^2 there is more than one intersection in the upper half of the diagram, that is, there is more than one eigenvalue for the s-state. The corresponding eigenstates are labeled $1s, 2s, \ldots, (n + 1)s, \ldots$ where n is the principal quantum number. n is the number of nodes in the wave function, not counting the nodes at the origin and at infinity. For $\eta < \pi/2$ there is no bound s-state.

The intersections of the circles with the corresponding curves for p-states give $(n + 1)p$ states, the values of n depending on how large VR^2 is. Thus larger potentials can bind more nucleons.

For an infinite square well the radial wave functions are $j_l(Kr)$ with the boundary conditions that the well radius R is at a node in the wave function since the wave function cannot exist outside the potential.

Figure 5.3 shows the levels of a harmonic oscillator in units of $\hbar\omega$ and an infinite square well in units of $\hbar^2/MR^2$. The cumulative totals of particles in the infinite square well give magic numbers

$$2, 8, 20, 34, 40, 58, 92, 132, 138.$$

Only the first three of these are correct. Shells that are close together in energy are considered almost degenerate because the nuclear forces can cause virtual transitions between them quite easily. For states whose eigenvalues are far apart in energy, virtual transitions are much less probable, and the shells are distinct in momentum space.

The addition to the Schrödinger equation (5.3) of a spin-orbit coupling term of the form

$$V_S(r) = -\lambda \frac{1}{2M^2c^2} \frac{1}{r} \frac{\partial}{\partial r} V_C(r), \tag{5.15}$$

where λ is positive, splits the levels in such a way that the correct magic numbers are obtained. The levels with spin-orbit coupling are shown in the center of Fig. 5.3.

The form (5.15) for $V_S(r)$ is obtained by analogy with the Thomas (35) term of atomic physics which arises from a relativistic treatment of the wave equation for a particle in a central potential. For the Thomas term $\lambda = -1$. The shell model spin-orbit term must be made not only of the opposite sign, but also larger in magnitude than the pure Thomas term, indicating that the spin-orbit terms in the nuclear forces are mainly responsible for it. The maximum strength of the Thomas term is of the order of 0.1 MeV.

The spin-orbit term splits the levels so that the $j = l + \frac{1}{2}$ level lies below the $j = l - \frac{1}{2}$ level. Clearly the levels are close together at the top of Fig. 5.3 and the correct ordering of levels may not have been achieved. It is achieved by considering the spins of the ground states of nuclei.

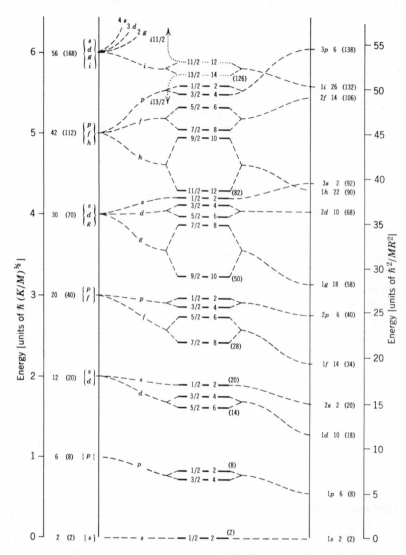

FIG. 5.3   Single-particle energy levels. Harmonic oscillator levels are on the left; infinite square well levels are on the right. In the center are levels computed in a finite potential with spin-orbit coupling. (Adapted from Haxel, Jensen, and Suess, 50.)

B. SPINS AND MOMENTS OF GROUND STATES

We have seen that the single-particle model makes certain simple predictions about the spins of nuclei. The closed-shell nuclei of course have zero spin. In order to minimize the energy, the nucleons outside the closed shell core tend to pair off in such a way that their angular momenta cancel. Thus, even nuclei are expected to have zero spin. The effect of the pairing forces reinforces this simple argument. It is experimentally verified. The spin of an odd-*A* nucleus is given by the angular momentum of the last unpaired nucleon in all but three cases.

Nucleus	$^{15}_{7}\text{N}$	$^{17}_{8}\text{O}$	$^{89}_{39}\text{Y}$	$^{91}_{49}\text{Nb}$	$^{207}_{82}\text{Pb}$	$^{209}_{83}\text{Bi}$
State of last particle	$1p_{1/2}$	$1d_{5/2}$	$2p_{1/2}$	$1g_{9/2}$	$3p_{1/2}$	$1h_{9/2}$
Ground state of nucleus	$\frac{1}{2}-$	$\frac{5}{2}+$	$\frac{1}{2}-$	$\frac{9}{2}+$	$\frac{1}{2}-$	$\frac{9}{2}-$

TABLE 5.1. Spins of ground states and single-particle states of the last particle for particular nuclei.

The predictions concerning spin are verified by studying the ground states of nuclei. Odd-*A* nuclei can be studied, for example, by adding a neutron or a proton by means of a reaction such as (d, p) or (d, n). Properties of the angular distribution of the outgoing particle enable the orbital angular momentum of the residual nucleus to be determined (Tobocman, 61; Butler, 51). These reactions will be discussed in detail in Chapter 13.

The parity π of a single-particle state is $(-1)^l$. The spin and parity of a nuclear state are denoted by j, π. Thus if a nucleus has a $1p_{3/2}$ particle outside a spinless core, the state is denoted $\frac{3}{2}-$. Examples of the spins of odd-*A* nuclei are given in Table 5.1.

Nuclei which need one more particle to complete a closed shell are called single-hole nuclei. The hole acts like a particle whose spin is the spin of the shell containing the hole. In Table 5.1, ^{15}N and ^{207}Pb are single-hole nuclei, while ^{89}Y may be considered as having a proton hole in the $2p_{1/2}$ shell of the closed-shell nucleus ^{90}Zr. The large energy gap between the $2p_{1/2}$ level and the next level to which a virtual single-particle transition is allowed by parity conservation, namely the $1h_{11/2}$ level, makes ^{89}Y behave like an ideal single-particle nucleus in many experiments.

The extreme single-particle model is thus successful in predicting the spins of even nuclei and of nearly all odd-*A* nuclei. There exist no criteria in the model for predicting the spins of odd nuclei. Correlations between the odd proton and neutron must be taken into account in order to predict which of the possible states is the lowest in energy.

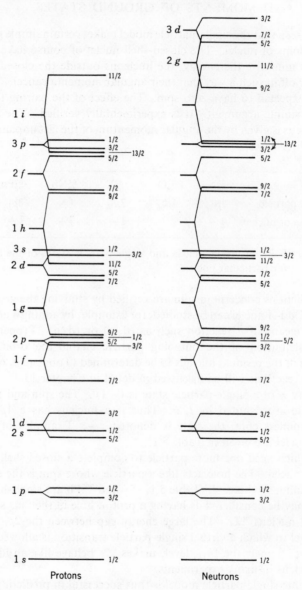

FIG. 5.4   Proton and neutron level schemes compiled from experimental data. (Adapted from Klinkenberg, 52.)

Observations of the spins of odd-A nuclei enable the order of levels to be determined. It is slightly different for protons and neutrons because of the Coulomb potential. Figure 5.4 shows the proton and neutron level ordering determined from experiments, largely (d, p) or similar reactions which add a single particle to a nucleus.

[i] LOCAL SHELL-MODEL POTENTIAL FOR PREDICTING LEVEL ORDERING

If the single-particle potential is to be approximated by a local model with spin-orbit coupling, the model must be chosen quite critically to reproduce all the level orders, since many of the levels are extremely close. A potential which is almost successful in achieving this is that of Ross, Mark, and Lawson (56). It was chosen with the restriction that it should be the same for all nuclei except that the radius is proportional to $A^{1/3}$.

The radial shape chosen for the potential is a very popular one in nuclear physics because it has the main properties of the charge-density distribution, namely a diffuse surface and a fairly constant internal value. It is given by the form factor

$$f(r) = \left\{ 1 + \exp\frac{r - R}{a} \right\}^{-1}, \qquad (5.16)$$

which is known as the Eckart, Fermi or Woods-Saxon form in different contexts. The half-density radius is R, the diffuseness parameter is a.

The Ross-Mark-Lawson potential is

$$V(r) = V_C f(r) - \lambda \frac{1}{2M^2c^2} V_C \frac{1}{r} \frac{d}{dr} f(r) \mathbf{l} \cdot \mathbf{s}, \qquad (5.17)$$

where

$$V_C = -42.8 \text{ MeV}$$
$$\lambda = 39.5$$
$$R = 1.3A^{1/3} \text{ fm}$$
$$a = 0.69 \text{ fm}.$$

It is interesting to compare the depth of this potential with the one derived in Chapter 1B from the Fermi gas model. Its depth was about 50 MeV.

[ii] MAGNETIC MOMENTS OF ODD-A NUCLEI

Having seen that the single-particle shell model predicts ground-state spins very well, we must consider the next refinement. Magnetic moments μ of single particles are given by their orbital angular momenta and spins. The nuclear magneton is the unit defined as the magnetic moment of a charge e with orbital angular momentum $l = 1$. The proton and neutron also have intrinsic magnetic moments in the direction of the spin. The magnetic moment of a nucleus is measured by nuclear magnetic resonance techniques. The Larmor precession frequency for an atom depends on the nuclear magnetic moment.

The magnetic moment of a nucleus is given by the expectation value in the ground state of the vector sum of the magnetic moment operators of the individual nucleons. The magnetic moment of each nucleon is

$$\boldsymbol{\mu} = (g_l a_l + g_s a_s)\mathbf{j}, \tag{5.18}$$

where the gyromagnetic ratios g_l and g_s for orbital angular momentum and spin are given by Table 5.2, and a_l and a_s give the projections of $\mathbf{l}$ and $\mathbf{s}$ on $\mathbf{j}$.

$$a_l = \mathbf{l} \cdot \mathbf{j}/j^2 = \frac{[j(j+1) + l(l+1) - s(s+1)]}{2j(j+1)}$$

$$a_s = \mathbf{s} \cdot \mathbf{j}/j^2 = \frac{[j(j+1) + s(s+1) - l(l+1)]}{2j(j+1)}. \tag{5.19}$$

	p	n
g_l	1	0
g_s	2.79	−1.91

TABLE 5.2.   Gyromagnetic ratios for nucleons.

For even nuclei, each nucleon is paired with one of the same charge and opposite $\mathbf{j}$. The ground-state spin is zero, the magnetic moment is zero.

For nuclei with one unpaired nucleon, the magnetic moment becomes, using $s = \frac{1}{2}$, $l = j \pm \frac{1}{2}$ in (5.19),

$$\mu = (j + \tfrac{1}{2})g_l + g_s, \qquad l = j - \tfrac{1}{2},$$

$$= \frac{j}{j+1}\{(j + \tfrac{3}{2})g_l - g_s\}, \qquad l = j + \tfrac{1}{2}. \tag{5.20}$$

The graphs of μ against j for Equation (5.20) are the Schmidt lines (Schmidt, 37). Comparison of theoretical and experimental values of μ for some odd-A nuclei is given in Table 5.3.

Nuclei near closed shells, which are expected to provide the best magnetic moment predictions, do not in general obey the predictions at all closely. The magnetic moment is seen to be a much more sensitive test of the single-particle character of a nucleus than the spin. The nuclei near the closed shell ^{90}Zr obey the single-particle prediction quite well for both protons and neutrons. A neutron hole in ^{208}Pb also acts like a single hole. Nuclei far from closed shells have magnetic moments in between the Schmidt values for $l = j + \frac{1}{2}$ and $l = j - \frac{1}{2}$.

The reason why a nucleus does not have the single-particle magnetic moment must be that virtual transitions of the originally paired particles to higher states are not impossible, so that the nuclear wave function, instead of being a pure single-particle wave function, is a superposition of products of single-particle wave functions, each with a different magnetic moment, but with the same $j\pi$.

Nucleus	$j\pi$	μ (Single particle)	μ (Experiment)
^{7}Li	$\frac{3}{2}-$	3.8	3.26
^{9}Be	$\frac{3}{2}-$	-1.9	-1.18
^{11}B	$\frac{3}{2}-$	3.8	2.69
^{13}C	$\frac{1}{2}-$	0.60	0.70
^{15}N	$\frac{1}{2}-$	-0.2	-0.28
^{17}O	$\frac{5}{2}-$	-0.2	-0.1373
^{89}Y	$\frac{1}{2}-$	-1.9	-1.9
^{91}Zr	$\frac{5}{2}+$	-1.9	-1.9
^{207}Pb	$\frac{1}{2}-$	0.60	0.5895
^{209}Bi	$\frac{9}{2}-$	2.63	4.080

TABLE 5.3. Magnetic moments (in nuclear magnetons) of nuclei near closed shells compared with the single-particle model.

As an example we shall consider ^{7}Li. The extreme single-particle model says that the two extra-core neutrons are paired to give a total extra-core neutron spin $J_N = 0$, while the proton angular momentum j is $\frac{3}{2}$. However, states with $J_N = 1, 2$, or 3 can be formed from neutrons in the $1p_{3/2}$ shell. Considerations of isospin and symmetry, which will be developed in Chapter 7, forbid $J_N = 1$ and 3. However, the $J_N = 2, j = \frac{3}{2}$ level is quite close enough for it to play a part in the wave function, which may be written as

$$|^7\text{Li}\rangle = |^4\text{He core}\rangle\{|J_N = 0\rangle\,|j = \tfrac{3}{2}\rangle + a\,|J_N = 2\rangle\,|j = \tfrac{3}{2}\rangle\}. \quad (5.21)$$

The amplitude a of the $J_N = 2$ state in the superposition is fairly small, since the single-particle magnetic moment is not far from the correct value.

[iii] ELECTRIC QUADRUPOLE MOMENTS

The electric quadrupole moment is a measure of the departure of the charge density of the nucleus from a spherical shape. Nuclei with a single particle outside a spherical core are of course not spherical unless the single particle is in an s-state. The angular dependence of the spherical harmonics in Equation (5.4) is such that a nucleus with a single proton outside a spherical core is oblate (negative quadrupole moment). A nucleus with a single proton hole is therefore prolate (positive quadrupole moment). The z-axis is chosen so that the projection of the single-particle angular momentum is maximum.

Nuclei with spin zero have zero quadrupole moment. If there is no angular momentum, there is no axis to define the direction of measurement of the quadrupole moment. This does not mean that the nucleus may not be intrinsically deformed from a spherical shape. It simply means that the expectation value of the charge distribution for the 0+ state is spherical. Nuclei with spin $\frac{1}{2}$ also have zero quadrupole moment [see Equation (7.89)].

The components of the electric quadrupole moment of a nucleus are conventionally defined as the expectation value for the ground state of the quadrupole operator Q_m.

$$\langle Q_m \rangle \equiv (16\pi/5)^{1/2} \langle \sum_{i=1}^{Z} er_i^2 Y_2^m(\theta_i', \phi_i') \rangle, \tag{5.22}$$

where r_i, θ_i', ϕ_i' are a set of coordinates relative to body-fixed axes for each of the protons. If the axes are chosen to be axes of symmetry, the terms for $m = \pm 1$ are zero due to reflection symmetry. Only Q_0, Q_2, and Q_{-2} ($= Q_2$) are nonvanishing.

For a single particle the nucleus is axially symmetric. The operators Q_2 and Q_{-2} vanish by the orthogonality of the spherical harmonics. The quadrupole moment is defined now by taking the expectation value in a substate with $m = j$, denoted by $|jm\rangle = |jj\rangle$.

The state $|jm\rangle$ is formed by vector coupling the orbital wave functions $|lm_l\rangle$ and the spin wave functions $|sm_s\rangle$.

$$|jm\rangle = r^{-1}R_{nl}(r) \sum_{m_s} C_{l\ s\ j}^{m_l m_s m} |lm_l\rangle |sm_s\rangle. \tag{5.23}$$

We now have, by inserting this expansion on both sides of the matrix element (5.22) of Q_0 for a single particle and using the orthogonality of the spin functions,

$$Q = \langle Q_0 \rangle = e \left(\frac{16\pi}{5} \right)^{1/2} \bar{r}^2 \sum_{m_s} (C_{l\ s\ j}^{m_l m_s j})^2 \langle lm_l| Y_2^0 |lm_l\rangle, \tag{5.24}$$

where $\bar{r}^2$ is the mean-square radius defined by

$$\bar{r}^2 = \int dr [R_{nl}(r)]^2 r^2. \tag{5.25}$$

Using the Wigner-Eckart theorem and the numerical values of the Clebsch-Gordan coefficient, all of which are discussed in Appendix 4, Equation (5.24) becomes

$$Q = - \frac{2j - 1}{2j + 2} e\bar{r}^2. \tag{5.26}$$

Since the relevant particle for the quadrupole moment is the least bound proton, we would expect $\bar{r}$ to be somewhat larger than the rms radius of the charge distribution, but not very much larger. Thus quadrupole moments should be of the order of the square of the rms radius, that is, about $A^{\frac{2}{3}}$ fm², or a few tenths of a barn.

As we have seen from the magnetic moments, nuclei, even near most closed shells, are described by a superposition of several independent particle configurations. Thus we do not expect the single-particle model to predict quadrupole moments accurately, and it does not.

There are, however, two striking anomalies (one qualitative, one quantitative) for certain nuclei. First, nuclei with one unpaired neutron have quadrupole moments similar to nuclei with one unpaired proton. For example, the quadrupole moment of ⁸⁷Sr, which has a neutron hole in the $N = 50$ closed shell, is 0.36 barns. Even ¹⁷O, with a neutron outside a doubly closed shell, has a quadrupole moment of −0.027 barns.

Second, although nuclei near closed shells have quadrupole moments of the right order of magnitude, those in two regions of the periodic table, $150 < A < 190$ and $A > 230$, have quadrupole moments of several barns, an order of magnitude larger than expected. For example, the quadrupole moment of ¹⁸¹Ta is 3.9 barns, whereas for ²⁰⁹Bi it is −0.4 barns, compared with $A^{\frac{2}{3}} = 0.35$ barns.

Both these facts suggest that the core of an anomalous nucleus is intrinsically deformed. Its deformation axis is correlated with the quantization axis of the single-particle motion through the action of the nuclear forces, so that the intrinsic deformation does lead to a measurable quadrupole moment. In Chapter 6, we shall see how the nuclear forces can lead to intrinsic deformations and, in Chapter 7, we shall study the parametrization in terms of deformed cores which is used to predict experimental data.

[iv] SUMMARY OF SINGLE-PARTICLE SPECTROSCOPY

We have seen that the extreme single-particle model is quite a good starting point for the understanding of nuclear structure. It gives a description of many outstanding qualitative features of nuclei, the most detailed being the spins. The spin is quantized and the model can only be right or wrong. In general, it is good enough to be right.

Properties of nuclei which depend on a more detailed description of nuclear wave functions, such as nuclear moments, are not predicted well by the model. Two possible methods of improving on the model are suggested by studying moments. Anomalous magnetic moments suggest that the nucleus could be described by a superposition of several different products of independent particle wave functions which are close to each other in energy. This is expected from the general considerations of Chapter 1*B*.

Virtual transitions for nucleons in the upper single-particle states are not inhibited by the Pauli principle as they are for nucleons in lower states.

Anomalous electric quadrupole moments suggest that the correlations in the upper states may take the form of deformations of the nuclear surface. Examination of the single-particle wave functions, which are similar to $j_l(Kr)$, show that nucleons in upper momentum states are in general further away from the center in the space distribution, particularly if they correspond to large l. Of course, levels with large l contain many more nucleons than levels with smaller l because of the $2j + 1$ degeneracy.

So far we have only considered the relevance of the single-particle model to spectroscopy. That is, we have taken nuclei as they exist in nature, and have considered their measurable properties. Fortunately, in nuclear physics we do not have to be content with this information. We can perform reaction experiments which force nuclei to yield further information about points which the reaction is designed to test. We have already mentioned the (d, p) reaction in which a single neutron is added to a nucleus. Properties of the reaction amplitude clearly depend on the wave function of the single neutron, even though the single-particle model may not be good. A more striking reaction is the (p, 2p) reaction in which a single proton is knocked out of the nucleus and the momentum-transfer distribution measured. The momentum-transfer distribution clearly is closely correlated with the distribution of momenta which the nuclear proton had before it was knocked out, and therefore with its wave function.

It is therefore possible to ask questions whose answers depend on a knowledge of the wave function of a single particle in the nucleus regardless of whether the single-particle model describes the spectroscopic data. If the single-particle model is a poor description of the data, the properties of the reaction are very different from the situation where it is a good description. This will be discussed in detail in Chapter 13 with reference to the (d, p) reaction.

C. SINGLE-PARTICLE ENERGY LEVELS AND WAVE FUNCTIONS IN REAL NUCLEI

Thus far we have been interested only in the ground states of nuclei. We shall now consider the excited states, concentrating on the ones that can be understood from a single-particle point of view. A real nucleus may be characterized by a Hamiltonian of the form

$$H = \sum_{i=1}^{A} K_i + \sum_{i=1}^{A} V(r_i) + \sum_{i<j}^{A} \bar{H}_{ij} + a \sum_{i=1}^{A} \mathbf{l}_i \cdot \mathbf{s}_i$$

$$= K + H_C + \bar{H}_{\text{int}} + H_S, \tag{5.27}$$

where the K_i are the kinetic energy operators of the nucleons i, $V(r_i)$ is a central shell-model potential, $\bar{H}_{\text{int}}$ is the residual two-body interaction term and H_S is the single-particle spin-orbit coupling term. The actual two-body interaction term H_{int} is given by

$$H_{\text{int}} = H_C + \bar{H}_{\text{int}} + H_S. \qquad (5.28)$$

This can be considered as a definition of the residual interaction $\bar{H}_{\text{int}}$.

In order to find the eigenvalues of the Hamiltonian, that is, the energy levels of the nucleus, and the eigenvectors, that is, the state vectors of the nucleus, we must express the Hamiltonian in a matrix representation and diagonalize it. In practice we can only use a representation of finite dimension. The practical aspects of this problem will be investigated in Chapters 6 and 7.

If we are able to find a representation in which H is diagonal, the problem is of course solved. The approximate validity of the single-particle shell model gives us a representation in which we hope H is not far from diagonal. The shell-model Hamiltonian is often defined to exclude the spin-orbit coupling term. It is

$$H_0 = K + H_C. \qquad (5.29)$$

The eigenstates of H_0 are a complete orthonormal set of antisymmetric state vectors which form the basis of the shell-model representation. Since it is possible to give closed forms for the matrix elements, the single-particle potential is usually taken to be the harmonic oscillator, sometimes with different oscillator constants for different shells, since this is more realistic as we shall see.

Several operators commute with H. They represent observables which are conserved. In other words, the corresponding quantum numbers are good. The most important of these are the total angular momentum J and the parity π. It is generally assumed that the isospin T is a good quantum number. This will be discussed more fully in Chapter 7. Matrix elements connecting states with different values of good quantum numbers are zero. Hence the Hamiltonian matrix is a direct sum of disjoint submatrices $K^{J\pi T}$, each corresponding to one set of values of J, π, T. The submatrices can be separately diagonalized.

Nucleons in the same subshell are said to be equivalent. This means that they have the same values of n, of l, and also of j if we use a representation in which j is specified. A configuration is a definite set of nlj.

Let us fix our attention on a single nucleon in a nucleus. In the extreme single-particle model, excited states may be formed by putting a particle in one of the unoccupied single-particle levels or by putting a hole in one of the occupied levels. In fact neither of these processes preserves particle number. The nucleus after the process has one nucleon more or less than it had before.

However, one of the assumptions of the single-particle model is that one nucleon more or less has a small effect on the single-particle energy levels. A process which does preserve particle number is the promotion of a single unpaired nucleon from one single-particle state to a higher state.

If the final nucleus is well described by the single-particle model, we may say that the process of adding or removing a nucleon is a means of investigating single-particle states. We shall investigate what this means in terms of the shell-model representation of a real nucleus.

Instead of an explicit shell-model representation, let us choose a single-particle representation in which the state vector $|m\rangle$ of the basis is given by

$$|m\rangle = A\phi_i(x_i)\psi_\alpha(\xi_i), \tag{5.30}$$

where x_i symbolizes all the coordinates of the single-particle i including spin and isospin, and ξ_i symbolizes all the coordinates of the other particles. ϕ_i is the single-particle wave function for particle i, ψ_α will be called the core wave function, and A is the antisymmetrization operator. This representation is often called the weak coupling representation (Macfarlane and French, 60). We shall take the separate submatrices $K^{J\pi T}$ one at a time, so that the basis state $|m\rangle$ is obtained by vector coupling the angular momenta and isospins of ϕ_i and ψ_α to the values $J\pi$, T.

The core state ψ_α is related to the states of the core nucleus which, for example, is the nucleus $[A]$ in the reaction

$$[A](d, p)[A + 1],$$

where the nuclei are specified by their mass numbers. We shall consider the case where a particle is added. The case where a hole is added to $[A]$ is completely parallel. An example of this case is

$$[A](p, 2p)[A - 1].$$

The core may be described by a nuclear model. At present we are not interested in a specific description. However, it must be realized that, in general, the core states ψ_α are not eigenstates of the nucleus $[A]$ if the basic vectors $|m\rangle$ are orthonormal. This will be understood when we consider the shell-model description of the core, but it is not surprising in view of the fact that the $|m\rangle$ are antisymmetrized. We shall choose the ground-state core function ψ_0 to be the ground-state eigenfunction of the nucleus $[A]$. The other core wave functions for $\alpha \neq 0$ are linear combinations of the eigenstates of $[A]$.

We shall now diagonalize the Hamiltonian H, that is, we shall transform it with an operator U, and shall express it in terms of a new representation $|\rho\rangle$ given by

$$|\rho\rangle = U|m\rangle, \tag{5.31}$$

where the set of all $|\rho\rangle$ is the set of eigenvectors of the transformed operator UHU^{-1}. The transformed operator is expressed in the transformed representation as

$$\langle\sigma|\ UHU^{-1}\ |\rho\rangle = E_\rho\delta_{\rho\sigma}$$
$$= \langle n|\ U^\dagger UHU^{-1}U\ |m\rangle. \tag{5.32}$$

This is identical to H in the original $|m\rangle$ representation if

$$U^\dagger U = 1. \tag{5.33}$$

U is a unitary operator. Its matrix elements in the $|m\rangle$ representation are

$$\langle n|\ U\ |m\rangle = \langle n\ |\ \rho\rangle. \tag{5.34}$$

We may now express the eigenstate $|\rho\rangle$ in terms of the original notation (5.30) for $|m\rangle$.

$$|\rho\rangle = \textstyle\sum_m |m\rangle\langle m\ |\ \rho\rangle$$
$$= \textstyle\sum_{i\alpha} t_{i\alpha}^{(\rho)} A\phi_i(x_i)\psi_\alpha(\xi_i) \tag{5.35}$$

where $t_{i\alpha}^{(\rho)}$ is seen by (5.34) to be an element of the unitary transformation matrix U.

Using the completeness relation for the eigenstates, we write the normalization of the basis state (5.30) as

$$\textstyle\sum_\rho\langle m\ |\ \rho\rangle\langle\rho\ |\ m\rangle \equiv \textstyle\sum_\rho |t_{i\alpha}^{(\rho)}|^2 = 1 \tag{5.36}$$

for all sets of indices $i\alpha$ and, in particular, for the set $i0$.

The state ρ of the nucleus $[A+1]$ is said to be a single-particle state if the expansion (5.35) is dominated by a single transformation matrix element $t_{i0}^{(\rho)}$. It is then quite well described by the single-particle wave function ϕ_i. Single-particle states defined in this way are as near as we can get experimentally to the original mathematical idea of the state of a single particle in a potential.

If we choose the shell-model potential $V(r_i)$ as realistically as possible, it will minimize the role of coefficients other than $t_{i0}^{(\rho)}$ in the actual state vector (5.35).

The philosophy behind the identification of single-particle states by means of the (d, p) or (d, n) reaction is as follows. If it is easy to make the state ρ by putting a single particle into it, then it is a single-particle state. The magnitude of the (d, p) cross section is a measure of whether a state is a single-particle state. A detailed model must be made for the reaction before the relationship can be stated quantitatively. Attempts to do this will be discussed in the chapters on reactions. It turns out approximately, and the assumption is often made, that the cross section is proportional to the spectroscopic factor $S^\rho(\phi_i)$.

$$S^\rho(\phi_i) = |t_{i0}^{(\rho)}|^2. \tag{5.37}$$

If ρ is an exact single-particle state then S^ρ is unity.

Spectroscopic factors are obtained from a theory of the (d, p) reaction by extracting a quantity θ^2, called the reduced width by analogy with the theory of resonances (see Chapter 8). The reduced width is determined by the square of the overlap of the wave functions of the initial and final nuclei $\langle[A + 1] | [A]\rangle$. It is a property of the reaction which is independent of the experimental conditions; for example, it is independent of the incident energy. For a single-particle reaction the reduced width is determined by the square of the single-particle wave function ϕ_i. It is then called the single-particle reduced width $\theta_0{}^2$. The spectroscopic factor is given by

$$\theta^2 = S^\rho\theta_0{}^2. \tag{5.38}$$

The theory of the (d, p) reaction has not quite reached the stage where the absolute reduced width is determined reliably (see Chapter 13). However, relative reduced widths for different states of a particular final nucleus are good indications of the single-particle strength of a particular transition. The reduced width for the ground state is taken as unity.

If S^ρ is not unity, then several states ρ contain terms in ϕ_i. The single-particle strength is said to be shared among several states of the nucleus $[A + 1]$. If the number of states ρ is small, the weak coupling approximation is said to be valid, and the weak coupling representation is a useful one.

An extremely useful relationship is the sum rule obtained from (5.36, 37)

$$\sum_\rho S^\rho(\phi_i) = 1. \tag{5.39}$$

This means that, if the theory of the reaction is well enough understood, the whole of the single-particle strength can be traced in the states ρ. The (d, p) cross section will be weighted according to the single-particle strength. If we have a nucleus whose spectroscopy is well understood, the sum rule may also be used to check the reaction theory. The energy of the single-particle state ϕ_i is often said to be at the "center of gravity" of the energies E_ρ, where they are weighted according to the (d, p) reduced widths.

[i]   LEVELS EXCITED BY (d, p) AND (p, 2p) REACTIONS

If coefficients $t_{i\alpha}^{(\rho)}$ for $\alpha \neq 0$ are important in the expansion (5.35) of the nuclear state vector in weak coupling states, the core cannot be inert. The state involves superpositions of configurations, including configurations with core excitation. We would expect this effect to be minimized when the core is a closed shell nucleus whose first excited state is high in energy.

Examples of such nuclei are ^{12}C, whose first excited state is at 4.43 MeV and ^{16}O, whose first excited state is at 6.06 MeV. The levels revealed by adding a neutron in (d, p) reactions and by adding a proton hole in (p, 2p) reactions are shown in Table 5.4. The orbital angular momentum transfer can be deduced from the reaction theory. This enables single-particle states to be easily assigned to the nuclear states, provided the core is inert.

Reaction	Level (MeV)	$J\pi$	s.p. State	Relative θ^2
^{16}O(d, p)^{17}O	0.93	$\frac{3}{2}+$	$1d_{3/2}$	0.80
	0.408	$\frac{3}{2}-$	Core excited	0.25
	−0.299	$\frac{5}{2}-$	Core excited	0.23
	−1.090	$\frac{1}{2}-$	Core excited	—
	−3.217	$\frac{1}{2}+$	$2s_{1/2}$	2.2
	−4.145	$\frac{5}{2}+$	$1d_{5/2}$	1
^{16}O(p, 2p)^{15}N	−12.4	$\frac{1}{2}-$	$1p_{1/2}$	—
	−19.1	$\frac{3}{2}-$	$1p_{3/2}$	—
	−44	$\frac{1}{2}+$	$1s_{1/2}$	—
^{12}C(d, p)^{13}C	−1.10	$\frac{5}{2}+$	$1d_{5/2}$	2.3
	−1.27	$\frac{3}{2}-$	Core excited	0.19
	−1.86	$\frac{1}{2}+$	$2s_{1/2}$	4.9
	−4.945	$\frac{1}{2}-$	$1p_{1/2}$	1
^{12}C(p, 2p)^{11}B	−16	$\frac{3}{2}-$	$1p_{3/2}$	—
	−34	$\frac{1}{2}+$	$1s_{1/2}$	—

TABLE 5.4.   The energy levels obtained by adding a single neutron and adding a single proton hole to ^{16}O and ^{12}C. The zero of energy is taken to be the ground-state energy of ^{16}O and ^{12}C, respectively. The experimental data are from Riou (65), McGruer, Warburton, and Bender (56), and Green and Middleton (56). Energy levels for particles with the opposite charge can be estimated by adding or subtracting the average Coulomb potential which is about 3 MeV in each case.

It is clear that neither ^{12}C nor ^{16}O act like perfect inert cores, since the core-excited states are mixed up with the single-particle states in both ^{13}C and ^{17}O.

Nuclei away from closed shells act very much less like inert cores. For example, the $1p_{3/2}$ single proton hole strength in the reaction ^{10}B(p, 2p)Be^9 is split between levels at 7, 12, and 17 MeV. This is to be expected, since ^{10}B is an odd nucleus with very close levels at 0, 0.717, 1.74, and 2.15 MeV corresponding to different couplings of the $1p_{3/2}$ shell nucleons.

Table 5.4 also serves to illustrate the way in which the level ordering is determined from (d, p) experiments. The level orders are not always consistent; for example, the $2s_{1/2}$ and $1d_{5/2}$ levels are interchanged in ^{13}C and ^{17}O. However the $2s_{1/2}$ level is higher than the $1d_{5/2}$ level in nearly all cases.

[ii]   POTENTIAL MODELS FOR SINGLE-PARTICLE WAVE FUNCTIONS

Having explained the means by which single-particle states are identified we must now consider how to choose a single-particle potential $V(r)$ which gives the best estimate of the single-particle wave function. This is particularly important because of its application to reaction theory. The first step in a reaction theory is to consider a collision between a projectile nucleon and a nucleon in the nucleus. The wave function of the nucleon in the nucleus must be known. The best chance of knowing it is when single-particle states are involved in the reaction. Momentum-transfer distributions are particularly sensitive to details of the wave function, the coarsest detail being the rms radius.

The theory of the (p, 2p) reaction at high energy is so well understood that the momentum-transfer distribution gives a very reliable estimate of the rms radius of the single-particle wave function (Lim and McCarthy 64b).

One other very prominent feature of the wave function is determined experimentally. This is the shape of the tail or the part outside the potential. Since its form is $h_l^{(1)} i\beta r$, it is determined entirely by the binding energy.

The spin and parity for many states may be inferred from the level order, an analysis of the cross section for a reaction, or from other spectroscopic methods.

In fact radial wave functions for which the spin and parity, the binding energy, and the rms radius are all equal are very similar, regardless of the potential. Many reaction theories have used finite square well potentials, other have used Woods-Saxon form factors in an attempt to introduce greater realism, although the differences between the corresponding wave functions are trivial, particularly when the integrations are performed to obtain the matrix elements.

In a survey of high energy (p, 2p) data on p-shell nuclei, Lim and McCarthy (64b) used wave functions computed in finite square wells making particular attempts to determine the rms radius. The experimental value of the binding energy was used. The rms radius of the charge distribution can be compared with the value obtained from high energy electron elastic scattering as an external check on the wave functions. The results of the survey are given in Table 5.5.

The most striking feature of the potentials is their state dependence. Wells for s-states are invariably narrower and deeper than for p-states. We might expect from our study of nuclear matter that this dependence reflects a dependence of the potential on the velocity of the single particle, given by the internal wave number K. This idea is supported by the fact that the difference is larger when the binding energy difference is larger (compare ^{11}B and ^{12}C).

State		E	V	R	$\langle r \rangle_{\mathrm{p, 2p}}$	$\langle r \rangle_{\mathrm{e}}$
^{6}Li	s	22.4	49.8	2.0	2.86	2.83
	p	4.0	13.0	5.2		
^{7}Li	s	25.5	49.8	2.2	2.85	2.83
	p	10.0	19.8	5.4		
^{10}B	s	31.5	55.0	2.3	2.60	*
	p	7.0	27.5	3.5		
^{11}B	s	34.0	59.5	2.2	2.64	2.55
	p	10.0	28.3	3.8		
^{12}C	s	36.0	58.0	2.4	2.48	2.42
	p	16.0	38.4	3.5		

TABLE 5.5.   Parameters of square well wave functions used to fit binding energies and momentum-transfer distributions in (p, 2p) experiments. Energies are in MeV, distances in fm. The last two columns give the rms radius for the whole nucleus as computed from (p, 2p) and electron scattering experiments. [From Lim and McCarthy (64b).]

The idea of velocity dependence was pursued by Elton and Swift (67) who used a Woods-Saxon form factor with the diffuseness parameter a approximately constant at 0.55 fm to 0.65 fm. The results were insensitive to a. With the restriction that the well radius should be the same for all states of the same nucleus, state-dependent values of the depth were obtained by fitting two types of experimental data. The eigenvalues were required to fit the observed binding energies and the charge density was required to fit electron elastic scattering cross sections.

In the effective mass approximation, in which the potential depends linearly on the internal energy $E = \hbar^2 K^2/2\mu$, the following velocity dependence of the central depth V_0 was found for protons.

$$V_0 = 39 - 0.64(E - 1.38ZA^{-\frac{1}{3}}) + \frac{25(N - Z)}{A}. \qquad (5.40)$$

The effective mass was

$$M^* = 0.36M,$$

in good agreement with the value found by Brueckner, Lockett, and Rotenberg (61) for finite nuclei (see Chapter 6B). The radius and spin-orbit coupling parameters for different nuclei are given in Table 5.6. Note that radii are not strictly proportional to $A^{\frac{1}{3}}$.

It is interesting to note that another criterion for obtaining the radial shape of nuclear wave functions has already been mentioned. This is the determination of a static potential whose depth is constant and whose radius

Nucleus	r_0(fm)	a(fm)	λ_p	λ_d
^{7}Li	1.38	0.65	40	—
^{12}C	1.36	0.55	30	—
^{16}O	1.41	0.65	45	—
^{28}Si	1.39	0.55	75	20
^{31}P	1.33	0.55	60	60
^{32}S	1.38	0.55	75	65
^{40}Ca	1.30	0.60	90	40

TABLE 5.6.   Parameters of the single-particle potential of Elton and Swift (67). The radius of the Woods-Saxon potential is $r_0 A^{1/3}$. The depth is given by (5.40), the spin-orbit coupling parameters are λ_p and λ_d for $1p$ and $1d$ states, respectively.

is proportional to $A^{1/3}$ so that level orders are correctly reproduced. The potential of Ross, Mark, and Lawson (56) in fact gives bad predictions for the rms radii of light nuclei. It is compared with the empirical wave function of Table 5.5 in Fig. 5.5. The differences in shape compensate for the binding energy difference in such a way as to make the rms radii more nearly equal.

It is essential to have a reliable estimate of the shapes of single-particle wave functions in order to predict momentum-transfer distributions for nuclear reactions. The potential of Elton and Swift gives a simple and reliable description. However, in fitting the momentum-transfer distribution in a (p, 2p) experiment, more data are fitted. This must be considered the best method at present for an empirical determination of single-particle wave functions.

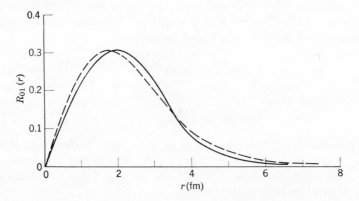

FIG. 5.5   The $1p_{3/2}$-radial wave function of ^{12}C using the empirical potential of Table 5.5 (full line) and the potential of Ross, Mark, and Lawson (56) (dashed line).

FURTHER READING

1. H. A. Bethe and R. F. Bacher, *Rev. Mod. Phys.*, **8,** 82 (1936).
   Early review of nuclear structure containing basic shell-model theory.

2. W. M. Elsasser, *J. Phys. et Radium*, **5,** 389, 635 (1934).
   Early discussion of periodicity in nuclear properties.

3. M. G. Mayer, *Phys. Rev.*, **74,** 235 (1948); **75,** 1969 (1949); **78,** 16, 22 (1950).
   O. Haxel, J. H. D. Jensen, and H. E. Suess, *Phys. Rev.*, **75,** 1766 (1949); *Z. Phys.*, **128,** 295 (1950).
   Comparison with experimental data of the predictions of the single-particle model with spin-orbit coupling.

4. M. G. Mayer and J. H. D. Jensen, *Elementary Theory of Nuclear Shell Structure*, John Wiley and Sons, Inc., New York, 1955.
   J. P. Elliott and A. M. Lane, "The Nuclear Shell Model," *Encyclopedia of Physics*, Vol. XXXIX, Berlin: Springer-Verlag, 1957.
   Comprehensive reviews.

5. M. H. Brennan and A. M. Bernstein, *Phys. Rev.*, **120,** 927 (1960).
   B. L. Cohen, *Am. J. Phys.*, **33,** 1011 (1965).
   M. Riou, *Rev. Mod. Phys.*, **37,** 375 (1965).
   Experimental determination of single-particle levels.

6. M. H. Macfarlane and J. B. French, *Rev. Mod. Phys.*, **32,** 567 (1960).
   Theory of the shell model in relation to stripping.

7. A. Ross, H. Mark, and R. D. Lawson, *Phys. Rev.*, **104,** 401 (1956).
   L. R. B. Elton and A. Swift, *Nucl. Phys.*, **A94,** 52 (1967).
   Determination of single-particle potentials.

PROBLEMS

1. Draw the radial wave functions for *all* the bound states in the square well potential $V = -40$ MeV, $R = 3$ fm.

2. Compare the shell models for atoms and nuclei. Are the shells as well localized radially in the nuclear model as they are in the atomic model?

3. Assume that the single particle shell model potential is velocity-dependent. The static part is the same as that of Problem 1. The effective mass M^* is 0.5 M. What velocity-independent potentials produce wave functions for the $1s$ and $1p$ states which have roughly the same rms radii as the wave functions for the velocity-dependent potential? Use graphical computation methods.

4. Calculate the electric quadrupole moment and the magnetic dipole moment of a proton in the $1p_{3/2}$ state of Problem 1.

5. Obtaining estimates of $\hbar\omega$ from Table 5.4, use harmonic oscillator wave functions to calculate the electric quadrupole moments of ^{11}B and ^{14}N. The experimental values are $+0.036$ and $+0.01$, respectively.

6. Show that the rms radius of a harmonic oscillator wave function is $(\hbar/M\omega)$ $(2n + l + 3/2)$.

7. Compare the rms radius of the $1p_{3/2}$ state in ^{12}C, calculated using the harmonic oscillator function of Problem 5, with the value 2.79 fm obtained by the analysis of high energy (p, 2p) experiments.

8. Find the value of $\hbar\omega$ for the $1s$ state of ^{12}C which gives the correct rms radius (2.83 fm) for the whole nucleus when used in conjunction with the wave function of Problem 7.

6

NUCLEAR STRUCTURE— GROUND STATES

We have seen that long-range correlations are to be expected in nuclei because of the interaction of nucleons in states near the Fermi surface. In order to discover what form these correlations take, we must now calculate the nuclear wave function in an approximation in which the nuclear forces are taken into account explicitly. The success of the theory of infinite nuclear matter suggests that the free nucleon-nucleon forces are sufficient for predicting properties of nuclei. The only many-body effect that we would expect to find necessary is the effect of the Pauli exclusion principle on the relative two-body scattering wave function in the presence of other nucleons.

In this chapter, we shall consider first a simple example to show how nuclear forces can induce a long-range correlation. We shall then consider the principles involved in the calculation of the nuclear wave function, which must be done in a representation of finite dimension using potentials that are very singular at short distances. Finally we shall discuss the principles of two types of calculation and illustrate their results.

The study of the single-particle shell model leads us to expect that a good approximation to the problem of the finite nucleus may be obtained by treating the nucleons in the lower occupied states as if they formed an inert closed shell core, and by considering the interaction only of the particles in the upper unfilled shell. There is no reason why, given powerful enough computing techniques, we should not include the particles in the topmost filled shell in our many-body calculation, or even include all the particles in the nucleus, as will be done in the calculations discussed in this chapter. All calculations are done by expanding the wave function in terms of an independent particle basis. The interaction of particles in a single-particle potential created by all the particles of the nucleus is calculated. Some major principles are illustrated by the simplest example of the interaction of two particles in a potential.

A nucleus for which we expect the model of two nucleons in a potential created by an inert core to be a good approximation is ^{6}Li. The first excited state of ^{4}He is at about 20 MeV, so it should obey the assumption of an inert core very well. The outer nucleons, one neutron and one proton, are both in the $1p_{3/2}$ shell. Their angular momenta can couple to $J = 0$, 1, 2, or 3. If the single-particle model were good, all these states should have about the same energy. In fact the states are separated by several MeV as shown in Fig. 6.1.

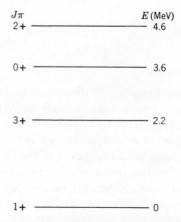

FIG. 6.1   The states of ^{6}Li which can be attributed to the $(p_{3/2})^2$ configuration.

In the extreme single-particle model the angular momenta of the two particles are separately coupled to the single-particle well by means of the spin-orbit term. Each nucleon has angular momentum j independent of the angular momentum of the other. This extreme case is called jj coupling. If the interparticle forces are very strong compared to the spin-orbit potential, the space wave function (including the orbital angular momentum) of one particle is determined largely by the space wave function of the other. This limit is called LS coupling.

Let us consider the LS coupling limit for ^{6}Li and take the situation for the ground state ($J = 1$) where the two spins couple to $S = 1$ and the two-orbital angular momenta couple to $L = 0$. There is a space correlation between the particles given by

$$\cos \xi = \frac{\mathbf{r}_1 \cdot \mathbf{r}_2}{r_1 r_2},$$

$$(6.1)$$

where ξ is the angle between the radius vectors. The strength of the forces influences the occurrence of particular values of ξ. Equation (6.1) means that *if* one particle is found in a given direction, it is most probable to find the other particle in a cone about that direction. The correlation produces an intrinsic quadrupole moment. The ^{6}Li nucleus is not spherical. This type of correlation may be expected in nuclei away from closed shells. The simple model of ^{6}Li enables us to understand in principle how it arises.

Another important principle is illustrated by considering the method of calculating the problem of two particles bound in a potential using an independent particle basis to expand the wave function.

A. THE USE OF THE *t*-MATRIX IN A SIMPLE BOUND-STATE CALCULATION

The computation of the matrix elements of the Hamiltonian for a bound-state calculation has a very serious difficulty when realistic local nuclear potentials with hard cores are used. The matrix elements of the potential are infinite.

In this section we shall consider the difficulty in the simplest possible bound-state calculation, two nonidentical particles interacting with an inert core. The formalism used here is due to Greider (65). We shall expand the wave function for the three-body system in a perturbation series in terms of the particle-core potential V_0 and the particle-particle potential V. We shall then rearrange the series in such a way that the leading term does not give infinite Hamiltonian matrix elements. The principles illustrated here apply to calculations with larger numbers of bound particles.

The Schrödinger equation for the problem is

$$(H - E)\Psi = 0, \tag{6.2}$$

where

$$H = K + V. \tag{6.3}$$

The Hamiltonian of the independent particle problem is K. It includes the kinetic energy K_0 of both particles, labeled by 1 and 2, and the potentials V_0 binding each to the core.

$$K = K_0 + 2V_0. \tag{6.4}$$

The independent particle problem can be solved. Its eigenstates ϕ_α form a complete orthonormal set which can be used as a basis for representing the wave function Ψ of the total problem.

$$(K - E_\alpha)\phi_\alpha = 0. \tag{6.5}$$

ϕ_α is a two-particle wave function and α indicates the state of the 1, 2 pair.

We use discrete notation for ϕ_α even though the set contains continuum states (states with continuous eigenvalues). If it were necessary to enumerate the states, we could impose periodic boundary conditions by putting the complete system in a box whose volume could be expanded to infinity at the correct point in the calculation. We shall not discuss this further in the present section.

For a numerical solution of (6.2) we must use a truncated basis of finite dimension. In the shell model we take a finite number of states, cutting off at the point where the energy is so much greater than the energy of the highest occupied state that virtual transitions are unlikely. Defining P to be the operator which projects out this shell-model basis from the complete set of ϕ_α we have, denoting the truncated sum by $\sum'$,

$$P = \sum_\alpha' |\phi_\alpha\rangle \langle\phi_\alpha|, \tag{6.6}$$

and

$$P\Psi = \psi_{SM}, \tag{6.7}$$

where ψ_{SM} is the shell model wave function, which is expected to be a good approximation to Ψ. Let Q be the projection operator for all states ϕ_α not included in the shell model set.

$$P + Q = 1. \tag{6.8}$$

Using the operator notation $(K - E)^{-1}$ for the Green's function of (6.5), we may use (6.6, 7) to obtain

$$\Psi = \psi_{SM} + (1 - P) \frac{1}{K - E} (K - E)\Psi. \tag{6.9}$$

From (6.2, 3) and the fact that $1 - P$ and $(K - E)^{-1}$ commute, we have the integral equation

$$\Psi = \psi_{SM} - \frac{1}{K - E} (1 - P)V\Psi$$

$$= \psi_{SM} - \frac{1}{K - E} V\Psi + \frac{1}{K - E} PV\Psi. \tag{6.10}$$

We shall now consider the expansion of (6.10) by perturbation theory using ψ_{SM} as the unperturbed wave function. The use of the zeroth order solution ψ_{SM} to represent Ψ leads to infinite Hamiltonian matrix elements when V has a hard core. The perturbation series is formed by iteratively substituting ψ_{SM} for Ψ in (6.10). We are particularly interested in the second term of (6.10). It may be further expanded in a series involving both V_0 and V explicitly, in which the only Green's functions that appear are those for the propagation of two free particles.

$$\frac{1}{K - E} V\Psi = \frac{1}{K_0 + 2V_0 - E} V\Psi$$

$$= \frac{1}{K_0 - E} V\Psi - \frac{1}{K_0 - E} 2V_0 \frac{1}{K_0 - E} V\Psi + \cdots . \quad (6.11)$$

Each of the terms of (6.11) is expanded further by the iterative substitution of ψ_{SM} for Ψ, generating a set of diagrams analogous to those described for the scattering problem in Chapter 2C[ii]. Some of the diagrams are shown in Fig. 6.2. The Green's function operator $(K_0 - E)^{-1}$ is the propagator for the two free particles 1 and 2. In all the diagrams representing the iteration of the first term of (6.11), particles 1 and 2 are connected by wavy lines representing the potential V. The core line is disconnected from the particle lines. For the diagrams representing all the terms of (6.10) and (6.11) except the first term of (6.11), the diagrams are fully connected by wavy lines representing the potentials V_0 and V.

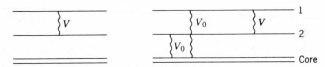

FIG. 6.2   Lowest-order diagrams for the iteration of the first and second terms of Equation 6.11.

The disconnected diagrams represent the propagation without interaction of a particle (the core) whose initial wave vector is **k** and whose final wave vector is **k′**. Matrix elements for the problem involve the function $\delta(\mathbf{k} - \mathbf{k}')$ which is not integrated over either **k** or **k′** because both can be measured. Thus the matrix elements have a singularity of the δ-function type. In a two-body problem the δ-function represents the conservation of momentum and cancels out when the transformation to C.M. and relative coordinates is performed. In a many-body problem, momentum is not conserved in the separate two-body systems, so that disconnected diagrams represent real singularities.

The series can be rearranged so that the disconnected diagram singularities do not appear explicitly. The singularities were of course introduced by making the perturbation expansion in both V_0 and V. It is quite possible that the rearrangement (6.10) is convergent for physically interesting matrix elements of V if V is small enough. However, this is certainly not so for a hard core.

Another rearrangement which leads to finite matrix elements in a matrix representation of the Schrödinger equation (6.2) is given by adding and subtracting $(K_0 - E)^{-1}V\Psi$ in (6.10). Note that the third term of (6.10) does not have disconnected diagram singularities, since P projects out only bound states from the set ϕ_α.

$$\Psi = \psi_{SM} - \left[\frac{1}{K - E}(1 - P)V - \frac{1}{K_0 - E}V\right]\Psi - \frac{1}{K_0 - E}V\Psi. \quad (6.12)$$

The kernel in square brackets converges since we have subtracted off the singular part. Equation (6.12) may be rewritten as

$$\Psi = \left[1 + \frac{1}{K_0 - E}V\right]^{-1}\psi_{SM}$$

$$- \left[1 + \frac{1}{K_0 - E}V\right]^{-1}\left[\frac{1}{K - E}(1 - P)V - \frac{1}{K_0 - E}V\right]\Psi. \quad (6.13)$$

In both terms of (6.13) we have the factor

$$\left[1 + \frac{1}{K_0 - E}V\right]^{-1} = 1 - \frac{1}{K_0 + V - E}V = \Omega_V. \quad (6.14)$$

This is the distortion operator for the interaction of particles 1 and 2 only (see Chapter 2C[iii]).

We will now obtain approximate solutions to the original Schrödinger equation (6.2) in terms of the shell-model set of states ϕ_α, using the first term of the rearrangement (6.13) of the perturbation series.

Expand the shell-model wave function ψ_{SM} in terms of the truncated set of two-body wave functions ϕ_α.

$$\psi_{SM} = \sum_\alpha' a_\alpha \phi_\alpha. \quad (6.15)$$

The Schrödinger equation (6.2, 3) may be expressed in a matrix representation as

$$\sum_\alpha' a_\alpha \langle\phi_\alpha|E|\Psi\rangle = \sum_\alpha' a_\alpha \langle\phi_\alpha|K + V|\Psi\rangle,$$

or

$$\sum_\alpha' (E - E_\alpha)\langle a_\alpha \phi_\alpha|\Psi\rangle = \sum_\alpha' a_\alpha \langle\phi_\alpha|V|\Psi\rangle. \quad (6.16)$$

At this stage we define the normalization of ψ_{SM} as follows

$$\langle\phi_\alpha|\Psi\rangle = \sum_\beta a_\beta \langle\phi_\alpha|\Omega_V|\phi_\beta\rangle = \sum_\beta a_\beta \delta_{\alpha\beta} = a_\alpha. \quad (6.17)$$

The energy eigenvalue is given by putting $\Psi = \Omega_V \psi_{SM}$, using (6.15, 17) and the orthonormality of the ϕ_α.

$$E = \frac{\sum_\alpha' |a_\alpha|^2 E_\alpha}{\sum_\alpha' |a_\alpha|^2} + \frac{\langle\sum_\alpha' a_\alpha \phi_\alpha|V|\Omega_V \sum_\beta' a_\beta \phi_\beta\rangle}{\sum_\alpha' |a_\alpha|^2}$$

$$= \frac{\sum_\alpha' |a_\alpha|^2 E_\alpha}{\sum_\alpha' |a_\alpha|^2} + \frac{\sum_{\alpha\beta}' a_\alpha a_\beta}{\sum_\alpha' |a_\alpha|^2} T_{\alpha\beta}, \quad (6.18)$$

where $T_{\alpha\beta}$ is the *t*-matrix element for the interaction of the two nucleons while the core does not interact.

$$T_{\alpha\beta} = \langle \phi_\alpha | \, V\Omega_V \, | \phi_\beta \rangle = \langle \phi_\alpha | \, T \, | \phi_\beta \rangle. \tag{6.19}$$

The calculation of the quantities a_α and E_α in (6.18) is performed by diagonalizing the Hamiltonian matrix with the two-body potential V replaced by T.

This simple illustration shows in principle how to do a nuclear structure calculation. For n bodies there are disconnected diagrams in the perturbation series representing the interaction of different sets of m particles while the remaining $n - m$ do not interact with them. Divergences associated with such diagrams are removed by summing the appropriate disconnected diagrams to form the corresponding many-body *t*-matrix.

So far we have considered only nonidentical particles. If the particles are identical, the basic two-body wave functions ϕ_α must be antisymmetrized. In a many-body problem they may be written as determinants (5.2).

There is no reason why we should have used the eigenstates of K as basis vectors. Each particle feels a potential $V_0 + V$ rather than just V_0. It is possible to construct a single-particle potential, the Hartree-Fock potential, which gives a much better basis ϕ_α. The criterion of a good basis is that it is the set of antisymmetrized products of states of a single-particle potential which minimizes the energy of the three-body bound state. This type of basis is used in the calculations to be discussed in the rest of the present chapter.

We expect the calculated eigenvalues and eigenvectors to be close to the correct ones if the basic states ϕ_α are a good enough approximation and if we take enough of them so that the matrix element $T_{\alpha\beta}$ is small for all pairs of omitted states. $T_{\alpha\beta}$ is of course the amplitude for a virtual transition of two particles from the state β to the state α. In the nuclear case the single-particle model is good enough to expect the ϕ_α to be a reasonable basic set. We can only omit states from the set which are so different in energy that $T_{\alpha\beta}$ is small. High-energy radial wave functions oscillate rapidly over a distance comparable to the range of T, so that the radial integration involved in $T_{\alpha\beta}$ averages out. Also, for two states of very different energy, the radial wave function for the higher-energy state oscillates more rapidly than that of the lower-energy state, so that $T_{\alpha\beta}$ again tends to average out.

Matrix elements of the *t*-matrix are finite both on and off the energy shell, in contrast to matrix elements of the potential if it has a hard core. For example, scattering amplitudes for nucleon-nucleon potentials with hard cores are finite and comparable in magnitude with those from smoother nonlocal potentials.

B. THE LOCAL NUCLEAR MATTER MODEL

In the theory of nuclear matter (Chapter 4) we have already seen how matrix elements of the t-matrix are relevant. An effect of the Pauli exclusion principle which was not considered in the previous section is that it modifies the t-matrix itself, producing what is in effect a many-body force. The nuclear matter t-matrix is obtained by solving the Brueckner-Bethe-Goldstone equation which contains an operator forbidding scattering to occupied states. In this respect it is different from the free two-body t-matrix. It is distinguished by calling it the K-matrix or reaction matrix.

Brueckner, Gammel, and Weitzner (58) proposed that a finite nucleus should be considered as consisting at any point of nuclear matter that has the properties of infinite nuclear matter whose density is the same as the local density at the point. This model may be compared with the Thomas-Fermi model of the atom.

[i] THE REACTION MATRIX

For infinite nuclear matter the Brueckner-Bethe-Goldstone form of the Schrödinger equation can be converted to an integral equation by methods similar to those of Chapters 2C and 6A. It is equivalent to scattering by a potential with a nonlocal term $v(r)G(\mathbf{r} - \mathbf{r}')$ where

$$G(\mathbf{r} - \mathbf{r}') = (2\pi)^{-3} \int_0^{k_F} d^3k\, e^{i\mathbf{k}\cdot(\mathbf{r}-\mathbf{r}')}. \tag{4.18}$$

The nonlocal potential depends through k_F on the density. For particles 1 and 2 we may call it $V^{(\rho)}(\mathbf{r}_{12}, \mathbf{r}_{12}')$.

We shall now derive the K-matrix and discuss its role in the nuclear matter calculation. The derivation and discussion are entirely parallel to those of the t-matrix for the problem of two bodies. The analogy will be helpful in understanding both situations. The Hamiltonian for the nucleus may be written

$$H = \sum_i \mathcal{K}_i + \sum_{i<j} V_{ij}, \tag{6.20}$$

where the kinetic energy operator is now denoted by $\mathcal{K}_i$ and V_{ij} is understood as an integral operator or nonlocal potential defined by

$$V_{ij}\psi_{ij} = \int d^3r_{ij}' V^{(\rho)}(\mathbf{r}_{ij}, \mathbf{r}_{ij}')\psi(\mathbf{r}_{ij}'). \tag{6.21}$$

The index ρ is dropped for convenience at this stage. We introduce an auxiliary single-particle potential U_i and write H as

$$H = H_0 + \sum_\alpha V_\alpha', \tag{6.22}$$

where

$$H_0 = \sum_i (\mathscr{K}_i + U_i),$$

$$\sum_\alpha V_\alpha' = \sum_\alpha (V_\alpha - U_\alpha). \tag{6.23}$$

$\alpha = ij$ is a pair index and U_α is defined so that

$$\sum_\alpha U_\alpha = \sum_i U_i. \tag{6.24}$$

Define the unperturbed eigenvalue problem by

$$H_0 \phi_n = E_n \phi_n. \tag{6.25}$$

The ϕ_n are antisymmetrized products of single-particle wave functions for $i = 1, \ldots, A$. The Schrödinger equation for the total problem is written

$$(E - H_0)\Psi = \sum_\alpha V_\alpha' \Psi. \tag{6.26}$$

Multiplying on the left by $\phi_0^\dagger$ and integrating over the coordinates we obtain

$$E = E_0 + \langle \phi_0 | \sum_\alpha V_\alpha' | \Psi \rangle. \tag{6.27}$$

Expanding Ψ in the complete set ϕ_n,

$$\Psi = \sum_n a_n \phi_n, \tag{6.28}$$

we may write (6.26) as

$$\sum_n a_n (E - E_n)\phi_n = \sum_\alpha V_\alpha' \Psi. \tag{6.29}$$

In (6.27) we used the normalization $a_0 = 1$. Formal manipulation of Equation (6.29) gives the integral equation for Ψ,

$$|\Psi\rangle = |\phi_0\rangle + \sum_n \frac{|\phi_n\rangle\langle\phi_n| \sum_\alpha V_\alpha' |\Psi\rangle}{E - E_n}. \tag{6.30}$$

The methods of Chapter 2C extended to the many-body case may be used to verify this formal procedure.

We may iteratively substitute the expression for Ψ obtained in Equation (6.30) into (6.27) to obtain the perturbation series

$$E = E_0 + \langle \phi_0 | V' - V'G_0 V' + V'G_0 V'G_0 V' - \cdots | \phi_0 \rangle, \tag{6.31}$$

where the Green's function for the unperturbed problem G_0 and the potential operator V' are defined by

$$G_0 = -\sum_{n \neq 0} \frac{|\phi_n\rangle\langle\phi_n|}{E - E_n},$$

$$V' = \sum_\alpha V_\alpha'. \tag{6.32}$$

We now introduce the operator K defined so that

$$\langle \phi_m | V' | \Psi \rangle = \langle \phi_m | K | \phi_0 \rangle. \tag{6.33}$$

K is given by

$$K = V' - V'G_0K. \tag{6.34}$$

Equation (6.31) for the total energy may now be written

$$E = E_0 + \langle \phi_0 | K | \phi_0 \rangle. \tag{6.35}$$

The main approximation in nuclear matter calculations is to write K as a sum of two-body terms. This is the pair correlation approximation or independent pair model treated in Chapter 4.

$$K = \sum_\alpha K_\alpha, \tag{6.36}$$

where

$$K_\alpha = V_\alpha' - V_\alpha' G_0 K_\alpha. \tag{6.37}$$

K_α is the reaction matrix of Brueckner. It depends on the density ρ and is calculated from the Brueckner-Bethe-Goldstone equation for two bodies in infinite nuclear matter which scatter from state i, j to states k, l, under the condition that states with wave numbers less than k_F are forbidden.

The integral equation for the two-body wave function ψ_α is

$$\psi_\alpha(\mathbf{r}) = \phi_\alpha(\mathbf{r}) - \int d^3r' G_\alpha(E_k; \mathbf{r}, \mathbf{r}') \int d^3r'' V_\alpha'(\mathbf{r}', \mathbf{r}'') \psi_\alpha(\mathbf{r}''), \tag{6.38}$$

where V_α' includes the auxiliary single-particle potential U. $G_\alpha(E_k; \mathbf{r}, \mathbf{r}')$ is the Green's function corresponding to the nonlocal potential V_α' for relative wave number k. This equation may be written formally as

$$\psi_\alpha = \phi_\alpha - G_\alpha V_\alpha' \psi_\alpha. \tag{6.39}$$

Using the equation for a single pair corresponding to (6.33) we see immediately that the reaction matrix K_α is given in terms of the Green's function G_α by

$$G_0 K_\alpha = G_\alpha V_\alpha'. \tag{6.40}$$

Thus we have seen in principle how to calculate K_α, given the Brueckner-Bethe-Goldstone equation. It depends on the density and the potential. In nuclear matter the potential depends on the quantum states of the two particles.

[ii] SINGLE-PARTICLE ENERGIES

Denoting the spin, isospin and momentum states by single indices, i, j, etc., we have for the total energy

$$E = \sum_i \langle \chi_i | K | \chi_i \rangle + \tfrac{1}{2} \sum_{ijkl} \int d^3r_1' \int d^3r_2' \int d^3r_1 \int d^3r_2 \chi_i^*(\mathbf{r}_1) \chi_j^*(\mathbf{r}_2)$$
$$\times \langle \mathbf{r}_{12} | K | \mathbf{r}_{12}' \rangle [\chi_k(\mathbf{r}_1') \chi_l(\mathbf{r}_2') - \chi_k(\mathbf{r}_2') \chi_l(\mathbf{r}_1')] \tag{6.41}$$

where $\langle \mathbf{r}_{12} | K | \mathbf{r}_{12}' \rangle$ is the matrix element of K in the plane wave coordinate representation. In a finite nucleus the single-particle wave functions ϕ_i are not plane waves. They are eigenstates of the single-particle potential V_i, denoted by χ_i.

The next problem is to determine the single-particle potentials V_i for the different angular momentum states self-consistently, starting with the auxiliary potentials U_i. For this we use the Hartree-Fock method, which is based on the variation principle. The method will be explained in more detail in the next section. Treating the wave function χ_i as a variation function, we know that the best (that is the minimum) value of E is obtained when

$$\frac{dE}{d\chi_i} = 0. \tag{6.42}$$

In solving this problem, we use at each point $\mathbf{r}$ the K-matrix corresponding to the local density

$$\rho = \sum_i \chi_i^*(\mathbf{r})\chi_i(\mathbf{r}). \tag{6.43}$$

This is a very large computing problem, which was solved by Brueckner, Lockett, and Rotenberg (61). We shall be content with the present statement of the problem. After summing up the variation for all single-particle states, one has the single-particle equation for the quantum state i,

$$(E - \mathcal{H}_i)\chi_i(\mathbf{r}) = \int d^3r' V_i(\mathbf{r}, \mathbf{r}')\chi_i(\mathbf{r}'). \tag{6.44}$$

[iii] NUMERICAL RESULTS

We shall illustrate the results of the calculation for ^{40}Ca, using the two-body potentials of Table 6.1.

The local nuclear matter approximation is justified by the fact that the potential and, therefore, the K-matrix, which is the potential with a correction

State	Strength (MeV)	$\mu(\text{fm}^{-1})$
Triplet central even	−877.4	2.0908
Tensor even	−159.4	1.0494
Spin-orbit even	−5000	3.70
Singlet even	−434.0	1.45
Triplet central odd	−14.0	1.00
Tensor odd	22.0	0.80
Spin-orbit odd	−7315	3.70
Singlet odd	130.0	1.00

TABLE 6.1. Potential parameters determined by Gammel and Thaler and used in the ^{40}Ca calculation of Brueckner, Lockett, and Rotenberg (61). The potentials all have the Yukawa form and a repulsive core of radius 0.4 fm.

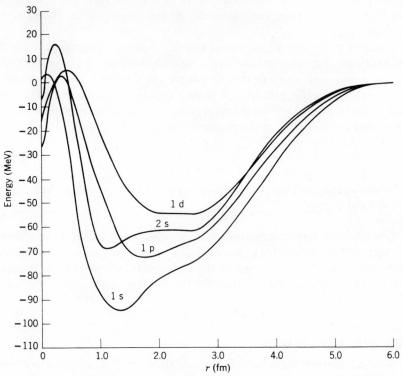

FIG. 6.3 Equivalent local single particle potentials for neutrons in ^{40}Ca. Spin-orbit potentials have been omitted. (Adapted from Brueckner 59.)

term, varies rapidly over distances less than about 0.5 fm for the strong potentials, while the distance over which the density changes from 90% to 10% of its central value is about 2.5 fm.

The self-consistent single-particle potentials are nonlocal, but they can be compared with local potentials by integrating $V_i(\mathbf{r}, \mathbf{r}')$ over $\mathbf{r}'$ to obtain the equivalent static potential [see Equation (3.82)]. The integrated potentials are illustrated in Fig. 6.3.

The striking feature of the single-particle potentials is the dependence on angular momentum. The dependence is in the same sense and of the same order of magnitude as that found for p-shell nuclei in the (p, 2p) experiments.

The single-particle wave functions are again more like the realistic wave functions obtained from (p, 2p) experiments than, for example, harmonic oscillator functions, although their overlaps with harmonic oscillator functions with state-dependent constants ω are at least 90 per cent. They are illustrated in Fig. 6.4 for the protons in ^{40}Ca. They have the same general

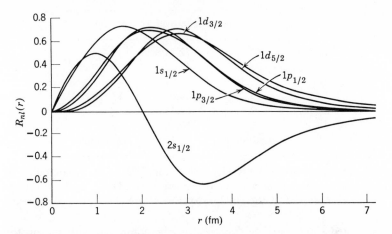

FIG. 6.4   Single particle wave functions for the protons in ^{40}Ca calculated by Brueckner Lockett and Rotenberg. (Adapted from Brueckner, Lockett and Rotenberg 61.)

shape as single-particle wave functions in a simple well such as the Ross-Mark-Lawson well because they must have the right tail and the right number of nodes. However, they have more curvature.

In Fig. 6.5 the $1d_{3/2}$ wave function is compared with the $1d_{3/2}$ wave function in the Ross-Mark-Lawson potential. The differences are qualitatively the same as they are for the $1p_{3/2}$ state in ^{12}C where the wave function determined by fitting the (p, 2p) experiment is compared with that of Ross, Mark, and Lawson (see Fig. 5.5).

The single particle energy eigenvalues for ^{40}Ca are given in Table 6.2.

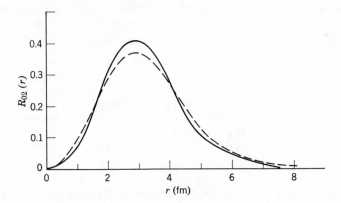

FIG. 6.5   The $1d_{3/2}$ wave function of Brueckner, Lockett and Rotenberg (61) (full curve) for neutrons ^{40}Ca Compared with the $1d_{3/2}$ wave function computed in the single particle potential of Ross, Mark and Lawson (56) (dashed curve).

State	Proton	Neutron	(p, 2p)
$1s_{1/2}$	62.50	72.34	—
$1p_{3/2}$	35.22	47.43	—
$1p_{1/2}$	32.36	41.54	—
$1d_{5/2}$	15.22	24.07	15, 19
$2s_{1/2}$	9.81	19.44	11
$1d_{3/2}$	8.24	16.71	8.4
$1f_{7/2}$	Unbound	6.47	Unbound

TABLE 6.2. Single-particle energy eigenvalues for ^{40}Ca in MeV, computed by Brueckner, Lockett, and Rotenberg (61). Those levels which can be observed in the (p, 2p) experiment are shown for comparison.

The calculated single-particle energies may be compared with the proton values obtained in the (p, 2p) experiment. For the lower single-particle states these values include one or two MeV for the rearrangement of the residual nucleus into its ground state after the removal of the proton (see Chapter 14).

Table 6.3 shows the eigenvalues for ^{16}O compared with the proton eigenvalues obtained from (p, 2p) experiments and the neutron eigenvalues obtained from (p, d) experiments. In this case the predicted eigenvalues are too small but the differences between neutrons and protons are in the right sense and of the correct order of magnitude.

The calculation predicts that the protons are on the average a little further out than the neutrons, the rms radii being 2.962 fm and 2.901 fm, respectively, for ^{40}Ca.

One very interesting aspect of the calculation is that the even-state spin-orbit part of the early Gammel-Thaler potential gave much too large a spin-orbit splitting. The $f_{5/2}$ level for neutrons dropped below the $d_{3/2}$ level

State	Proton		Neutron	
	Theory	Experiment	Theory	Experiment
$1s_{1/2}$	39.6	44	44.3	51
$1p_{3/2}$	14.6	19	19.0	21.7
$1p_{1/2}$	10.7	13	14.9	15.6

TABLE 6.3. Eigenvalues for single particles in ^{16}O obtained by Brueckner, Lockett and Rotenberg (61). In this calculation the hard core contributions were arbitrarily reduced by a factor 0.85 to allow for possible overestimate because of the assumption of an infinite core.

for protons, so that the system would be beta-unstable. Since there is no direct evidence for an even-state spin-orbit force in scattering experiments Brueckner, Lockett, and Rotenberg reduced it considerably in the calculation. This is an example of the use of off-energy-shell information about the nuclear force to improve the information obtained from scattering analysis.

The significant failure of the model is in the prediction of the rms radius for the proton distribution. The electron scattering value is about 3.5 fm for ^{40}Ca, compared with 2.962 fm for the calculation.

Although the calculation is completely stable and self-consistent in that the potentials calculated from the wave functions reproduce the same wave functions, the chief trouble is the obvious self-inconsistency of the local nuclear matter approximation, which is the basis of the method. Although measurements of nuclear form factors indicate that the surface of a nucleus has a low average density, the concept of infinite nuclear matter of low density is invalid. Nuclear matter saturates at a density of 0.217 particles/fm^3. A plausible picture of a nuclear surface is that it consists of clusters of nucleons having roughly the saturation density, which move in and out of the nucleus, so that the time average density appears to be low in the surface.

The possible existence of such surface clusters is a very interesting point which can be investigated by reaction experiments.

C. NUCLEAR HARTREE-FOCK CALCULATIONS

We have shown in Section A that a shell-model calculation for nuclear structure is performed by considering the interaction of extra-core particles in a single-particle potential due to themselves and to all the other nucleons in the problem. For several nucleons outside a closed shell, the nucleons which are treated as interacting with each other also provide a large contribution to the single-particle potential. It is therefore necessary to perform the calculation self-consistently so that the single-particle potential, in which each particle's wave function is calculated, is given by the density of all the particles determined, in turn, from all the single-particle wave functions. It is of course better to perform a self-consistent calculation for all the particles in the nucleus, rather than to treat some of them as an inert core.

This is done, for example, in the local nuclear matter model, which is particularly suited to the determination of single-particle wave functions in nuclei that might be expected to be spherical, such as the closed-shell nuclei ^{16}O, ^{40}Ca and ^{90}Zr.

In the present section we shall discuss a calculation, suited to the determination of intrinsic shapes of nuclei away from closed shells, by Pal and Stamp (67). (References to Hartree-Fock calculations by other authors are given in this paper.) The simple example of ^{6}Li has illustrated the fact that extra-core nucleons may be correlated in such a way as to produce an intrinsic nonspherical shape. In classical language this means that the nucleus would be nonspherical if it could be observed at rest. For an even nucleus the ground state is 0+, so no electric quadrupole moment is observable. There is no axis defined for the ground state with respect to which the quadrupole moment can be defined. Nonspherical nuclei can be expected to have excited states which are described by a rotational model. This will be discussed in Chapter 7C.

We have seen in Section *A* that a description of a nuclear wave function is given by using matrix elements of the *t*-matrix in a shell-model representation. The basis states in this representation are antisymmetrized products of single-particle shell-model wave functions, which take the form of determinants (5.2). The many-body effect of the Pauli exclusion principle on the two-body *t*-matrix is taken into account by replacing T with K.

[i] THE HARTREE-FOCK EQUATIONS

The Hartree-Fock method assumes that the nuclear ground-state wave function may be described as a determinant of single-particle wave functions computed in the self-consistent potential. The occupied single-particle states are denoted by $|l\rangle, |m\rangle, \ldots,$ etc.

The basis states $|\alpha\rangle$ are single-particle wave functions computed in a simple potential such as the harmonic oscillator.

The ground-state wave function is expressed as a superposition of basis states

$$|l\rangle = \sum_\alpha x_\alpha{}^l |\alpha\rangle, \tag{6.45}$$

with the normalization condition

$$\langle l \,|\, l \rangle = \sum_\alpha |x_\alpha{}^l|^2 = 1. \tag{6.46}$$

The superposition coefficients $x_\alpha{}^l$ are treated as variational parameters for the minimization of the expectation value E of the many-body Hamiltonian (6.20) in the ground state, which is a determinant of states $|l\rangle$, called the Hartree-Fock states. The Hartree-Fock ground state $|\phi_0\rangle$ is therefore the antisymmetrized independent particle wave function (in the form of a determinant of single-particle wave functions) which gives the minimum expectation value of the total energy.

$$|\phi_0\rangle = \begin{vmatrix} |l_1\rangle & |m_1\rangle \cdots \\ |l_2\rangle & |m_2\rangle \cdots \\ \cdot & \cdot \\ \cdot & \cdot \\ \cdot & \cdot \end{vmatrix}. \tag{6.47}$$

The particle indices have been indicated explicitly on the single-particle wave functions. Just as it was in the previous section, the ground-state expectation value E of the total energy is given by Equation (6.35), which may be written out in more detail in terms of the Hamiltonian (6.20). Denoting the total kinetic energy operator by $\mathscr{K}$, we have

$$E = \langle \phi_0 | \mathscr{K} | \phi_0 \rangle + \langle \phi_0 | K | \phi_0 \rangle. \tag{6.48}$$

We do not use an auxiliary single-particle potential in the present section. Equation (6.48) may be written in terms of single-particle states $|l\rangle$. As an example we shall consider the first term of the right-hand side. Both the bra and ket vectors are determinants. Each is an antisymmetric linear combination of direct products of all the single-particle states $|l\rangle$, each product having a different permutation of the particle indices i. If the single-particle states are orthogonal, that is, if

$$\langle l_i | m_i \rangle = 0, \qquad l_i \neq m_i, \tag{6.49}$$

only the diagonal single-particle matrix elements remain. Remembering that the $|l\rangle$ are normalized (6.46), and writing the second term of (6.48) explicitly in the same way, we have

$$E = \sum_{l=1}^{A} \langle l | \mathscr{K} | l \rangle + \sum_{l<m}^{A} \langle lm | K | lm \rangle_a. \tag{6.50}$$

The subscript a on the matrix element indicates that it is antisymmetric. It consists of the difference of direct and particle-exchange terms.

Substituting (6.45) for $|l\rangle$, we have

$$E = \sum_l \sum_{\alpha\beta} x_\alpha^{l*} x_\beta^l \langle \alpha | \mathscr{K} | \beta \rangle + \sum_{lm} \sum_{\alpha\beta\gamma\delta} x_\alpha^{l*} x_\beta^l x_\gamma^{m*} x_\delta^m \langle \alpha\gamma | \mathscr{K} | \beta\delta \rangle_a. \tag{6.51}$$

The total energy is now minimized with respect to the superposition coefficients x_α^{l*}. This is done by decomposing E into single-particle energies ϵ_l and minimizing each separately.* Using the normalization condition (6.46) we have

$$E = \sum_l \epsilon_l \sum_\alpha x_\alpha^{l*} x_\alpha^l. \tag{6.52}$$

Differentiating (6.51) and (6.52) with respect to x_α^{l*} and setting

$$\frac{\partial \epsilon_l}{\partial x_\alpha^{l*}} = 0, \tag{6.53}$$

* Alternatively, a technique of more general value is to consider the ϵ_l as Lagrange multipliers for the minimization of E while taking into account the normalization condition (6.46). Equation (6.59) then shows that the ϵ_l, defined in this way, are the single-particle eigenvalues.

we obtain a set of equations for the $x_\alpha{}^l$, from which the Hartree-Fock states can be determined.

$$\sum_\beta x_\beta{}^l \langle \alpha | \mathcal{K} | \beta \rangle + \sum_{m=1}^A \sum_{\beta\gamma\delta} x_\delta{}^m x_\gamma{}^{m*} x_\beta{}^l \langle \alpha\gamma | K | \beta\delta \rangle_a = \epsilon_l x_\alpha{}^l. \quad (6.54)$$

We now define the single-particle Hartree-Fock potential V^l by

$$\langle \alpha | V^l | \beta \rangle = \sum_{\gamma\delta} \langle \alpha\gamma | K | \beta\delta \rangle_a \rho_{\delta\gamma}, \quad (6.55)$$

where

$$\rho_{\delta\gamma} = \sum_{m=1}^A x_\delta{}^m x_\gamma{}^{m*} \equiv \sum_{m=1}^A \langle \delta | m \rangle \langle m | \gamma \rangle. \quad (6.56)$$

The projection operator

$$\sum_{m=1}^A |m\rangle\langle m| \quad (6.57)$$

is the single-particle density operator. Its matrix elements in the shell-model representation are $\rho_{\delta\gamma}$.

We must now make the approximation that the shell-model representation $\langle \alpha\gamma | K | \beta\delta \rangle_a$ of K is independent of the state l. We set

$$V^l \cong V. \quad (6.58)$$

If the single-particle potentials V^l are state-dependent, the orthogonality condition (6.49) is not satisfied and (6.54) is not true. Single-particle states calculated with different Hamiltonians are not orthogonal.

Using the definition (6.55) with the approximation (6.58) in (6.54), the Hartree-Fock states are determined by

$$\sum_\beta \langle \alpha | \mathcal{K} | \beta \rangle x_\beta{}^l + \sum_\beta \langle \alpha | V | \beta \rangle x_\beta{}^l = \epsilon_l x_\alpha{}^l. \quad (6.59)$$

At this stage the methods of the present section and the previous section on the local nuclear matter model diverge. The analogue of (6.51) in Section B is (6.41). The assumption that K is the reaction matrix for nuclear matter of the local density enabled us to write a density-dependent coordinate representation of K. After performing the variation it remained only to solve independent Schrödinger equations (6.44) for the single-particle wave functions. These wave functions determined a second approximation to the density which was used in solving the equations (6.44) iteratively until the same density was reproduced by successive iterations. The nonlocal single-particle potential $V(\mathbf{r}, \mathbf{r}')$ turned out to be quite strongly state-dependent. It was preferred to ignore the overlaps of the different states $|l\rangle$.

The Hartree-Fock equation (6.59) in the present approximation becomes an eigenvalue equation for eigenvectors x^l and eigenvalues ϵ_l. It is solved by diagonalizing $(\mathcal{K} + V)$ in the shell-model representation. The single-particle potential operator V is defined in terms of the x^l. Therefore V and x^l must be determined self-consistently. This is achieved by repeated diagonalization of $\mathcal{K} + V$ starting with a guess for ρ, then recalculating ρ, and hence V, from the eigenvectors at each iteration until the same V is reproduced by successive iterations.

[ii] MATRIX ELEMENTS OF THE NUCLEAR FORCE

In order to compute the Hartree-Fock potential (6.55, 6.58), it is necessary to have matrix elements of K for basis states $|\alpha\rangle$, $|\beta\rangle$, . . . , etc. Three types of basis states will be distinguished. First, there are those which are occupied in the ground state. Second, there are those which lie above but near the Fermi surface. Virtual transitions to these states are responsible for long-range correlations. Third, we have the states at very high energy. Virtual transitions to these states are mainly caused by the short-range part of the force and are responsible for short-range correlations.

We have seen that short-range correlations are responsible for the saturation of nuclear matter. Hence they are most important in determining the effective single-particle potential (6.55). The high-lying states play the role of intermediate states in the definition of the K-matrix. They may be approximated by plane waves. Since they are well above the occupied states the mathematical complication involved in excluding the occupied states from the intermediate set is not worthwhile. The Pauli exclusion principle operator Q^F is set equal to unity and K becomes the free two-body t-matrix T. Setting the two-body potential V_{12} equal to v, the definition (2.106) of T becomes for particles 1 and 2,

$$T = v - v \frac{1}{\tilde{K}_1 + \tilde{K}_2 - E} T, \qquad (6.60)$$

where $\tilde{K}_1$ and $\tilde{K}_2$ are the Hamiltonians for the independent motion of particles 1 and 2 in the harmonic oscillator potential used for computing the basis.

We now use the property, which is peculiar to plane waves and harmonic oscillator wave functions, that the wave function for particles 1 and 2 may be written as a product of one-body wave functions either of the particle coordinates r_1 and r_2 or of the coordinates $\mathbf{r}$ and $\mathbf{R}$ for the relative and C.M. motion, respectively. This transformation will be treated in detail in Chapter 7B[ii].

The wave functions for harmonic oscillator states may be identified by their quantum numbers. For $\mathbf{r}$ and $\mathbf{R}$ they are written $|nl\rangle$ and $|NL\rangle$, respectively. The matrix elements of T are written, making the approximation that T depends only on $\mathbf{r}$, as

$\langle nl| \langle NL| T(\mathbf{r}) |N'L'\rangle |n'l'\rangle$

$= \langle nl| \langle NL| v(\mathbf{r}) |N'L'\rangle |n'l'\rangle - \langle nl| v(\mathbf{r})\langle NL| \dfrac{1}{\tilde{K}_r + \tilde{K}_R - E} |N'L'\rangle T(\mathbf{r}) |n'l'\rangle.$

$$(6.61)$$

The operators $\tilde{K}_r$ and $\tilde{K}_R$ are the Hamiltonians for the relative and C.M. harmonic oscillators. Here we have used the fact that $|NL\rangle$ commutes with functions of $\mathbf{r}$. We denote the eigenvalue of $\tilde{K}_R$ for the oscillator state $|NL\rangle$ of the C.M. by $\delta(\epsilon_1, \epsilon_2)$, where ϵ_1 and ϵ_2 are the energies of particles 1 and 2 in the nucleus.

$$\langle NL| \tilde{K}_R = \langle NL| \delta(\epsilon_1, \epsilon_2). \qquad (6.62)$$

The approximation that $T = T(\mathbf{r})$ means that $\langle NL| N'L'\rangle$ factorizes out from (6.61), leaving an integral equation in one variable $\mathbf{r}$. The total energy E is written

$$E = \epsilon_1 + \epsilon_2. \qquad (6.63)$$

Using the distortion operator Ω, defined by

$$T = v\Omega, \qquad (6.64)$$

we may write the following equation for the operators in (6.61).

$$v\Omega = v - v \frac{1}{\tilde{K}_r - \Delta} v\Omega, \qquad (6.65)$$

where

$$\Delta = \delta - \epsilon_1 - \epsilon_2. \qquad (6.66)$$

Since we cannot define a Hartree-Fock equation with a state-dependent t-matrix, the approximation is made that Δ is a constant. We now operate with (6.65) on a harmonic oscillator wave function $\phi_{nl}(\mathbf{r})$ and convert (6.65) into a differential equation, formally multiplying by $\tilde{K}_r - \Delta$.

$$(\tilde{K}_r - \Delta)(\phi_{ln} - \psi_{nl}) = v\psi_{nl}. \qquad (6.66)$$

The t-matrix elements are calculated numerically from (6.66).

$$\langle \phi_{n'l'}| T |\phi_{nl}\rangle = \langle \phi_{n'l'}| v |\psi_{nl}\rangle. \qquad (6.67)$$

The remaining difficulty is the definition of the energy constant Δ. Calculations show that t-matrix elements are very insensitive to Δ.

A good initial guess is that ϵ_1 and ϵ_2 are each equal to the average binding energy of the particles in the nucleus, say about 10 MeV. Of course the $1s$ particles are much more strongly bound, but they do not contribute much to the average. In order to improve on this estimate, a double self-consistency procedure must be adopted where the Hartree-Fock equation is written at each iteration in the representation defined by the Hartree-Fock single-particle states computed at the previous iteration. The ϵ_1 and ϵ_2 are then Hartree-Fock single-particle energies. The computing problem for this is enormous.

[iii] NUCLEAR DEFORMATION

It is expected that the self-consistent solution of the Hartree-Fock equation (6.59) will yield a deformed single-particle potential, particularly for nuclei away from closed shells. The lowest-order and, presumably, the most important, terms describing the shape of a nonspherical nucleus are the quadrupole (ellipsoidal) deformation terms. The deformed nuclear surface is written

$$R = R_0[1 + \sum_m a_m Y_2{}^m(\theta', \phi')], \tag{6.68}$$

where θ', ϕ' are the coordinates relative to body-fixed principal axes.

Because of reflection symmetry a_1 and a_{-1} are zero. There is obvious physical significance in the quantities β and γ defined by

$$
\begin{aligned}
a_0 &= \beta \cos \gamma, \\
a_2 &= a_{-2} = 2^{-\frac{1}{2}} \beta \sin \gamma.
\end{aligned}
\tag{6.69}
$$

With this definition,

$$R - R_0 = (\tfrac{5}{16}\pi)^{\frac{1}{2}} R_0 \beta [\cos \gamma (3 \cos^2 \theta' - 1) + 3^{\frac{1}{2}} \sin \gamma \sin^2 \theta' \cos 2\phi']. \tag{6.70}$$

The quantity β measures the total deformation of the nucleus. The significance of γ is seen by writing the increments in length of the three axes.

$$
\begin{aligned}
R(0, \phi') - R_0 &= \left(\frac{5}{4\pi}\right)^{\frac{1}{2}} R_0 \beta \cos \gamma \\
R\left(\frac{\pi}{2}, 0\right) - R_0 &= \left(\frac{5}{4\pi}\right)^{\frac{1}{2}} R_0 \beta \cos \left(\gamma - \frac{2\pi}{3}\right) \\
R\left(\frac{\pi}{2}, \frac{\pi}{2}\right) - R_0 &= \left(\frac{5}{4\pi}\right)^{\frac{1}{2}} R_0 \beta \cos \left(\gamma - \frac{4\pi}{3}\right).
\end{aligned}
\tag{6.71}
$$

The quantity γ is called the angle of asymmetry. Only values $0 < \gamma < \pi/3$ are relevant since higher values of γ mean a repetition of the same ellipsoidal shape with the axes relabeled.

The intrinsic quadrupole moments of the deformed nucleus are

$$\langle Q_m \rangle = \left(\frac{3}{5\pi}\right)^{\frac{1}{2}} R_0{}^2 a_m. \tag{6.72}$$

Note that these are the matter quadrupole moments in which neutrons as well as protons are included.

The Hartree-Fock quadrupole moments are evaluated for the Hartree-Fock ground state $|\phi_0\rangle$ (6.47) using the analogue of (5.22) for all nucleons,

$$\langle Q_m \rangle = \left(\frac{16\pi}{5}\right)^{1/2} \langle \phi_0 | \sum_{i=1}^{A} r_i^2 Y_2^m(\theta_i', \phi_i') | \phi_0 \rangle. \tag{6.73}$$

From the Hartree-Fock ground state, β and γ are evaluated using (6.69), (6.72), and (6.73).

[iv] NUMERICAL RESULTS

Hartree-Fock calculations for even nuclei up to ^{40}Ca were carried out by Pal and Stamp (67) using t-matrix elements of the Yale potential. The truncated harmonic oscillator basis included the $1s$, $2s$, $1p$ and $1d$ states. Interest was centered in obtaining the lowest minimum for the binding energy per

State	PS	BLR	EX
$2s_{1/2}$	1.5		−3.2
$1d_{3/2}$	6.0		0.9
$1d_{5/2}$	−1.0		−4.1
$1p_{1/2}$	−17.6	−14.9	−15.6
$1p_{3/2}$	−23.3	−19.0	−21.7
$1s_{1/2}$	−52.8	−44.3	−51

TABLE 6.4. Single-particle energies for the neutrons in ^{16}O computed by Pal and Stamp (PS) compared with the values of Brueckner, Lockett, and Rotenberg (BLR) and with experimental values (EX).

particle, denoted by BE/A. In some nuclei, minima in BE/A occurred for different shapes. The shape parameters β, γ and the single-particle binding energies ϵ_i were determined for each nucleus as Lagrange multipliers introduced by the shape and normalization conditions.

The harmonic oscillator basis used did not permit accurate determination of the shapes of radial wave functions in the nuclear surface. At least three nodes should be included for this purpose. This is estimated to cause up to 20 per cent error in the quadrupole moments. A measure of the importance of basis states which have been omitted is the energy gap between occupied and unoccupied Hartree-Fock states.

To obtain an idea of the overall quality of the calculation, the single-particle binding energies for the closed-shell nucleus ^{16}O are compared in Table 6.4 with experiment and with the values obtained by Brueckner, Lockett, and Rotenberg (61) from the local nuclear matter model. In the calculation of Pal and Stamp, Coulomb corrections were ignored. Hence, only the experimental values for neutrons are relevant. Agreement for the Hartree-Fock values is considerably better than agreement obtained with the local nuclear matter model. The energies of the unoccupied states have a discrepancy of about 4 MeV in comparison with those determined by (d, p) on ^{16}O. This is due to several things among which are the fact that the minimization procedure concentrates on the occupied states and the fact that the (d, p) experiment populates single-particle states in ^{17}O, not ^{16}O.

The overall results for the nuclei considered are shown in Table 6.5. Several interesting qualitative facts can be discovered from the table.

1. The energy gaps up to ^{16}O are very large, indicating that virtual transitions to the unoccupied states are most improbable. Hence the single-particle states are expected to be very well described by the Hartree-Fock theory.

2. Nuclei with several particles outside a closed shell have positive deformations β, while those with several holes outside a closed shell have negative β. Positive β corresponds to a prolate shape.

3. The rms radii are too small. This is due to the small number of nodes in the radial wave functions of the basis set. The experimental value for protons in ^{12}C is, for example, 2.42 fm as compared with 2.245 fm for neutrons in the calculation.

4. Only ^{24}Mg and ^{32}S are not axially symmetric. The closed-shell nuclei are spherical. These shapes are all confirmed by experimental properties of the rotational states (see Chapter 7C).

A very interesting case was ^{28}Si where three minima were obtained corresponding to oblate, prolate, and approximately spherical Hartree-Fock potentials. The oblate and prolate shapes are expected since ^{28}Si is midway between the closed shells ^{16}O and ^{40}Ca. The nearly spherical shape is expected in the *jj* coupling shell model since the $1d_{5/2}$ subshell is filled. Presumably all these states occur in ^{28}Si, but the oblate state is the ground state. A similar effect was noticed in ^{20}Ne, where the lowest minimum is prolate and axially symmetric, although another minimum corresponding to axial asymmetry was found.

D. SUMMARY AND DISCUSSION

The outstanding feature of the work discussed in this chapter is that at least semiquantitative agreement with experimental data relevant to ground states of nuclei can be obtained using realistic phenomenological nuclear forces. It is perhaps surprising that there are no surprises. The simplest assumptions give the correct answers. Local potentials which fit two-body data on the energy shell provide an adequate description of nuclei, although in the case of

	^{8}Be	^{12}C	^{16}O	^{20}Ne	^{24}Mg	^{28}Si	^{32}S	^{40}Ca
BE/A (MeV)	−5.507	−7.039	−6.775	−6.601	−6.931	−7.539	−8.128	−7.506
Oscillator constant $\hbar/M\omega$ (fm)^2	2.3716	2.3716	3.100	3.100	3.100	3.100	3.100	4.36
rms Radius (fm)	2.156	2.245	2.596	2.754	2.854	2.925	2.911	—
β	0.786	−0.343	0	0.335	0.324	−0.282	−0.190	0
γ	0	0	0	0	17°52'	0	23°33'	0
Energy gap (MeV)	18.436	18.849	16.574	7.423	7.161	8.889	6.063	—

TABLE 6.5. Results of the Hartree-Fock calculation of Pal and Stamp (67) for the even nuclei up to ^{40}Ca.

the even-state spin-orbit part of the early Gammel-Thaler potential, the finite nucleus calculation supplemented the two-body data in determining the potential.

Three- and more-body correlations do not need to be introduced. There is no need for many-body forces except in the sense of the Pauli exclusion principle correction. The calculations are insensitive to matrix elements of the two-body forces off the energy shell provided that the forces give correct on-shell predictions. This conclusion is drawn from the fact that the separable potential of Tabakin (64) also gives acceptable results (Pal and Kerman, 67).

Much has been learnt about methods for nuclear bound-state calculations. In order to obtain finite matrix elements for a realistic two-nucleon interaction, the diagonalization of the Hamiltonian is performed with the two-nucleon potential v replaced by the t-matrix T, possibly with the Pauli exclusion principle correction built in. For many years the Hartree-Fock method was not tried seriously for nuclei, possibly because of the fear that the strong interactions would preclude its convergence. In fact the understanding of the role of the t-matrix, first introduced by Brueckner and his collaborators, has enabled the Hartree-Fock method to be formulated in such a way that it is convergent, although some computational problems remain when Coulomb forces are introduced.

Even the basically meaningless concept of unsaturated nuclear matter introduced in the local nuclear matter model does not prevent good results from being obtained. In fact this model has some features which are extremely difficult to reproduce in Hartree-Fock calculations of the type discussed in Section C of this chapter, because of the simplification introduced by the plane-wave representation of K which is state-independent. This is the characteristic assumption of the model. Realistically state-dependent single-particle potentials are determined, whereas the potentials must be state-independent for a proper definition of the Hartree-Fock equations using a finite-well basis.

We have already discussed the experiments which check the single-particle properties. Experiments are capable of estimating single-particle binding energies and the rms radii of single-particle wave functions from which the state-dependence of the single-particle potentials can be estimated. The rms radii are not determined very reliably by present Hartree-Fock calculations because not enough states are taken in the basis. Binding energies are not affected so much by this, since the single-particle wave functions have large overlaps with harmonic oscillator functions. Only the surface parts of the wave functions are incorrect.

We have not yet discussed the experiments relevant to the intrinsic deformations. The deformations show up in the study of excited states, where they lead to rotational bands in the spectra. From these spectra and from transitions between the collective states the deformation parameters can be determined. This will be discussed in Chapter 7C.

FURTHER READING

1. W. Heisenberg, *Z. Phys.*, **96**, 473 (1935).
   Variational calculation using smooth exchange forces.

2. K. A. Brueckner, A. M. Lockett, and M. Rotenberg, *Phys. Rev.* **121**, 225 (1961).
   R. J. Eden and V. J. Emery, *Proc. Roy. Soc.*, **A248**, 226 (1958); **A253**, 117, 186 (1959).
   R. J. McCarthy and H. S. Köhler, *Nucl. Phys.*, **A99**, 65 (1967).
   Local nuclear matter model.

3. I. Kelson and C. A. Levinson, *Phys. Rev.*, **134**, B269 (1964).
   Hartree-Fock calculation with smooth potentials.

4. K. T. R. Davies, S. J. Krieger, and M. Baranger, *Nucl. Phys.*, **84**, 545 (1966).
   Examination of the principles of nuclear Hartree-Fock theory.

5. M. K. Pal and A. P. Stamp, *Phys. Rev.* (1967) (and references therein).
   Hartree-Fock calculation with realistic *t*-matrix.

6. R. E. Peierls and J. Yoccoz, *Proc. Phys. Soc.* (*London*), **A70**, 381 (1957).
   Projection of excited states from the Hartree-Fock wave function.

PROBLEMS

1. Calculate the *s*-wave partial scattering amplitude for the scattering of a 1 MeV neutron from a proton at rest where the potential is a repulsive square well of radius 0.4 fm and strength 100 MeV. Find the wave function for the *s*-wave, and use it to calculate the corresponding *t*-matrix element $\langle \mathbf{k}' | T(E) | \mathbf{k} \rangle_0$ in a plane-wave representation, where E and $\mathbf{k}$ correspond to 1 MeV scattering and $\mathbf{k}'$ corresponds to 2 MeV scattering. Compare these two *t*-matrix elements with the Born approximation $\langle \mathbf{k}' | V | \mathbf{k} \rangle_0$.

2. Prove Equation (6.50).

3. Give as many physical arguments as you can think of for using the two-nucleon *t*-matrix in a nuclear structure calculation rather than the potential.

4. Deduce Equation (6.44) from Equation (6.41).

5. Using Table 6.5 calculate the principal moments of inertia of ^{24}Mg assuming it is a rigid body.

6. What is the significance of the energy gap in Table 6.5? Justify your answer with rough numerical examples taken from the literature or from Chapter 7B.

7

NUCLEAR STRUCTURE—
EXCITED STATES

Although the methods of the previous chapter can, in principle, be applied to the calculations of excited states of nuclei, this is a very difficult computing problem, and very little work has been done on it thus far. Excited states are understood at present in terms of nuclear models, in which certain groups of nucleons are treated as if they had far fewer degrees of freedom than the co-ordinates, momenta, spins, and isospins of their individual nucleons. In the single-particle model, for example, all the nucleons but one are treated as an inert core that exerts a collective potential on the preferred particle.

The shell model treats the particles in filled shells as an inert spherical core, and calculates the energy levels due to interactions of the extra-core particles. The collective model treats the whole nucleus as a nonrigid deformed or deformable system which may have vibrational or rotational degrees of free-dom. We have seen that the rotational model applies particularly to nuclei with many particles outside closed shells. A unified model, due originally to Bohr and Mottelson, treats particle motion and collective degrees of freedom in different approximations for nuclei in appropriate regions of the periodic table. Certain states may also be understood in terms of cluster substructures, in which the binding forces between the nucleons of a particular group have more effect than the binding forces between these nucleons and the other ones in the nucleus. Closed shell substructures such as ^{4}He or ^{16}O in certain cir-cumstances may act in such a way as to have a large effect on energy levels.

Thus far we have assumed the charge independence of nuclear forces. Evidence for this comes, in fact, mainly from the study of excited states of nuclei in terms of isospin. Therefore we shall begin this chapter with a dis-cussion of the role of isospin in nuclei. Much of the material has been adapted from Wigner (58).

A. ISOSPIN IN NUCLEI

The conservation of isospin is equivalent to the charge independence of nuclear forces. This is violated by the Coulomb forces but not to a great extent, as far as can be seen from scattering experiments and the properties of mirror nuclei, by the nuclear forces.

Examples of mirror nuclei are ^{11}C and ^{11}B for which T_3 $[=\frac{1}{2}(Z - N)]$ is $+\frac{1}{2}$ and $-\frac{1}{2}$, respectively. Approximately the first nine levels of these nuclei correspond within a few tenths of an MeV. The existence of corresponding levels in mirror nuclei is evidence of the equality of n-n and p-p forces, but not of the equality of n-n and n-p forces.

The full charge independence hypothesis means that the properties of a nuclear state are independent of T_3; that is, they are independent of the orientation of the isospin in isospin space. This indicates that the total isospin T is a good quantum number. Charge independence does not imply that all nuclei with the same A should have the same spectra and energy levels (except for Coulomb shifts). The Pauli principle invalidates this because neutrons are distinguishable from protons. States that are symmetrical for space and spin coordinates are compatible with the Pauli principle for a p-n pair, but not for p-p or n-n pairs.

Nuclei with N and Z more nearly equal are expected to have more low-lying states than nuclei for which the ratio N/Z is further from one. This is because there is most chance of p-n pairs being important in determining the low-lying states if $N = Z$ (see Fig. 7.2).

Let us consider the $A = 6$ nuclei. The shell model would predict that the low-lying states of the ones with a ^{4}He core are due entirely to the interaction of the two extra-core particles. Figure 7.1a shows schematically what would be expected if the Pauli principle did not operate and if Coulomb forces were negligible, assuming charge independence. Figure 7.1b shows the actual situation with the Coulomb shifts eliminated. There are no known states of ^{6}H or ^{6}B corresponding to the states of ^{6}Be, ^{6}Li, and ^{6}He shown in the diagram. This verifies the idea that states of maximum symmetry have less energy than less symmetric states. It also argues against the existence of nuclei consisting entirely of neutrons.

The idea that states of maximum symmetry have lower energies than less symmetric configurations is illustrated schematically in the single-particle model for $A = 12$ in Fig. 7.2.

We see how states of different isospin are related. In this model it is obvious that there can be no states in ^{12}B and ^{12}N corresponding to the ground states of ^{12}C. The groups of states in Figs. 7.1a and 7.1b are called isospin multiplets. Although T_3 is $+1, 0$, and -1 for ^{6}Be, ^{6}Li, and ^{6}He, respectively, this tells us nothing about T. Any integral value of T may have these projections on the axis in isospin space. However, the nonexistence of $T_3 = \pm 1$ states corresponding to the first two levels of ^{6}Li tells us that they are $T = 0$ states. Similarly, the states that exist in ^{6}Be, ^{6}Li, and ^{6}He but not in ^{6}B and ^{6}H are isospin triplets with $T = 1$. The states of ^{11}C and ^{11}B are generally isospin doublets.

The states of an isospin multiplet have the same spin and parity, but they exist in different nuclei so that they are not always easy to identify experimentally.

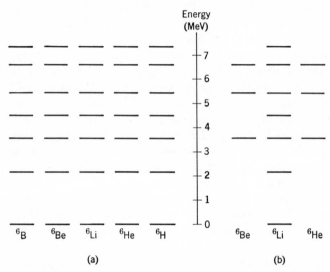

FIG. 7.1   Level scheme (based on ^{6}Li) for the $A = 6$ nuclei: (*a*) shows the situation for charge-independent forces if the Pauli exclusion principle did not operate; (*b*) shows the actual situation. Coulomb shifts have been eliminated. (Adapted from Wigner, 58.)

The Coulomb forces cause proton-rich nuclei to have higher energies than neutron-rich nuclei. For larger Z the effect of the Coulomb forces is of course larger. This is illustrated in Fig. 7.3 which shows the experimental situation for $A = 6$ and $A = 18$ nuclei, both nuclei having simple interpretations as closed-shell-plus-two systems. Even at low but odd A where the lowest state is an isospin doublet, the nucleus with the larger neutron number is more stable. At higher A, the electrostatic forces become so strong that the neutron richest component of the lowest isospin triplet becomes the lowest energy level of any of the three nuclei. $A = 18$ is the lowest mass number for which this happens.

At higher A, the ground state of a nucleus is always the last member of a T-multiplet with $T = T_3$. The $T_3 = -T + 1$ member of this multiplet is always a rather highly excited state of the isobar with one less neutron.

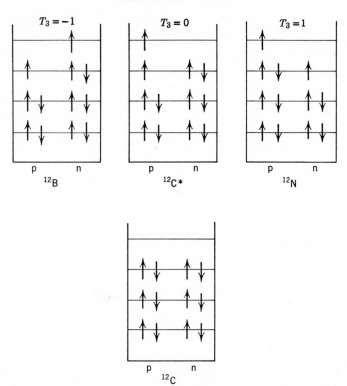

FIG. 7.2   Isospin singlet and triplet for $A = 12$ showing the greater symmetry of the isospin singlet.

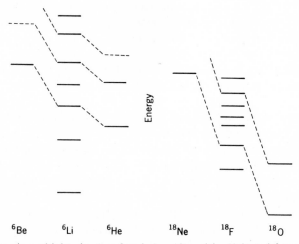

FIG. 7.3   Isospin multiplets in $A = 6$ and $A = 18$ nuclei. (Adapted from Wigner, 58.)

Usually the excitation energy is so high that it is difficult to find it. This greatly hinders the identification of T-multiplets with $T > \frac{3}{2}$ and, in fact, few bound T-multiplets are known beyond $A = 30$. For larger nuclei the higher members of T-multiplets can sometimes be identified as states with positive energy, that is, as resonances in nuclear reactions between two nuclei which together constitute the relevant nucleus. These states are sometimes called Coulomb analogue states.

The existence of T-multiplets is strong evidence for charge independence of nuclear forces. Of course it is difficult accurately to assess the effects of the Coulomb forces, and the evidence is only accurate to within a few per cent. The pion-exchange model of nucleon-nucleon interactions leads us to expect a breakdown of charge independence because the mass of the neutral pion is about 3 per cent less than the mass of the charged pions.

The modification of the wave function due to electrostatic forces should be most important if the number of protons is large, because the effective potential acting on a proton is very different from the effective potential acting on a neutron. Thus the concept of isospin has not been regarded as useful for large nuclei. This is not to say that it is invalid for large nuclei. If valid, it would be useful if more than one member of an isospin multiplet could be identified.

The concept of the validity of the isospin assumption can be understood by considering the nuclear wave function as a superposition of independent particle wave functions. It is valid if states in two different nuclei with the same A are described in terms of products of single-particle wave functions all of which have the same isospin and whose shape is roughly independent of T_3. The single-particle eigenvalues *measured from the bottom of the well* will be independent of T_3. The other necessary condition is that the coefficients in the superposition must be very similar for both nuclei. This means that the probability amplitudes of virtual transitions are largely unaffected by whether the particles undergoing transitions are protons or neutrons. The amplitude for a virtual transition to an independent particle configuration whose isospin is different from the others in the superposition must be small.

The validity of the assumption of isospin conservation depends on the effects of the Coulomb force. The shell-model concept of a closed-shell core has been shown to be valid in many cases to a good approximation. The core is in a state of maximum symmetry which is a $T = 0$ state. There are many protons in the core, so one would possibly expect isospin not to be a good quantum number in this case. However, we shall disregard isospin impurity of the ground state of the core because it has little effect on the motion of the extra-core nucleons except to provide the shell-model potential.

Extra-core nucleons have three kinds of electrostatic interaction.

1. The protons are influenced by each other.
2. The protons are influenced by the core charge.
3. The protons are influenced by core fluctuations.

The p-p Coulomb force at the average internucleon distance is about 1 MeV. This compares with about 20 MeV for nuclear forces (see Table 3.3). It is not enough to make virtual transitions of two protons to higher single-particle states much more probable than virtual transitions of two unlike particles or two neutrons. Thus it cannot cause much difference between the independent particle superposition coefficients for wave functions of nuclei in states that are similar except for T_3.

Charge fluctuations of the core are presumably not as significant as charge fluctuations in the nuclear forces due to the appearance and disappearance of charged virtual mesons. We know these have a small effect. If they did not, charge independence would be very significantly violated in the two-nucleon system.

The average effect of the core charge in deforming the single-particle wave functions of extra-core protons must be the most significant cause of isospin impurity. The core charge tries to push the extra-core protons to the surface of the nucleus in a square-well picture. However, in a sloping-edge well, the protons are reflected from the edge of the well at a smaller radius than the neutrons because of the Coulomb barrier, causing the opposite effect.

It is hard to form an experimental estimate of how important this effect is. The calculation of Brueckner, Lockett, and Rotenberg showed a very small difference between the rms radii for protons and neutrons in ^{40}Ca. Since it predicted relative energy levels of protons and neutrons quite well, we should perhaps believe it for relative radii, even though the absolute radii were in error by nearly 20 per cent.

Assuming that the self-consistent potential wells for neutrons and protons are almost the same in the absence of the average Coulomb potential, the difference is given by the average Coulomb potential itself. For a uniformly charged sphere the Coulomb potential is

$$V_C = \frac{Ze^2}{2R_C}\left(3 - \frac{r^2}{R_C^2}\right) \qquad r \leq R_C$$

$$= \frac{Ze^2}{r} \qquad\qquad r \geq R_C. \tag{7.1}$$

Over the nuclear volume, this potential varies remarkably little. For example, for $A = 140, Z = 58, R_C = 6$ fm, it is 17.2 MeV at 4 fm, 13.5 MeV at 6 fm, and 10.2 MeV at 8 fm. The 7 MeV difference over the volume occupied by most of the nucleons is quite small compared to the average depth of about 50 MeV for the nuclear part of the well. Therefore, proton and neutron potentials have approximately the same shape, and single-particle wave functions are very similar for both. Even large nuclei therefore do not significantly violate the idea that isospin is a good quantum number.

The usefulness of isospin for large nuclei depends on the possibility of identifying at least the second member of a multiplet. The isospin analogue of the ground state of a nucleus specified by N, Z is expected to occur at positive (unbound) energies in the nucleus $N - 1, Z + 1$. Resonances corresponding to such states have been identified. For example, the isospin analogue of the ground state of ^{89}Sr occurs with a Coulomb energy of 11.8 MeV in ^{89}Y. The Coulomb potential of ^{89}Y at $R_C = 5$ fm is 11 MeV.

We can conclude that for many nuclear states isospin is a good quantum number. The shape of single-particle wave functions is fairly independent of T_3 because the average Coulomb potential does not cause significant differences in the shapes of the neutron and proton single-particle potentials. The superposition coefficients in the expansion of the nuclear wave function in independent particle wave functions can be understood as probability amplitudes for virtual excitations caused by effective nucleon-nucleon forces. For excited single-particle states that are separated by several MeV, the 1 MeV difference between the p-p force and the n-n and n-p forces due to the Coulomb interaction cannot have much effect on the virtual excitation amplitudes. For higher excited states, the single-particle level separation is of the order of 1 MeV and significant dependence of the superposition coefficients on T_3 can occur. Energy differences between members of a T-multiplet are accounted for by the average Coulomb potential felt by the extra proton in the next higher member. For a review of further details of the use of isospin for nuclei, the reader is referred to Wigner (58).

B.   THE SHELL MODEL

We are now in a position to study the quantitative description of the interaction of several particles in a spherical potential provided by a closed-shell core. We shall study the problem of two particles in detail because it illustrates most of the principles without the straightforward but tedious complications introduced by the proliferation of angular momentum substates for larger problems.

The mathematical problem involved in the calculation of the shell model is the diagonalization of the Hamiltonian with the two-nucleon potential replaced by the t-matrix. The basis states in the matrix representation are a truncated set of antisymmetrized independent particle states. Each state is denoted by a product of factors, one factor for each shell-model configuration, with a superscript indicating the number of particles in the configuration.

Two different types of basis are used, *jj* coupling and *LS* coupling. Physically neither is preferred, since the representation is just a mathematical device. However, for certain nuclei fewer basis states may be needed if *jj* coupling is used. For *jj* coupling the configuration is labeled by the quantum number $n + 1$ and a letter of the old spectroscopic notation denoting the orbital quantum number *l*, with a subscript denoting *j*. For *LS* coupling, only the principal and orbital quantum numbers are specified.

For two particles in the $1p_{3/2}$ shell for example, the wave function is denoted by $(1p_{3/2})^2$, or simply by $(p_{3/2})^2$ if the omission of the principal quantum number does not cause ambiguity. For one particle in the $1p_{3/2}$ shell and one in the $1p_{1/2}$ shell the notation is $(p_{3/2} p_{1/2})$. A hole is denoted by a negative index.

The number of wave functions used in the basis depends on the virtual transitions which are expected to be important in the Hamiltonian matrix. The virtual transition amplitude between two basis states is the matrix element for those states. States which lie much higher in energy than the topmost occupied states need not be included. In a limited basis, only a finite number of excited states of the nucleus can exist. For a large basis, the methods of group theory are very helpful in counting the states. We shall illustrate the different types of states by considering two particles in the $1p$ shell.

The Hamiltonian matrix is a direct product of independent submatrices, one for each set of good quantum numbers. For two particles the good quantum numbers are the total spin *J*, the total isospin *T*, and of course the parity which is not denoted explicitly.

[i] ANTISYMMETRIC WAVE FUNCTIONS

For particles in the same *jj* configuration, the Pauli exclusion principle restricts the sets of *JT* that can occur. To understand this we consider the construction of antisymmetric single-particle wave functions for two particles. Since the radial wave function is symmetric, it is sufficient to consider the spin-angle functions in a discussion of symmetry. The two-particle wave function of angular momentum *JM* formed by coupling single particles of angular momenta $j_1 m_1$ and $j_2 m_2$ is given by

$$|j_1 j_2 JM\rangle = \sum_{m_1 m_2} C_{j_1 \; j_2 \; J}^{m_1 m_2 M} |j_1 m_1\rangle |j_2 m_2\rangle. \tag{7.2}$$

Two particles may have $T = 0$ or 1. The isospin function is

$$|\tfrac{1}{2}\tfrac{1}{2} T T_3\rangle = \sum_{\tau_1 \tau_2} C_{\frac{1}{2}\frac{1}{2} \; T}^{\tau_1 \; \tau_2 \; T_3} |\tfrac{1}{2}\tau_1\rangle |\tfrac{1}{2}\tau_2\rangle. \tag{7.3}$$

The convention adopted for identifying the particles is that the quantum numbers of particle 1 are written to the left of the quantum numbers of particle 2.

If the particles are exchanged in (7.3), the original form (7.3) is regained by interchanging τ_1 and τ_2. Using the symmetry properties of the Clebsch-Gordan coefficients under exchange of quantum numbers we have, since the relevant Clebsch-Gordan coefficient has equal single-particle isospin quantum numbers $\frac{1}{2}$,

$$|\tfrac{1}{2}\tfrac{1}{2}TT_3\rangle = (-1)^T |\tfrac{1}{2}\tfrac{1}{2}TT_3\rangle_{\text{ex}}. \tag{7.4}$$

The subscript ex denotes that particles have been exchanged. The wave function is symmetric in isospin if $T = 0$ and antisymmetric if $T = 1$.

Similar considerations apply to (7.2) if the single-particle spin quantum numbers j_1 and j_2 are equal, that is, if the particles belong to the same jj configuration.

$$|jjJM\rangle = (-1)^J |jjJM\rangle_{\text{ex}}. \tag{7.5}$$

Configuration	T	J
$(p_{3/2})^2$	1	0, 2
	0	1, 3
$(p_{1/2})^2$	1	0
	0	1
$(p_{3/2}p_{1/2})$	1	1, 2
	0	1, 2

TABLE 7.1.   Values of T and J allowed by the Pauli exclusion principle for two particles in the $1p$ shell.

If j_1 and j_2 are unequal, we apply the properties (A4.26) of the Clebsch-Gordan coefficients to obtain

$$|j_1j_2JM\rangle \pm |j_2j_1JM\rangle = (-1)^{j_1+j_2-J}[|j_1j_2JM\rangle_{\text{ex}} \pm |j_2j_1JM\rangle_{\text{ex}}]. \tag{7.6}$$

The wave function of two particles in the same configuration is antisymmetric with respect to spin and isospin exchange if J is even for $T = 1$ and if J is odd for $T = 0$. For a mixed configuration $(p_{3/2}p_{1/2})$ all values of J are allowed for each T. Table 7.1 shows the allowed values of J and T for different configurations of two particles in the p shell.

Table 7.1 may be used to see immediately which basis configurations must be used in the JT submatrices of the Hamiltonian matrix. The dimension of the submatrix is of course equal to the number of eigenstates. In this way the number of possible eigenstates of particular JT can easily be counted, and it can be seen which matrix elements must be computed for each submatrix. This is indicated in Table 7.2.

From Table 7.2 it can be seen that only ten states are expected for two p-shell particles outside a closed core if core excitations or higher configurations are unimportant. The most obvious such nucleus is ^{6}Li. All the states given by Table 7.2 are expected in ^{6}Li, whereas only the $T = 1$ states are expected in ^{6}He and ^{6}Be. Another nucleus which might be considered in this way is ^{14}N. It is extremely simple if it is regarded as having two particles in the $1p_{1/2}$ shell outside a ^{12}C core. In this case there are only two states, $T = 0$, $J = 1$ and $T = 1, J = 0$. Since the $T = 0$ states have more symmetry, it is not surprising that the ground state of ^{14}N has $J = 1$. The nucleus ^{14}N could also be considered as two $1p$ holes in ^{16}O. Ten states are then expected. In fact the sd shell is close enough for virtual transitions to take place with

$T = 0, J = 1$	$T = 1, J = 0$
$(p_{3/2})^2$	$(p_{3/2})^2$
$(p_{1/2})^2$	$(p_{1/2})^2$
$(p_{3/2} p_{1/2})$	
$T = 0, J = 2$	$T = 1, J = 1$
$(p_{3/2} p_{1/2})$	$(p_{3/2} p_{1/2})$
$T = 0, J = 3$	$T = 1, J = 2$
$(p_{3/2})^2$	$(p_{3/2})^2$
	$(p_{3/2} p_{1/2})$

TABLE 7.2.   Antisymmetric basis states in the JT submatrices of the Hamiltonian matrix for two particles in the $1p$ shell using jj coupling.

quite high probability for ^{14}N, and neither ^{12}C nor ^{16}O are sufficiently inert closed shells for core-excited states to be very high in energy. The results of a calculation of ^{14}N including the sd shell will be given later.

We shall not examine the details of the LS coupling basis at this stage. It is described, for example, in the review article of Elliott and Lane (57). The jj and LS coupling wave functions may be transformed into each other. For two particles with LS coupling, we couple the spins and orbital angular momenta separately.

$$\mathbf{S} = \mathbf{s}_1 + \mathbf{s}_2,$$
$$\mathbf{L} = \mathbf{l}_1 + \mathbf{l}_2. \tag{7.7}$$

The LS coupling wave function is denoted

$$|LSJM\rangle \equiv |(l_1 l_2)L(s_1 s_2)SJM\rangle. \tag{7.8}$$

For jj coupling, we couple the spin of each particle to its orbital angular momentum

$$\mathbf{j}_1 = \mathbf{l}_1 + \mathbf{s}_1,$$
$$\mathbf{j}_2 = \mathbf{l}_1 + \mathbf{s}_2. \tag{7.9}$$

The *jj* coupling wave function may be written out in full as

$$|j_1 j_2 JM\rangle \equiv |(l_1 s_1) j_1 (l_2 s_2) j_2 JM\rangle. \qquad (7.10)$$

The transformation coefficient between the two sets of basis vectors is

$$\langle (l_1 l_2) L (s_1 s_2) SJM \,|\, (l_1 s_1) j_1 (l_2 s_2) j_2 JM\rangle$$

$$\equiv \{(2L + 1)(2S + 1)(2j_1 + 1)(2j_2 + 1)\}^{1/2} \begin{Bmatrix} S & \tfrac{1}{2} & \tfrac{1}{2} \\ L & l_1 & l_2 \\ J & j_1 & j_2 \end{Bmatrix}.$$

$$(7.11)$$

The symbol in braces is the Wigner 9*j* symbol. It is computed by techniques which are standard in nuclear theory. It is discussed, for example, by Elliott and Lane (57) and in Appendix 4*F*.

In the discussion of the single-particle basis, the problem of center of mass motion should be mentioned. The shell model assumes that the core has no degrees of freedom, so that the center of mass of the extra-core nucleons is actually moving with respect to the origin of coordinates. One of the great advantages of the harmonic oscillator basis is that the motion of the center of mass may be separated out. This has been done, for example, by Elliott and Skyrme (55). For *k* particles outside the core we have products of single-particle wave functions representing *k* particles with their center of mass in a harmonic oscillator state. If the wave function of the relative motion of the *k* particles is the same in two eigenstates which differ only by the center of mass wave function, the higher of the two eigenstates is spurious.

In the harmonic oscillator model, if all shells with energy lower than the topmost are filled, the center of mass is in a 1*s* state. If the center of mass is specified to be in a 1*s* state, there will be no spurious states if only states of the lowest configuration are included in the basis. If an excited configuration is included in the basis, spurious states will occur. One way of finding them is to diagonalize the matrix of R^2, where **R** is the coordinate of the centre of mass of the *k* particles.

It is an interesting exercise, which will be left to the reader, to verify this in the case of two particles, where the transformation from the particle co-ordinates $\mathbf{r}_1$, $\mathbf{r}_2$ to the center of mass and relative coordinates **R**, **r** is easy. In the circumstances indicated, the basis wave function will be proportional to $\exp(-M\omega R^2/\hbar)$ multiplied by a polynomial in R, so that the center of mass is not in a 1*s* state.

If there are more than two particles in the configurations which it is decided to take into account, it is convenient to express the basis wave functions in terms of the wave functions of the two-particle basis. This is most easily done using *LS* coupling. Consider the case where there are k particles in the configuration $(l)^k$. Each state of the configuration $(l)^{k-1}$ is considered as a parent of the nucleus in which we are interested.

Let ψ and $\bar{\psi}$ be antisymmetric wave functions for $(l)^k$ and $(l)^{k-1}$, respectively. We would like to form an antisymmetric state ψ from $\bar{\psi}$ by vector coupling $\bar{\psi}$ with the single-particle wave function ϕ_k. In the present section this vector coupling will be denoted by

$$\bar{\psi} = \{\bar{\psi}, \phi_k\}\psi. \tag{7.12}$$

It corresponds to Equation (5.30) in the discussion of the single-particle model. In that discussion, problems of antisymmetry were avoided. We face these problems here by defining fractional parentage coefficients (c.f.p.) which are the coefficients in a linear combination of terms of the form (7.12) which is antisymmetric.

$$\psi = \sum_{\bar{\psi}} (\psi \{| \bar{\psi})\{\bar{\psi}, \phi_k\}\psi. \tag{7.13}$$

The sum extends over all states $\bar{\psi}$ of the complete set for the configuration $(l)^{k-1}$. The c.f.p. are orthogonal in the sense that

$$\sum_{\bar{\psi}} (\psi \{| \bar{\psi})(\psi' \{| \bar{\psi}) = \delta(\psi, \psi'). \tag{7.14}$$

They have been tabulated by various authors, for example, de Shalit and Talmi (63) and Bayman and Lande (66).

It is often necessary to express wave functions of the configuration $(l)^k$ in terms of linear combinations of states of the complete set ψ of the configuration $(l)^{k-2}$, vector coupled to all states ϑ of the last two particles $k - 1$ and k. Coefficients in this combination have also been worked out. They are called c.f.p. of the $(k \,|\, k - 2, 2)$ set in contrast to the first kind which are called c.f.p. of the $(k \,|\, k - 1, 1)$ set. The two sets are related by

$$(\psi \{| \tilde{\psi}\vartheta) = \sum_{\bar{\psi}} \{(2j_{\bar{\psi}} + 1)(2j_\vartheta + 1)\}^{1/2} W(\tilde{\psi}l\psi l, \bar{\psi}\vartheta)(\psi \{| \bar{\psi})(\bar{\psi} \{| \tilde{\psi}). \tag{7.15}$$

The coefficient W is the product of three Racah coefficients containing quantum numbers of the states ψ, $\bar{\psi}$, $\tilde{\psi}$, ϑ in the T, L, and S spaces, respectively. Racah coefficients are used in the theory of the coupling of three angular momenta. They are described in Appendix 4.

[ii] MATRIX ELEMENTS

Elements of the two-body t-matrix are now computed using the basis states. We shall again consider only the case of two particles in detail, but shall first indicate how matrix elements for more than two particles are reduced to matrix elements for two particles using the c.f.p.

Most shell-model calculations thus far have used central pseudopotential approximations to T_{ij}, with exchange character. We wish to compute the matrix element

$$\langle \psi | \mathscr{T} | \psi' \rangle,$$

where

$$\mathscr{T} = \sum_{i<j} T_{ij}(r_{ij}), \tag{7.16}$$

and ψ, ψ' are antisymmetric states of the configuration $(l)^k$. From antisymmetry, we have

$$\langle \psi | \mathscr{T} | \psi' \rangle = \frac{k(k-1)}{2} \langle \psi | T_{(k-1)k} | \psi' \rangle. \tag{7.17}$$

We use the $(k \mid k-2, 2)$ c.f.p. to expand (7.17) in the form

$$\langle \psi | \mathscr{T} | \psi' \rangle = \frac{k(k-1)}{2} \sum_{\tilde{\psi}\vartheta\vartheta'} (\psi \{ | \tilde{\psi}\vartheta)(\psi' \{ | \tilde{\psi}\vartheta')\langle \vartheta | T_{(k-1)k} | \vartheta' \rangle. \tag{7.18}$$

In this expansion the $\tilde{\psi}$ in the expansions of ψ and ψ' must be the same for all nonzero contributions, since $T_{(k-1)k}$ does not involve the coordinates of particles 1 to $k-2$ from which the $\tilde{\psi}$ are constructed. The importance of (7.18) is that the k-body matrix element has been expressed as a linear combination of two-body matrix elements

$$\langle \vartheta | T_{12} | \vartheta' \rangle.$$

The kinetic energy matrix element for a particular configuration is the expectation value of the sum of the single-particle kinetic energies for the states $|nl\rangle$. For the harmonic oscillator this is

$$\langle nl | -\frac{\hbar^2}{2M} \nabla^2 | nl \rangle = \tfrac{1}{2}(2n + l + \tfrac{3}{2})\hbar\omega. \tag{7.19}$$

The center of mass effect is taken into account for the lowest configuration by subtracting $\tfrac{3}{4}\hbar\omega$ from the total kinetic energy.

A particularly useful feature of the harmonic oscillator basis is that the two-particle matrix elements of (7.18) may be expressed in terms of harmonic oscillator functions of the relative coordinate $\mathbf{r}$ and the coordinate $\mathbf{R}$ of the center of mass of the two particles. For the present purpose, these coordinates are defined in terms of the coordinates $\mathbf{r}_1, \mathbf{r}_2$ of the particles with respect to the center of the well by

$$\mathbf{r} = 2^{-\frac{1}{2}}(\mathbf{r}_1 - \mathbf{r}_2),$$
$$\mathbf{R} = 2^{-\frac{1}{2}}(\mathbf{r}_1 + \mathbf{r}_2). \tag{7.20}$$

The principal and orbital quantum numbers in the $(\mathbf{r}_1, \mathbf{r}_2)$ system are n_1, l_1 and n_2, l_2. The principal and orbital quantum numbers for the relative motion are n, l and for the center of mass they are N, L. The total orbital angular momentum of the two particles is λ.

$$l_1 + l_2 = \lambda = l + L. \tag{7.21}$$

The energy associated with the $(\mathbf{r}_1, \mathbf{r}_2)$ system is of course equal to the energy associated with the $(\mathbf{r}, \mathbf{R})$ system.

$$E = 2n_1 + l_1 + 2n_2 + l_2 = 2n + l + 2N + L. \tag{7.22}$$

The single-particle eigenstates in the two systems are given by

$$|n_1 l_1, n_2 l_2, \lambda\mu\rangle = \sum_{m_1 m_2} C^{m_1 m_2 \mu}_{l_1 \ l_2 \ \lambda} |n_1 l_1 m_1\rangle |n_2 l_2 m_2\rangle$$
$$|nl, NL, \lambda\mu\rangle = \sum_{mM} C^{m M \mu}_{l \ L \ \lambda} |nlm\rangle |NLM\rangle, \tag{7.23}$$

where the single-particle wave functions are denoted, for example, by

$$|nlm\rangle = \rho^{-1} R_{nl}(\rho) Y_l^m(\Omega). \tag{7.24}$$

and $R_{nl}(\rho)$ is given by (5.11). The radial coordinate ρ includes the scale factor $(M\omega/\hbar)^{1/2}$.

The transformation from the $(\mathbf{r}, \mathbf{R})$ system to the $(\mathbf{r}_1, \mathbf{r}_2)$ system has been studied by Moshinsky (59). It is written as

$$|n_1 l_1, n_2 l_2, \lambda\mu\rangle = \sum_{nlNL} |nl, NL, \lambda\mu\rangle\langle nl, NL, \lambda \,|\, n_1 l_1, n_2 l_2, \lambda\rangle. \tag{7.25}$$

Note that the transformation is independent of μ. The calculation of the coefficients $\langle nl, NL, \lambda \,|\, n_1 l_1, n_2 l_2, \lambda\rangle$ is one of the standard procedures of nuclear theory. It is discussed and tables are given by Brody and Moshinsky (60).

Calculations with the harmonic oscillator basis have been further simplified by precomputation and tabulation of the radial integrals for central forces. In terms of the $(\mathbf{r}, \mathbf{R})$ system, the matrix element is written

$$\langle nl, NL, \lambda\mu| T(r) |n'l', N'L, \lambda\mu\rangle = \delta_{ll'}\delta_{NN'}\delta_{LL'}\langle nl\| T(r) \|n'l\rangle. \tag{7.26}$$

The simplification (7.26) occurs because T depends only on r. Remember that l is a good quantum number for a central force.

The reduced matrix element of (7.26) is defined by

$$\langle nl\| T(r) \|n'l'\rangle \equiv \int d\rho R_{nl}(\rho) T(\rho) R_{n'l'}(\rho). \tag{7.27}$$

It may be expanded in a series of Talmi integrals I_p (Talmi, 52).

$$\langle nl\| T(r) \|n'l'\rangle = \sum_p B(nl, n'l', p) I_p, \tag{7.28}$$

where

$$I_p = \frac{2}{\Gamma(p + 3/2)} \int d\rho \, \rho^2 \rho^{2p} e^{-\rho^2} T(\rho). \tag{7.29}$$

The calculation of the coefficients $B(nl, n'l', p)$ is also standard. It is discussed by Brody, Jacob, and Moshinsky (60).

The integrals I_p of course depend on the radial shape of $T(\rho)$. The most common radial shapes are the Yukawa and the Gaussian. With these forces, even the radial integrals are standard calculations.

We may now summarize the steps involved in computing matrix elements of T for k particles in the configuration $(l)^k$. First the k-particle states are reduced to two-particle states using the c.f.p. by means of the transformation (7.18). jj coupling states may be reduced to LS coupling states by the transformation (7.11). The two-body matrix elements are then reduced to radial integrals by using the Moshinsky bracket transformation (7.26) and the Talmi integral expansion (7.28).

The calculation of a two-particle matrix element for a central force, starting with harmonic oscillator wave functions in LS coupling as a basis, is summarized, for example, by

$$\langle n_1 l_1, n_2 l_2, \lambda\mu| \ T(r) \ |n_1' l_1', n_2' l_2', \lambda\mu\rangle$$
$$= \sum_{nn'lLN} \langle nl, NL, \lambda \mid n_1 l_1, n_2 l_2, \lambda\rangle\langle n'l, NL, \lambda \mid n_1' l_1', n_2' l_2', \lambda\rangle$$
$$\times \langle nl\| \ T(r) \ \|n'l\rangle. \quad (7.30)$$

If the single-particle wave functions belong to harmonic oscillator states of the same energy, then Equation (7.22) for the energy index E gives, in the light of the reduction (7.26) of the quantum numbers for the case of a central potential,

$$n' = n. \quad (7.31)$$

This simple situation occurs for example in the sd shell.

The calculations of two-particle matrix elements for tensor and spin-orbit forces are more complicated but no different in principle. They will not be discussed. Matrix elements for mixed configurations will not be discussed for the same reason. The reader is referred to de Shalit and Talmi (63).

[iii] CENTRAL FORCES

The Moshinsky bracket transformation is extremely useful for the calculation of matrix elements for the t-matrix of difficult realistic nucleon-nucleon potentials like the Yale or Hamada-Johnston potentials. In this case, integrals (7.29) must be computed.

Early shell-model calculations used local central pseudopotentials with simple radial forms (often the Gaussian) and wave functions in the $(\mathbf{r}_1, \mathbf{r}_2)$ system. The central force (3.86) was found to reproduce experimental results quite well. For this force it is necessary to compute both direct and space-exchange radial integrals.

$$T(S, T, r) = (W + BP^\sigma + MP^r + HP^rP^\sigma)t(r). \quad (3.86)$$

Using the isospin formulation and *LS* coupling, we shall write the matrix element, displaying only the necessary quantum numbers, as

$$\langle n_1 l_1, n_2 l_2, LMST| \ T(S, T, r) \ |n_1' l_1', n_2' l_2', LMST\rangle$$

$$= \langle n_1 l_1, n_2 l_2, LM| \ [W + M(-1)^{T+S+1} + H(-1)^{T+1} + B(-1)^{S+1}]t(r)$$

$$\times \ |n_1' l_1', n_2' l_2', LM\rangle. \quad (7.32)$$

The space-exchange operator may be written in terms of the spin- and isospin-exchange operators since the wave functions are antisymmetrized.

$$P^r P^\sigma P^\tau = -1. \quad (3.41)$$

For the orbital part of the matrix element we use the multipole expansion of $t(r)$.

$$t(|\mathbf{r}_1 - \mathbf{r}_2|) = \sum_{\lambda\mu} t_\lambda(r_1, r_2) Y_\lambda^{\mu *}(\Omega_1) Y_\lambda^{\mu}(\Omega_2). \quad (7.33)$$

The matrix element of $t(r)$ becomes

$$\langle n_1 l_1, n_2 l_2, LM| \ t(r) \ |n_1' l_1', n_2' l_2', LM\rangle$$

$$= \sum_{\lambda\mu} \langle l_1 l_2 LM| \ Y_\lambda^{\mu *}(\Omega_1) Y_\lambda^{\mu}(\Omega_2) \ |l_1' l_2' LM\rangle F_\lambda(n_1 l_1, n_2 l_2, n_1' l_1', n_2' l_2'). \quad (7.34)$$

The angular integral is evaluated by standard techniques of angular momentum algebra (see Appendix 4). The radial integral is

$$F_\lambda = \int dr_1 \int dr_2 R_{n_1 l_1}(r_1) R_{n_1' l_1'}(r_1) R_{n_2 l_2}(r_2) R_{n_2' l_2'}(r_2) t_\lambda(r_1, r_2). \quad (7.35)$$

The order of the quantum numbers in (7.35) depends on whether direct or exchange integrals are being evaluated. Details of the evaluation of two-body matrix elements will be given in Chapter 12B.

[iv] INTERMEDIATE COUPLING

We have now seen that most of the difficulties of a shell-model calculation are included in standard calculations whose results are written as coefficients depending on angular momentum and isospin quantum numbers. One chooses the configurations which are to be included. This choice defines the matrix elements to be calculated. It then remains only to choose the parameters of the effective two-body interaction. The oscillator constant is generally chosen in order to reproduce the rms radius of the nucleus or the spacing of the single-particle levels. The Hamiltonian matrix is diagonalized. The lowest eigenvalue is chosen to be the ground state and taken to be the zero on the energy scale.

The earliest and simplest shell-model calculations were called intermediate coupling calculations. The name arises from the fact that strong central interparticle forces with weak single-particle spin-orbit forces couple orbital angular momenta (*LS* coupling limit), while the opposite situation couples total single-particle angular momenta (*jj* coupling limit). The situation where the relative strength of spin-orbit and interparticle forces is specified to have some intermediate value is called intermediate coupling. The first such calculations included only the $1p$ shell. Consequently they could only predict states whose parity is $(-1)^k$, where there are k particles in the $1p$ shell. They are called states of normal parity. States of nonnormal parity require admixtures of configurations whose parity is opposite.

The two-particle and two-hole nuclei $A = 6$ and $A = 14$ were calculated by Inglis (53). The remainder of the $1p$ shell nuclei were calculated by Kurath (56). The shape of the pseudopotential was chosen to be Gaussian. With this choice the radial functions are such that the calculated level schemes depend only on the ratio of the radial parameters in the Gaussian and the shell-model harmonic oscillator, r_p and r_0, respectively. This may be seen by considering the form of the radial integrals (7.35). The best value is approximately

$$\frac{r_p}{r_0} = 1.3.$$

Only the exchange mixture and the strengths of the potentials now remain to be specified. The exchange mixture was

$$W = H = 0, \qquad M = 0.8, \qquad B = 0.2.$$

This is a simplified version of a mixture found by Rosenfeld (48) to produce saturation in nuclear matter.

Rather than specify r_p/r_0, we may specify the values of three parameters

$$L = F_0 + (\tfrac{4}{25})F_2,$$

$$K = (\tfrac{3}{25})F_2,$$

$$a = \text{the spin-orbit energy.}$$

The F_λ are the radial integrals (7.35).

Alternatively, if r_p/r_0 is specified, one needs only to specify a and K. Taking K as the unit of energy, the level scheme depends on L/K and a/K. For reasonable values of r_p/r_0,

$$\frac{L}{K} = 6.$$

The ratio a/K of spin-orbit to central force matrix elements is the intermediate coupling parameter. If a/K is small, we have the *LS* coupling limit. If a/K is large, we have the *jj* coupling limit. a/K is positive for particles, negative for holes.

The energy levels for $A = 6$ and $A = 14$ are shown in Fig. 7.4 as a function of a/K. In the extreme *jj* coupling limit there are three degenerate levels, one for each of the configurations $(p_{3/2})^2$, $(p_{3/2}p_{1/2})$, and $(p_{1/2})^2$, separated by the spin-orbit splitting energy, $a/2$. In the extreme LS coupling limit the $1p$ shell

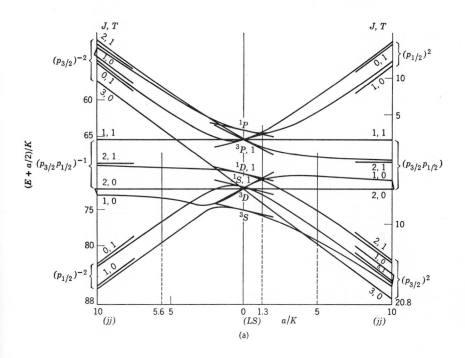

(a)

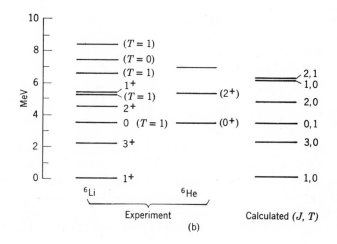

(b)

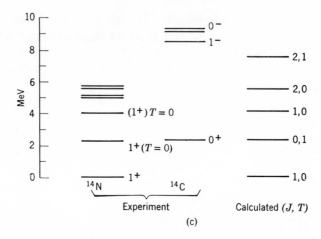

FIG. 7.4 (a) The calculated spectra for $A = 6$ and 14 plotted against a/K with $L/K = 6$. The spectra of $(1p)^2$ for $A = 6$ and $(1p)^{-2}$ for $A = 14$ are on the right and left, respectively. (b) Comparison with experiment for $A = 6$, taking $a/K = 1.3$, $K = -1.23$ MeV. (c) Comparison with experiment for $A = 14$, taking $a/K = 5.0$, $K = -0.8$ MeV. (Adapted from Elliott and Lane, 57.)

nucleons can couple to S, P or D states (denoting L). The multiplicities of the states $(2S + 1)$ are written as left superscripts and the isospin is indicated with the spin by writing the states as

$$T = 0: \quad {}^3S; {}^3D; {}^1P,$$

$$T = 1: \quad {}^1S, 1; {}^1D, 1; {}^3P, 1.$$

The best fits to the experimental level schemes are found for $A = 6$ with $a/K = 1.3$ and for $A = 14$ with $a/K = 5.0$. The difference suggests that the spin-orbit strength increases as the shell is filled, an indication which is confirmed by studying the levels of other nuclei in the $1p$ shell.

In general energy levels for the $1p$ shell are fitted quite well by this model with a few anomalies, most of which can be attributed to higher configurations. The values of the parameters a/K and K for the $1p$ shell are illustrated in Figs. 7.5 and 7.6.

Fitting of energy levels is only the first step in the determination of nuclear structure wave functions. The wave functions are checked by using them to calculate spectroscopic data such as magnetic moments and electric quadrupole moments. Electromagnetic transition rates provide a sensitive test of wave functions.

The transition rates for magnetic dipole ($M1$) and electric quadrupole ($E2$)

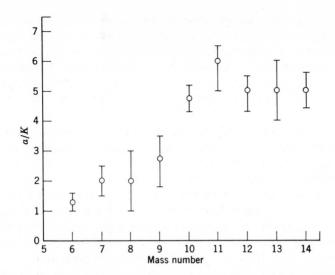

FIG. 7.5   Values of a/K for best fits using $r_p/r_0 = 1.3$. The "limits of error" are the values by which significantly worse fit to experimental level schemes (with sympathetic adjustment of K) is found.   (Adapted from Wilkinson, 58.)

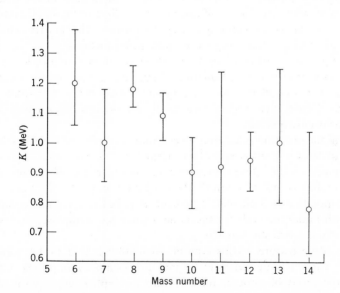

FIG. 7.6   Values of K for best fits using $r_p/r_0 = 1.3$. The "limits of error" are the values by which significantly worse fit to experimental level schemes (with sympathetic adjustment of a/K) is found.   (Adapted from Wilkinson, 58.)

radiation are proportional to the squares of the magnetic and intrinsic electric quadrupole moments, respectively. $E2$ radiation will be considered in Section C of this chapter in connection with the collective model. The theory of electromagnetic radiation is discussed for example by Blatt and Weisskopf (52). The cross sections for nuclear reactions such as inelastic scattering or (d, p) provide an even more sensitive test. They will be discussed in later chapters.

The intermediate coupling model predicts magnetic moments of $1p$-shell nuclei generally within 10 per cent. Electric quadrupole moments have not been well enough determined in the $1p$ shell.

Electromagnetic transitions which involve $\Delta L = 1$ are predicted quite well. The matrix elements for these transitions involve single-particle wave functions for L and $L + 1$, which overlap sufficiently for the values of the single-particle matrix elements to be large. Single-particle matrix elements for $\Delta L = 2$ are small. The experimental transition rates for these are often at least comparable with those for $\Delta L = 1$. This is a serious anomaly which suggests small in-phase contributions to the transition from many higher configurations.

[v] Matrix Elements of the Effective Interaction

The effective interaction of two nucleons in the shell model is expected to be the t-matrix with possible modification for the effect of the Pauli exclusion principle. Its matrix elements are used in forming the matrix which is diagonalized to obtain the energy levels and eigenfunctions.

If the simplification of considering the effective interaction as a local, central pseudopotential is made, Equation (7.30) gives a very simple means of calculating the matrix elements. If jj coupling is used, it has been found that a very limited basis gives satisfactory results for the low-lying energy levels of nuclei near closed shells.

In view of the selection rules, only a very limited number of matrix elements are nonzero, and it is often possible to treat them as parameters which are overdetermined by the relevant experimental energy levels. By means of the jj to LS coupling transformation (7.11) and Equation (7.30), the radial integrals corresponding to these matrix elements may be extracted and compared directly with radial integrals for the same relative harmonic oscillator states computed from a realistic t-matrix.

An interesting feature of this type of calculation is that by knowing the levels of a particular nucleus and by making certain assumptions, we can compute the levels of another nucleus with no explicit description of the forces.

As an example we shall consider a calculation by Pandya (63) for ^{17}O, ^{18}O, ^{19}O, and ^{20}O. Figure 7.7 shows the experimental energy levels of these

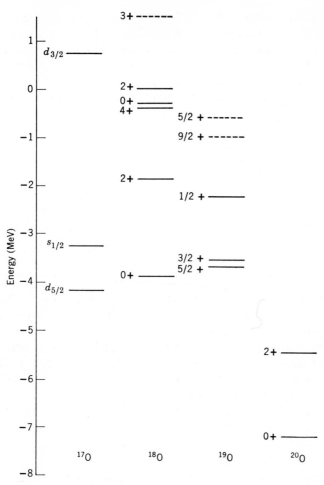

FIG. 7.7   Energy levels of ^{17}O, ^{18}O, ^{19}O, and ^{20}O. Levels predicted by the shell model and subsequently discovered are shown as dotted lines.

four nuclei. The zero of energy in each case has been adjusted so that all four sets of energy levels correspond. The binding energy of the ^{16}O ground state and the contribution of the single-particle energy to the ground state are subtracted out. For example, for ^{19}O we have for the energy of the ground state,

$$\text{B.E.}(^{19}\text{O}) - \text{B.E.}(^{16}\text{O}) - 3[\text{B.E.}(^{17}\text{O}) - \text{B.E.}(^{16}\text{O})].$$

The same single-particle potential is assumed for extra-core nucleons in all four nuclei. That this is a reasonable assumption may be seen from the potential of Elton, which is discussed in Chapter 5C.

The single-particle information is obtained from ^{17}O. It is clear that only the $1d_{5/2}$ and $2s_{1/2}$ states are important for a discussion of low-lying levels. These states have equal energy in the harmonic oscillator model, so that we have the simplification (7.31) in the basis. For two-neutron states we need consider only the configurations shown in Table 7.3. They are of course $T = 1$ states, for which only the singlet-even and triplet-odd forces act. The central force approximation is much better for these states than for the case $T = 0$.

Configuration	T	J
$(d_{5/2})^2$	1	0, 2, 4
$(s_{1/2})^2$	1	0
$(d_{5/2} s_{1/2})$	1	2, 3

TABLE 7.3. Two-neutron configurations in the $s_{1/2} d_{5/2}$ shell.

Of the six states listed in Table 7.3, five had been observed at the time of Pandya's calculation. The 3+ state was subsequently found at 1.5 MeV.

In the limited configuration space that has been assumed, there are eight two-body matrix elements, shown in Table 7.4. From these matrix elements the three- and four-body matrix elements for ^{19}O and ^{20}O can be determined by the use of fractional parentage coefficients in the expansion (7.18). In addition to these eight parameters, we have a parameter $\Delta = 0.87$ MeV which is the separation of the single-particle states in ^{17}O.

As an example of the determination of the matrix elements, we shall consider ^{18}O. The $J(T = 1)$ submatrices are as follows.

$$
J = 0: \quad \begin{bmatrix} V_0 & V_{00} \\ V_{00} & V_0' + 2\Delta \end{bmatrix},
$$

$$
J = 2: \quad \begin{bmatrix} V_2 & V_{22} \\ V_{22} & V_2' + \Delta \end{bmatrix}, \qquad (7.36)
$$

$$
J = 3: \quad V_3 + \Delta,
$$

$$
J = 4: \quad V_4.
$$

The matrix elements of the submatrices for the larger nuclei are linear combinations (7.18) of the matrix elements of Table 7.4.

From (7.36), V_4 is determined directly.

$$
V_4 = -0.37 \text{ MeV}.
$$

If the 3+ state were known, V_3 could also be determined directly. For

$J = 0, 2$ we have 2×2 matrices with both eigenvalues known. They can be partially inverted. For a given assumed value of V_{00} (or V_{22}) one can deduce V_0 and V_0' (or V_2 and V_2') in terms of the observed energies of the $0+$ (or $2+$) states. In a similar but more complicated way, values of all the matrix elements can be determined for all the energy levels. Since the basis is too restricted for complete accuracy, different methods of determination within the overcomplete set of methods lead to slightly inconsistent values of the matrix elements.

$$V_0 = \langle (d_{5/2})^2 0 | \ T \ | (d_{5/2})^2 0 \rangle \qquad V_2 = \langle (d_{5/2})^2 2 | \ T \ | (d_{5/2})^2 2 \rangle$$
$$V_0' = \langle (s_{1/2})^2 0 | \ T \ | (s_{1/2})^2 0 \rangle \qquad V_2' = \langle (d_{5/2} \, s_{1/2}) 2 | \ T \ | (d_{5/2} \, s_{1/2}) 2 \rangle$$
$$V_{00} = \langle (d_{5/2})^2 0 | \ T \ | (s_{1/2})^2 0 \rangle \qquad V_{22} = \langle (d_{5/2})^2 2 | \ T \ | (d_{5/2} \, s_{1/2}) 2 \rangle$$
$$V_3 = \langle (d_{5/2} \, s_{1/2}) 3 | \ T \ | (d_{5/2} \, s_{1/2}) 3 \rangle$$
$$V_4 = \langle (d_{5/2})^2 4 | \ T \ | (d_{5/2})^2 4 \rangle$$

TABLE 7.4.   Two-neutron matrix elements for the $s_{1/2} \, d_{5/2}$ shell. The wave functions are denoted by the single-particle configuration and the value of J. (From Pandya, 63.)

The values of the matrix elements obtained by three different methods of determination, labeled *A*, *B*, and *C*, are shown in Table 7.5. In the last column of Table 7.5 are shown the matrix elements determined by Dawson, Talmi, and Walecka (62) from the free *t*-matrix of the Brueckner-Gammel-Thaler potential. The correspondence is remarkably close, considering the crude nature of the approximations. The value of V_3, which is determined from the more recently discovered $3+$ level of ^{18}O to be $+0.6$ MeV, provides the main discrepancy.

There are several things to be learned from this calculation. One is that the slight inconsistency of the determinations *A*, *B*, and *C* of the matrix elements reflects the breakdown of the assumptions of the shell model. The most important point of breakdown probably is the assumption that ^{16}O is an inert core. We have already noted that the electric quadrupole moment of ^{17}O is inconsistent with this assumption.

In fact there is strong evidence that the probability of the ^{16}O core being excited in the ground state of ^{18}O is quite large. One important piece of evidence is the large cross section for the reaction $^{18}O(^3He, d)^{19}F$ populating the low-lying $\frac{1}{2}-$ state of ^{19}F. This state has nonnormal parity. It is understood in terms of the shell model as involving an excitation of a $1p_{1/2}$ proton from ^{16}O. It may be understood in terms of a cluster model, and will be discussed in Section *D*. If the $p_{1/2}$ subshell is full in ^{18}O, the $(^3He, d)$ reaction can only put a proton into the *sd* shell, forming a state of positive parity. Analysis of the reaction shows that the probability of this type of core excitation in the ^{18}O ground state is about 20 per cent.

In spite of the large probability of core excitation, the shell-model calculation gives remarkably good agreement with spectroscopic data including magnetic dipole radiative transition rates. It even enabled two levels in ^{19}O to be predicted: a $\frac{9}{2}+$ level at about -1 MeV in Fig. 7.7 and a $\frac{5}{2}+$ level at about -0.6 MeV in Fig. 7.7. Both of these levels were subsequently identified experimentally.

	A	B	C	DTW
V_0	-3.00	-2.97	-2.97	-1.96
V_2	-1.20	-1.24	-1.20	-1.60
V_4	-0.37	-0.15	-0.10	-0.77
V_0'	-2.90	-2.99	-2.99	-3.02
V_2'	-1.65	-1.58	-1.83	-1.09
V_3	$+1.50$	$+1.40$	$+1.40$	-0.65
V_{00}	-1.50	-1.60	-1.60	-0.95
V_{22}	-0.93	-0.93	-0.85	-0.78

TABLE 7.5. Values of the two-neutron matrix elements for the $s_{1/2} d_{5/2}$ shell. Columns *A*, *B*, and *C* list values from three different methods of determination from the experimental energy levels. The column headed *DTW* gives the values computed from the *K*-matrix of the Brueckner-Gammel-Thaler potential by Dawson, Talmi, and Walecka (62). (From Pandya, 63.)

A strong note of caution about the agreement of the shell model with certain spectroscopic data has been voiced by Cohen, Lawson, and Soper (66). These authors set up a theoretical nucleus called "pseudonium" (Ps) which had only neutrons in two isolated degenerate single-particle levels, the $1d_{3/2}$ state and the $1f_{7/2}$ state. An effective interaction and oscillator parameters similar to those found in shell-model calculations were postulated and the spectroscopic properties of the nucleus were calculated. A shell-model calculation using only the single configuration $1f_{7/2}$ was then performed by the method of this section for pseudonuclei formed from various numbers of neutrons. Agreement for absolute energy levels, magnetic moments, and dipole radiative transitions was obtained, which was just as good as agreement found in a shell-model calculation for real nuclei.

Because the two configurations were chosen to be degenerate in energy, the probability of excitation from the $1d_{3/2}$ core is unrealistically high. For example, the probability that the ^{41}Ps ground state is a closed $1d_{3/2}$ shell plus a single $1f_{7/2}$ neutron outside it was only 17.3 per cent. However, the magnetic moment using the shell model calculation with the $1f_{7/2}$ configuration was within 1 per cent of the value calculated with both configurations.

Conclusions drawn from the fitting of energy levels by using matrix elements as parameters are therefore subject to large errors. Errors similar to those found in actual shell-model fits were found in the pseudonium calculation for quadrupole transition rates and nuclear reaction cross sections.

Of course the extremely degenerate situation assumed in the pseudonium model does not apply to the oxygen isotopes. The $1p_{1/2}$ and $1d_{5/2}$ single-particle levels are separated by 6 MeV, which is much larger than any of the matrix elements involved in the calculation (see Table 7.5). There certainly is significance in the correspondence of the matrix elements with those calculated from realistic forces.

A shell-model calculation using a realistic nucleon-nucleon t-matrix is that of Dawson, Talmi, and Walecka (62) which has been mentioned. This calculation predicts the correct ordering of levels of ^{18}O. The great improvement over earlier shell-model calculations is that the predicted absolute binding energy is very close to the experimental value. Level spacings are also predicted quite well.

Other regions of the periodic table, where the shell model using a very limited number of configurations is found to be internally consistent by over-determining experimental values of matrix elements, are the $1p$ shell, the region near ^{90}Zr, and the region near ^{208}Pb. Not only are the energy levels predicted by the matrix elements consistent, but other spectroscopic properties such as magnetic moments, β-decay rates, and electromagnetic transition rates for dipole radiation are predicted quite well by the eigenfunctions. Electric quadrupole moments and transition rates are predicted better in some of these cases than in the sd shell.

[vi] CALCULATIONS WITH CONFIGURATION MIXING

The shell-model calculations considered so far have used a basis formed from single-particle states which have the same energy in the harmonic oscillator well. Only states of normal parity are reproduced. The inclusion of configurations of different parity enables states of nonnormal parity to be predicted.

As an example we shall consider the calculation by True (63) of ^{14}N. Using the states of the $1p$ shell as a basis there are only ten states predicted in ^{14}N. The spectrum is actually much more complicated than this. True considered the $1s_{1/2}$ and $1p_{3/2}$ shells to be filled in order to produce an inert ^{12}C core. The harmonic oscillator basis consisted of two-particle states in the $1p_{1/2}$, $1d_{5/2}$, $2s_{1/2}$, and $1d_{3/2}$ shells.

A central force with exchange character was used, and the oscillator parameter $M\omega/\hbar$ was allowed to be different for the p and sd shells. The

$J\pi, T$	E_{exp}(MeV)	E_{th}(MeV)	Eigenfunctions
0−, 0	4.91	3.31	$(p_{1/2}s_{1/2})$ 1.000
0+, 1	2.312	2.94	$(p_{1/2})^2$ −0.9501, $(s_{1/2})^2$ 0.1219, $(d_{5/2})^2$ 0.2635, $(d_{3/2})^2$ 0.1139
	8.63	8.46	$(p_{1/2})^2$ −0.2056, $(s_{1/2})^2$ −0.9360, $(d_{5/2})^2$ −0.2754, $(d_{3/2})^2$ −0.0760
0−, 1	8.71	8.37	$(p_{1/2}s_{1/2})$ 1.000
1+, 0	0	0	$(p_{1/2})^2$ 0.9666, $(s_{1/2})^2$ 0.0643, $(d_{5/2})^2$ 0.1839, $(s_{1/2}d_{3/2})$ 0.1012, $(d_{3/2}d_{5/2})$ 0.0105, $(d_{3/2})^2$ −0.1318
	6.23	6.34	$(p_{1/2})^2$ 0.1303, $(s_{1/2})^2$ −0.8732, $(d_{5/2})^2$ −0.3268, $(s_{1/2}d_{3/2})$ 0.0201, $(d_{3/2}d_{5/2})$ −0.3308, $(d_{3/2})^2$ 0.0628
	8.99	9.92	$(p_{1/2})^2$ 0.1346, $(s_{1/2})^2$ 0.4713, $(d_{5/2})^2$ −0.7457, $(s_{1/2}d_{3/2})$ −0.0398, $(d_{3/2}d_{5/2})$ −0.4357, $(d_{3/2})^2$ 0.1108
1−, 0	5.69	4.90	$(p_{1/2}s_{1/2})$ 0.9931, $(p_{1/2}d_{3/2})$ 0.1175
1−, 1	8.06	7.26	$(p_{1/2}s_{1/2})$ −0.9945, $(p_{1/2}d_{5/2})$ 0.1050
2−, 0	5.10	4.83	$(p_{1/2}d_{5/2})$ 0.9829, $(p_{1/2}d_{3/2})$ 0.1842
3+, 0	6.44	7.61	$(s_{1/2}d_{5/2})$ −0.8969, $(d_{5/2})^2$ −0.4082, $(d_{3/2}d_{5/2})$ −0.1673, $(d_{3/2})^2$ 0.0312
3−, 0	5.83	5.60	$(p_{1/2}d_{5/2})$ 1.000
3−, 1	8.91	7.71	$(p_{1/2}d_{5/2})$ 1.000
1+, 0	3.945		*Core excited*
(2+), 0	7.03		*Core excited*

TABLE 7.6. States of ^{14}N found by True (63) compared with experimental levels, spins, parities, and isospins below 9 MeV excitation. (From True, 63.)

single-particle interactions of protons and neutrons with the ^{12}C core were determined from the energy levels of ^{13}C and ^{13}N. The single-particle energy levels in these nuclei are identified by the ^{12}C(d, p)^{13}C and ^{12}C(d, n)^{13}N reactions. An arbitrary zero on the energy scale was adopted so that the lowest $1+$, $T = 0$ level was set equal to zero to correspond with the ground state.

The nuclear force was taken to be

$$V(r) = V_0 e^{-\beta r^2}[(1 + \alpha) + (1 + \alpha)P^r + (\alpha - 1)P^\sigma + (\alpha - 1)P^r P^\sigma], \quad (7.37)$$

where

$$V_0 = -8.125 \text{ MeV}, \qquad \beta = 0.2922 \text{ fm}^{-2}.$$

The results to be quoted used the following values of α and the oscillator constants.

$$\alpha = 1.6 \qquad \frac{M\omega_p}{\hbar} = 0.32 \text{ fm}^{-2} \qquad \frac{M\omega_{sd}}{\hbar} = 0.27 \text{ fm}^{-2}.$$

Of the 29 experimental energy levels up to 10.42 MeV, the spins and parities are known for 24. Of these the calculation predicted 18 with the correct spin and parity and with energy within an MeV except in two cases where errors of about 2 MeV occurred. For some of the higher states, isospins have not been determined experimentally. In describing the states the spin, parity, and isospin quantum numbers will be given in that order. Four levels, including the second excited $1+$, 0 state were attributed to excitations of the ^{12}C core. Only two are not accounted for.

It is interesting to consider the amplitudes or superposition coefficients with which the different configurations occur in the eigenstates. A pure jj coupling state has an amplitude 1 for the relevant single-particle configuration. The squares of the amplitudes for a particular eigenstate add to 1. Amplitudes for some of the lower-lying states are given in Table 7.6.

There are some facts concerning the table which should be pointed out. The states of the simple $(p_{1/2})^2$ configuration are the ground state and the first excited state at 2.312 MeV. Neither has very strong contributions from the sd shell. The sd shell therefore is sufficiently above the p shell for configuration mixing not to alter the level order. Indeed the effect of excitations from the $p_{3/2}$ shell to the $p_{1/2}$ shell is so great that the second excited state is one of these. It is not predicted by this model, although it is predicted by the intermediate coupling calculation in the $p_{3/2} p_{1/2}$ shell (see Fig. 7.4c). Most of the other states have a very dominant jj configuration. Some, of course, have only one configuration permitted by the Pauli exclusion principle within the basis. However, there are others, notably the 8.99 MeV $1+$, 0 state, which are shared among several configurations of the sd shell.

This type of calculation is much more sensitive to the exchange parameters of the effective interaction than to its shape. The parameters A_{TS} of (3.99) which correspond to the value $\alpha = 1.6$ are

$$A_{00} = A_{11} = 0, \qquad A_{01} = 1, \qquad A_{10} = 0.625.$$

This roughly corresponds to what is known about the free two-body force. Singlet-odd and triplet-odd interactions are small. The singlet-even interaction (given by p-p scattering at 90°) is not quite as strong as the triplet-even (given by the deuteron).

[vii] PARTICLE-HOLE CALCULATIONS

It is possible to extend the shell model to describe core excitations and excitations of closed-shell nuclei in terms of effective forces between the excited particles and the holes left behind in the closed shells by their excitation.

$1p_{3/2}$	$1p_{3/2}$	$1p_{3/2}$	$1p_{3/2}$	$1p_{3/2}$	$1s$	$1s$
$1p_{1/2}$	$1f_{5/2}$	$1f_{7/2}$	$2p_{1/2}$	$2p_{3/2}$	$1d_{3/2}$	$1d_{5/2}$
0.91	−0.08	0.30	0.11	−0.12	0.20	−0.29

$1p_{1/2}$	$1f_{5/2}$	$1f_{7/2}$	$2p_{1/2}$	$2p_{3/2}$	$1d_{3/2}$	$1d_{5/2}$
$1p_{3/2}$	$1p_{3/2}$	$1p_{3/2}$	$1p_{3/2}$	$1p_{3/2}$	$1s$	$1s$
0.05	0.06	0.02	0.08	−0.09	−0.14	−0.20

TABLE 7.7. Amplitudes for particle-hole configurations in the eigenvector for the first excited $2+, 0$ state of ^{12}C calculated by Gillet and Vinh Mau (64). The hole quantum numbers are shown in the top row; the particle quantum numbers are shown in the second row. The top set of amplitudes are direct; the bottom set are exchange amplitudes due to inclusion of correlations in the ground state. (From Gillet and Vinh Mau, 64.)

The construction of the antisymmetric basis states for the diagonalization of the Hamiltonian matrix in this model is a little more complicated than for the situations we have considered. However, there are some very interesting features of the eigenfunctions which should be noticed.

For example, we shall consider a calculation of ^{12}C by Gillet and Vinh Mau (64). The interesting state is the first excited $2+, 0$ state at 4.43 MeV. On the single-particle, single-hole model it is an excitation of a particle to the $1p_{1/2}$ state leaving a hole in the $1p_{3/2}$ state. In the calculation the energy is 4.8 MeV. The amplitudes of different single-particle, single-hole configurations are shown in Table 7.7.

The remarkable thing about this state is the range of single-particle and single-hole levels which contribute. The amplitude for taking a particle out of the $1s$ state and putting it into the $1d_{3/2}$ state is far from negligible, although these states are separated by at least 40 MeV. Even if the $(1p_{3/2})^{-1}(1p_{1/2})$ configuration is dominant, there are strong contributions from much higher excitations whose phases evidently combine in the correct way to produce a low-lying level.

As is obvious from this example, such a state requires a very difficult and sophisticated shell-model description. For such states a much simpler description is afforded by the collective model. Note that all the nucleons, not just the upper 10 per cent as for nuclear matter, are correlated in the first 2+ state of such a light nucleus.

C.   COLLECTIVE MODELS OF NUCLEI

While nuclei near closed shells are the easiest to understand in terms of particle motion, they are really very exceptional cases. Most nuclei lie between closed shells. The large electric quadrupole moments in the regions $150 < A < 190$ and $A > 230$ indicate that these nuclei are deformed from the spherical shape in the ground state. The shell model would require a large basis of independent particle wave functions in a spherical well to describe them. The Hartree-Fock calculation predicts deformed shapes in the ground state for nuclei in the middle of the *sd* shell. A much simpler description of such nuclei is afforded by collective models in which the motions of the particles are correlated in such a way that the effective nuclear potential that each particle feels is nonspherical, at least in certain low-lying states.

The first collective description of nuclei was the liquid drop model of N. Bohr (36) and N. Bohr and Kalckar (37). The long-range correlations between the nucleons near the top of the momentum distribution produce surface tension effects. The energy due to different collective effects is determined by investigating all the nuclei in the periodic table by means of the semiempirical mass formula of Weizsäcker (35).

[i]   THE SEMIEMPIRICAL MASS FORMULA

General considerations of Coulomb forces, the Pauli exclusion principle and the liquid drop model lead to a formula for the atomic masses that contains seven terms and four constants. These are determined by fitting masses in the periodic table. Expressing masses in MeV, the formula is

$$M = M_n N + M_p Z - \alpha A + \beta A^{2/3} + \frac{\gamma T_3^2}{A} + \frac{3}{5} \frac{Z(Z-1)}{A^{1/3}} \frac{e^2}{r_{0C}} + \delta(A, Z).$$

$$(7.37)$$

The term in α expresses the saturation of nuclear forces. The binding energy is proportional to A. This is the volume energy which is attributed to infinite nuclear matter.

The term in β is the surface tension term due to unbalanced forces at the surface of a finite nucleus. It corrects the binding energy for the overestimate made by the term in α which ignores the surface.

The term in γ is the symmetry energy due to the Pauli principle and the collective Coulomb repulsion of the protons. Nuclear matter is not actually charge symmetric. Assuming charge independence of the nuclear forces, the single-particle well for the protons is shallower than that for neutrons. If the wells are not occupied to approximately the same level, the nucleus can β-decay until they are. Consider the Fermi gas for neutrons.

The number of neutron states per unit momentum interval is

$$\frac{dN}{dp} = \frac{\Omega p^2}{\pi^2 \hbar^2}.$$ (7.38)

For a degenerate gas the neutron number N is

$$N = \int_0^{p_F} \frac{dN}{dp}\, dp = \frac{\Omega}{3\pi^2\hbar^3}\, p_F{}^3.$$ (7.39)

From (7.39) we obtain the formula for E_F in terms of the density ρ. The total kinetic energy of the neutrons is

$$E_n = \int_0^{E_F} E\,\frac{dN}{dE}\, dE = \int_0^{E_F} E\,\frac{dN}{dp}\frac{dp}{dE}\, dE$$

$$= CN^{5/3}/A^{2/3}.$$ (7.40)

For a symmetrical gas the total energy is

$$\frac{C}{A^{2/3}}\, (N^{5/3} + Z^{5/3}).$$

This value is larger than the energy computed for $N = Z$. We can make a binomial expansion of the difference to second order in $T_3 = \frac{1}{2}(Z - N)$.

$$\frac{C}{A^{2/3}}\left[N^{5/3} + Z^{5/3} - 2\left(\frac{A}{2}\right)^{5/3} \right]$$

$$= \frac{C}{A^{2/3}}\left[\left(\frac{A}{2} - T_3\right)^{5/3} + \left(\frac{A}{2} + T_3\right)^{5/3} - 2\left(\frac{A}{2}\right)^{5/3} \right]$$

$$\cong \frac{\gamma T_3{}^2}{A}.$$ (7.41)

The next term is the Coulomb repulsion term. The electrostatic energy between a pair of protons in single-particle states ψ_i, ψ_j is

$$(E_C)_{ij} = \langle \psi_{ij}(\mathbf{r}_1, \mathbf{r}_2) | \frac{e^2}{r_{12}} | \psi_{ij}(\mathbf{r}_1, \mathbf{r}_2) \rangle. \tag{7.42}$$

The two-body wave function ψ_{ij} must be symmetric in space if the protons are in a singlet state, antisymmetric if they are in a triplet state.

$$(E_C)_{ij} = \int d^3r_1 \int d^3r_2 \, |\psi_i(\mathbf{r}_1)|^2 \, |\psi_j(\mathbf{r}_2)|^2 \frac{e^2}{r_{12}}$$
$$\pm \int d^3r_1 \int d^3r_2 \psi_i{}^*(\mathbf{r}_1)\psi_j{}^*(\mathbf{r}_2)\psi_i(\mathbf{r}_2)\psi_j(\mathbf{r}_1)\frac{e^2}{r_{12}}. \tag{7.43}$$

The expression (7.43) must be summed over all proton pairs ij. If there were as many singlet pairs as triplet pairs the exchange terms would vanish. In fact, since we know that the p-p force is strongly attractive in singlet states and weak in triplet states, the sum over pairs leaves us with a positive exchange term which is considerably smaller than the sum of the first terms.

In the main term for E_C the pair Coulomb repulsion is integrated over the product of the particle densities. In a crude model these densities are constant inside the effective Coulomb radius $R_C = r_{0C}A^{1/3}$. Each particle produces a charge density $\rho = 3e/4\pi R_C{}^3$ and a potential $U(r) = 2\pi\rho[R_C{}^2 - r^2/3]$. The energy of the charge density of proton i in the potential due to proton j is

$$(E_C)_{ij} = \int_0^{R_C} d^3r U(r)\rho = \frac{6}{5}\frac{e^2}{R_C}. \tag{7.44}$$

Applied to a nucleus containing Z protons and thus $Z(Z-1)/2$ proton pairs we have

$$E_i = \frac{3}{5}\frac{Z(Z-1)}{A^{1/3}}\frac{e^2}{r_{0C}}. \tag{7.45}$$

Since the effective Coulomb radius parameter can be determined by electron scattering, it is not a parameter to be obtained by fitting the masses in the periodic table.

The term in δ describes the effects of pairing.

The coefficients turn out to be approximately

$$\alpha = 14 \text{ MeV}$$
$$\beta = 13 \text{ MeV}$$
$$\gamma = 77 \text{ MeV}$$
$$\delta = -35A^{-3/4} \text{ MeV} \qquad \text{for even nuclei}$$
$$= 0 \qquad \qquad \text{for odd-}A \text{ nuclei}$$
$$= +33A^{-3/4} \text{ MeV} \qquad \text{for odd nuclei.}$$

These numbers were obtained by Fermi (50). Slightly different numbers are obtained by various refinements (Feenberg, 47).

[ii] THE UNIFIED MODEL OF BOHR AND MOTTELSON

The advantage of a collective description of nuclear properties is that it requires far fewer coordinates than a description in terms of all the individual particles. Assuming that the nucleus has a small compressibility, the collective coordinates are defined so that the only degrees of freedom involve changes of shape while the volume is constant. Assuming a sharp surface, the normal coordinates of collective oscillations are the expansion parameters of the nuclear surface function $R(\theta', \phi')$ in terms of spherical harmonics.

$$R(\theta', \phi') = R_0[1 + \sum_{\lambda\mu} \alpha_{\lambda\mu} Y_\lambda^\mu(\theta', \phi')]. \qquad (7.46)$$

The coordinates θ', ϕ' are in a body-fixed system.

The collective effects are average effects produced by the motion of the particles. The assumption is made that the frequencies ω_p associated with particle motion are much greater than the frequencies ω_c associated with collective motion. This is the adiabatic approximation. The nuclear wave function is then

$$\Psi_{n\nu}(x) = \psi_\nu(\alpha)\phi_n(x, \alpha), \qquad (7.47)$$

where x represents the coordinates of all the particles in the nucleus including spin and isospin. The wave function $\phi_n(x, \alpha)$ is characterized by a set of quantum numbers n. It is the shell-model wave function for a fixed potential specified by the collective parameters α. The wave function $\psi_\nu(\alpha)$ specifies the oscillations of the whole nucleus. It is characterized by a further set of quantum numbers ν.

The theory of nuclei in this approximation has been given in a series of papers by A. Bohr and Mottelson (57). (This paper provides a good introduction to the theory and gives earlier references.) A nucleus is pictured as having a particular particle structure described by ϕ_n. The particle correlations do not change much relative to a body-fixed coordinate system while the collective density distribution changes shape or rotates. Since for heavy nuclei, which are presumably like nuclear matter, approximately the upper 10 per cent of particles have effective long-range correlations, the nucleons in the lower filled shells do not contribute much to the collective effect.

For a particular set of particle quantum numbers n, there is a set of collective states ν described by a Hamiltonian of the form

$$H_c = T(\dot{\alpha}) + E_n(\alpha), \qquad (7.48)$$

where the potential energy $E_n(\alpha)$ is the energy of the particle structure n calculated for fixed α. The kinetic energy of the nucleons is of course given by the $\dot{x}$. This generalized velocity coordinate may be considered as the sum of the collective velocity $\dot{\alpha}$ and the velocity of the nucleon relative to the collective motion. We shall consider particular cases of this model.

[iii] VIBRATIONS OF SPHERICAL NUCLEI

In some of our Hartree-Fock examples (Chapter 6B), the particle structure preferred a spherical shape in the ground state. For such nuclei the deformation may be expanded about the equilibrium configuration $\alpha_{\lambda\mu} = 0$. Small oscillations are assumed to be harmonic. The surface Hamiltonian is then

$$H_S = \sum_{\lambda\mu} \{ \tfrac{1}{2} B_\lambda \,|\dot{\alpha}_{\lambda\mu}|^2 + \tfrac{1}{2} C_\lambda \,|\alpha_{\lambda\mu}|^2 \}. \tag{7.49}$$

Since the function R of (7.46) is real, we have

$$\alpha_{\lambda\mu} = (-1)^\mu \alpha^*_{\lambda(-\mu)}. \tag{7.50}$$

H_S describes a set of harmonic oscillators with frequencies

$$\omega_\lambda = \left(\frac{C_\lambda}{B_\lambda} \right)^{\!1/2}. \tag{7.51}$$

The real and imaginary parts of $\alpha_{\lambda\mu}$ are treated as independent variables.

The generalized momentum coordinate which is canonically conjugate to $\alpha_{\lambda\mu}$ is $\pi_{\lambda\mu}$ defined by

$$\pi_{\lambda\mu} = \frac{\partial}{\partial \dot{\alpha}_{\lambda\mu}} \,(\tfrac{1}{2} \sum_{\lambda\mu} B_\lambda \,|\dot{\alpha}_{\lambda\mu}|^2)$$

$$= B_\lambda \dot{\alpha}_{\lambda\mu}{}^*. \tag{7.52}$$

The vibrational motion is quantized (Dirac, 58) in terms of the generalized coordinates and momenta by requiring the commutation rule

$$[\alpha_{\lambda\mu}, \pi_{\lambda'\mu'}] = i\hbar \delta_{\lambda\lambda'} \delta_{\mu\mu'}, \tag{7.53}$$

where the square bracket denotes the commutator of the operators $\alpha_{\lambda\mu}$ and $\pi_{\lambda'\mu'}$.

We now define operators $b_{\lambda\mu}$ by the following transformation.

$$\alpha_{\lambda\mu} = \left(\frac{\hbar}{2B_\lambda \omega_\lambda} \right)^{\!1/2} [b_{\lambda\mu} + (-1)^\mu b^*_{\lambda(-\mu)}]$$

$$\dot{\alpha}_{\lambda\mu} = -i\omega_\lambda \left(\frac{\hbar}{2B_\lambda \omega_\lambda} \right)^{\!1/2} [b_{\lambda\mu} - (-1)^\mu b^*_{\lambda(-\mu)}]. \tag{7.54}$$

In the $b_{\lambda\mu}$ representation the Hamiltonian becomes

$$H_S = \tfrac{1}{2} \sum_{\lambda\mu} \hbar\omega_\lambda (b_{\lambda\mu}{}^* b_{\lambda\mu} + b_{\lambda\mu} b_{\lambda\mu}{}^*). \tag{7.55}$$

The quantization rule (7.53) becomes

$$[b_{\lambda\mu}, b^*_{\lambda'\mu'}] = \delta_{\lambda\lambda'}\delta_{\mu\mu'}. \tag{7.56}$$

The number operator $n_{\lambda\mu}$ is defined by

$$n_{\lambda\mu} = b_{\lambda\mu}{}^* b_{\lambda\mu}. \tag{7.57}$$

The Hamiltonian H_S is diagonal in the $n_{\lambda\mu}$ representation. Its eigenvalues are obtained from (7.55, 7.56, 7.57).

$$\begin{aligned} E_\lambda &= \hbar\omega_\lambda \sum_\mu (n_{\lambda\mu} + \tfrac{1}{2}) \\ &= \hbar\omega_\lambda\left(N_\lambda + \frac{2\lambda + 1}{2}\right). \end{aligned} \tag{7.58}$$

The eigenstates are degenerate in μ. We have in fact a $(2\lambda + 1)$-dimensional oscillator. The number of excitation quanta or phonons of type λ, μ is $n_{\lambda\mu}$. Because of the μ degeneracy we define a new phonon number N_λ which is the number of phonons of type λ.

$$N_\lambda = \sum_\mu n_{\lambda\mu} = 0, 1, 2, \dots . \tag{7.59}$$

The $n_{\lambda\mu}$-th eigenstate is

$$(b_{\lambda\mu}{}^*)^{n_{\lambda\mu}}|0\rangle,$$

where $|0\rangle$ is the ground state. The operator $b_{\lambda\mu}{}^*$ is called the creation operator of a phonon of type λ, μ. The corresponding annihilation operator is $b_{\lambda\mu}$. Each phonon has angular momentum λ. It is a boson. This can be seen by writing the angular momentum operator M_z in the $n_{\lambda\mu}$ representation, in which it is diagonal with eigenvalues

$$M_z^{(\lambda)} = \hbar \sum_\mu \mu n_{\lambda\mu}. \tag{7.60}$$

The angular momentum I of the nucleus in an excited state with a given N_λ is given for $\lambda = 2$ (quadrupole vibrations) by

$$\begin{aligned} N_2 &= 0, \quad & I &= 0, \\ N_2 &= 1, \quad & I &= 2, \\ N_2 &= 2, \quad & I &= 0, 2, 4. \end{aligned}$$

An example of the reasoning used in obtaining these assignments is the two-phonon excitation. Two phonons, each of spin 2, can couple to $I = 0, 1, 2, 3, 4$. Since the phonons are bosons the collective wave functions must be symmetric under two-phonon exchange. This eliminates $I = 1, 3$.

Since phonon energies are equal in the harmonic vibrator model, a vibrational spectrum for given λ is expected to have first and second excited states whose energies are in the ratio

$$E_2 : E_1 = 2. \tag{7.61}$$

The two-phonon excitation E_2 may have $J\pi$ equal to $0+$, $2+$, or $4+$. In fact the collective model does not predict how this degeneracy is resolved, and the order is haphazard in nuclei.

In the regions $60 < A < 150$ and $190 < A < 220$ there are many even nuclei whose first two excited states with positive parity are approximately in the ratio $2:1$. Such states are presumably vibrational. Ratios of excitation energies for positive parity states of even nuclei are shown in Fig. 7.8.

In many nuclei one of the low-lying excited states is $3-$, indicating the presence of $\lambda = 3$ vibrations (octupole vibrations). The parity of the state is of course the parity of the spherical harmonic in the surface expansion (7.46).

The exact energies of vibrational states can only be calculated by assuming a detailed model for the collective motion. Bohr and Mottelson used a hydrodynamic model to obtain the right order of magnitude—about 1 MeV or somewhat less for $A > 100$. However, such a model is not to be taken too seriously.

The vibrational model is checked by using it to predict transitions between the states. The most important of these are electromagnetic transitions and inelastic scattering of a nuclear particle. The latter will be treated in detail in Chapter 12. The electromagnetic transition due to a change of charge density vibration with $\Delta L = 2$ is called an electric quadrupole transition.

The electric quadrupole ($E2$) transition operator is defined to be (Blatt and Weisskopf, 52)

$$\Omega_\mu(E2) = \int d^3r \ r^2 \rho(\mathbf{r}) Y_2^\mu(\theta', \phi'). \qquad (7.62)$$

In order to predict $E2$ transition rates we assume that the charge density $\rho(\mathbf{r})$ is constant inside the nucleus with a value

$$\rho_0 = 3Ze/4\pi R_0^3 \qquad (7.63)$$

and zero outside. We use the first two terms of (7.46) and the properties of the operators $b_{2\mu}$, $b_{2\mu}{}^*$ to perform the integrals in (7.62) and express $\Omega_\mu(E_2)$ in the $b_{\lambda\mu}$ representation.

$$\Omega_\mu(E2) = \frac{3Ze}{4\pi\sqrt{5}} \frac{\beta_2}{\omega_2} R_0^2 \{b_{2\mu} + (-1)^\mu b^*_{2(-\mu)}\}, \qquad (7.64)$$

where β_2 is called the rms deformation parameter for quadrupole vibrations. The rms deformation parameter is given in general by

$$\beta_\lambda{}^2 = \langle 0| \sum_\mu |\alpha_{\lambda\mu}|^2 |0\rangle$$

$$= \frac{(2\lambda + 1)\hbar\omega_\lambda}{2B_\lambda}. \qquad (7.65)$$

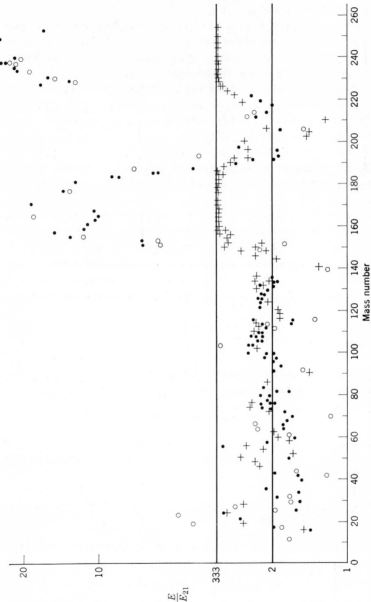

FIG. 7.8   The energy ratios E/E_{21} plotted against mass number for 0+ (open circles), 2+ (closed circles), and 4+ (crosses) states of even nuclei. E_{21} is the excitation energy of the lowest 2+ state.   In nonspherical nuclei the ratio E_{41}/E_{21} is close to the rotational prediction 3.33, whereas the other two ratios are of the order 10–20.   The corresponding 0+, 2+ states are probably β- or γ-vibrations (see Section 7C(v)).   (Adapted from Nathan and Nilsson, 65.)

The electric quadrupole operator can thus create or annihilate one phonon. Two-phonon states 0+, 2+, 4+ can decay only to a one-phonon state 2+, not to the ground state 0+. The one-phonon state can decay to the ground state. Since the $E2$ operator is proportional to the total charge Ze, all the protons take part collectively in the transition. The rate is therefore much stronger than would be predicted by a shell model using only simple configurations. In fact it was just this type of transition that was underestimated by the shell model and is predicted correctly by the collective model.

The simple assumptions which lead to (7.64) predict transition rates of the correct order of magnitude. The value of β_2 for a given transition is often checked for internal consistency between electromagnetic transitions and inelastic scattering of different nuclear particles, where of course all the nucleons contribute to the transition, not merely the protons.

The $E2$ transition rate from initial state i to final state f is given for a photon energy E_γ by

$$B(E2) = \frac{4\pi}{\hbar} \frac{3}{\sqrt{15}} \left(\frac{E_\gamma}{\hbar c}\right)^5 \sum_\mu |\langle f| \, \Omega_\mu(E2) \, |i\rangle|^2. \tag{7.66}$$

It is easily calculated from (7.64) using the properties of the $n_{\lambda\mu}$ and the fact that an eigenstate with $n_{\lambda\mu}$ phonons is given by

$$|n_{\lambda\mu}\rangle = (b_{\lambda\mu}{}^*)^{n_{\lambda\mu}} |0\rangle. \tag{7.67}$$

A good example of a vibrational nucleus is ^{106}Pd. Its level structure (Yoshizawa, 62) is shown, together with the strong $E2$ transitions characteristic of vibrational states in Fig. 7.9. Note also the vibrational appearance of the level structure of ^{18}O in Fig. 7.7. This is deceptive since there is no strong $E2$ transition from the second 2+ state to the first. Thus it is important to consider spectroscopic data other than spins and parities.

[iv] ROTATIONAL STATES

We shall primarily consider spheroidal nuclei, which have axial symmetry and symmetry under a rotation by 180° about any line through the center perpendicular to the symmetry axis. The body-fixed axes are conveniently taken to be a set of principal axes called the x', y', z' axes to distinguish them from the x, y, z axes which are fixed in space. The z' axis is the axis of symmetry. The principal moments of inertia are

$$\mathscr{I} = \mathscr{I}_{x'} = \mathscr{I}_{y'}; \qquad \mathscr{I}_{z'}.$$

The components of angular momentum along the body-fixed axes are

$$I_{x'}, \quad I_{y'}, \quad I_{z'}.$$

The total angular momentum is I.

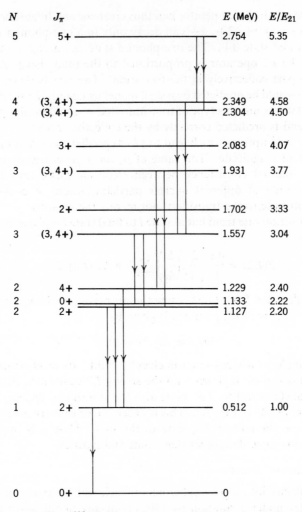

N	J_π	E (MeV)	E/E_{21}
5	5+	2.754	5.35
4	(3, 4+)	2.349	4.58
4	(3, 4+)	2.304	4.50
	3+	2.083	4.07
3	(3, 4+)	1.931	3.77
	2+	1.702	3.33
3	(3, 4+)	1.557	3.04
2	4+	1.229	2.40
2	0+	1.133	2.22
2	2+	1.127	2.20
1	2+	0.512	1.00
0	0+	0	

FIG. 7.9 Energy levels of ^{106}Pd. The assignments of the phonon number N are shown in the first column. The last column shows the ratio of the excitation energy to that of the first 2+ state. Strong $E2$ transitions are indicated by arrows; weak transitions are not shown. (Adapted from Yoshizawa, 62.)

The system is called the symmetric top (Pauling and Wilson, 35). Its Hamiltonian is

$$H_{\text{top}} = \frac{\hbar^2}{2\mathscr{I}}\left(I^2 - I_{z'}^2\right) + \frac{\hbar^2}{2\mathscr{I}_{z'}} I_{z'}^2. \qquad (7.68)$$

The eigenfunctions of the Hamiltonian (7.68) are the rotation functions $D^\lambda_{\mu\rho}$.

These functions are the transformation coefficients involved in the transformation of the spherical harmonics $Y_\lambda{}^\mu(\theta, \phi)$ in the x, y, z system into spherical harmonics $Y_\lambda{}^\rho(\theta', \phi')$ in the x', y', z' system, where the x', y', z' system is obtained from the x, y, z system by a rotation through the Euler angles α, β, γ. This rotation is performed as follows. First perform a right-handed rotation α $(0 < \alpha < 2\pi)$ about the z-axis. Then perform a right-handed rotation β $(0 < \beta < \pi)$ about the y'-axis. Finally perform a right-handed rotation γ $(0 < \gamma < 2\pi)$ about the z'-axis. The transformation of the spherical harmonics is

$$Y_\lambda{}^\mu(\theta, \phi) = \sum_\rho Y_\lambda{}^\rho(\theta', \phi') D_{\mu\rho}^\lambda(\alpha, \beta, \gamma). \tag{7.69}$$

The rotation functions are simultaneous eigenfunctions of the operators $I_z, I_{z'}$ and I^2.

$$I_z D_{MK}^I = M D_{MK}^I$$

$$I_{z'} D_{MK}^I = K D_{MK}^I \tag{7.70}$$

$$I^2 D_{MK}^I = I(I + 1) D_{MK}^I.$$

Thus the quantum numbers defining an eigenstate of the symmetric top are the total angular momentum I and its projection M, also a quantum number K for the projection of the angular momentum I on the z'-axis. Conditions on K and M are

$$|K| \leq I, \; |M| \leq I. \tag{7.71}$$

The orthonormality properties of the rotation functions are given by

$$\int \sin \beta \, d\beta \, d\alpha \, d\gamma D_{MK}^{I*}(\alpha, \beta, \gamma) D_{M'K'}^{I'}(\alpha, \beta, \gamma) = \frac{8\pi^2}{2I + 1} \delta_{MM'} \delta_{KK'} \delta_{II'}. \tag{7.72}$$

For a spherical nucleus there are no rotational states. This indicates that the moment of inertia of a nucleus about a symmetry axis is zero.

$$\mathscr{I}_{z'} = 0. \tag{7.73}$$

In terms of the adiabatic approximation to the unified model (7.47), the collective wave function $\psi_\nu(\alpha)$ is $D_{MK}^I(\alpha, \beta, \gamma)$. The intrinsic wave function $\phi_n(x, \alpha)$ for particles in a static, deformed potential is not an eigenfunction of angular momentum because the potential is not central. However, the z' component of the angular momentum is a constant of the motion, denoted by Ω, because of the axial symmetry. We select Ω from the set of quantum numbers n and write it explicitly, denoting the remaining quantum numbers by τ.

The intrinsic wave function is most easily understood when it describes only one nucleon with a deformed core. We shall mainly consider this case.

It can be generalized in the same way as the single-particle shell model is generalized to take into account more particles in the upper shell. The intrinsic wave function is now written as $\phi_\Omega^\tau(\mathbf{r}')$, where $\mathbf{r}'$ is the coordinate of the particle in the body-fixed (x', y', z') system.

The total angular momentum is now divided into intrinsic and rotational parts $\mathbf{j}$ and $\mathbf{I} - \mathbf{j}$. The nuclear Hamiltonian is expressed as

$$H = H_{\text{intr}}(\mathbf{r}') + T_{\text{rot}}, \tag{7.74}$$

where T_{rot} is the total kinetic energy of rotation, given by

$$T_{\text{rot}} = \frac{\hbar^2}{2\mathscr{I}} [(\mathbf{I} - \mathbf{j})^2 - (I_{z'} - j_{z'})^2]. \tag{7.75}$$

We may further express T_{rot} as a sum of a term diagonal in a representation defined by basis vectors $\phi_\Omega^\tau D_{MK}^I$ and a coupling term.

$$T_{\text{rot}} = T_{\text{rot}}^0 + T_{\text{coupl}}, \tag{7.76}$$

where

$$T_{\text{rot}}^0 = \frac{\hbar^2}{2\mathscr{I}} [I^2 + j^2 - (I_{z'} - j_{z'})^2],$$

$$\tag{7.77}$$

$$T_{\text{coupl}} = \frac{\hbar^2}{2\mathscr{I}} [-2\mathbf{I} \cdot \mathbf{j}].$$

For the present we shall neglect the coupling term. Our description therefore applies particularly to even nuclei. The nuclear Hamiltonian becomes

$$H = H_{\text{intr}}(\mathbf{r}') + \frac{\hbar^2}{2\mathscr{I}} [I^2 + j^2 - (I_{z'} - j_{z'})^2]. \tag{7.78}$$

A normalized eigenfunction of this Hamiltonian is

$$\Psi = \left(\frac{2I + 1}{8\pi^2}\right)^{\frac{1}{2}} \phi_\Omega^\tau(\mathbf{r}') D_{MK}^I(\alpha, \beta, \gamma). \tag{7.79}$$

There are some restrictions imposed on the values of the quantum numbers by the two symmetry properties. The first property is the invariance of the wave function Ψ of (7.79) under a rotation through an arbitrary angle ϕ about the symmetry axis z'. The second is the invariance of Ψ under a rotation by 180° about any axis through the center perpendicular to the symmetry axis.

A rotation by ϕ about z' transforms the Euler angles into $\alpha, \beta, \gamma + \phi$. The rotation and intrinsic functions transform as follows

$$D_{MK}^I \rightarrow e^{iK\phi} D_{MK}^I,$$

$$\phi_\Omega^\tau \rightarrow e^{-i\Omega\phi} \phi_\Omega^\tau. \tag{7.80}$$

This may be understood from the properties of the spherical harmonics. The signs of the exponents in the two equations (7.80) are opposite because the rotation function is the wave function of the body-fixed system with respect to the space-fixed system, while the intrinsic function depends on coordinates in the body-fixed system.

The new eigenfunction (7.79) in the transformed system is the same as the old one. Hence, under the condition of axial symmetry,

$$K = \Omega. \tag{7.81}$$

A rotation by 180° transforms the rotation function as follows.

$$D^I_{MK} \rightarrow e^{i\pi(I+K)} D^I_{M(-K)}. \tag{7.82}$$

The transformation of the intrinsic function is understood by expanding it in eigenfunctions of j.

$$\phi_\Omega^\tau = \sum_j c_j \phi_\Omega^{\tau, j}. \tag{7.83}$$

The rotation has the effect

$$\phi_\Omega^{\tau, j} \rightarrow e^{-i\pi(j+\Omega)} \phi_{-\Omega}^{\tau, j}. \tag{7.84}$$

For $K = \Omega \neq 0$, invariance requires that the wave function be a linear combination of two wave functions (7.79). The normalized wave function is

$$\Psi = \left(\frac{2I+1}{16\pi^2}\right)^{1/2} [\phi_K^\tau(\mathbf{r}') D^I_{MK}(\alpha, \beta, \gamma) + (-1)^{I-j} \phi_{-K}^\tau(\mathbf{r}') D^I_{M(-K)}(\alpha, \beta, \gamma)]. \tag{7.85}$$

For $K = \Omega = 0$ the normalized wave function that satisfies the symmetry condition is

$$\Psi = (2\pi)^{-1/2} \phi_0^\tau(\mathbf{r}') Y_I^M(\theta', \phi'). \tag{7.86}$$

If the intrinsic wave function (7.85) contains even values of j, the wave function vanishes for $K = 0$ if I is odd. The total angular momentum I of the nucleus in this case is even. Low-lying intrinsic states of even nuclei, in fact, have $j = 0$, so I is even for $K = 0$.

The energy levels of rotational nuclei are determined by the Hamiltonian (7.78) if the coupling is neglected. For a given intrinsic wave function (given K) we have a set of energy levels for different values of I, called a rotational band. Wave functions of the form (7.85) correspond to energy levels

$$E_K(I) = E_K^0 + \frac{\hbar^2}{2\mathcal{J}} I(I+1), \tag{7.87}$$

where E_K^0 is a constant. The lowest level in the band has $I = K$; the higher levels in the case $K \neq 0$ have $I = K+1, K+2, \ldots$, etc. If $K = 0$ we have a set of levels

$$0+, 2+, 4+, \ldots, \text{etc.}$$

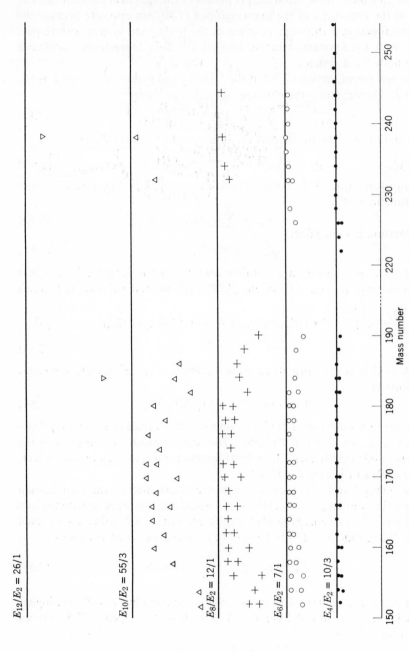

FIG. 7.10 Ground-state rotational energy ratios E_I/E_2 in even nuclei. The horizontal lines represent the ratios expected for an $I(I + 1)$ dependence. (Adapted from Nathan and Nilsson, 65.)

K is called the band quantum number. This situation occurs in even nuclei. Theoretical energy ratios of excited states are

$$\frac{E_4}{E_2} = 3\tfrac{1}{3}$$

$$\frac{E_6}{E_2} = 7$$

$$\frac{E_8}{E_2} = 12.$$

Here E_I denotes the energy of the transition from the state with spin I to the ground state.

These ratios are followed very closely by even nuclei in the rotational regions. For $0+, 2+, 4+,$ and $6+$ states they are often within a few per cent. The rotational regions are strikingly distinguished from other regions of the periodic table in Fig. 7.8. The $I(I+1)$ rule is illustrated in Fig. 7.10. Ratios are generally less than the rotational value because of weak coupling with particle or vibrational modes.

The moment of inertia $\mathscr{I}$ may be determined by fitting energy levels.

$$\frac{3\hbar^2}{\mathscr{I}} \simeq 0.095 \text{ MeV}, \qquad 150 < A < 200$$

$$\simeq 0.043 \text{ MeV}, \qquad A > 220.$$

The moment of inertia increases with increasing mass, but it is much less than the rigid body moment of inertia. This is to be expected, since the rotational correlation only occurs for nucleons near the top of the momentum distribution.

Odd-A nuclei have moments of inertia similar to those of even nuclei with neighboring mass numbers.

One of the primary reasons for expecting nuclei in certain regions to be deformed in the ground state was the large electric quadrupole moments. We shall show how to obtain the measured quadrupole moment in terms of the intrinsic quadrupole moment. The intrinsic quadrupole moment operator Q_m (6.73) contains the function $Y_2{}^m(\theta', \phi')$. It therefore transforms into the space-fixed system by means of a set of rotation functions,

$$Q_0(\theta, \phi) = \sum_m D^2_{0m}(\alpha, \beta, \gamma) Q_m(\theta', \phi'). \tag{7.88}$$

The expectation value of Q_0 in the ground state is obtained by evaluating the matrix element of Q_0 between collective wave functions of the form (7.85, 7.86) with $M = I$. The matrix element includes an integral of three rotation functions over the Euler angles, which is a standard result in the theory of angular momentum. The result is

$$\langle Q_0(\theta, \phi) \rangle = \frac{3K^2 - I(I + 1)}{(I + 1)(2I + 3)} \langle Q_0(\theta', \phi') \rangle. \tag{7.89}$$

Note that the measured ground-state quadrupole moment is zero for $I = 0$ or $\frac{1}{2}$, since $K = I$ in the ground state.

The electric quadrupole transition operator $\Omega_\mu(E2)$ (7.62) is directly proportional to the electric quadrupole moment operator Q_μ (6.73). Hence nuclei with large quadrupole moments have large $E2$ transition rates. For further details the reader is referred to the review article by Moszkowski (57).

[v] VIBRATIONS OF DEFORMED NUCLEI

Spheroidal deformed nuclei can vibrate about their equilibrium shape. For these nuclei the surface function $R(\theta', \phi')$ of (7.46) may be written in the simpler form (6.68) where

$$a_m = \alpha_{2m}, \tag{7.90}$$

It is convenient to discuss the changing shape of a nucleus in terms of the deformation parameter β and the angle of asymmetry γ defined by (6.69). In the equilibrium spheroidal configuration,

$$a_0 = \beta, \qquad \gamma = 0.$$

If the nucleus remains spheroidal during the vibration, γ remains equal to zero, while β changes with time. This is a β-vibration mode. Since $\beta = a_0$ the projection quantum number is zero and the rotational band quantum number K for this mode in an even nucleus is zero. Thus we expect to see a $0+$ excited state corresponding to the one-phonon β-vibration with a band of rotational levels built on it as the band head.

Another mode of vibration is the γ-vibration in which β remains constant but γ oscillates about zero. For small vibrations we set

$$\cos \gamma \cong 1, \sin \gamma \cong \gamma,$$

so that

$$a_0 = \beta, \qquad a_2 = a_{-2} \cong \frac{\beta\gamma}{\sqrt{2}}.$$

The γ-vibration has a projection quantum number 2 (from a_2). The band quantum number K is 2 and there is a rotational band built on a band head of spin and parity $2+$ with one quantum of γ-vibrational energy.

A discussion of experimental data on vibrations of deformed nuclei is given by Sheline (60). Second excited states with $J\pi$ values $2+$ and $0+$ are shown in Fig. 7.8.

The second 2+ level of a nucleus in the rotational region has an explanation which is alternative to the γ-vibration picture. It was first pointed out by Davydov and Filippov (58) that such a level appears in the model of an asymmetric rotator. The Hartree-Fock theory predicts several nuclei with asymmetric ground states in the sd shell and several more asymmetric states which do not correspond to absolute minima in binding energy. It is difficult to choose between these two explanations of rotational bands built on the second excited 2+ state. The reader is referred to a discussion of the asymmetric rotator by Davidson (65).

[vi] COUPLING OF VIBRATIONS AND SINGLE-PARTICLE MOTION

In the regions where even nuclei have spherical ground states and vibrational low-lying excited states, the odd-A nuclei made by adding a nucleon to such a nucleus can be described by a specially simple form of the weak coupling model [see Equation (5.30)].

The Hamiltonian of the system is

$$H = H_C + H_p + H_{\text{int}}, \qquad (7.91)$$

where H_C, H_p and H_{int} are, respectively, the Hamiltonians for the core, particle, and interaction. The Hamiltonian is diagonalized using as a basis the eigenfunctions of $H_C + H_p$. The eigenfunctions of H are linear combinations of eigenfunctions of the type (7.47). For the eigenstate ρ the eigenfunction is

$$|\rho\rangle = \sum_{i\alpha} t_{i\alpha}^{(\rho)} \psi_\alpha(\xi_i)\phi_i(x_i). \qquad (7.92)$$

Contrast this expression with (5.35). We have lost the complication of antisymmetrization between the particle and the core.

The core quantum numbers are α, including the core spin J. The single-particle quantum numbers are i, including the single-particle angular momentum j. The particle coordinates x_i include spin and isospin.

A calculation of the energy levels of ^{63}Cu was performed in this model by Thankappan and True (65). The vibrational core in this case is ^{62}Ni. Its vibrational spectrum is shown in Fig. 7.11. The two-phonon excitations are approximately 1 MeV above the one-phonon excitation. Hence it should be a good approximation to include only the 0+ and 2+ states in the basis.

The single-particle basis consists of single-particle wave functions in a spherical potential. For the proton in ^{63}Cu only the $p_{3/2}$, $p_{1/2}$, and $f_{5/2}$ single-particle states were included. They were calculated in a harmonic oscillator well.

The interaction was taken to be

$$H_{\text{int}} = -\xi \mathbf{J} \cdot \mathbf{j} - \eta \sum_\mu Q_\mu^{(c)} Q_\mu^{(p)} \qquad (7.93)$$

where $Q_\mu^{(c)}$ and $Q_\mu^{(p)}$ are the core and particle quadrupole moment operators respectively. The constants ξ and η are obtained by fitting magnetic dipole and electric quadrupole transition rates in ^{62}Ni.

The values of the superposition coefficients $t_{i\alpha}^{(\rho)}$ provide us with a model which is extremely interesting in connection with reactions that add a proton to ^{62}Ni or take a proton out of ^{63}Cu. They are given in Table 7.8. Only the ground state can be considered seriously as a single-particle state, whereas

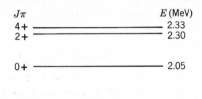

FIG. 7.11   Lowest-energy levels of ^{62}Ni in MeV.

the $\frac{7}{2}-$ state appears as almost a pure excitation of the core to the $2+$ state while the single particle remains in the $p_{3/2}$ state. The spectroscopic factor S^ρ is $|t_{i0}^{(\rho)}|^2$ for each eigenstate ρ.

The spins, parities, and approximate level spacings of the first five levels of ^{63}Cu are predicted quite well.

[vii]   SINGLE-PARTICLE MOTION IN A DEFORMED POTENTIAL—THE NILSSON MODEL

In the previous section we considered cases where the intrinsic motion of a particle, described by the spherical shell model, is weakly coupled to collective vibrations of a spherical core. We shall now consider the strong coupling situation where the core is deformed and in its vibrational ground state. Single-particle motion in a deformed potential was considered by Nilsson (55).

The potential is essentially a fixed spheroidal harmonic oscillator with spin-orbit coupling.

$$H = -\frac{\hbar^2}{2M}\nabla^2 + \frac{M\omega_0^2}{2}[(1 + \tfrac{2}{3}\delta)(x'^2 + y'^2) + (1 - \tfrac{4}{3}\delta)z'^2]$$

$$+ C\mathbf{l}\cdot\mathbf{s} + Dl^2. \quad (7.94)$$

			Eigenfunctions					
E_{exp}	E_{th}	$I\pi$	$0,p_{3/2}$	$0,p_{1/2}$	$0,f_{5/2}$	$2,p_{3/2}$	$2,p_{1/2}$	$2,f_{5/2}$
0	0	$\frac{3}{2}-$	0.9221			−0.3264	0.1779	0.1076
0.668	0.834	$\frac{1}{2}-$		0.8663		−0.4387		−0.2389
0.961	1.069	$\frac{5}{2}-$			0.6141	−0.7603	−0.0409	−0.2077
1.327	1.296	$\frac{7}{2}-$				0.9869		0.1612
1.412	1.489	$\frac{5}{2}-$			0.6384	0.6002	−0.4257	−0.2258
	2.017	$\frac{3}{2}-$	0.1841			0.7888		−0.1307

TABLE 7.8. Energies, spins, and amplitudes $t_{i\alpha}^{(\rho)}$ of the levels of ^{63}Cu calculated by Thankappan and True (65). The amplitudes are labeled by α, i where α is the angular momentum of the core and i denotes the single-particle quantum numbers. (From Thankappan and True, 65.)

The coordinates in the body-fixed system are x', y', z'. The term in l^2 gives a correction to the oscillator potential especially at large distances (large l^2) which simulates a finite potential. The deformation parameter is δ. C and D are chosen to reproduce the correct level order in the spherical case (see Fig. 5.4).

The calculation consists of diagonalizing the Hamiltonian (7.94) using the eigenstates of an isotropic harmonic oscillator as the basis for the matrix representation. It is convenient to define new coordinates ξ, η, ζ, which include the oscillator scale factor $(M\omega_0/\hbar)^{1/2}$.

$$\xi = (M\omega_0/\hbar)^{1/2}x', \ldots, \text{etc.} \quad (7.95)$$

We impose the condition that the volume of the nucleus is independent of δ. This amounts to a condition on ω_0.

$$\omega_0(\delta) = \omega_0(0)(1 - \tfrac{4}{3}\delta^2 - \tfrac{16}{27}\delta^3)^{-1/6}. \quad (7.96)$$

The Hamiltonian H_0 of the anisotropic oscillator is split into that of an isotropic oscillator plus a correction term.

$$H_0 = H_0^{(0)} + H_\delta$$
$$= \tfrac{1}{2}\hbar\omega_0(-\nabla^2 + \rho^2) - \delta\hbar\omega_0\tfrac{4}{3}\left(\frac{\pi}{5}\right)^{1/2}\rho^2 Y_2^0, \qquad (7.97)$$

where ρ is the radius vector in the ξ, η, ζ system, as in the formula (5.11) for the isotropic oscillator wave function. The deformation parameter β of (6.69) is related to δ by

$$\delta \simeq 0.95\,\beta. \qquad (7.98)$$

The representation is chosen with $H_0^{(0)}$ diagonal. The operators l^2, l_ζ, s_ζ, which commute with $H_0^{(0)}$ are also diagonal. The corresponding quantum numbers are l, Λ, and Σ. In addition the ζ-component of the total angular momentum $j_\zeta = l_\zeta + s_\zeta$ commutes with the total Hamiltonian H. The corresponding quantum number, as in the case of rotational motion, is denoted by Ω. The total Hamiltonian matrix splits into disjoint submatrices, one for each value of Ω.

For a given Ω, the basis vectors are denoted

$$|Nl\Lambda\Sigma\rangle, \qquad \Lambda + \Sigma = \Omega.$$

The quantum number N represents the total number of oscillator quanta.

$$H_0^{(0)}\,|Nl\Lambda\Sigma\rangle = (N + \tfrac{3}{2})\hbar\omega_0\,|Nl\Lambda\Sigma\rangle. \qquad (7.99)$$

We may separate N into quantum numbers n_ξ, n_η, n_ζ representing quanta of excitation of the ξ, η, ζ components of oscillator motion,

$$N = n_\xi + n_\eta + n_\zeta. \qquad (7.100)$$

The quantum numbers for the components are not constants of the motion, but for large positive deformation where the ξ, η excitation energies are very different from the excitation energy for ζ,

$$\hbar\omega_\xi - \hbar\omega_\zeta \gg 0, \qquad (7.101)$$

we may treat n_ζ as an approximately good quantum number. It is called an asymptotic quantum number for large deformation.

The matrix elements of the different terms of H (7.94, 7.97) are given as follows.

$H_0^{(0)}$ and l^2 are diagonal.

The matrix elements $\langle l'\Lambda'\Sigma'| \mathbf{l} \cdot \mathbf{s} |l\Lambda\Sigma\rangle$ have the following selection rules.

$$l = l',$$

$$\Lambda = \Lambda', \Lambda' \pm 1,$$

$$\Sigma = \Sigma' \pm 1, \Sigma',$$

$$\Lambda + \Sigma = \Lambda' + \Sigma'.$$

The nonvanishing matrix elements of $\mathbf{l} \cdot \mathbf{s}$ are

$$\langle l(\Lambda \pm 1)\pm| \mathbf{l} \cdot \mathbf{s} |l\Lambda\pm\rangle = \tfrac{1}{2}[(l \mp \Lambda)(l \pm \Lambda + 1)]^{1/2},$$

$$\langle l\Lambda\pm| \mathbf{l} \cdot \mathbf{s} |l\Lambda\pm\rangle = \pm\tfrac{1}{2}\Lambda. \tag{7.102}$$

The quantum numbers $\Sigma = \pm\tfrac{1}{2}$ are denoted simply by $\pm$.

Since $|l\Lambda\rangle$ is Y_l^Λ, the Wigner-Eckart theorem (Appendix 4) gives immediately for the angular matrix element of H_δ,

$$\langle l'\Lambda'| Y_2^0 |l\Lambda\rangle = \left[\frac{5(2l + 1)}{4\pi(2l' + 1)}\right]^{1/2} C_{l\,2\,l'}^{\Lambda 0\Lambda'} C_{l2l'}^{000}. \tag{7.103}$$

Matrix elements of ρ^2 are as follows:

$$\langle Nl| \rho^2 |Nl\rangle = N + \tfrac{3}{2}$$

$$\langle N(l - 2)| \rho^2 |Nl\rangle = [(N - l + 2)(N + l + 1)]^{1/2}$$

$$\langle (N - 2)l| \rho^2 |Nl\rangle = \tfrac{1}{2}[(N - l)(N + l + 1)]^{1/2} \tag{7.104}$$

$$\langle (N - 2)(l - 2)| \rho^2 |Nl\rangle = \tfrac{1}{2}[(N + l + 1)(N + l - 1)]^{1/2}$$

$$\langle (N - 2)(l + 2)| \rho^2 |Nl\rangle = \tfrac{1}{2}[(N - l)(N - l - 1)]^{1/2}.$$

The others vanish. The selection rules for the matrix elements of H_δ are

$$\Lambda = \Lambda',$$

$$\Sigma = \Sigma',$$

$$l = l', l' \pm 2,$$

$$N = N', N' \pm 2.$$

Shells with quantum numbers N and $N \pm 2$ are separated by an energy of about $2\hbar\omega_0$, which is much larger than the values of the off-diagonal matrix elements. Therefore the submatrices for Ω split approximately into further disjoint submatrices for N. It remains to diagonalize the submatrices of H for particular values of N and Ω. This is done numerically.

Tables of eigenvectors $|N\Omega\rangle$ are given in Nilsson's article (Nilsson, 55). In the calculation the parameters were redefined for convenience.

$$\eta = \frac{2\delta\hbar\omega_0(\delta)}{C},$$

$$\kappa = \frac{C}{2\hbar\omega_0(0)}, \tag{7.105}$$

$$\mu = \frac{2D}{C}.$$

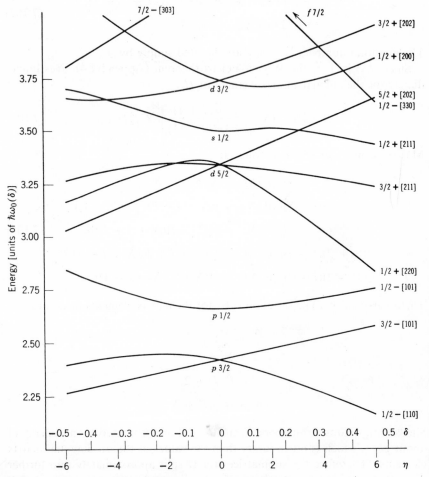

FIG. 7.12 Single-particle levels for $8 < Z < 20$ and $8 < N < 20$. The potential parameters are $\mu = 0$, $\kappa = 0.08$. (Adapted from Mottelson and Nilsson, 59.)

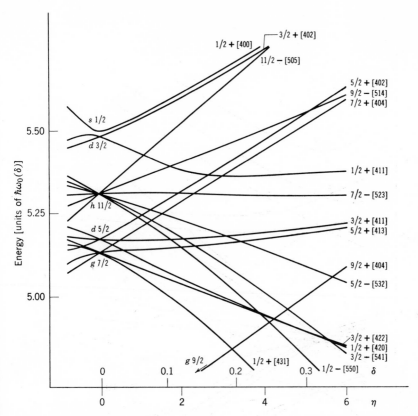

FIG. 7.13 Single-particle levels for $50 < Z < 82$. The value of the potential parameter μ is 0.55 for $N = 4$ and approximately 0.50 for $N = 5$. (Adapted from Mottelson and Nilsson, 59.)

Values determined by fitting energy levels in the spherical shell model are roughly

$$\hbar\omega_0(0) = 41A^{-\frac{1}{3}} \text{ MeV},$$
$$\kappa = 0.05, \quad Z > 50,$$
$$0.08, \quad Z < 20.$$

The value of μ depends strongly on A and is given in the captions of the appropriate figures.

The single-particle levels plotted against η or δ are shown for the rotational regions $A \cong 25$, $50 < Z < 82$ and $Z > 82$ in Fig. 7.12, 7.13, and 7.14. Each single particle level is indicated by the value of Ω and the parity together with the set of asymptotic quantum numbers for large deformation

$$[Nn_\zeta\Lambda].$$

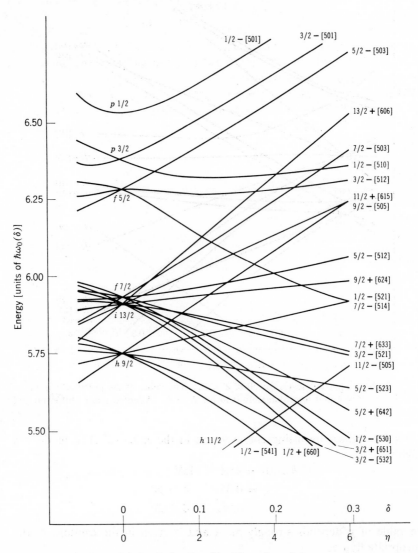

FIG. 7.14   Single-particle levels for $Z > 82$. The value of the potential parameter μ is 0.70 for $N = 5$ and approximately 0.62 for $N = 6$. (Adapted from Mottelson and Nilsson, 59.)

It has already been explained that n_ζ becomes a good quantum number as $\eta \to \infty$. In this limit we may treat $\mathbf{l} \cdot \mathbf{s}$ and l^2 as small perturbations on a pure anisotropic harmonic oscillator for which the good quantum numbers are N, n_ζ, Λ and Σ.

In the Nilsson diagrams there are as many lines corresponding to each state of an isotropic potential as there are different projections $\Omega = |m_j|$ of the single-particle angular momentum j, that is, $(2j + 1)/2$. Lines which slope upward for large deformation correspond to oscillations in the direction of the small axes. The asymptotic quantum numbers help us to understand the construction of the eigenvectors.

$$N = 5, \Omega = \tfrac{7}{2} \quad |5\,3\,3+\rangle$$

Basis Vectors: $|553+\rangle$, $|553+\rangle$, $|554-\rangle$

$\eta = -6$	-4	-2	0	2	4	6	$+\infty$
-16.090	-15.493	-14.007	-11.400	-8.393	-5.255	-2.055	
-0.615	-0.485	-0.214	0	0.094	0.144	0.177	
-0.583	-0.723	-0.954	1	-0.994	-0.987	-0.982	[503]
0.531	0.493	0.210	0	-0.055	-0.067	-0.068	
-20.498	-18.153	-16.194	-15.000	-13.961	-12.885	-11.757	
0.082	0.254	0.432	-0.426	-0.372	-0.321	-0.279	
-0.717	-0.655	-0.285	0	-0.086	-0.111	-0.117	[514]
-0.692	-0.712	-0.856	0.905	0.924	0.941	0.953	
-27.812	-26.755	-26.199	-26.000	-26.046	-26.260	-26.588	
0.784	-0.837	-0.876	0.905	-0.924	-0.936	-0.944	
-0.382	0.220	0.092	0	-0.066	-0.114	-0.149	[523]
0.489	-0.501	-0.473	0.426	-0.378	-0.333	-0.295	

TABLE 7.9.   An example of Nilsson's tables of eigenvalues and the coefficients $a_{l\Lambda}$ of the basis vectors in the eigenvectors. This table was adapted and the coefficients normalized to $\sum_{l\Lambda} a_{l\Lambda}^2 = 1$ by Preston. (M. A. Preston, *Physics of the Nucleus*, Addison-Wesley, Reading, Mass., 1962.)

Nilsson's table for $N = 5$, $= \Omega \tfrac{7}{2}$ is reproduced in Table 7.9 as an example. In this case the selection rules allow three basis vectors $|N l \Lambda \Sigma\rangle$ for which the values of the quantum numbers are listed at the top. There are three eigenstates for a 3×3 matrix. Each is listed in a row of the table for different values of η. The first subrow of each row lists the energy of the state in units of $\hbar\omega_0$. The next three subrows give the values of the coefficients $a_{l\Lambda}$ in the expansion

$$|N\Omega\rangle = \sum_{l\Lambda} a_{l\Lambda} |Nl\Lambda\Sigma\rangle. \tag{7.106}$$

The state described by the first row has, for the isotropic case ($\eta = 0$), $l = 3$, $\Omega = \frac{7}{2}$. It is therefore an $f_{\frac{7}{2}}$ state. Only one projection of l, $\Lambda = 3$, is allowed by the selection rules, so the eigenvector contains the basis vector $|533+\rangle$ with an amplitude $a_{l\Lambda}$ of 1. As $|\eta|$ is increased, the states of different l and Λ become important. If η is made very large, only the states with $\Lambda = 3$ contribute in the combination corresponding to $n_\zeta = 0$. (The assignment of n_ζ is explained below.) Hence the trend of the sizes of the amplitudes as η increases is denoted by [503].

The second state has, for $\eta = 0$, $l = 5$, $\Omega = \frac{7}{2}$. Two projections of l, $\Lambda = 3$ and 4, are allowed by the selection rules. The same is true for the third state. They correspond to $h_{\frac{9}{2}}$ and $h_{\frac{11}{2}}$ in that order because the spin-orbit coupling forces the energy of the third state below that of the second state. As η is increased, only the basis states with $\Lambda = 4$ and 3, respectively, survive, and their asymptotic amplitudes correspond to $n_\zeta = 1$ and 2, respectively. The three states of Table 7.9 are found in Figs. 7.13 and 7.14.

The assignment of n_ζ can be made, knowing the energy eigenvalues, without resorting to a detailed understanding of the amplitudes. For positive (prolate) deformation, $\omega_\zeta \ll \omega_\xi$, so that the state of highest energy has the lowest value of n_ζ for a given N. Thus the states in Table 7.9 have $n_\zeta = 0$, 1, 2, respectively.

The assignment of Λ is also straightforward. Since $\Lambda + \Sigma = \Omega$, Λ is determined if we know whether it is even or odd. The properties of the three-dimensional oscillator are such that Λ is even or odd according as $N - n_\zeta$ is even or odd. The assignments of Λ in Table 7.9 obey this rule.

The Nilsson model is most simply checked by using it to predict the spins of ground states of odd-A nuclei. It is very successful in doing this, where the value of η is known accurately enough for a unique assignment. If this is not the case, the ground-state spin always has one of the possible values. The value of η is determined, for example, from $E2$ transition rates or quadrupole moments.

The low-lying states of an odd-A nucleus consist of rotational bands built on the Nilsson single-particle states as band heads. Moments of inertia for these rotational bands are similar to those for even nuclei. For example, the first and second rotational bands of ^{175}Lu have

$$\frac{3\hbar^2}{\mathscr{I}} \simeq 0.077 \text{ MeV}.$$

The spacing of the Nilsson levels is considerably less than the spacing of vibrational levels. Hence odd-A nuclei do not have vibrational band heads for low-lying states.

We shall consider ^{25}Al as an example of a light rotational nucleus. Quadrupole moments give $\delta \simeq 0.3$. (Compare this value of δ with the value $\beta = 0.324$, $\delta \simeq 0.308$ found for ^{24}Mg in the Hartree-Fock calculation of Pal and Stamp (67). (See Table 6.5.)) The relevant Nilsson level diagram is Fig. 7.12. The last particle is in either the $\frac{5}{2}+$[202] level or the $\frac{1}{2}+$[211]

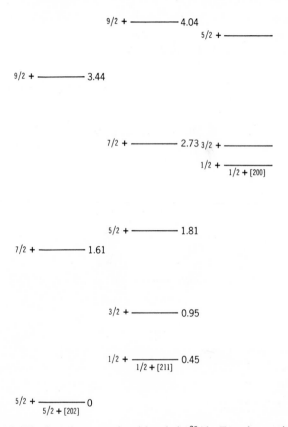

FIG. 7.15 The first three rotational bands in ^{25}Al. Energies are in MeV.

level, which are very close for $\delta \simeq 0.3$. The ground state is actually $\frac{5}{2}+$ and the first excited state is $\frac{1}{2}+$ at 0.45 MeV. The rotational bands built on these two states are shown in Fig. 7.15. Other Nilsson states identified in ^{25}Al are $\frac{1}{2}+$[202] at 2.50 MeV, $\frac{1}{2}-$[330] at 3.09 MeV and $\frac{3}{2}+$[211] at 4.22 MeV. The last is a hole state. For the lowest state of a rotational band, we have

$$I = K = \Omega, \quad (\Omega \neq \tfrac{1}{2}). \tag{7.107}$$

Thus the spin may be determined immediately for $\Omega \neq \frac{1}{2}$.

The case $\Omega = \frac{1}{2}$ is an exception which we have not yet treated. In this case the coupling between particle and rotational states is not negligible. The coupling term, defined in (7.77) is proportional to $\mathbf{I} \cdot \mathbf{j}$. This may be written out in terms of the angular momentum raising and lowering operators

$$I_{\pm} \equiv I_{\xi} \pm iI_{\eta},$$
$$j_{\pm} \equiv j_{\xi} \pm ij_{\eta}. \tag{7.108}$$

We have

$$2\mathbf{I} \cdot \mathbf{j} = I_{+}j_{-} + I_{-}j_{+} + 2I_{\zeta}j_{\zeta}. \tag{7.109}$$

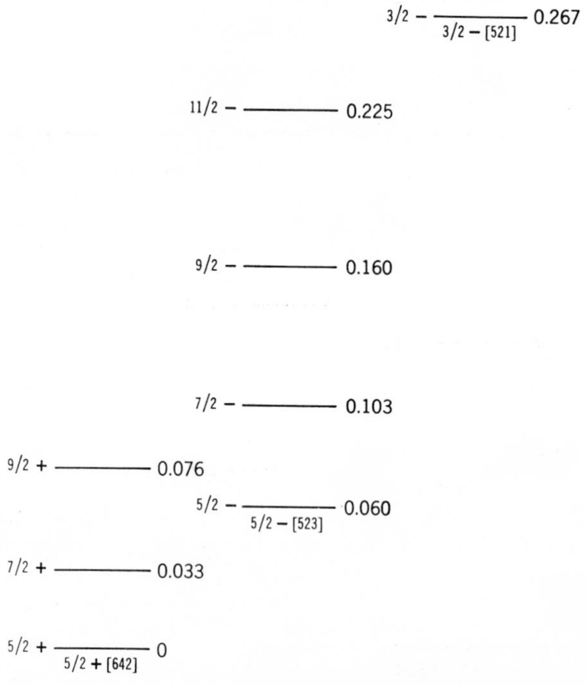

FIG. 7.16 Rational bands in ^{237}Np. Energies are in MeV.

The coupling term therefore connects states whose values of I differ by 1. It may be seen from the properly symmetrized wave function (7.85) that this perturbation is effective only for $K = \frac{1}{2}$. It can be strong enough to change the spacings and even the order of rotational energy levels away from the $I(I + 1)$ sequence. We will not pursue this complication further. In ^{25}Al for example the spin of the lowest $\frac{1}{2}-[330]$ state is actually $\frac{3}{2}$ rather than $\frac{1}{2}$.

A good example of a heavy rotational nucleus with odd Z is ^{237}Np. The relevant Nilsson level diagram is Fig. 7.14. The lowest single-particle band heads are identified as $\frac{5}{2}+[642]$, $\frac{5}{2}-[523]$ and $\frac{3}{2}-[521]$. Thus the deformation is given by $\delta \simeq 0.24$. The rotational bands are illustrated in Fig. 7.16.

The Nilsson wave functions may be used to predict electromagnetic transitions and other spectroscopic data. These predictions are essential in establishing the character of the states from the relevant experiments. Spectroscopic factors for (d, p) and similar reactions are also predicted by the wave functions. In Table 7.9, for example, the spectroscopic factor for putting a proton into the $f_{\frac{7}{2}}$ level corresponding to the first eigenstate is, for $\eta = 6$,

$$S^p = (-0.982)^2 = 0.96.$$

A further application of the Nilsson model is its use as an alternative to shell-model calculations which take into account several particles. For odd-A nuclei in the $1p$ shell, for example, we may consider all the $1p$-shell nucleons except the odd one as correlated in such a way as to produce an intrinsic deformation (remember the simple discussion of ^{6}Li in the introduction to Chapter 6). Clegg (61) obtained results for the $1p$ shell which are comparable with the results of intermediate coupling calculations. The values of the deformation parameter η turned out to be positive (prolate) for the first half of the shell and negative (oblate) for the upper half of the shell.

D. CLUSTER MODELS

It has long been known that there are certain properties of nuclei which suggest that nucleons tend to cluster in groups within a nucleus. This means that the binding forces between nucleons in the group have more effect than the binding forces between these nucleons and the other ones in the nucleus. Following the general idea that correlations are observed for nucleons near the top of the Fermi distribution, we might expect clustering to be most important on the nuclear surface.

The most tightly bound nucleus is the α-particle. We would expect this from its complete symmetry. Evidence that nucleons tend to form α-particle clusters is common. First, unstable heavy nuclei can decay by emitting α-particles as if they existed as essentially independent entities in nuclear matter. Light nuclei that have equal even numbers of protons and neutrons are called α-particle nuclei. They have especially high binding energies for the topmost nucleon. For example, it is 16 MeV for ^{12}C, compared with 20 MeV for ^{4}He and the average of 8 MeV. The α-particle model can approximately explain several low-lying levels of some α-particle nuclei. For example, the low-energy levels of ^{8}Be are explained as rotational levels produced by the two α-particles which rotate round each other. However, the fact that ^{8}Be is unbound indicates that the α-α interaction is quite weak. At the same time, the α-particles must be packed quite tightly so as to reproduce the observed nuclear density. Therefore the amplitudes of the zero-point oscillations of the α-particles in the ground state could not be small compared to their spacings. There must be a strong overlap between the internal wave functions of the α-particles so that a constant interchange of nucleons will occur, and it is hard to imagine that individual α-particles will retain their identity.

Nucleus	Number of α-Particles	Number of Bonds	B_α (MeV)	B_α/Bond
^{8}Be	2	1	-0.12	-0.12
^{12}C	3	3	7.33	2.45
^{16}O	4	6	14.4	2.42
^{20}Ne	5	8	19.3	2.41
^{24}Mg	6	12	28.8	2.40
^{28}Si	7	16	37.8	2.36
^{32}S	8	19	46.8	2.47

TABLE 7.10. Inter-α binding energies in light α-nuclei. (From Goldhammer, 63.)

The binding energies of α-particle nuclei provide the most striking evidence for the α-particle model. The binding energy of a nucleus is the difference between the rest energy of the nucleus and the sum of the rest energies of its constituent nucleons. If we consider, for example, ^{16}O, we find the binding energy is 127 MeV. The sum of the binding energies of four α-particles is 4 times 28.2 MeV. This is about 113 MeV. The α-particle model predicts 90 per cent of the binding of ^{16}O. The difference is the inter-α binding energy B_α.

If it is assumed that α-particles are clustered as tightly as possible so that the bonds between any adjacent pair are approximately the same, we can find the bond energy for several nuclei. This is shown in Table 7.10.

The bond energy, about 2.4 MeV for all except ^{8}Be, may be compared with other energy effects due to long-range internucleon forces such as the off-diagonal t-matrix elements of Table 7.5, or the splitting of the levels of ^{6}Li in Fig. 6.1.

Even in the independent particle model we can, if we like, focus our attention on certain clusters of nucleons. The interesting question is whether the internucleon forces give us a physical reason for preferring certain cluster substructures. For example the rms radii of the single-particle wave functions of the four nucleons in the $1s$ states of light nuclei are only a few per cent larger than that of an α-particle.

In the harmonic oscillator independent particle model, we shall show how cluster substructures can be formally separated, so that we can write cluster wave functions that are equivalent to independent particle ones. The fact that the harmonic oscillator Hamiltonian is separable enables us to do this. The Schrödinger equation is

$$\frac{1}{2M} \{ \textstyle\sum_{i=1}^{A} p_i^2 + M^2 \omega^2 \sum_{i=1}^{A} r_i^2 \} \Psi = E \Psi. \tag{7.110}$$

It can be rewritten in terms of k clusters, each containing n_i nucleons ($i = 1, \ldots, k$).

$$\left\{ \textstyle\sum_{i=1}^{k} H_i + \frac{1}{2M} \sum_{i=1}^{k} \frac{1}{n_i} P_i^2 + \frac{M^2 \omega^2}{2M} \sum_{i=1}^{k} n_i R_i^2 \right\} \Psi = E \Psi. \tag{7.111}$$

H_i is the Hamiltonian for the internal motion of the ith cluster and

$$\mathbf{P}_i = \textstyle\sum_{s=1}^{n_i} \mathbf{p}_s,$$
$$\mathbf{R}_i = \frac{1}{n_i} \textstyle\sum_{s=1}^{n_i} \mathbf{r}_i. \tag{7.112}$$

We can give a complete set of cluster wave functions for (7.111) corresponding to the complete set of independent particle wave functions for (7.110). After introducing the spin and isospin coordinates and antisymmetrizing, all these cluster-function systems are equivalent to the antisymmetrized independent particle system. The practical question is whether the expansion of the actual nuclear wave function in the complete set of cluster wave functions of a certain system has fewer relevant terms than the expansion in the independent particle wave function system.

In calculating bound states the Hamiltonian matrix is formed in terms of the matrix elements between antisymmetrized cluster wave functions. For even the simplest cluster nucleus, ^{8}Be, the antisymmetrization of the cluster wave functions with respect to all the nucleons is very involved.

We shall be content to treat the possible existence of cluster substructures as an experimental question. If only spectroscopic information is used to determine the preference of a nucleus for a particular cluster substructure, the evidence is very indirect; it usually requires a lengthy calculation, and it is often inconclusive.

In a few cases the spins of apparently anomalous low-lying levels can be understood in terms of the cluster model. In ^{19}F there are two possible cluster substructures involving closed-shell nuclei. The ^{4}He, ^{15}N substructure has an intercluster binding energy of only 4 MeV. Assuming that the clusters are in a relative s state, its spin and parity are $\frac{1}{2}-$. The ^{16}O, ^{3}H substructure, which is the one we would expect from the shell model, has an intercluster binding energy of 12 MeV. Its spin and parity are $\frac{1}{2}+$. In fact the ground state is $\frac{1}{2}+$ as we would expect from the shell model, and the first excited state, which is $\frac{1}{2}-$, is only 0.11 MeV higher in energy. Its simple shell-model interpretation is an excitation of a proton to the $2s$ state leaving a hole in the $1p_{\frac{1}{2}}$ state, which we would naively expect to involve several MeV of excitation energy. Evidently the tendency of nucleons to cluster in closed-shell substructures is sufficient to reduce the excitation energy by a few MeV.

Consider ^{6}Li. It requires 1.5 MeV to break it up into an α-particle and a deuteron. Is the α,d cluster substructure relevant? To answer this question, knowing only the binding energies, involves asking whether the 1.5 MeV cluster binding is small compared to the 2.2 MeV binding of the two nucleons to form a deuteron.

A direct answer to the question of the probability of finding cluster substructures can be obtained by reaction experiments with the same principle as the (p, 2p) experiment. For ^{6}Li, it is found that the cross section for (p, pd) is comparable with that for (p, 2p). Thus the α,d substructure is certainly significant. The cross section for knocking out other clusters such as that for (p, pt) is insignificant.

For ^{7}Li it is found that the (p, 2p) and (p, pt) cross sections are appreciable but that the (p, pd) cross section is not.

We thus have striking experimental evidence for the validity of the cluster model. The fact that the results of (p, 2p) experiments are well understood on the basis of the single-particle model argues very strongly for the idea, which we have already developed, that the cluster structure is the result of a weak perturbation of the single-particle picture. It is another type of long-range correlation due to the long-range part of the nucleon-nucleon force, resulting in level shifts of a few MeV.

E. SUMMARY: LONG-RANGE CORRELATIONS IN NUCLEI

Long-range correlations in nuclei are understood most fundamentally by calculating the virtual transition amplitudes between independent particle states, which are antisymmetrized products of single-particle states. Single particle states are best calculated by the Hartree-Fock method. However, a reasonable approximation to them is obtained by using the states of a harmonic oscillator. In the shell model the virtual transition amplitudes between the model independent particle states are the corresponding matrix elements of the nucleon-nucleon t-matrix. Typically they are of the order of a few MeV in light nuclei, so that they result in splittings of independent particle levels of this order of magnitude. This is much smaller than the spacing of the harmonic oscillator shells, which is typically about 15 MeV from the $1p$ shell to the sd shell. Configuration mixing, therefore, is unimportant for the lower states. In the example of ^{14}N (Table 7.6), states that require configuration mixing for their description start at about 5 MeV of excitation.

The *sd* shell can be thought of as a microcosm of the periodic table. Extensive calculations covering most aspects of nucleon-nucleon correlation have been done for these nuclei. The shell model works extremely well, for example, on the isotopes of oxygen, in predicting energy levels and dipole moments and transitions. Quadrupole moments and transitions are badly underestimated by this model, showing the necessity for including more states in the basis. However the effective *t*-matrix elements are encouragingly close to the values predicted by using the *t*-matrix of the nucleon-nucleon potential.

Instead of including more configurations in the shell model, remarkably good results have been achieved by using collective models. Turning for a moment to the $1p$ shell, the $2+$ first excited state of ^{12}C may be thought of as a collective state. More sophisticated shell-model calculations, which include holes in all the bound states and particles in many unbound configurations, are necessary to describe this state, indicating that all the particles take part in the collective oscillation. There is strong evidence that the ^{16}O core of the *sd* shell can be excited quite easily. The simple single-particle picture of this is the excitation of a $1p_{1/2}$ particle to the *sd* shell. This acts as a warning against too-literal interpretation of the shell model. The extra-core proton in ^{17}O, for example, stretches the ^{16}O core in order to produce a measurable quadrupole moment.

In the *sd* shell the Hartree-Fock calculations lead us to expect nuclei that are deformed in their ground state in the middle of the shell. There are both axially symmetric nuclei and asymmetric nuclei. The quadrupole moment of ^{25}Al, for example, gives a deformation $\delta \simeq 0.3$ which is remarkably close to the Hartree-Fock prediction. Rotational bands (Fig. 7.15) are observed for this nucleus. They are observed for all nuclei in the middle of the *sd* shell.

The *sd* shell also provides a remarkable example of a simplified description of a state in terms of a cluster substructure. The $\frac{1}{2}-$ state of ^{19}F, which is only 0.11 MeV above the $\frac{1}{2}+$ ground state can be considered as an α-particle in the *sd* shell created by promoting one proton from the $1p_{1/2}$ shell. The strong binding of the α-particle causes this state to be so favored energetically that it is almost the ground state.

It is perhaps significant that the qualitative facts about the shapes of light α-particle nuclei, which are revealed by the Hartree-Fock calculation, agree with the simplest predictions made from the close packing of α-particles. ^{8}Be is prolate and very elongated, ^{12}C is oblate, ^{16}O is spherical, ^{20}Ne is prolate, and ^{24}Mg is asymmetric.

This study of the *sd* shell emphasizes the point that nuclear models are interrelated. In some cases a very good start has been made in actually relating them numerically. For example, the Hartree-Fock calculations start with single-particle states and realistic nucleon-nucleon interactions and produce rotational nuclei, both models even predicting the same deformations. The study has also shown that many shell-model configurations are necessary to describe some states, emphasizing the value of the simplification introduced by collective descriptions, which work remarkably well for heavy nuclei (Figs. 7.8 and 7.10).

For heavy nuclei, the fact that the moments of inertia are much less than the rigid body values shows that at least a large proportion of the nucleons do not participate in the correlations. This is more in accord with our understanding of nuclei from infinite nuclear matter than are the results of calculations in the $1p$ and sd shells. For these nuclei, all the particles must be considered as sufficiently close to the Fermi surface to participate in correlations.

FURTHER READING

1. E. P. Wigner, *Phys. Rev.*, **51**, 106 (1937).

   E. P. Wigner, "Isotopic Spin—A Quantum Number for Nuclei," *Proceedings of the Robert A. Welch Foundation Conferences on Chemical Research*, Vol. I, edited by W. O. Milligan, Rice University, Houston, 1958, p. 67.

   Discussions of isospin in nuclei.

2. D. R. Inglis, *Rev. Mod. Phys.*, **25**, 390 (1953).

   Intermediate coupling.

3. J. P. Elliott and A. M. Lane, "The Nuclear Shell Model," *Encyclopedia of Physics*, Vol. XXXIX, Berlin: Springer-Verlag, 1957.

   A. de Shalit and I. Talmi, *Nuclear Shell Theory*, Academic Press, New York, 1963.

   Comprehensive reviews of shell-model theory using smooth two-body forces.

4. T. A. Brody and M. Moshinsky, *Tables of Transformation Brackets*, Universidad Nacional Autonoma de Mexico, 1960.

   Very lucid account of the calculation of matrix elements.

5. T. T. S. Kuo and G. E. Brown, *Nucl. Phys.*, **85**, 40 (1966).

   Shell-model calculation with matrix elements of a realistic t-matrix.

6. I. Talmi and I. Unna, *Annual Reviews of Nuclear Science*, **10**, 353 (1960).

   The effective matrix-element approach.

7. G. E. Brown and M. Bolsterli, *Phys. Rev. Letters*, **3**, 472 (1959).

   A. M. Lane, *Nuclear Theory*, W. A. Benjamin, Inc., New York, 1964.

   M. Baranger, "Theory of Finite Nuclei," *1962 Cargese Lectures in Theoretical Physics*, edited by M. Levy, W. A. Benjamin, Inc., New York, 1963.

B. R. Mottelson, "Nuclear Structure," *The Many-body Problem*, edited by C. DeWitt, John Wiley and Sons, New York, 1959.

Accounts of advanced nuclear structure theory involving particle-hole interactions.

8. S. A. Moszkowski in α, β, γ *Ray Spectroscopy*, edited by K. Siegbahn, North-Holland Publishing Company, Amsterdam, 1961.

Theory of electromagnetic transitions with applications.

9. A. Bohr and B. R. Mottelson, *Kgl. Danske Videnskab. Selskab, Mat-fys. Medd.*, **27**, No. 16 (1953, second edition, 1957).

S. A. Moszkowski, "Models of Nuclear Structure," *Encyclopedia of Physics*, Vol. XXXIX, Berlin: Springer-Verlag, 1957.

O. Nathan and S. G. Nilsson, "Collective Nuclear Motion and the Unified Model," α, β, γ *Ray Spectroscopy*, edited by K. Siegbahn, North-Holland Publishing Company, Amsterdam, 1965.

Collective models.

10. Y. C. Tang, K. Wildermuth, and L. D. Pearlstein, *Nucl. Phys.*, **32**, 504 (1952) (and references therein).

K. Wildermuth and T. Kanellopoulos, *The Application of the "Cluster" Model to Nuclear Physics*, CERN Report No. 59–23, Geneva, 1959.

Cluster models.

PROBLEMS

1. Using the eigenfunction of Table 7.6 for the ground state of ^{14}N, calculate its magnetic moment and electric quadrupole moment to two significant figures. Use the form (5.5) for the jj coupling wave functions. The relevant angular momentum algebra and values of the Clebsch-Gordan coefficients are discussed in Appendix 4. The experimental values are +0.40 nuclear magnetons and +0.71 fm^2, respectively.

2. Using the experimental values of the energy levels of ^{14}N from Table 7.6 and the single-particle levels of ^{13}C from Table 5.4 calculate the values of all the independent effective t-matrix elements in the $1p_{1/2}$ configuration.

3. Estimate the moment of inertia of $^{180}_{72}$Hf assuming that (1) it is a rigid body, and (2) the upper 10 per cent of the nucleons are responsible for rotations. Use the fact that the electric quadrupole moment of $^{181}_{73}$Ta is +3.9 barns. Calculate the experimental value of the moment of inertia from the energies of the ground-state rotational band, 0, 0.0933 MeV, 0.3093 MeV, 0.6417 MeV, 1.0853 MeV.

4. Show in the independent particle model with LS coupling that the "α-particle" configurations of the four nucleons outside the core of ^{8}Be, that is, the configurations with maximum symmetry $S = 0$, $T = 0$, form a rotational band with angular momenta and parities $0+, 2+, 4+$.

5. How would you interpret the $0+$ first excited states at 6.06 MeV in ^{16}O and 3.35 MeV in ^{40}Ca?

6. Estimate the deformation and the moment of inertia of $^{184}_{73}$Ta from the spectrum

$J\pi$	E (MeV)
$\frac{5}{2}+$	0.480
$\frac{11}{2}+$	0.303
$\frac{9}{2}-$	0.152
$\frac{9}{2}+$	0.136
$\frac{7}{2}+$	0

Compare the moment of inertia with the rigid body value. At what energy would you look for a $\frac{13}{2}+$ state?

7. Estimate the moment of inertia of ^{25}Al.

8. Estimate the value of $B(E2)$ for the decay of ^{28}Si from the first $2+$ state to the ground state.

9. Estimate the value of $B(E2)$ for the decay of ^{62}Ni from the first $2+$ state to the ground state.

8

THEORY OF NUCLEAR
REACTIONS

At this stage we have a general idea of the properties of nucleons bound to form nuclei. We must now consider the situation where a nuclear system has positive total energy so that it cannot remain bound together indefinitely. Our study of bound nuclei has shown that it makes sense to consider the motion of a single nucleon in the presence of the others. This motion is described by a complicated nonlocal potential, but for many purposes we can get quite a long way by considering the nucleon as if it moves independently in a local potential well.

A. RESONANCES

We shall first consider what happens to a single nucleon when it enters a nuclear system to form a compound nucleus. Again our initial approach will be to consider the nucleus as a local potential which acts on the nucleon. Nucleons bound in a potential well can only exist in certain discrete shell-model states where the continuity of the wave function inside and outside the potential permits the correct boundary condition. The tail of the radial wave function must be $h_l^{(1)}(i\beta r)$ so that the particle cannot be found at infinity. β is determined by the binding energy.

In the positive energy case, the boundary conditions are as follows. In the external region, that is for $r > r_0$ where r_0 is the radius beyond which the potential is negligible, the radial wave function is

$$e^{i\sigma_l}u_l(r) = \tfrac{1}{2}e^{i\sigma_l}[u_l^{(-)}(r) - \eta_l u_l^{(+)}(r)], \tag{8.1}$$

where the outgoing and ingoing wave functions $u_l^{(\pm)}$ are given by

$$u_l^{(\pm)}(r) = [G_l(r) \pm iF_l(r)]. \tag{8.2}$$

223

Here G_l and F_l are the Coulomb functions defined in Equation (2.28) and σ_l is the Coulomb phase shift.

In order to express the boundary conditions simply, we shall introduce some new notation. The continuity of the wave function at r_0 is expressed by the continuity of the logarithmic derivative at r_0, L_l.

$$L_l = \left[\frac{r}{u_l} \frac{\partial u_l}{\partial r} \right]_{r_0}. \tag{8.3}$$

We want to express the S-matrix element η_l in terms of L_l.

For the outgoing wave we define the real numbers Δ_l and P_l by

$$L_l^{(+)} \equiv \left[\frac{r}{u_l^{(+)}} \frac{\partial u_l^{(+)}}{\partial r} \right]_{r_0} \equiv \Delta_l + iP_l. \tag{8.4}$$

Δ_l and P_l are given in terms of F_l and G_l by

$$\Delta_l = r_0 \left[\frac{G_l G_l' + F_l F_l'}{G_l^2 + F_l^2} \right]_{r_0},$$

$$P_l = r_0 \left[\frac{G_l F_l' - F_l G_l'}{G_l^2 + F_l^2} \right]_{r_0}. \tag{8.5}$$

The quantity v_l, given by

$$v_l \equiv [G_l^2 + F_l^2]_{r_0}^{-1}, \tag{8.6}$$

is called the penetration factor. If it is much less than unity, it means that the particle does not penetrate the potential. For large Z the penetration factor is very small for low-energy protons. The proton does not penetrate the Coulomb barrier. We can express P_l in terms of v_l, using (8.2) and (2.32).

$$P_l = kr_0 v_l. \tag{8.7}$$

This quantity is called the penetrability. We shall also introduce the hard-sphere phase shift ξ_l by

$$e^{2i\xi_l} = \frac{u_l^{(-)}(r_0)}{u_l^{(+)}(r_0)}. \tag{8.8}$$

It is easily seen from (8.1) that this is the phase shift for the situation where $u_l(r_0) = 0$, as would occur for a hard sphere of radius r_0.

Using (8.4) and its complex conjugate relation, we substitute (8.1) and (8.8) into (8.3) to obtain, after some manipulation,

$$\eta_l = \frac{L_l - \Delta_l + iP_l}{L_l - \Delta_l - iP_l} e^{2i\xi_l}. \tag{8.9}$$

We have thus expressed the S-matrix element η_l in terms of Δ_l and P_l, which are properties only of the external conditions k and r_0; ξ_l, which is a property only of k and r_0; and the logarithmic derivative L_l. The logarithmic derivative thus has the same information content as the phase shift and can be used to parametrize the scattering.

Up until this stage, we have considered only elastic scattering. In this case the absolute value of the reflection coefficient η_l is unity. As much probability flux comes out as goes in, but there may be a phase shift.

If, however a reaction can occur, we may lose flux from the initial quantum state, which is described by the wave number k. The initial quantum state is called the entrance channel. Flux is lost from the entrance channel when the nucleus is excited in any way. We say the flux goes into another channel. If there is a reaction, we have $|\eta_l| < 1$. In this case, L_l is a complex number.

Let us first consider the situation where no other channel but the entrance channel is open; that is, the incident particle has too little energy to excite the nucleus. For simplicity we will consider a square well of radius r_0. The wave function just inside the surface may be approximated by ignoring the curvature of the surface

$$u_l \cong e^{-ik'r_0} + e^{i(k'r_0+2\zeta)}. \tag{8.10}$$

The internal wave number is k'. The ingoing and outgoing waves have the same flux but there is a phase shift 2ζ. The logarithmic derivative is now

$$L_l = -k'r_0 \tan (k'r_0 + \zeta). \tag{8.11}$$

We may rewrite the expression (8.10) for the wave function just inside the boundary as

$$u_l^{\text{in}}(r) = A \cos (k'r + \zeta). \tag{8.12}$$

The wave function just outside the boundary is

$$u_l^{\text{out}}(r) = B \sin (kr + \delta). \tag{8.13}$$

We have to join a periodic function of high wave number inside to one of low wave number outside.

In general this can only be done if the amplitude of the internal wave function is small (Fig. 8.1a). However, if the tangent to $u_l(r)$ is horizontal at r_0, the internal wave function has a large amplitude (Fig. 8.1b). In terms of an a-c circuit analogy, we have an impedance mismatch away from resonance.

We can see that the conditions for resonance are very like the conditions for a bound state. For bound states the internal wave function does not exist unless the internal wave number is such that the wave function can join smoothly to the external wave function, which is one that vanishes at infinity. For resonances the internal wave function is very small unless the internal wave number is such that the wave function can join smoothly to the external wave function where the tangent is horizontal. This depends on the external wave number. Resonances for a given l occur at different energies. These energies are sometimes called positive energy eigenvalues. At resonance the phase shift in the external wave function is an odd multiple of $\pi/2$.

A resonance wave function is an eigenstate of the Hamiltonian for positive energy whose internal amplitude is large. A bound-state wave function is an eigenstate of the Hamiltonian for negative energy whose internal amplitude is finite. The probability of finding a particle inside the potential is large at

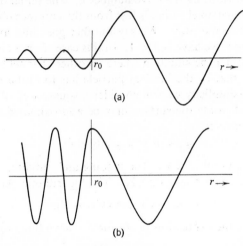

FIG. 8.1 Schematic diagram of radial wave function $u_l(k, r)$ near the surface r_0 of a square potential well. The picture is actually valid only for distances to the left and right of r_0 shorter than a wavelength, except for $l = 0$. (a) shows the off-resonance situation (impedance mismatch); (b) shows the situation at resonance (impedance matching).

resonance. However, the compound nucleus will eventually decay by emitting the particle in the entrance channel if no other channel is open, or by emitting the same particle or perhaps a cluster in another channel if this is possible. The nucleus can always lose energy by emitting a γ-ray. Because electromagnetic interactions are weaker than nuclear interactions, we shall neglect such a possibility at this stage.

We shall now formulate the theory of the compound nucleus, which is the nucleus formed in a state with positive energy by the addition of the projectile to the target.

B. FORMULATION OF THE THEORY OF THE COMPOUND NUCLEUS

The theory of the compound nucleus has been formulated very generally and elegantly by C. Bloch (57). We shall follow this formulation with some changes in notation for the sake of consistency with previous chapters. The general formalism is best understood as the generalization of a simple single channel case to a multichannel case. We shall first consider the simple example of the scattering of neutrons of energy ϵ in an *s*-state by a central potential $V(r)$ cut off at r_0. The quantum mechanics of this example is the same as that of the more complicated case but there are fewer indices and quantum numbers to worry about.

In the more general theory we make a distinction between the *interior region* and the *exterior region* in a configuration space of $3A$ dimensions. The particles can interact in the interior region Ω. This region is bounded by the channel surface which is a generalization of the nuclear surface to $3A$ dimensions. The distinction between the interior and exterior regions is important because in the exterior region we can solve exactly the radial wave equations and calculate the penetration factors which are important for low-energy charged particles. The surface Σ is not unique. Obviously we can put it anywhere outside a certain minimum interaction volume.

In the interior the problem consists in solving the Schrödinger equation with appropriate boundary conditions at the surface Σ. These boundary conditions are determined by the actual dynamical situation. They may be given by a set of logarithmic derivatives. In the case of a real nucleus the potential felt by a nucleon is too complicated to describe exactly; in fact it is not even uniquely known. However, we have seen that the asymptotic situation is uniquely described by the boundary conditions on Σ.

Bloch's method consists of the formal solution of the boundary-value problem. The essential step is the construction of the Green's function appropriate to the nuclear collision problem. As we have seen in Chapter 2 the Green's function for elastic scattering comes from the inversion of a differential operator which is the Hamiltonian for the problem. When we build the boundary conditions into the integral equation we determine the Green's function. The same is true in the present formulation. We build the boundary conditions in at the start by means of a boundary condition operator $\mathscr{L}$. $\mathscr{L}$ is a differential operator. The Green's function comes from the inversion of an operator which is the sum of the Hamiltonian H of the problem and the operator $\mathscr{L}$. A convenient choice of basis vectors gives us a general formal expression for the collision matrix (S-matrix) of the problem.

The choice of basis vectors is the starting point of the different methods in common use for describing reactions. The method most useful for describing experiments at low energies is the Wigner-Eisenbud (47) R-matrix theory. The Kapur-Peierls (38) method is especially adapted to theoretical consideration of reactions at higher energy.

[i] SCATTERING OF A NEUTRON IN AN *s* STATE

In this case the configuration space has three dimensions which reduce to one because *s* states are spherically symmetric. In the interior region,

$0 \le r \le r_0$, the wave function satisfies the Schrödinger equation

$$(\epsilon - H)\psi(r) = 0, \tag{8.14}$$

where the Hamiltonian H is written

$$H = -\frac{\hbar^2}{2\mu}\frac{1}{r}\frac{\partial^2}{\partial r^2}r + V(r). \tag{8.15}$$

In the exterior region, $r > r_0$, the wave function is a linear combination of ingoing and outgoing waves $\psi^{(\mp)}$.

$$\psi(r) = \psi^{(-)}(r) - \psi^{(+)}(r). \tag{8.16}$$

where

$$\psi^{(-)}(r) = \frac{1}{r}e^{-ikr},$$

$$\psi^{(+)}(r) = \frac{\eta_0}{r}e^{ikr}. \tag{8.17}$$

The s-state reflection coefficient, partial scattering amplitude, or S-matrix element is η_0. Note that η_0 has been absorbed in the definition of $\psi^{(+)}$ in contrast to previous notation [for example (8.1)]. We shall express η_0 in terms of k, r_0 and a Green's function describing the boundary conditions. To do this we solve the Schrödinger equation (8.14) in the interior region with boundary conditions at $r = r_0$ such that the incident amplitude is unity.

The operator H, *restricted to the interior region*, which plays a central role in the theory, *is not Hermitian*. The proof of this is as follows. If $\psi_1(r)$ and $\psi_2(r)$ are any two functions, we have as a consequence of Green's theorem

$$\int_0^{r_0} r^2\, dr\{\psi_1{}^*(H\psi_2) - (H\psi_1)^*\psi_2\} = -\frac{\hbar^2}{2\mu}\left[r\psi_1{}^*\frac{d}{dr}(r\psi_2) - \frac{d}{dr}(r\psi_1{}^*)r\psi_2\right]_{r_0}. \tag{8.18}$$

We shall choose a new operator corresponding to H, which is *Hermitian for the interior region*, by defining a surface term which compensates (8.18). We set

$$\mathscr{H} \equiv H + \frac{\hbar^2}{2\mu r_0}\delta(r - r_0)\frac{d}{dr}r. \tag{8.19}$$

It is easily verified that

$$\int_0^{r_0} r^2\, dr\{\psi_1{}^*(\mathscr{H}\psi_2) - (\mathscr{H}\psi_1)^*\psi_2\} = 0. \tag{8.20}$$

In spite of the singular character of the operator $\mathscr{H}$, its matrix elements are well-defined. Thus, for any two wave functions ψ_1, ψ_2,

$$\int_0^{r_0} r^2\, dr\, \psi_1{}^* \mathscr{H} \psi_2 = \int_0^{r_0} r^2\, dr \left\{ \frac{\hbar^2}{2\mu} \frac{d}{dr} (r\psi_1{}^*) \frac{d}{dr} (r\psi_2) + \psi_1{}^* V \psi_2 \right\}. \quad (8.21)$$

If $\psi(r)$ is continuous and differentiable, $\mathscr{H}\psi(r)$ is continuous for $r < r_0$, but at $r = r_0$ it has a singularity of the δ-function type given by

$$\frac{\hbar^2}{2\mu r_0} \delta(r - r_0) \left[\frac{d}{dr} (r\psi) \right]_{r_0}.$$

We shall now consider the meaning of the differential equation with the operator $\mathscr{H}$. It has the form

$$(\epsilon - \mathscr{H})\psi(r) = F(r). \quad (8.22)$$

The left-hand side is a function of r of the form $g(r) + B\delta(r - r_0)$. The equality of a function of this form to a similar one $f(r) + A\delta(r - r_0)$, where $f(r)$, $g(r)$ are continuous for $r < r_0$, implies the separate equality of the singular and continuous parts. Thus (8.22) is equivalent to

$$(\epsilon - H)\psi(r) = f(r); \qquad r < r_0 \qquad \text{(general solution for } r < r_0\text{)},$$

$$-\frac{\hbar^2}{2\mu r_0} \left[\frac{d}{dr} (r\psi) \right]_{r_0} = A; \qquad r = r_0 \qquad \text{(logarithmic derivative at } r_0\text{)}.$$

$$(8.23)$$

This is a differential equation with a boundary condition specifying the value of the logarithmic derivative at r_0.

It will shortly be seen that it is convenient to replace $\mathscr{H}$ by the operator $\mathscr{K}$ where

$$\mathscr{K} = H + \frac{\hbar^2}{2\mu r_0} \delta(r - r_0) \left(\frac{d}{dr} - ik \right) r. \quad (8.24)$$

We are interested in the situation where we know the conditions of the incident wave $\psi^{(-)}$ but not the conditions of the outgoing wave $\psi^{(+)}$. We shall define the *boundary-condition operator* $\mathscr{L}$ so that $\mathscr{L}\psi^{(+)} = 0$.

$$\mathscr{L} = \mathscr{K} - H = \frac{\hbar^2}{2\mu r_0} \delta(r - r_0) \left(\frac{d}{dr} - ik \right) r. \quad (8.25)$$

It is clear that

$$\mathscr{L}\psi^{(+)} = \frac{\hbar^2}{2\mu r_0} \delta(r - r_0) \left(\frac{d}{dr} - ik \right) \eta_0 e^{ikr} = 0.$$

The Schrödinger equation (8.14) may be written for $r < r_0$

$$(\epsilon - H - \mathscr{L})\psi(r) = -\mathscr{L}\psi(r). \quad (8.26)$$

Substituting the definition of $\mathcal{K}$ into (8.26) gives

$$(\epsilon - \mathcal{K})\psi(r) = -\mathcal{L}\psi^{(-)}(r); \qquad r < r_0. \tag{8.27}$$

For $r = r_0$ we have

$$\mathcal{L}\psi(r) = \mathcal{L}\psi^{(-)}(r), \tag{8.28}$$

since

$$\mathcal{L}\psi^{(+)}(r) = 0.$$

If the operator $\epsilon - \mathcal{K}$ has an inverse, that is, if $(\epsilon - \mathcal{K})\psi(r) = 0$ implies that $\psi(r)$ is identically zero, we can write the solution (8.27) in the form

$$\psi(r) = -\frac{1}{\epsilon - \mathcal{K}}\mathcal{L}\psi^{(-)}(r). \tag{8.29}$$

From (8.29) and (8.16) we obtain the expression for $\psi^{(+)}(r_0)$, which is unknown, in terms of $\psi^{(-)}(r_0)$, which is given.

$$\psi^{(+)}(r_0) = \psi^{(-)}(r_0) + \left[\frac{1}{\epsilon - \mathcal{K}}\mathcal{L}\psi^{(-)}\right]_{r_0}. \tag{8.30}$$

Using (8.17) we can now find the S-matrix element η_0.

At this stage we have seen the reason for defining the operators $\mathcal{K}$ and $\mathcal{L}$. They enable us formally to express $\psi^{(+)}$ in terms of $\psi^{(-)}$. $\mathcal{K}$ is the Hamiltonian plus the boundary-condition operator. $(\epsilon - \mathcal{K})^{-1}$ is the Green's function operator resulting from transforming the differential equation (8.27) into an integral equation as we did in Chapter 2. $\mathcal{L}$ is known if the logarithmic derivative at r_0 is known.

The difference between the present method and that of Chapter 2 is that the inhomogeneous term $\mathcal{L}\psi^{(-)} = F(r)$ contains a singularity $A\,\delta(r - r_0)$, whereas the inhomogeneous term of Chapter 2 was $V(r)\psi(r)$, which is regular.

We can justify and explain the present method by putting

$$F(r) = f(r) + A\,\delta(r - r_0 + \eta), \tag{8.31}$$

where η is a small positive number and $f(r)$ is regular.

Our differential equation and boundary conditions are

$$(\epsilon - H)\psi(r) = f(r); \qquad r < r_0,$$

$$-\frac{\hbar^2}{2\mu r_0}\left[\left(\frac{d}{dr} - ik\right)r\psi\right]_{r_0} = A. \tag{8.32}$$

The formal solution of (8.32) may be written with the Green's function $G(r, r')$ as

$$\psi(r) = \int_0^{r_0} r'^2\,dr'\,G(r, r')F(r'). \tag{8.33}$$

With the definition (8.31) of $F(r)$ the solution of (8.33) is the solution of

$$(\epsilon - H)\psi(r) = F(r) \tag{8.34}$$

with the boundary condition

$$\left[\left(\frac{d}{dr} - ik \right) r\psi \right]_{r_0} = 0. \tag{8.35}$$

This corresponds to Chapter 2, where the boundary condition was also nonsingular. The present equation is similar to this up to and in the neighborhood of $r_0 - \eta$. If we integrate (8.34) term by term on the small interval $(r_0 - 2\eta, r_0)$ we get

$$\left[\frac{\hbar^2}{2\mu r_0} \frac{d}{dr} r\psi \right]_{r_0 - 2\eta}^{r_0} = A. \tag{8.36}$$

In this interval, ψ is a continuous function, but $(d/dr)(r\psi)$ is discontinuous.

We have thus shown that when $\psi(r)$ satisfies the boundary conditions (8.35) at r_0, it satisfies (8.32) at $r_0 - 2\eta$. Making $\eta \to 0$, we see that the formal solution (8.29) is justified.

Introducing (8.17) and (8.25) into (8.29) we have for the S-matrix element

$$\eta_0 = e^{-2ikr_0} \left[1 - \frac{i\hbar^2 k r_0^2}{\mu} G(r_0, r_0) \right], \tag{8.37}$$

where $G(r, r')$ is the Green's function corresponding to the integral operator $(\epsilon - \mathscr{K})^{-1}$. This may be alternatively written as

$$\eta_0 = e^{2ikr_0} \frac{\left[\left(\frac{d}{dr} + ik \right) r\psi \right]_{r_0}}{\left[\left(\frac{d}{dr} - ik \right) r\psi \right]_{r_0}}, \tag{8.38}$$

where $\psi(r)$ is the solution of the Schrödinger equation which is regular at the origin. It is interesting to compare (8.38) with (8.9).

Since this formalism bears very little resemblance to the formalism of Chapter 2, we should perhaps explain its significance further. In Chapter 2 we were dealing with the wave function for scattering defined in all space. In order to find it, we had to solve the Schrödinger equation or the corresponding integral equation explicitly. The scattering amplitude or the S-matrix elements were expressed in terms of this wave function. In the present formulation, we have expressed the wave function in the exterior region in terms of a Green's function operator defined in the interior region by the Schrödinger equation and on the boundary by the logarithmic derivative. We can thus express the S-matrix elements in terms of the dynamic properties of the system, namely the Hamiltonian and the boundary-condition operator. In formulating a nuclear reaction theory we do not actually know the Hamiltonian, so we cannot find the explicit wave function. However, we shall see that there are properties of the operators in terms of which the S-matrix is formulated that enable us to understand what happens in a nuclear reaction without ever having to solve the Schrödinger equation. Instead of formulating the S-matrix in terms of potential parameters, it will be formulated in terms of parameters of resonances, whose relationship to the Hamiltonian and the boundary conditions will be demonstrated.

[ii] General Formulation of the Multichannel Case

We now shall formulate the theory of reactions in which more than one channel can be excited. For simplification we shall assume that only two-particle channels are important. We are thus neglecting electromagnetic channels and three-particle channels such as (p, 2p).* A channel is specified by the nature of the particles, the energy, the relative orbital angular momentum, the isospin, and the spin coupling with the orbital angular momentum. It is a quantum state of the compound system. All the quantum numbers characterizing a channel will be denoted by λ.

The exterior region of configuration space where the particles in each channel are well separated (that is, the separation distance r_λ of the centers of mass of the two particles is greater than the channel radius R_λ), the wave function of the system can be written

$$|\Psi\rangle = \sum_\lambda |\lambda\rangle \psi_\lambda(r_\lambda), \qquad r_\lambda \geq R_\lambda. \tag{8.39}$$

The interior region Ω of configuration space is now defined as being the region where $r_\lambda < R_\lambda$ for all channels λ. ψ_λ is a purely radial wave function, and $|\lambda\rangle$ is the product of the wave functions of two particles in channel λ and the spherical harmonic describing their relative angular motion. The different functions $|\lambda\rangle$ are orthogonal to one another, and we suppose that they are relatively normalized.

The notation $|\ \rangle$ is used to describe the complete wave functions depending on all the coordinates. The notation $|\ )$ is for the incomplete wave functions depending on all the coordinates except r. In a simple case, $|\lambda)$ might be the spin-angle function (5.5) for jj coupling.

A useful notation is the scalar product $(\lambda|\Psi\rangle$ of a complete and an incomplete wave function. This is calculated by holding r_λ constant and integrating over the other coordinates that describe the direction of $\mathbf{r}_\lambda$, the

---

* A comprehensive reaction theory including many-body channels has been formulated by Sasakawa (67).

vector joining the centers of mass. The scalar product is then a function of r_λ and

$$(\lambda \,|\, \Psi) = \psi_\lambda(r_\lambda), \qquad r_\lambda \geq R_\lambda. \tag{8.40}$$

The element of volume in $\mathbf{r}_\lambda$ space is $r_\lambda^2 \, dr_\lambda \, d\Omega_\lambda$. We transform the incomplete scalar product (8.40) into a complete scalar product by integrating over $r_\lambda^2 \, dr_\lambda$.

For a given value of the energy, there exist a certain number of open channels and a certain number of closed channels. In an open channel, ψ_λ is a linear combination of ingoing and outgoing wave functions

$$\psi_\lambda(r_\lambda) = \psi_\lambda^{(-)}(r_\lambda) - \psi_\lambda^{(+)}(r_\lambda). \tag{8.41}$$

The ingoing and outgoing wave functions are defined by

$$\psi_\lambda^{(-)}(r_\lambda) = (\lambda \,|\, -) \frac{u_\lambda^{(-)}(r_\lambda)}{r_\lambda V_\lambda^{\frac{1}{2}}},$$

$$\psi_\lambda^{(+)}(r_\lambda) = (\lambda \,|\, +) \frac{u_\lambda^{(+)}(r_\lambda)}{r_\lambda V_\lambda^{\frac{1}{2}}}. \tag{8.42}$$

Equations (8.41) and (8.42) are analogous to Equations (8.16) and (8.17). $u_\lambda^{(\pm)}(r_\lambda)$ are the asymptotic radial wave functions for channel λ. They are defined for orbital angular momentum l in the same way as the $u_l^{(\pm)}$ of Equation (8.2) and of Chapter 2A. The $u_\lambda^{(\pm)}$ are related by

$$u_\lambda^{(-)} = u_\lambda^{(+)*}. \tag{8.43}$$

The logarithmic derivative for outgoing waves in channel λ at the channel radius R_λ is defined in analogy with (8.4, 8.6, 8.7) as

$$L_\lambda^{(+)} \equiv \left[\frac{r_\lambda}{u_\lambda^{(+)}} \frac{\partial u_\lambda^{(+)}}{\partial r_\lambda} \right]_{R_\lambda}$$

$$\equiv \Delta_\lambda + ik_\lambda R_\lambda v_\lambda$$

$$\equiv \Delta_\lambda + iP_\lambda. \tag{8.44}$$

The imaginary part P_λ of the logarithmic derivative is the penetrability, defined by (8.7). For s-wave neutrons it is kr_0 [compare Equations (8.9) and (8.38)]. At the channel radius we have in analogy with (8.6, 8.8)

$$u_\lambda^{(+)}(R_\lambda) = v_\lambda^{-\frac{1}{2}} e^{-i\xi_\lambda}. \tag{8.45}$$

The penetration factor, defined by (8.6), is v_λ, and ξ_λ is the hard sphere phase shift, defined by (8.8).

In the closed channels there is only one radial wave function, denoted by $w_\lambda(r_\lambda)$. It is a standing wave linear combination of $u_\lambda^{(+)}$ and $u_\lambda^{(-)}$, which vanishes for $r_\lambda \to \infty$. We write

$$\left[\frac{r_\lambda}{w_\lambda}\frac{\partial w_\lambda}{\partial r_\lambda}\right]_{R_\lambda} = L_\lambda^c. \tag{8.46}$$

This is always real. The superscript c stands for "closed."

The complex numbers $(\lambda \mid +)$ and $(\lambda \mid -)$ in (8.42) are the amplitudes of the outgoing and ingoing waves. The factors $V_\lambda^{1/2}$, where V_λ is the relative velocity of the two particles in channel λ, normalize the amplitudes to unit incident flux. The amplitudes $(\lambda \mid -)$ are determined by properties of the incident beam. They are regarded as known. The amplitudes $(\lambda \mid +)$ depend linearly on the $(\lambda \mid -)$. This linear dependence is described by the *S-matrix*. In the literature on reaction theory, this matrix is sometimes called the collision matrix and denoted by U.

The S-matrix is defined by

$$(\lambda \mid +) = \sum_\mu (\lambda \mid S \mid \mu)(\mu \mid -). \tag{8.47}$$

The S-matrix contains all the physically observable quantities, since it relates all possible amplitudes of ingoing and outgoing waves in all channels.

In the last section we found S for a single channel case. We shall now use a parallel argument to find S in the multichannel case. We formally solve the Schrödinger equation for the whole nuclear problem in the interior region. The Schrödinger equation is

$$(\epsilon - H)|\Psi\rangle = 0, \tag{8.48}$$

where H is given by

$$H = -\sum_i \frac{\hbar^2}{2M_i}\nabla_i^2 + V. \tag{8.49}$$

Here again we begin by noticing that H is not Hermitian in the interior region Ω. By application of Green's theorem we find for any two functions Ψ_1, Ψ_2,

$$\int_\Omega [\Psi_1^*(H\Psi_2) - (H\Psi_1)^*\Psi_2]\,dT$$

$$= -\int_\Omega \sum_\lambda \frac{\hbar^2}{2\mu_\lambda}[\Psi_1^*(\nabla_\lambda^2\Psi_2) - (\nabla_\lambda^2\Psi_1)^*\Psi_2]\,dT$$

$$= \sum_\lambda \frac{\hbar^2}{2\mu_\lambda}\left[r_\lambda\psi_{1\lambda}^*\frac{\partial}{\partial r_\lambda}(r_\lambda\psi_{2\lambda}) - \frac{\partial}{\partial r_\lambda}(r_\lambda\psi_{1\lambda})^*r_\lambda\psi_{2\lambda}\right]_{R_\lambda}, \tag{8.50}$$

where μ_λ are the reduced masses in the various channels and $\psi_{1\lambda}$, $\psi_{2\lambda}$ are the radial wave functions defined for Ψ_1, Ψ_2 and channel λ in analogy with (8.40).

To make the Hamiltonian Hermitian, we again add a surface term defined on the channel surface Σ, in analogy with (8.19)

$$\mathcal{H} = H + \sum_\lambda |\lambda)\frac{\hbar^2}{2\mu_\lambda R_\lambda}\delta(r_\lambda - R_\lambda)\frac{\partial}{\partial r_\lambda}r_\lambda(\lambda|. \tag{8.51}$$

We can easily verify that with $\mathscr{H}$ instead of H, (8.50) is zero. $|\lambda)(\lambda|$ is a projection operator which selects the different intrinsic and angular parts of $\mathscr{H}$ at Σ.

To obtain a formal solution of the Schrödinger equation in the interior region with the boundary conditions of the collision problem and with the entrance channel amplitudes $(\lambda \,|\, -)$ given, we define a new operator $\mathscr{K}$ in analogy with (8.24, 8.25).

$$\mathscr{K} = H + \mathscr{L}. \tag{8.52}$$

The *boundary-condition operator* is defined by

$$\mathscr{L} = \sum_\lambda |\lambda) \frac{\hbar^2}{2\mu_\lambda R_\lambda} \delta(r_\lambda - R_\lambda)\left(\frac{\partial}{\partial r_\lambda} - \frac{L_\lambda}{r_\lambda}\right) r_\lambda(\lambda|, \tag{8.53}$$

with

$$L_\lambda = L_\lambda^{(+)} \qquad \text{for the open channels,}$$

$$= L_\lambda^{\,c} \qquad \text{for the closed channels.} \tag{8.54}$$

For the single-channel case we chose the boundary-condition operator $\mathscr{L}$ so that $\mathscr{L}\psi^{(+)} = 0$. This enabled us to get rid of $\psi^{(+)}$ from the right-hand side of our formal expression for $\psi^{(+)}$, leaving an explicit expression rather than an integral equation. It is easily verified that the choice (8.54) of L_λ gives

$$\left[\left(\frac{\partial}{\partial r_\lambda} - \frac{L_\lambda}{r_\lambda}\right) u_\lambda^{(+)}\right]_{R_\lambda} = 0,$$

$$\left[\left(\frac{\partial}{\partial r_\lambda} - \frac{L_\lambda}{r_\lambda}\right) w_\lambda\right]_{R_\lambda} = 0, \tag{8.55}$$

so that again $\mathscr{L}|\Psi\rangle$ depends only on entrance channel amplitudes.

$$\mathscr{L}|\Psi\rangle = \mathscr{L} \sum_\lambda^0 |\lambda)\psi_\lambda^{(-)}(r_\lambda). \tag{8.56}$$

The sum extends only over open channels. It is a known quantity. In the interior region Ω the situation is described by (8.48). At the surface Σ it is described by (8.56). The equation

$$(\epsilon - \mathscr{K})|\Psi\rangle = -\mathscr{L} \sum_\lambda^0 |\lambda)\psi_\lambda^{(-)}, \tag{8.57}$$

which is obtained from (8.48, 8.52, 8.56) in analogy with (8.27), is valid in the domain $\Omega + \Sigma$.

In order to define an inverse of the operator $(\epsilon - \mathscr{K})$, we must have a situation where $\mathscr{K}$ does not have real eigenvalues. If this is not true, $(\epsilon - \mathscr{K})|\Psi\rangle = 0$ may have a solution that is not identically zero.

The formal solution of (8.57) is, in analogy with (8.29),

$$|\Psi\rangle = -\frac{1}{\epsilon - \mathscr{K}} \mathscr{L} \sum_\lambda^0 |\lambda)\psi_\lambda^{(-)}. \tag{8.58}$$

This expression gives $|\Psi\rangle$ in the whole domain $\Omega + \Sigma$. On the surface Σ we can write, using (8.40),

$$\psi_\lambda(R_\lambda) = -\sum_\mu^0 {}_{R_\lambda}(\lambda| \frac{1}{\epsilon - \mathscr{K}} \mathscr{L} |\mu)\psi_\mu^{(-)}. \tag{8.59}$$

Here we have used the notation

$$_{R_\lambda}(\lambda \,|\, \Psi\rangle \equiv [(\lambda \,|\, \Psi\rangle]_{R_\lambda}. \tag{8.60}$$

From (8.41, 8.59) we can obtain the amplitudes of the outgoing waves in the open channels. At the nuclear surface we have

$$\psi_\lambda^{(+)}(R_\lambda) = \psi_\lambda^{(-)}(R_\lambda) + \sum_\mu^0 {}_{R_\lambda}(\lambda| \frac{1}{\epsilon - \mathscr{K}} \mathscr{L} |\mu)\psi_\mu^{(-)}. \tag{8.61}$$

This equation, together with (8.42), gives the amplitudes $(\lambda \,|\, +)$ in terms of the $(\lambda \,|\, -)$, thus defining the S-matrix.

[iii] INTRODUCTION OF BASIS VECTORS IN THE INTERIOR REGION

To obtain an explicit expression for the S-matrix from (8.61), we must introduce in the interior region a complete orthonormal set $|s\rangle$, $|t\rangle$, etc., which we shall regard at this time as entirely arbitrary. Note that this definition means that integrations are over the interior region only, where $\mathscr{H}$ is Hermitian.

We can write the expansion

$$\frac{1}{\epsilon - \mathscr{K}} = \sum_{st} |s\rangle\langle s| \frac{1}{\epsilon - \mathscr{K}} |t\rangle\langle t|. \tag{8.62}$$

When this expression is substituted into (8.61) we have expressions like $_{R_\lambda}(\lambda \,|\, s\rangle$, which we will redefine by introducing new quantities.

$$g_s^{(\lambda)} = \left(\frac{\hbar^2 R_\lambda}{2\mu_\lambda} \right)^{1/2} {}_{R_\lambda}(\lambda \,|\, s\rangle \tag{8.63}$$

$$|s\rangle = \sum_\lambda |\lambda)\phi_s^{(\lambda)}(r_\lambda). \tag{8.64}$$

The definition (8.64) of the radial parts $\phi_s^{(\lambda)}(r_\lambda)$ of the basis vector $|s\rangle$ is obtained by analogy with (8.39).

The quantities $g_s^{(\lambda)}$ are given in analogy with (8.40) by

$$g_s^{(\lambda)} = \left(\frac{\hbar^2 R_\lambda}{2\mu_\lambda} \right)^{1/2} \phi_s^{(\lambda)}(R_\lambda). \tag{8.65}$$

They depend on the interior region and the choice of basis vectors. They are called the *reduced width amplitudes* of the basis functions, and are essentially equal to the radial parts of the basis functions evaluated at the channel radii R_λ.

When (8.62) is substituted into (8.61) we have to the right of the operator $(\epsilon - \mathcal{H})^{-1}$ the following quantities.

$$\langle t| \mathcal{L} |\mu) \psi_\mu^{(-)} = \langle t| \mu)(\mu| -) \frac{\hbar^2 R_\mu}{2\mu_\mu V_\mu^{1/2}} \left[\left(\frac{\partial}{\partial r_\mu} - \frac{L_\mu}{r_\mu} \right) u_\mu^{(-)} \right]_{R_\mu}. \quad (8.66)$$

Equation (8.66) is derived from (8.42, 8.53, 8.56). With the aid of the relations (8.44, 8.45) and the complex conjugate relations, we may write, using (8.56, 8.66),

$$\langle t| \mathcal{L} |\mu) \psi_\mu^{(-)} = \frac{\hbar^{1/2}}{i} (\mu| -) G_t^{(\mu)*} e^{i\xi_\mu} \quad (8.67)$$

where

$$G_s^{(\lambda)} = (2k_\lambda R_\lambda v_\lambda)^{1/2} g_s^{(\lambda)}$$
$$= (2P_\lambda)^{1/2} g_s^{(\lambda)}. \quad (8.68)$$

The quantities $G_s^{(\lambda)}$ are each given by the product of the reduced width amplitude $g_s^{(\lambda)}$ and the square root of twice the penetrability P_λ which is defined by (8.44). They are the *partial width amplitudes* of the basis functions $|s\rangle$ in the different channels λ. They are essentially the values of the radial parts $\phi_s^{(\lambda)}$ of the basis functions at the channel surface Σ multiplied by suitable normalizing factors which are energy dependent.

On substituting in (8.61) the expressions (8.42, 8.62, 8.63, 8.67, 8.68) we obtain the exit-channel amplitudes as a function of the known entrance-channel amplitudes.

$$(\lambda| +) = \sum_\mu^0 e^{i\xi_\lambda} [\delta_{\lambda\mu} - i \sum_{st} \langle s| \frac{1}{\epsilon - \mathcal{H}} |t\rangle G_s^{(\lambda)} G_t^{(\mu)*}] e^{i\xi_\mu} (\mu| -). \quad (8.69)$$

This immediately gives the S-matrix in the form

$$S = e^{i\xi} \left[1 - i \sum_{st} \langle s| \frac{1}{\epsilon - \mathcal{H}} |t\rangle \mathbf{G}_s \times \mathbf{G}_t^* \right] e^{i\xi}. \quad (8.70)$$

We should explain the notation of (8.70). By $\mathbf{G}_s$ we mean a vector in the symbolic space of open channels, whose components are the $G_s^{(\lambda)}$. The product $\times$ is the direct product of the two vectors. $e^{i\xi}$ means a diagonal matrix in the space of open channels whose elements are the $e^{i\xi_\lambda}$. The S-matrix operates on vectors in the space of open channels.

Equation (8.70), which is the matrix notation for (8.69), now contains numbers, not operators. Instead of the operator $(\epsilon - \mathcal{H})^{-1}$ we have its matrix elements between the basis vectors $|s\rangle, |t\rangle$, which are so far arbitrary.

In order to write numbers in a specific representation, we must make a convenient choice of the basis vectors.

The most natural basis is the one in which $\mathscr{K}$ is diagonal. This is the basis of Kapur and Peierls. Unfortunately, the nature of $\mathscr{K}$ introduces certain difficulties. First, $\mathscr{K}$ is not Hermitian because the $L_\lambda^{(+)}$ of the open channels which figure in the definition (8.53) of the operator $\mathscr{L}$ are complex numbers. Indeed this is essential because otherwise we could not define the inverse of $\epsilon - \mathscr{K}$. Second, the L_λ and, hence, the operator $\mathscr{K}$ depend on the energy ϵ. As a result, the basis functions which diagonalize $\mathscr{K}$, and consequently the eigenvalues, depend on the energy in a complicated way.

[iv] THE R-MATRIX THEORY OF WIGNER AND EISENBUD

In order to calculate with real and energy-independent numbers, Wigner and Eisenbud (47) introduce a basis in which not $\mathscr{K}$, but the operator $\mathscr{K}_W$, where

$$\mathscr{K}_W = H + \mathscr{L}(b), \tag{8.71}$$

is diagonal. $\mathscr{L}(b)$ is the analogue of the boundary-condition operator obtained by replacing the L_λ in all channels, open and closed, by real constants b_λ. In open channels the L_λ are complex and energy-dependent. The operator $\mathscr{K}_W$ is

$$\mathscr{K}_W = H + \sum_\lambda |\lambda) \frac{\hbar^2}{2\mu_\lambda R_\lambda} \delta(r_\lambda - R_\lambda) \left[\frac{\partial}{\partial r_\lambda} - \frac{b_\lambda}{r_\lambda} \right] r_\lambda (\lambda|. \tag{8.72}$$

We have thus defined an eigenvalue problem independent of the energy. The eigenvalues are given by constant parameters characteristic of the interior region. Unfortunately, in this case the inverse operator $(\epsilon - \mathscr{K})^{-1}$ is not completely diagonalized, and its inversion presents a difficult problem that can only be solved approximately.

The operator $\mathscr{K}_W$ is Hermitian, its eigenvalues ϵ_s are real, and its eigenfunctions $|s\rangle$ define a complete orthonormal set.

$$\mathscr{K}_W |s\rangle = \epsilon_s |s\rangle. \tag{8.73}$$

This equation (8.73) is equivalent to the system

$$H|s\rangle = \epsilon_s |s\rangle$$
$$\left[\left(\frac{\partial}{\partial r_\lambda} - \frac{b_\lambda}{r_\lambda} \right) r_\lambda \phi_s^{(\lambda)}(r_\lambda) \right]_{R_\lambda} = 0, \tag{8.74}$$

where the $\phi_s^{(\lambda)}$ are the radial wave function parts of $|s\rangle$ in channel λ according to Equation (8.64).

The reduced width amplitudes $g_s^{(\lambda)}$, which are proportional to $\phi_s^{(\lambda)}(R_\lambda)$, are eigenfunctions of a Hermitian operator. They are real if the phases of $|s\rangle$

and $|\lambda\rangle$ are chosen appropriately. The partial width amplitudes $G_s^{(\lambda)}$ are real positive or negative quantities.

In order to have a concrete picture of the quantities we are using, we return briefly to the single-channel problem. Resonance occurs when the logarithmic derivative of the internal wave function is a constant b (for example, zero) at the channel radius r_0. This is what is meant by the set of eigenstates ϕ_s of the internal Schrödinger equation. By the use of Green's theorem one can obtain a linear relation between the internal wave function $\phi_E(r)$ for an arbitrary energy E and its logarithmic derivative at the surface. The constant in the relation was called the R-function by Wigner, and its generalization to the many-channel case was called the R-matrix, thus accounting for the name of the theory. However, in the present Green's function formalism, we can consider directly the inversion of the complete operator $(\epsilon - \mathcal{K})$ to obtain the S-matrix without discussing the R-matrix which, of course, depends on the values of R_λ and is only an intermediate step in the calculation of the S-matrix. The S-matrix must be independent of the values of R_λ.

We shall now proceed to discuss the complete $\mathcal{K}$ operator

$$\mathcal{K} = \mathcal{K}_W + [\mathcal{L} - \mathcal{L}(b)]. \tag{8.75}$$

The last term in (8.75) is not diagonal in our representation. Following (8.53) we have

$$\mathcal{L} - \mathcal{L}(b) = \sum_\lambda |\lambda\rangle \frac{\hbar^2}{2\mu_\lambda R_\lambda} \delta(r_\lambda - R_\lambda)(b_\lambda - L_\lambda)\langle\lambda|, \tag{8.76}$$

where the sum extends over all the channels. On using the definitions (8.63, 8.68) of the reduced-width amplitudes $g_s^{(\lambda)}$ and partial-width amplitudes $G_s^{(\lambda)}$, we obtain for the matrix elements of the operator $\mathcal{L} - \mathcal{L}(b)$

$$\langle s| \mathcal{L} - \mathcal{L}(b) |t\rangle = \sum_\lambda g_s^{(\lambda)}(b_\lambda - L_\lambda)g_t^{(\lambda)}$$

$$= \sum_\lambda g_s^{(\lambda)}(b_\lambda - \operatorname{Re} L_\lambda)g_t^{(\lambda)} - \frac{i}{2}\sum_\lambda^0 G_s^{(\lambda)}G_t^{(\lambda)}. \tag{8.77}$$

The last relationship is obtained from (8.44, 8.68). L_λ has an imaginary part only for open channels, so the second sum extends only over open channels. $\operatorname{Re} L_\lambda$ is equal to L_λ^c for closed channels and to Δ_λ, defined by (8.44), for open channels.

It is convenient to define the matrices E, ΔE, and Γ by the relations

$$\langle s| E |t\rangle = \epsilon_s \delta_{st},$$

$$\langle s| \Delta E |t\rangle = \sum_\lambda g_s^{(\lambda)}(b_\lambda - \operatorname{Re} L_\lambda)g_t^{(\lambda)}, \tag{8.78}$$

$$\langle s| \Gamma |t\rangle = \sum_\lambda^0 G_s^{(\lambda)}G_t^{(\lambda)}.$$

We now have in our present representation

$$\mathscr{K}_W = E,$$
$$\mathscr{L} - \mathscr{L}(b) = \Delta E - \frac{i\Gamma}{2}. \tag{8.79}$$

Substituting (8.79) in (8.70) we have the *S-matrix for the theory of Wigner and Eisenbud.*

$$S = e^{i\xi}\left[1 - i\sum_{st}\langle s|\frac{1}{\epsilon - E - \Delta E + i\Gamma/2}|t\rangle \mathbf{G}_s \times \mathbf{G}_t\right]e^{i\xi}. \tag{8.80}$$

This form of the S-matrix involves a double sum and many different products of partial width amplitudes. If we neglect the overlap of different resonances in the same channel we can obtain a much simpler formula. This is the *Breit-Wigner many-level formula* (Breit and Wigner, 36).

$$S = e^{i\xi}\left[1 - i\sum_s\frac{\mathbf{G}_s \times \mathbf{G}_s}{\epsilon - \epsilon_s - \Delta\epsilon_s + i\Gamma_s/2}\right]e^{i\xi}, \tag{8.81}$$

where the level shift and total width for the level s are defined by

$$\Delta\epsilon_s = \sum_\lambda [g_s^{(\lambda)}]^2(b_\lambda - \text{Re}\,L_\lambda)$$
$$\Gamma_s = \sum_\lambda{}^0 [G_s^{(\lambda)}]^2. \tag{8.82}$$

For a single isolated level, the numerator of the resonance term is Γ_s. The S-matrix in the form (8.80) or the approximation (8.81) is clearly a sum of resonance terms. If the b_λ are chosen to be equal to Re L_λ, then the resonance will occur at the eigenvalues ϵ_s in the approximation (8.81). If the b_λ are chosen to be zero there is a level shift $\Delta\epsilon_s$. The widths of the resonances depend on the basis radial wave functions $\phi_s^{(\lambda)}(R_\lambda)$ and the imaginary parts of the L_λ which, in turn, depend on the energy and the penetration factors for particular channel radii R_λ. The partial width for channel λ is $[G_s^{(\lambda)}]^2$. The total width is the sum of the partial widths, which are nonzero only for open channels.

The approximation of neglecting the overlap of different channels is equivalent to the assumption of well-separated resonances. In practice, well-separated resonances occur for low-energy neutron scattering. Resonances in neutron scattering are discussed in detail in Chapter 9. Examples are shown in Fig. 9.1a. There are other examples of states of the compound nucleus whose internal wave functions $\phi_s^{(\lambda)}$ are so large that the S-matrix element near the energy $\epsilon_s^{(\lambda)}$ can be considered practically as being due to the excitation of this state alone. In this energy region a single resonance is then a good description of the reaction. Isospin analogue states are examples of such exceptionally strong states.

For a particular S-matrix element, we can consider ξ, $\epsilon_s + \Delta\epsilon_s$, Γ_s, and $\mathbf{G}_s \times \mathbf{G}_s$ as approximately energy-independent parameters of the scattering. They provide a very much simpler set, for a restricted energy region, than any realistic set of potentials. In the theory of Wigner and Eisenbud, they are real numbers. The theory is particularly applicable to situations where single resonances are isolated, or where they are very much stronger than their neighbors.

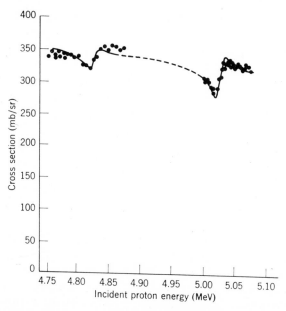

FIG. 8.2   Differential cross section at 90° for the elastic scattering of protons from ^{89}Y. The line is the Wigner-Eisenbud theory with the parameters given in the text. (Adapted from Fox, Moore, and Robson, 64.)

A good example of the use of the resonance expansion is the identification of isospin analogue states in the elastic scattering of protons from ^{89}Y (Fox, Moore, and Robson, 64). In this case the differential cross section at 90° was plotted against the incident energy (Fig. 8.2). In the neighborhood of 4.82 MeV and 5.02 MeV the curve has the characteristic shape for isolated resonances corresponding to compound states in ^{90}Zr with spins and parities 2− and 3−. The widths in both cases were about 10 KeV. The energy separation of these states is 0.204 MeV. The ground and first excited states of the isospin analogue ^{90}Y have spins and parities 2− and 3− and an energy separation of 0.202 MeV. The Coulomb energy is very clearly identified as 11.63 ± 0.05 MeV by making use of the mass relationships between the nuclei (Appendix 2). The method of obtaining information about spins and parities of resonances from cross sections may be understood by referring to Section C of this chapter on the relationship between S-matrix elements and cross sections. Note that for elastic scattering there are two terms in (8.81), the hard-sphere scattering and the resonance term. Figure 8.2 shows a pattern resulting from the interference of these two terms.

[v]   THE BASIS OF KAPUR AND PEIERLS

The formally simplest basis for a representation of the Green's function operator $(\epsilon - \mathscr{K})^{-1}$ is the one which diagonalizes $\mathscr{K}$. The basis vectors $|s\rangle$ are the eigenvectors of $\mathscr{K}$ with eigenvalues E_s.

$$\mathscr{K}|s\rangle = E_s|s\rangle. \tag{8.83}$$

This equation is equivalent to the system

$$H|s\rangle = E_s|s\rangle,$$
$$\left[\left(\frac{\partial}{\partial r_\lambda} - \frac{L_\lambda}{r_\lambda}\right) r_\lambda \phi_s^{(\lambda)}(r_\lambda)\right]_{R_\lambda} = 0. \tag{8.84}$$

The operator $\mathscr{K}$ depends on energy through L_λ. Hence the whole system of eigenfunctions and eigenvalues is given at a particular energy, and changes when the energy is varied.

We shall study certain formal properties of the eigenvalues and state vectors in this representation so that we can use them in our subsequent discussion of reactions in the region of overlapping resonances at higher incident energies. Resonances overlap at higher energies because many channels are open so that a large number of partial widths contribute to the total width of each resonance. Total widths become larger than spacings on the average.

First we shall show that the eigenvalues E_s are all complex and below the real axis in the complex plane if there exists at least one open channel. From (8.83) and its Hermitian conjugate equation we deduce

$$(E_s - E_s^*)\langle s \mid s\rangle = \langle s| \mathscr{K} - \mathscr{K}^\dagger |s\rangle$$
$$= \langle s| \mathscr{L} - \mathscr{L}^\dagger |s\rangle$$
$$= \sum_\lambda^0 \frac{\hbar^2 R_\lambda}{2\mu_\lambda} (L_\lambda^{(-)} - L_\lambda^{(+)}) |\langle \lambda \mid s\rangle|^2$$
$$= -i \sum_\lambda^0 |G_s^{(\lambda)}|^2. \tag{8.85}$$

To prove (8.85) we have used (8.43), (8.44) and its complex conjugate definition, and (8.53), (8.63), and (8.68).

Thus the imaginary part of $E_s - E_s{}^*$ is negative definite if there is at least one term in the sum over open channels. If we define ϵ_s and Γ_s by

$$E_s = \epsilon_s - \frac{i\Gamma_s}{2}, \tag{8.86}$$

we have

$$\Gamma_s = \frac{\sum_{\lambda}^{0} |G_s^{(\lambda)}|^2}{\langle s \mid s \rangle}. \tag{8.87}$$

It will be shown that $\langle s \mid s \rangle$ is not unity in the Kapur-Peierls formalism, so that the total width is not given by the sum of the partial widths.

We shall now discuss the behavior of the state vectors $|s\rangle$ under the time reversal operator T. $\mathcal{H}$ is not Hermitian because of the presence in $\mathcal{L}$ of the complex numbers $L_{\lambda}^{(+)}$. It has the following property

$$\mathcal{H}^{\dagger} = T\mathcal{H}T^{-1}. \tag{8.88}$$

This is proved by considering the operators $\mathcal{H}$ and $\mathcal{K} - \mathcal{H}$. If $\mathcal{H}$ is invariant under time reversal we have

$$T\mathcal{H}T^{-1} = \mathcal{H} = \mathcal{H}^{\dagger}. \tag{8.89}$$

The operator $\mathcal{K} - \mathcal{H}$ transforms as follows.

$$T(\mathcal{K} - \mathcal{H})T^{-1} = T\left[\sum_{\lambda} |\lambda\rangle \frac{\hbar^2}{2\mu_{\lambda}R_{\lambda}} \delta(r_{\lambda} - R_{\lambda})L_{\lambda}(\lambda| \right]T^{-1}. \tag{8.90}$$

The time-reversal operator is $\sigma_2 u$, where u is the complex conjugation operator and σ_2 is the Pauli spin operator. Its properties are studied in Appendix 4j. It reverses the angular momenta in $|\lambda\rangle$, and changes the projection quantum numbers of the angular momenta from m to $-m$. Since all the $|\lambda\rangle$ are included in the sum, the effect of T on $|\lambda\rangle$ just rearranges the terms. The $L_{\lambda}^{(+)}$ are replaced by $L_{\lambda}^{(-)}$. The operation of taking the Hermitian conjugate has the same effect. Thus we have proved (8.88).

On applying the operator T to (8.83) and using (8.88) we obtain

$$\mathcal{H}^{\dagger}T|s\rangle = E_s{}^*T|s\rangle. \tag{8.91}$$

Thus $T|s\rangle$ is an eigenfunction of $\mathcal{H}^{\dagger}$ with eigenvalue $E_s{}^*$. The eigenfunctions of $\mathcal{H}^{\dagger}$ for open channels are purely ingoing waves.

We next shall show that if $E_s \neq E_t$ the functions $T|s\rangle$ and $|t\rangle$ are orthogonal. We write the Hermitian conjugate of (8.83)

$$\langle t|\mathcal{H}^{\dagger} = \langle t|E_t{}^*. \tag{8.92}$$

Multiplying (8.92) on the right by $T|s\rangle$, and multiplying (8.83) on the left by $\langle t|T$, we have

$$(E_t{}^* - E_s{}^*)\langle t|\{T|s\rangle\} = 0,$$

which is what we had to prove.

The eigenvalues E_s are, in general, degenerate because there are several partial waves in the process. That is, the total angular momentum is not zero. For simplicity we shall assume that this is the only degeneracy. To indicate angular momentum we use the notation $|sJM\rangle$. s indicates the energy eigenvalue, J and M are the total angular momentum and its projection, respectively. With the functions $|sJM\rangle$ we associate the functions

$$|s\widetilde{JM}\rangle = (-1)^{M-J}T|sJ-M\rangle. \tag{8.93}$$

T reverses the angular momenta and changes M to $-M$.

The function $|s\widetilde{JM}\rangle$ is orthogonal to all other functions $|s'J'M'\rangle$ for $E_s \neq E_{s'}$, $M \neq M'$. If the basis is complete, $|s\widetilde{JM}\rangle$ cannot be orthogonal to all the functions. Hence it is not orthogonal to $|sJM\rangle$. One can multiply $|sJM\rangle$ by an appropriate constant so that

$$\langle s\widetilde{JM} \mid s'J'M'\rangle = \delta_{ss'}\delta_{JJ'}\delta_{MM'}. \tag{8.94}$$

The functions $|sJM\rangle$ and $|s\widetilde{JM}\rangle$ form a biorthogonal system.

We abbreviate the notation to

$$\langle \tilde{s} \mid s'\rangle = \delta_{ss'}. \tag{8.95}$$

In the spinless case the functions in the biorthogonal basis system become

$$\tilde{\phi}_s = \phi_s{}^* \tag{8.93'}$$

and the orthonormality condition becomes

$$\int_\Omega \phi_s\phi_{s'} \, dT = \delta_{ss'}. \tag{8.95'}$$

It is the reversal of the spin projections with time reversal that prevents this equation holding in general and is thus responsible for the fact that $\langle s \mid s\rangle$ is not in general unity. For complete sets of $|s\rangle$ and $|\tilde{s}\rangle$ with orthonormality defined by (8.95), we have the unit operator

$$\sum |s\rangle\langle \tilde{s}| = 1. \tag{8.96}$$

The operator $\mathcal{K}$ may be written

$$\mathcal{K} = \sum_s |s\rangle E_s\langle \tilde{s}|, \tag{8.97}$$

and the inverse of $\epsilon - \mathcal{K}$, which is the Green's function for the nuclear problem, has the form

$$\frac{1}{\epsilon - \mathcal{H}} = \sum_s |s\rangle \frac{1}{\epsilon - E_s} \langle \tilde{s}|. \tag{8.98}$$

On substituting (8.98) into the definition (8.70) of the S-matrix, we obtain the quantities $(\lambda \,|\, s)$ and $(\tilde{s} \,|\, \lambda)$. These quantities are equal by the definition (8.93) of $|\tilde{s}\rangle$, if the phases are chosen in accordance with the usual definition of T.

$$T|\lambda JM) = (-1)^{M-J}|\lambda J - M). \tag{8.99}$$

This is proved as follows.

$$
\begin{aligned}
\langle s\widetilde{JM} \,|\, \lambda JM) &= (\lambda JM \,|\, s\widetilde{JM})^* \\
&= (-1)^{M-J}(\lambda JM|\{T|sJ - M\})^* \\
&= (-1)^{M-J}\{(\lambda JM|T\}|sJM\rangle \\
&= (\lambda J - M \,|\, sJ - M\rangle \\
&= (\lambda JM \,|\, sJM\rangle.
\end{aligned}
$$

Here we have used the facts that T is unitary and antilinear.

On defining the amplitudes $\mathbf{G}_s$ as in (8.65, 8.68) and on substituting (8.98) into (8.70), we obtain the *formula of Kapur and Peierls* (38).

$$S = e^{i\xi}\left[1 - i\sum_s \frac{\mathbf{G}_s \times \mathbf{G}_s}{\epsilon - \epsilon_s + i\Gamma_s/2}\right]e^{i\xi}. \tag{8.100}$$

This formula resembles the Breit-Wigner many-level formula, but it is a rigorous expression. The theoretical advantage of the Kapur-Peierls formalism is that the sum in the S-matrix is over only one index s, not s and t as in the exact Wigner-Eisenbud theory. The disadvantage is that ϵ_s and Γ_s depend on the energy ϵ in a much more complicated way. Another disadvantage from the point of view of dealing with particular experimental resonances is that the sum of the partial widths is not equal to the total width.

An alternative description, which has the advantage of not containing the channel radii explicitly, has been given by Humblet and Rosenfeld (61). In this theory the boundary conditions are complex, but are defined so that the total width is the sum of the partial widths. The theory is harder to work with for isolated resonances than the Wigner-Eisenbud theory and does not have the formal simplicity of the Kapur-Peierls theory.

C. DIFFERENTIAL CROSS SECTIONS
FROM S-MATRIX ELEMENTS

In order to consider cross sections for specific experiments involving two-body channels λ, we shall express the channel wave functions $|\lambda\rangle\psi_\lambda(r)$ more explicitly by using the channel-spin representation. The presentation will follow that of Lane and Thomas (58).

Separating out the motion of the center of mass, we may write the wave function for the channel λ, in which the two bodies are denoted by α_1, α_2, as

$$|\lambda)\psi_\lambda(r_\lambda) = \chi(\mathbf{r}_\lambda)\psi_1(q_1)\psi_2(q_2) \tag{8.101}$$

where $\chi(\mathbf{r}_\lambda)$ is the wave function of the relative motion of α_1 and α_2, and $\psi_1(q_1)$, $\psi_2(q_2)$ are the internal wave functions of α_1, α_2. If the effective potential between α_1 and α_2 is independent of the relative orientation of the respective spins $\mathbf{I}_1$, $\mathbf{I}_2$, we may represent the intrinsic wave functions of α_1, α_2 by a channel-spin wave function $\psi_{\alpha s v}$ defined by vector addition of the spins $\mathbf{I}_1$, $\mathbf{I}_2$ whose projections are m_1, m_2, to give a channel spin s with projection v. The The partition index α serves to specify the isospin.

$$\psi_{\alpha s v} = \sum_{m_1 m_2} C^{m_1 m_2 v}_{I_1 \ I_2 s} \psi_{1 I_1}^{m_1} \psi_{2 I_2}^{m_2}. \tag{8.102}$$

In order to reduce $\chi(\mathbf{r})$ to functions of one variable, we shall make a partial wave expansion and include the orbital angular momentum in our channel definition. It is a good idea to remember at this stage that the partial wave expansion is a mathematical device. The orbital angular momenta are not measurable, and are summed out in any expression for a matrix element of an observable quantity. The transformation (8.99) of $|\lambda)$ under time reversal is valid if $|\lambda)$ is defined as follows.

$$|\lambda) = \psi_{\alpha s v} i^l Y_l^m(\Omega_\lambda). \tag{8.103}$$

The complete channel wave functions for ingoing and outgoing waves normalized to unit flux are defined, respectively, by

$$\mathscr{I}_{\alpha s l v m} = i^l Y_l^m(\Omega_\lambda) \frac{u_l^{(-)}(k_\lambda, r_\lambda)}{r_\lambda V_\lambda^{\frac{1}{2}}} \psi_{\alpha s v},$$

$$\mathscr{O}_{\alpha s l v m} = i^l Y_l^m(\Omega_\lambda) \frac{u_l^{(+)}(k_\lambda, r_\lambda)}{r_\lambda V_\lambda^{\frac{1}{2}}} \psi_{\alpha s v}. \tag{8.104}$$

The indices $\alpha s l v m$ describing the nature of the two bodies, the channel spin, the orbital angular momentum, and the corresponding angular momentum projections now represent λ.

The total wave function for the nuclear problem Ψ may now be expressed in the external region as the multichannel generalization of (2.29).

$$\Psi = \sum_\lambda (x_\lambda \mathscr{O}_\lambda + y_\lambda \mathscr{I}_\lambda). \tag{8.105}$$

We have abbreviated the notation slightly by setting

$$x_\lambda = (\lambda \mid +), \qquad y_\lambda = -(\lambda \mid -). \tag{8.106}$$

The S-matrix is now defined by the equation

$$x_\lambda = -\sum_{\lambda\mu} S_{\lambda\mu} y_\mu, \tag{8.107}$$

which is equivalent to (8.47).

By substituting (8.107) into (8.105), we may express the complete solution Ψ in terms of the ingoing wave amplitudes y_μ.

$$\Psi = \sum_{\lambda\mu} (\delta_{\lambda\mu}\mathscr{I}_\mu - S_{\lambda\mu}\mathcal{O}_\lambda) y_\mu. \tag{8.108}$$

Consider now the wave function with the same y_μ, the radial parts of which are proportional to the regular Coulomb function F_λ in each channel λ.

$$\Psi' = \sum_{\lambda\mu} (\delta_{\lambda\mu}\mathscr{I}_\mu - e^{2i\sigma_\mu}\delta_{\lambda\mu}\mathcal{O}_\mu) y_\mu. \tag{8.109}$$

Adding Ψ' to and subtracting it from (8.108) gives

$$\Psi = \Psi' + \sum_{\lambda\mu} (e^{2i\sigma_\mu}\delta_{\lambda\mu} - S_{\lambda\mu})\mathcal{O}_\lambda y_\mu, \tag{8.110}$$

in which explicit reference to the ingoing waves has been eliminated.

We now choose y_μ so that Ψ' represents an ingoing Coulomb wave of particles of type α, channel spin s, ν. The z-axis is defined to be the incident direction.

$$y_\mu \equiv y_{\alpha s l \nu 0} = \frac{i\pi^{\frac{1}{2}}}{k_\mu} (2l+1)^{\frac{1}{2}}, \tag{8.111}$$

all others being zero.

From the definitions (8.2, 8.104) of the ingoing and outgoing waves in the exterior region and the relation

$$Y_l^0(\Omega) = [(2l+1)/4\pi]^{\frac{1}{2}} P_l(\cos\theta), \tag{8.112}$$

it follows that

$$\Psi'_{\alpha s \nu} = V_\lambda^{-\frac{1}{2}} k_\lambda^{-1} \sum_l i^l (2l+1) e^{i\sigma_\lambda} \frac{F_\lambda}{r_\lambda} P_l(\cos\theta_\lambda) \psi_{\alpha s \nu}. \tag{8.113}$$

The function $\Psi'_{\alpha s \nu}$ represents an ingoing Coulomb wave, that is, an incident plane wave of type $\alpha s \nu$ together with a wave scattered by the Coulomb field. The asymptotic form of the function as $r_\lambda \to \infty$ is

$$\Psi'_{\alpha s \nu} \sim V_\lambda^{-\frac{1}{2}} \psi_{\alpha s \nu} \left[\left(1 - \frac{\eta_\lambda^2}{i k_\lambda (r_\lambda - z_\lambda)}\right) \exp i\{k_\lambda z_\lambda - \eta_\lambda \ln k_\lambda (r_\lambda - z_\lambda) - \sigma_\lambda\} \right.$$
$$\left. - \frac{\pi^{\frac{1}{2}}}{k_\lambda r_\lambda} C_\lambda(\theta_\lambda) \exp i\{\rho_\lambda - \eta_\lambda \ln 2\rho_\lambda + \sigma_\lambda\} \right], \tag{8.114}$$

where

$$z_\lambda = r_\lambda \cos \theta_\lambda,$$

$$\eta_\lambda = \frac{Z_1 Z_2 e^2}{\hbar V_\lambda},$$

$$\rho_\lambda = k_\lambda r_\lambda,$$

$$C_\lambda(\theta_\lambda) = (4\pi)^{-\frac{1}{2}} \eta_\lambda \operatorname{cosec}^2 \frac{\theta_\lambda}{2} \exp\left[-2i\eta_\lambda \ln \sin \frac{\theta_\lambda}{2}\right]. \tag{8.115}$$

The quantity $C_\lambda(\theta_\lambda)$ is the Coulomb or Rutherford scattering amplitude.

We may now write the particular solution (8.110) of the Schrödinger equation, corresponding to the choice (8.111) of incident amplitudes, in our explicit channel-spin formalism. The asymptotic form of this solution is

$$\Psi_{\text{part}} \sim \Psi'_{\alpha s \nu} + \frac{i\pi^{\frac{1}{2}}}{k_\lambda} \sum_{\alpha' s' l' \nu' m' l} (2l + 1)^{\frac{1}{2}}$$

$$\times [e^{2i\sigma_{\lambda'}} \delta_{\lambda' s' l' \nu' m', \lambda s l \nu 0} - S_{\lambda' s' l' \nu' m', \lambda s l \nu 0}]$$

$$\times \frac{\exp i\{\rho_{\lambda'} - \eta_{\lambda'} \ln 2\rho_{\lambda'} + \sigma_{\lambda'}\}}{V_{\lambda'}^{\frac{1}{2}} r_{\lambda'}} Y_{l'}^{m'}(\Omega_{\lambda'}) \psi_{\alpha' s' \nu'}. \tag{8.116}$$

We are now in a position to define the amplitudes $A_{\alpha' s' \nu', \alpha s \nu}(\Omega_{\lambda'})$ of the outgoing waves of type $\alpha' s' \nu'$ at infinity, which are associated with the incident wave of type $\alpha s \nu$ with unit flux. To do this, we remember the fundamental way of extracting probability amplitudes from quantum mechanics. The probability amplitude for finding a system whose state vector is $|\Psi\rangle$ in the final state $|\Phi\rangle$ is the projection $\langle \Phi \mid \Psi \rangle$ of $|\Psi\rangle$ on $|\Phi\rangle$. In our explicit case we have

$$A_{\alpha' s' \nu', \alpha s \nu}(\Omega_{\lambda'}) = r_{\lambda'} V_{\lambda'}^{\frac{1}{2}} \exp i\{\rho_{\lambda'} - \eta_{\lambda'} \ln 2\rho_{\lambda'} + \sigma_{\lambda'}\}$$

$$\times \lim_{r_{\lambda'} \to \infty} \int \psi^*_{\alpha' s' \nu'} \Psi \, dq_{\alpha'}. \tag{8.117}$$

The dependence of the scattering and reaction amplitudes on the energies of the channels λ, λ' is implicit. The differential cross sections are defined to be

$$d\sigma_{\alpha s \nu, \alpha' s' \nu'} = |A_{\alpha' s' \nu', \alpha s \nu}(\Omega_{\lambda'})|^2 \, d\Omega_{\lambda'}. \tag{8.118}$$

The scattering and reaction amplitudes for the particular wave function (8.116) are

$$A_{\alpha' s' \nu', \alpha s \nu}(\Omega_{\lambda'}) = \frac{\pi^{\frac{1}{2}}}{k_\lambda} \{ -C_{\lambda'}(\theta_{\lambda'}) \delta_{\lambda' s' \nu', \lambda s \nu} + i \sum_{l' m' l} (2l + 1)^{\frac{1}{2}}$$

$$\times [e^{2i\sigma_{\lambda'}} \delta_{\lambda' s' l' \nu' m', \lambda s l \nu 0} - S_{\lambda' s' l' \nu' m', \lambda s l \nu 0}] Y_{l'}^{m'}(\Omega_{\lambda'}) \}. \tag{8.119}$$

At this stage we shall not discuss the measurement of polarization in the reaction products or cross sections for polarized beams. For unpolarized incident beam and target, the cross section is summed over the v' and averaged over the v to obtain the differential cross sections for the processes $\alpha s \to \alpha' s'$.

$$d\sigma_{\alpha s, \alpha' s'} = (2s + 1)^{-1} \sum_{vv'} |A_{\alpha' s' v', \alpha s v}(\Omega_{\lambda'})|^2 \, d\Omega_{\lambda'}. \tag{8.120}$$

We may also sum (8.120) over s' and average over s to obtain the differential cross section for the process $\alpha \to \alpha'$.

$$d\sigma_{\alpha \alpha'} = \{(2I_1 + 1)(2I_2 + 1)\}^{-1} \sum_{ss'vv'} |A_{\alpha' s' v', \alpha s v}(\Omega_{\lambda'})|^2 \, d\Omega_{\lambda'}, \tag{8.121}$$

where I_1 and I_2 are the spins of the particles of the pair α.

It is sometimes convenient to change from the $\{\alpha l s v m\}$ scheme to the $\{\alpha s l J M\}$ scheme where the total angular momentum of the pair α is

$$\mathbf{J} = \mathbf{l} + \mathbf{s}. \tag{8.122}$$

$\mathbf{J}$ is conserved in the reaction. Instead of (8.119) we have

$$A_{\alpha' s' v', \alpha s v}(\Omega_{\lambda'}) = \frac{\pi^{\frac{1}{2}}}{k_\lambda} [-C_{\lambda'}(\theta_{\lambda'})\delta_{\lambda' s' v', \lambda s v} + i \sum_{J M l l' m'} (2l + 1)^{\frac{1}{2}}$$
$$\times C_{l\,s\,J}^{0v\,M} C_{l'\,s'\,J}^{m'v'\,M} T_{\lambda' s' l', \lambda s l}^J Y_{l'}^{m'}(\Omega_{\lambda'})] \tag{8.123}$$

where

$$T_{\lambda' s' l', \lambda s l}^J = e^{2i\sigma_{\lambda'}}\delta_{\lambda' s' l', \lambda s l} - S_{\lambda' s' l', \lambda s l}^J. \tag{8.124}$$

The cross sections are obtained by squaring the scattering amplitudes A and summing over projection and spin quantum numbers as in (8.120, 8.121). In a computation this is often done by the computer, the sums over spin quantum numbers yielding coefficients depending on the other angular momentum indices. It is sometimes useful to use special coefficients which have been worked out for this purpose, thus obtaining a formally simpler answer. The coefficients are related to the functions used in the theory of angular momentum and described in Appendix 4.

We shall quote the result for the differential cross section (8.120). It involves squaring the A functions (8.123) using the sets of summing integers

$$\{J_1 M_1 l_1 l_1' m_1'\} \qquad \text{and} \qquad \{J_2 M_2 l_2 l_2' m_2'\}.$$

The differential cross section is given by

$$(2s + 1) \frac{k_\lambda^2}{\pi} d\sigma_{\alpha s, \alpha' s'} / d\Omega_{\lambda'}$$

$$= (2s + 1) |C_{\lambda'}(\theta_{\lambda'})|^2 \, \delta_{\lambda' s', \lambda s} + \pi^{-1} \sum_L B_L(\lambda' s', \lambda s) P_L(\cos \theta_{\lambda'})$$
$$+ (4\pi)^{-\frac{1}{2}} \sum_{Jll'} (2J + 1) 2 \, \text{Re} \, [i T_{\lambda' s' l', \lambda s l}^J C_{\lambda'}(\theta_{\lambda'}) P_l(\cos \theta_{\lambda'})] \tag{8.125}$$

where the T coefficient is given by (8.124) and

$$B_L(\lambda's', \lambda s) = \tfrac{1}{4}(-1)^{s-s'} \sum_{J_1 J_2 l_1 l_2 l_1' l_2'} \times Z(l_1 J_1 l_2 J_2, sL)Z(l_1'J_1 l_2'J_2, s'L)$$
$$\times (T^{J_1}_{\lambda's'l_1',\lambda s l_1})(T^{J}_{\lambda's'l_2',\lambda s l_2})^*. \quad (8.126)$$

The Z coefficients are related to the Racah coefficients W of (A4.32) by

$$Z(l_1 J_1 l_2 J_2, sL) = \{(2l_1 + 1)(2l_2 + 1)(2J_1 + 1)(2J_2 + 1)\}^{\frac{1}{2}}$$
$$\times C^{0\ 0\ 0}_{l_1 l_2 L} W(l_1 J_1 l_2 J_2, sL). \quad (8.127)$$

Note that much computing effort may be saved by the process of squaring and defining coefficients since the spherical harmonics $Y_l^m(\Omega_{\lambda'})$, which are extremely long and difficult to compute, become Legendre polynomials $P_l(\cos \theta_{\lambda'})$. The computation of Racah and Clebsch-Gordan coefficients is not difficult for a high-speed computer.

The differential cross section (8.125) contains three terms, a pure Coulomb scattering term, a pure nuclear scattering term, and an interference term.

The cross section integrated over angles is also of interest. Using the special value of the Z coefficient

$$Z(l_1 J_1 l_2 J_2, s0) = \delta_{l_1 J_1, l_2 J_2}(-1)^{J_1-s}(2J_1 + 1)^{\frac{1}{2}}, \quad (8.128)$$

we integrate (8.125) over $d\Omega_{\lambda'}$ to obtain

$$\sigma_{\alpha s,\alpha's'} = \frac{\pi}{k_\lambda^2(2s + 1)} \sum_{Jll'} (2J + 1)|T^{J}_{\lambda's'l',\lambda s l}|^2. \quad (8.129)$$

We have omitted the infinite contribution from the Coulomb term. The important fact is that the partial wave sums over J, l, l' are incoherent, whereas they are coherent in Equation (8.125) for the differential cross section.

We can write the generalization of Equation (2.40) for the total cross section in the situation where no polarizations are measured by summing over s', averaging over s, and summing over all possible channels λ' including $\lambda' = \lambda$. We define the spin statistical factor g_J by

$$g_J = \frac{2J + 1}{(2I_1 + 1)(2I_2 + 1)}. \quad (8.130)$$

Using the unitarity of the S-matrix (see Chapter 10B) we have

$$\sigma_\lambda = \frac{\pi}{k_\lambda^2} \sum_J g_J \sum_{sl} [1 - \text{Re}(S^{J}_{\lambda sl,\lambda sl})]. \quad (8.131)$$

For detailed accounts of nuclear reaction theory, see Lane and Thomas (58) and Lane and Robson (66).

FURTHER READING

1. G. Breit and E. P. Wigner, *Phys. Rev.*, **49**, 519 (1936).
Original time-dependent discussion of two-channel scattering.

2. H. A. Bethe, *Rev. Mod. Phys.*, **9**, 69 (1937).
Time-independent multichannel theory for isolated resonances.

3. P. L. Kapur and R. E. Peierls, *Proc. Roy. Soc.* (*London*), **A166**, 277 (1938).
E. P. Wigner and L. Eisenbud, *Phys. Rev.*, **72**, 29 (1947).
Exact formal theories depending implicitly on channel radii.

4. C. Bloch, *Nucl. Phys.*, **4**, 503 (1957).
Generalized formal theory, containing earlier formal theories as special cases.

5. H. Feshbach, *Ann. Phys.*, **5**, 357 (1958); **19**, 287 (1962).
L. S. Rodberg, *Phys. Rev.*, **124**, 210 (1961).
W. M. McDonald, *Nucl. Phys.*, **54**, 393 (1964); **56**, 636, 647 (1964).
Formal theories with modified Hamiltonians.

6. R. E. Peierls, *Proc. Roy. Soc.* (*London*), **A253**, 16 (1959).
J. Humblet and L. Rosenfeld, *Nucl. Phys.*, **26**, 529 (1961).
Formal theories based on analytic properties of the *S*-matrix.

7. A. M. Lane and D. Robson, *Phys. Rev.*, **151**, 774 (1966).
Generalized formal theory including previous theories as special cases.

8. J. M. Blatt and V. F. Weisskopf, *Theoretical Nuclear Physics*, John Wiley and Sons, Inc., New York, 1952.
Review including simplified discussion of resonances.

9. A. M. Lane and R. G. Thomas, *Rev. Mod. Phys.*, **30**, 257 (1958).
Review with discussions of applications.

PROBLEMS

1. Derive the elastic scattering amplitude $f(\theta)$ for the scattering of a spinless particle by a spherical potential from the Kapur-Peierls formula.

2. Plot the differential cross section at $45°$ as a function of energy for the elastic scattering of a spinless particle by a spinless nucleus of radius 4 fm according to the Breit-Wigner formula given the following information. The position of the resonance is at 5 MeV. The width of the resonance is 10 KeV. It occurs in (a) an s state and (b) a p state.

3. Plot the differential cross section at $45°$ in the energy region 5.1 MeV through 5.2 MeV for scattering of a spinless particle by a nucleus of radius 4 fm. when

the scattering amplitude is given essentially by three resonances all of which have $G_s^{(l)}G_s^{(l)} = 0.1$ MeV and $\Gamma_s = 0.2$ MeV. The resonances are further characterized by

	$\epsilon_s + \Delta\epsilon_s$	l
(i)	5 MeV	0
(ii)	4.8 MeV	1
(iii)	5.3 MeV	0

4. Give a rough numerical estimate of the resonance parameters for the first s-state resonance in the square potential well whose depth is 40 MeV, radius 3 fm.

5. Verify that $\mathscr{H}$, defined by (8.51) is Hermitian in the interior region of the nucleus Ω.

6. Derive the expression (8.70) for the S-matrix from (8.42, 8.53, 8.56, 8.65, 8.68).

7. Verify that the time-reversed conjugate of the jj coupling wave function of (5.5) satisfies (8.93).

8. Verify from the expressions (8.119, 8.120) for the differential cross section averaged over polarizations that the cross section for elastic scattering integrated over angles contains the sum over the partial wave quantum number l incoherently.

9

APPLICATIONS OF
REACTION THEORY

Our formal study of the theory of the compound nucleus has led to the idea that the formation and decay of the compound nucleus can be understood in terms of the resonant states involved in the various channels. A resonant state occurs at an energy for which there is a high probability of finding the compound nucleus in comparison with the probability at nearby energies. Its wave function is very similar to the wave function of a bound state as far as the interior region is concerned. Since a resonant state has positive energy, it must eventually decay. It is sometimes called an energy level in analogy with bound states.

Because of the effect of the penetration factor on charged-particle scattering, resonances are observed at lowest energies in neutron scattering from nuclei. Resonances can occur at energies of the order of electron volts. Their widths are also of the order of electron volts and their spacings are so large that any departure from the Breit-Wigner formula for one level due to the effects of neighboring levels is quite unobservable. An example is shown in Fig. 9.1a.

The total width Γ_s of a resonance is the sum of the partial widths for decay of the compound nucleus into each of the accessible open channels. Clearly, at high enough energies where many channels are open, the widths will become much larger than the spacings, which decrease with increasing energy, so that, in a given channel, the scattering at a particular energy is described by a coherent sum of many resonance contributions.

In this chapter we shall discuss the variation of the cross section with energy. Experiments with poor energy resolution (which will be defined more precisely) measure the average cross section. At energies above about

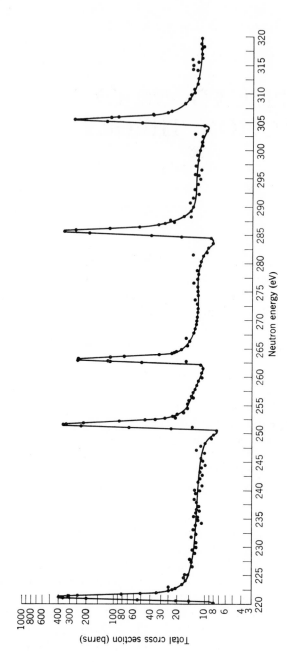

FIG. 9.1   (a) The total cross section for neutrons incident on ^{232}Th as a function of energy in the range 220 eV to 320 eV. The partial wave quantum numbers of the resonances are 0+. The solid curve is the Breit-Wigner many-level formula with parameters adjusted to fit. (Adapted from Goldberg, Mughabghab, Magurno, and May, 67.)   (b) Average total neutron cross sections for nuclei of similar sizes. The curves for Y and Zr are indistinguishable. (Adapted from Goldberg, Mughabghab, Magurno, and May, 67.)   (c) The total cross section for scattering of neutrons by ^{23}Na. The dashed curve is the optical-statistical theory of Hauser and Feshbach [Section 9C(iii)]. (Adapted from Krieger and Pearlstein, 65).

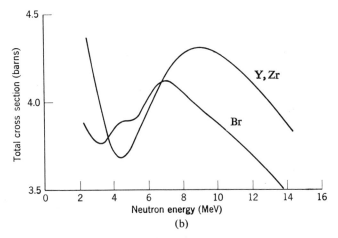

(b)

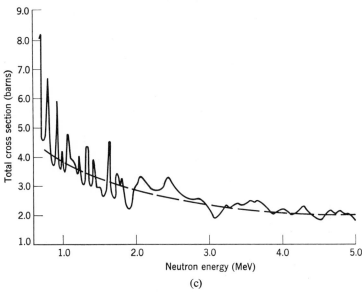

(c)

FIG. 9.1 (*b*) and (*c*)

1 MeV, average cross sections vary slowly with energy (see Fig. 9.1*b*). We shall see how it is possible to define pseudopotentials which reproduce the slowly varying average cross sections for elastic scattering and which can be used in models for other reactions based on simplifying assumptions that describe the reaction in terms of only a few degrees of freedom. The pseudopotential for elastic scattering is the optical model potential.

It is important to perform experiments with good enough energy resolution to distinguish the basic structure of the cross section as a function of energy if this is experimentally feasible. For overlapping resonances the cross section fluctuates with energy in a way that can be understood from the fact that reduced width amplitudes are real and normally distributed about zero mean. Statistical theories of nuclear reactions and cross-section fluctuations will be discussed. An example of the basic structure of a total neutron cross section at a few MeV is shown in Fig. 9.1c.

Normally, at high energies, no single resonance is sharp enough to dominate its many neighbors. Exceptions are states which are the isospin analogues of low-lying states of the nucleus with one proton replaced by a neutron. They have narrow total widths and large heights, since their decay through channels that are easily accessible in energy is restricted by lack of isospin conservation, so that the partial widths for the other channels do not contribute much to the total width.

The widths of resonances are easily translated by means of the uncertainty principle into lifetimes of the corresponding compound nucleus states. We have seen that the uncertainty principle is a short-cut method for predicting the result of an experiment. In order to understand more fully the time properties of scattering experiments, we shall work out the complete theory of experiments that would measure lifetimes of compound nuclei. The energy uncertainty in the position of a level in the scattering *amplitude* will be called *quantal uncertainty*. This uncertainty is basic to the quantum mechanics of the compound system.

In an actual experiment, there are other energy uncertainties resulting from limitations of experimental technique. For example a "50 MeV" beam from a cyclotron may include particles that have energies of 49.98 MeV and 50.01 MeV due to the different classical orbits each has described in the cyclotron. This type of uncertainty will be called *classical uncertainty*. It is tempting to apply the uncertainty principle to it and assign a corresponding lifetime property to an experiment. By giving an explicit account of the quantum mechanics of a beam, we shall show that it would be incorrect to do this. This point has caused much confusion in simple "explanations" of nuclear reaction experiments.

To avoid this confusion we have not so far mentioned time properties of reactions, that is, we have considered scattering amplitudes as functions of the complementary variable, energy. We shall continue to do this unless we are describing an experiment that is actually designed to measure time properties directly, not one that is designed to infer them from energy measurements. However, in order to see the correct relationship of energy and time properties we shall first consider the scattering of beams which are divided into wave packets so that the time of propagation of a wave packet can in principle be measured.

A. WAVE-PACKET SCATTERING

[i] Energy-Time Properties of a Beam of Particles

We shall consider a beam of particles which is not a pure state, that is, the motion of a particle in the beam is not specified as completely and accurately as possible without conflicting with the general principles of quantum mechanics. In particular, we consider that the energy resolution is capable of improvement, for example, by better magnetic analysis. The quantum mechanical way of understanding such a beam is to consider it as an ensemble of particles, each of which is in a pure state. It is an accident of the experiment that the different particles in the ensemble are mixed up. We could in principle do a separate experiment with each.

The ensemble is described by a density matrix

$$\rho = \sum_m |m\rangle P_m \langle m|, \tag{9.1}$$

where P_m is the probability of finding a beam particle in the mth pure state· In wave function notation, we may write the density matrix as

$$\rho(x, x') = \int dk_m P(k_m) \psi_m^*(k_m, x') \psi_m(k_m, x). \tag{9.2}$$

Here we are considering just one dimension of momentum $\hbar k_m$ in the beam direction. We are assuming that the collimation is sufficiently inaccurate, so that we do not need to consider momentum uncertainties perpendicular to the beam.

The wave function $\psi_m(k_m)$ will be described as a wave packet which is not an eigenstate of the momentum $\hbar k_m$. In this way we introduce quantal uncertainty into the beam. Neglecting dimensions other than the beam direction we may write

$$\psi_m(k_m, x) = \int dk F(k; k_m, W_m) e^{ik(x - x_m)}. \tag{9.3}$$

F is a weighting factor centered at k_m, defining a wave packet of width W_m. W_m is the quantal uncertainty. The position of the wave packet in configuration space, x_m, is known. It is defined, for example, by measuring the time of flight from a source position x_0.

The usual scattering experiment does not measure times of flight. Thus the variable x_m is completely undefined. In practice the shortest time we can resolve is about 10^{-10} sec. The shortest time that is allowed to be measured by the general principles of quantum mechanics is of the order of $\hbar / W_m$. We shall see in our discussion of wave packet scattering that time effects are negligible unless W_m is of the order of the resonance width. Even for a 1 eV width, $\hbar/\Gamma$ is $6.64 \cdot 10^{-16}$ sec, so that x_m is essentially unresolved even in the best possible experiment. (We might notice at this stage that this is not true for certain states which are metastable with respect to γ-decay. Lifetimes of the order of minutes are known.)

Thus the usual scattering experiment not only fails to resolve k_m as well as possible, but it does not resolve x_m at all. Even if we select a particular k_m, that is, if we remove the classical energy uncertainty, our experimental beam essentially is described by a density matrix in which the probability of finding a wave packet with a certain x_m is the same for all x_m. This density matrix may be written for quantal uncertainty W_m as

$$\rho_{W_m} = \int_{-\infty}^{\infty} dx_m \psi_m{}^*(k_m, x_m)\psi_m(k_m, x_m)$$

$$= \iiint dx_m\, dk\, dk' F^*(k'; k_m, W_m)F(k; k_m, W_m)$$

$$\times\ e^{i(k-k')x_m}e^{i(kx-k'x')}$$

$$= \iint dk\, dk' F^*(k'; k_m, W_m)F(k; k_m, W_m)\delta(k - k')e^{i(kx-k'x')}$$

$$= \int dk\ |F(k; k_m, W_m)|^2 e^{ik(x-x')}. \tag{9.4}$$

The experimental density matrix reduces to a density matrix describing a beam consisting of an ensemble of plane waves e^{ikx}, where the probability of finding a wave number k is $|F(k; k_m, W_m)|^2$.

The quantal uncertainty completely disappears if there is no time resolution in the experiment. In previous discussions of the conditions of the incident beam, we have assumed that it is a plane wave. We have now proved that, whatever the energy resolution in the experiment, if time is not resolved, the experiment may be considered as one of an ensemble of experiments, each with plane wave initial conditions.

[ii]   Time-Dependent Initial Conditions in Elastic Scattering

Although it is a fact imposed by the nature of measuring equipment that time dependence is negligible in the usual scattering experiment, it helps to clarify our understanding of reactions if we consider the scattering of a wave packet. We shall see also under what conditions time-dependent effects can be observed.

We shall consider wave packet states ξ_0 describing particles localized in the region R whose macroscopic distance from the scattering center is $\mathbf{r_0}$. The particles are moving towards the scattering center with mean momentum $\hbar\mathbf{k_0}$. The situation is illustrated in Fig. 9.2. ξ_0 describes the initial conditions when $\mathbf{r}_0$ is large. We are interested in the probability of a particle reaching the detector D as a function of time as well as of the position $\mathbf{r}_d$ of D.

Quantum mechanics tells us the time behavior of the eigenstates ψ_k of the total Hamiltonian for the problem.

$$\psi_{\mathbf{k}}(t) = \psi_{\mathbf{k}} e^{-iE_{\mathbf{k}}t/\hbar}. \tag{9.5}$$

For simplicity of notation we shall include the bound states in the set $\psi_{\mathbf{k}}$. If we normalize the scattering states by considering the whole system in a

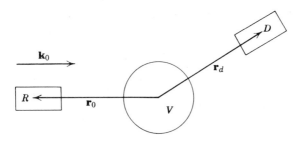

FIG. 9.2 Definition of the quantities used in the discussion of wave-packet scattering.

box as in Chapter 1B, the $\psi_{\mathbf{k}}$ form a complete orthonormal set in terms of which we can expand the initial state vector ξ_0.

$$\xi_0 = \int d^3k \omega(\mathbf{k}_0, \mathbf{k}) \psi_{\mathbf{k}}. \tag{9.6}$$

The integral is defined to include a discrete sum over the bound states. Using the orthonormality property of the $\psi_{\mathbf{k}}$, we find the coefficients ω of the expansion (9.6).

$$\omega(\mathbf{k}_0, \mathbf{k}) = \int d^3r \xi_0 \psi_{\mathbf{k}_0}{}^*. \tag{9.7}$$

The wave packet at time t becomes, using the time development (9.5) of the eigenstates $\psi_{\mathbf{k}}$,

$$\xi_0(t) = \int d^3k \omega(\mathbf{k}_0, \mathbf{k}) \psi_{\mathbf{k}} e^{-iE_{\mathbf{k}}t/\hbar}. \tag{9.8}$$

We shall now introduce a more explicit expression for the initial wave packet.

$$\xi_0 = (2\pi)^{-3/2} \int d^3k F(\mathbf{k}) e^{i\mathbf{k}\cdot(\mathbf{r}-\mathbf{r}_0)}. \tag{9.9}$$

The weight function $F(\mathbf{k})$ has mean value $\mathbf{k}_0$ and quantal uncertainty $\delta\mathbf{k}$. The corresponding localization in configuration space is $\delta\mathbf{r}$ about $\mathbf{r}_0$.

We shall now evaluate the expansion coefficients $\omega(\mathbf{k}_0, \mathbf{k})$. The overlap integral (9.7) is negligible for bound states since ξ_0 is negligible outside R and the bound-state wave functions are negligible outside the scattering region V. r_0 is a macroscopic distance.

It is sufficient to consider the scattering states, which may be written as a plane ingoing wave superposed on a spherical outgoing wave.

$$\psi_{\mathbf{k}}(\mathbf{r}) = (2\pi)^{-3/2}[e^{i\mathbf{k}\cdot\mathbf{r}} + \mathscr{F}(\mathbf{k}, \mathbf{r})]. \tag{9.10}$$

The second term is proportional to e^{ikr}/r for large r. We have for the expansion coefficients

$$\omega(\mathbf{k}_0, \mathbf{k}) = \int d^3r \xi_0(\mathbf{r})(2\pi)^{-3/2}[e^{-i\mathbf{k}\cdot\mathbf{r}} + \mathscr{F}^*(\mathbf{k}, \mathbf{r})]. \tag{9.11}$$

The plane wave term of (9.11) reduces with the definition (9.9) of the initial wave packet to

$$\omega(\mathbf{k}_0, \mathbf{k}) = F(\mathbf{k})e^{-i\mathbf{k}\cdot\mathbf{r}_0}. \tag{9.12}$$

The second term in (9.11) is negligible. Since ξ_0 vanishes outside R, we may restrict the integration to the region R where $\mathscr{F}(\mathbf{k}, \mathbf{r})$ has its asymptotic form

$$\mathscr{F}(\mathbf{k}, \mathbf{r}) \sim \frac{f(k, \theta)e^{ikr}}{r}. \tag{9.13}$$

$f(k, \theta)$ varies slowly with θ in the region R.

The magnitude of the second term in (9.11) is

$$\left| \int_K d^3k' F(\mathbf{k}')e^{-i\mathbf{k}'\cdot\mathbf{r}_0}f^*(k, \theta) \int_R \frac{d^3r e^{i\mathbf{k}\cdot\mathbf{r}} e^{-ikr}}{r} \right| \sim \frac{|f(k, \theta)|}{r_0}. \tag{9.14}$$

K is the region of momentum space corresponding to R. In nuclear scattering experiments $|f(k, \theta)|$, when multiplied by the appropriate constants, is of the order of fermis, while r_0 is of the order of centimeters. Thus (9.14) is very small, and we may write the wave packet at time t using (9.8, 9.12) as

$$\xi_0(\mathbf{r}, t) = \int d^3k F(\mathbf{k})e^{-i\mathbf{k}\cdot\mathbf{r}_0 - iE_{\mathbf{k}}t/\hbar}\psi_{\mathbf{k}}(\mathbf{r}). \tag{9.15}$$

This is just a superposition of wave functions describing the time development of the energy eigenstates with superposition coefficients equal to those of the incident wave packet.

The probability of detection at time t is

$$P(t) = |\xi_0(\mathbf{r}_d, t)|^2 r_d^2 \, d\Omega_d. \tag{9.16}$$

The differential cross section for a time-independent experiment is

$$\frac{d\sigma}{d\Omega_d} = v_0 r_d^2 \int_{-\infty}^{\infty} dt \, |\xi_0(\mathbf{r}_d, t)|^2 \tag{9.17}$$

where ξ_0 is given by (9.15) with appropriate normalization.

[iii] Time Dependence of the Detection Probability

The asymptotic solution of the wave-packet scattering problem is given by the time development of the wave packet (9.15). In order to evaluate (9.15), we shall make some special assumptions about the experiment.

We shall first make the approximation that the exponent of the integrand of (9.15) is linear in E. For nonrelativistic scattering, this involves neglecting the final term in the following expansion of E.

$$E = (\hbar^2/2m)[2\mathbf{k} \cdot \mathbf{k}_0 - k_0^2 + |\mathbf{k} - \mathbf{k}_0|^2]. \tag{9.18}$$

For photons this restriction is unnecessary. We have

$$E = \hbar c k. \tag{9.19}$$

The restriction means that the source, scatterer, and detector are so close that we can neglect the spreading of the wave packet. This situation is not realizable in an actual experiment except for a photon scattering experiment.

We can choose the shape of the weight function $F(\mathbf{k}_0, \delta\mathbf{k}; \mathbf{k})$ to simplify the calculation. Since we are not interested in the angular uncertainty, we write

$$F(\mathbf{k}_0, \delta\mathbf{k}; \mathbf{k}) = \frac{\delta(\theta_k - \theta_0)\delta(\phi_k - \phi_0)}{2\pi k^2 \sin\theta_k} \Delta(k_0, \delta k; k). \tag{9.20}$$

We shall be interested only in the scattered wave part of ξ_0 defined by (9.15). Using E instead of k according to (9.18) and using the particular wave-packet shape (9.20), we have for the amplitude of the scattered wave packet

$$\xi(\mathbf{r}, t) = (2\pi)^{\frac{1}{2}} \frac{e^{ik_0(r_0+r)/2}}{r} \int_0^\infty dE\, \Delta(E_0, \delta; E) e^{iE[(r_0+r)/v_0-t]/\hbar} f(E, \theta). \tag{9.21}$$

Here $\Delta(E_0, \delta; E)$ is the function of E corresponding to $\Delta(k_0, \delta k; k)$ and v_0 is the mean velocity of the wave packet.

At this stage we shall introduce the Kapur-Peierls expansion of the elastic scattering amplitude $f(k, \theta)$. The diagonal elements of the S-matrix (8.100) for elastic scattering may be written

$$\eta_l \equiv S_{ll} = e^{i\xi_l}\left[1 - i\sum_s \frac{G_s^{(l)}G_s^{(l)}}{E - \epsilon_s + i\Gamma_s/2}\right]e^{i\xi_l}. \tag{9.22}$$

According to (2.37) the scattering amplitude is given by

$$f(E, \theta) = (2ik)^{-1}\sum_l (2l+1)P_l(\cos\theta)\left\{e^{2i\xi_l} - 1 + \sum_s \frac{R_{ls}}{E - \epsilon_s + i\Gamma_s/2}\right\}, \tag{9.23}$$

where we have abbreviated the notation by defining the residues R_{ls} at the poles in the scattering amplitude by

$$R_{ls} = -ie^{2i\xi_l}\Gamma_s^{(l)} = -ie^{2i\xi_l}G_s^{(l)}G_s^{(l)}. \qquad (9.24)$$

If we consider only a limited energy range, we have a finite sum over s in (9.23), with resonances outside the range contributing a smoothly-varying term $C_l'(E)$ to the scattering amplitude owing to the coherent sums of the long tails of the resonance terms. The smoothly varying scattering amplitude could be derived in a limited energy range from a potential. We could define a potential scattering term $C_l(E)$ whose definition depends on the energy range.

$$C_l(E) = e^{2i\xi_l} - 1 + C_l'(E). \qquad (9.25)$$

Abbreviating the notation still further and using (9.23, 9.25) we have

$$\xi(\mathbf{r}, t) = K \sum_l (2l + 1)P_l(\cos\theta)$$

$$\times \int_0^\infty dE\,\Delta(E)\left[C_l(E) + \sum_s \frac{R_{ls}}{E - \epsilon_s + i\Gamma_s/2}\right]e^{iEX}, \qquad (9.26)$$

where

$$X = \frac{[(r_0 + r)/v_0 - t]}{\hbar} \qquad (9.27)$$

$$KK^* = \frac{1}{8\pi r^2}. \qquad (9.28)$$

The limited energy range for which $C_l(E)$ is defined includes the range for which the wave packet weight factor $\Delta(E_0, \delta; E)$ is significant. We shall assume that $C_l(E)$ is constant in this range.

The time properties of the scattering will be discussed in terms of the variable X. The quantity $(r_0 + r)/v_0$ is the time of flight of the center of a wave packet that is not retarded by the interaction. X is positive for times shorter than $(r_0 + r)/v_0$ and negative for times longer than $(r_0 + r)/v_0$.

[iv] POTENTIAL SCATTERING

We are now in a position to consider the probability of detecting a particle as a function of time. We shall see how the time dependence is related to the S-matrix. Let us first consider the case of propagation by potential scattering only. This includes the trivial case of free propagation, $C_l(E) = 1$.

There is one specific shape for $\Delta(E)$ which leads to very easy evaluation of the integral. We shall basically consider this shape always in this text.

$$\Delta(E_0, \delta; E) = \frac{i/2\pi}{E - E_0 + i\delta/2}. \qquad (9.29)$$

We may abbreviate the notation for ΔE by defining the complex number E_δ which represents the position and width parameters.

$$E_\delta = E_0 - \frac{i\delta}{2}. \tag{9.30}$$

In order to perform the integration very simply, one other approximation is needed: to extend the lower limit of the energy integration in (9.26) to $-\infty$. In doing this we assume that the contribution from bound states is small.

With the form (9.29) for ΔE the integral to be evaluated is

$$I = \int_{-\infty}^{\infty} dE \, \frac{i/2\pi}{E - E_\delta} C_l(E) e^{iEX}. \tag{9.31}$$

For $X > 0$ the integration is along the real axis and round an infinite semi-circle in the upper half plane on which the integrand vanishes. Since the pole E_δ is in the lower half plane, the integral is zero. For $X < 0$ we integrate round an infinite semicircle in the lower half plane, obtaining a contribution from the pole.

$$\begin{aligned} I &= C_l(E_\delta) e^{iE_\delta X}, & X &< 0, \\ &= 0, & X &> 0. \end{aligned} \tag{9.32}$$

The scattered wave packet does not exist for times before $t = (r_0 + r)/v_0$. For times after, this is propagated with a velocity v_0 and the probability of detection decays in time at a given point r with a time constant $\hbar/\delta$. This is seen by substituting the definitions (9.27, 9.30) of X and E_δ in (9.32) to obtain the explicit form

$$I = C_l(E_\delta) e^{iE_0 X - \delta(r_0 + r)/2v_0} e^{-(\delta/2\hbar)t}. \tag{9.33}$$

The detection probability $|\xi(\mathbf{r}, t)|^2$ is proportional to $e^{-(\delta/\hbar)t}$.

This form of $\Delta(E)$ is a wave packet that appears in nature. If we create a particle that can decay, for example, we may suddenly (in comparison with $\hbar/\delta$) excite a nuclear level whose energy is E_0 and lifetime $\hbar/\delta$, the wave function of the decay product is represented by this wave packet.

We have also shown that the propagation of the wave packet is not affected by the potential scattering term except for an amplitude factor $C_l(E_\delta)$.

The form

$$\Delta(E_0, \delta; E) = \frac{i/2\pi}{E - E_\delta^*} \tag{9.34}$$

would likewise correspond to a wave packet exponentially increasing in time. The form

$$\Delta(E_0, \delta; E) = \frac{\delta/2\pi}{(E - E_0)^2 + \delta^2/4} = \frac{i/2\pi}{E - E_\delta} - \frac{i/2\pi}{E - E_\delta^*} \tag{9.35}$$

corresponds to a wave packet increasing exponentially with a lifetime $\hbar/\delta$ up to $t = (r_0 + r)/v_0$ and then decaying exponentially with a lifetime $\hbar/\delta$. This type of wave packet is like the localized packet of our previous scattering theory. We shall see how it scatters in certain circumstances.

[v] RESONANCE SCATTERING

We shall now consider the case where the S-matrix has poles

$$E_s = \epsilon_s - i\frac{\Gamma_s}{2}, \tag{9.36}$$

which are so isolated that the scattering from the other poles is negligible compared with the scattering from E_s for energies where $\Delta(E)$, given by (9.35), is significant. When we see the form of the cross section we shall understand that this can be satisfied in practice. The detection probability amplitude is proportional to

$$I = \int_{-\infty}^{\infty} dE \, \frac{\delta/2\pi}{(E - E_\delta)(E - E_\delta{}^*)} \frac{R_{ls}}{E - E_s} e^{iEX}$$

$$= \frac{R_{ls}}{E_\delta{}^* - E_s} e^{iE_\delta{}^*X}, \qquad\qquad X > 0,$$

$$= \frac{R_{ls}}{E_\delta - E_s} e^{iE_\delta X} - i\delta \frac{R_{ls}}{(E_s - E_\delta)(E_s - E_\delta{}^*)} e^{iE_sX}, \qquad X < 0. \tag{9.37}$$

This form is very interesting and much can be learned about scattering from it.

First, we can use it to interpret the resonance term in the S-matrix physically. Thus far we have only a mathematical expansion. If we take the limit $\delta \to \infty$, that is, the limit in which the time width of the wave packet becomes very small so that we excite the scatterer suddenly and watch it decay, the time spectrum of the tail has the shape $e^{-\Gamma_s t/\hbar}$. The lifetime of the compound system is $\hbar/\Gamma_s$. We have thus derived the same result from a detailed scattering theory that we knew already from the uncertainty principle, an approximate scattering theory.

Second, we consider the propagation of the leading edge of the wave packet ($X > 0$). This is propagated without change of shape. Disturbances due to the scatterer appear *after* the center of the wave packet has passed the scatterer. This is still true in the case of the usual scattering experiment where δ is very small compared to Γ_s. The mathematical reason can be seen from (9.37). The S-matrix has no poles in the upper half energy plane [see Equation (8.87)]. A pole in the upper half plane would result in a second term for $X > 0$ with a time factor $e^{iE_\delta{}^*X}$ characteristic of the scatterer. The time factor for $X > 0$ is at present characteristic of the wave packet, not the scatterer.

Thus we have obtained a physical understanding of the fact that *causality requires the S-matrix to be analytic in the upper half E-plane.*

The cross section, obtained by integrating $|I|^2$ [given by (9.37)] over time, is proportional to

$$\frac{d\sigma_R}{d\Omega} = \frac{R_{ls}R_{ls}*[(E - \epsilon_s)^2\Gamma_s/2 + (\Gamma_s + \delta)^2(\Gamma_s/2 + \delta)/4]}{2\Gamma_s[(E - \epsilon_s)^2 + (\Gamma_s + \delta)^2/4]^2}. \tag{9.38}$$

In the usual scattering experiment, δ is negligible in comparison with Γ_s. In this case, (9.38) reduces to a form which is formally identical to the Breit-Wigner formula for a single level and which is approximately identical to it for a small energy range over which the differences in the Kapur-Peierls and Wigner-Eisenbud definitions of ϵ_s, Γ_s and R_{ls} are unimportant.

Equation (9.38) also tells us under what conditions the wave packet width is significant in an experiment. We must have time resolution $\hbar/\delta$ such that δ is comparable to the resonance width Γ_s.

[vi] EXPERIMENTS INVOLVING ISOLATED RESONANCES

The absorption of a γ-ray produced by the decay of a metastable nuclear level in a source by the same level in a target has an enormously wide application in all branches of physics because of the energy resolution available. The 14 KeV metastable level in ^{57}Fe has, for example, a lifetime of 10^{-7} sec and a width of 6.10^{-9} eV, so that the absorption cross section will be negligible unless the γ-ray energy is within a few times 10^{-9} eV of the level eigenvalue. This type of resonant absorption is the Mössbauer effect (Mössbauer, 58). It would not be possible for isolated nuclei in the source or target because the recoil of the nucleus in the decay and the absorption completely destroys the energy matching of the γ-ray and the level. However, if both nuclei are embedded in crystals, the recoil energy of a free nucleon is often not enough to excite a quantum state of the crystal with high probability. Thus the recoil momentum is absorbed collectively by the whole crystal with a sufficiently small change in energy.

The lifetime of 10^{-7} sec is long enough to make well-resolved time-dependent measurements of γ-ray probabilities. It has been confirmed, for example, by Holland, Lynch, Perlow, and Hanna (60), that the time dependence of the decay of the ^{57}Fe level is given by the square of the wave packet (9.33). It is a smooth exponential decay with lifetime 10^{-7} sec corresponding to $\hbar/\delta$.

The probability of absorption of the γ-ray in the target level is proportional to the differential cross section for scattering from that level. It is of course reemitted eventually after absorption, but not usually in the incident direction.

Using the physically realistic decaying wave packet (9.31) in our scattering formalism (9.26) instead of the symmetrical packet (9.35), and integrating over time, we find the differential cross section for the Mössbauer effect is proportional to

$$\frac{d\sigma}{d\Omega} = \frac{R_{ls}^2}{2\Gamma_s} \frac{1}{(E_0 - E_s)^2 + \Gamma_s^2}. \tag{9.39}$$

In this case the width of the wave packet is of course equal to the width of the scattering resonance Γ_s. The width of the resonance in the Mössbauer effect is twice Γ_s.

The measurement of the time dependence of the decay of the target level, in an experiment where the initial time of excitation of the source level is determined, constitutes a wave-packet scattering experiment. Two time measurements are necessary, that of the time of excitation of the source and that of the time of detection of the scattered γ-rays. This experiment was also performed by Holland, Lynch, Perlow, and Hanna. An account of more detailed experiments is given by Lynch, Holland, and Hamermesh (60).

Instead of a smooth exponential time dependence, an oscillating pattern was observed. The frequency of the oscillation increased as $E_0 - \epsilon_s$ increased. This corresponds to the interference of the two terms in the scattering amplitude which is again given by using a decaying wave packet (9.31). It is proportional to

$$I = \int_{-\infty}^{\infty} dE \frac{i/2\pi}{E - E_\delta} \frac{R_{ls}}{E - E_s} e^{iEX}$$
$$= 0, \qquad\qquad X > 0,$$
$$= \frac{R_{ls}}{E_s - E_\delta} e^{iE_s X} - \frac{R_{ls}}{E_s - E_\delta} e^{iE_\delta X}, \qquad X < 0. \tag{9.40}$$

In the experiment we are describing, $\Gamma_\delta = \Gamma_s$. If E_0 is exactly equal to ϵ_s, the detection probability decays smoothly as a function of time with a width $\hbar/2\Gamma_s$. If E_0 differs from ϵ_s, oscillations appear as a function of time. Equation (9.40) implies that the frequency of the oscillations increases as $\sin (E_0 - \epsilon_s)X$. This is illustrated in Fig. 9.3.

The experiment checks the superposition principle for energy and time in the same way that a diffraction experiment tests it for momentum and position. The width of the absorbing resonance corresponds to the width of the diffracting slit. The fact that the incident beam must have the right energy corresponds to the fact that the beam must hit the slit. The measured time distribution of photons corresponds to the measured momentum distribution of photons.

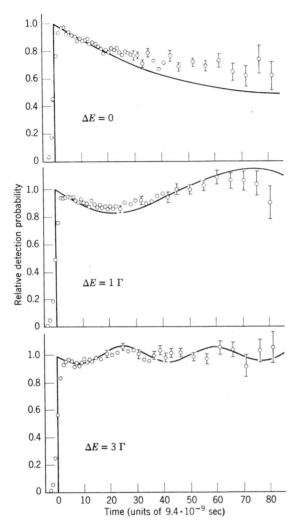

FIG. 9.3 Time spectra obtained in the wave-packet scattering experiment for various energy shifts of the emitted γ-ray. $\Delta E = E_0 - \epsilon_s$. The solid curves are theoretical predictions.

A very interesting application of resonance theory to nuclear and particle physics is the *Dalitz plot*. For many years our knowledge of particles was restricted to those which last long enough for their tracks to be observed in an emulsion or bubble chamber. A particle which decays may be thought of as a resonant state of the compound system consisting of the decay products. If a particle is produced in a reaction with a two-body final state, conservation of energy and momentum require the phase space it can occupy to be severely restricted.

Consider a reaction of the form

$$1 + 2 \rightarrow 3 + 4 + 5.$$

If particles 3 and 4 result from the decay of a long-lived parent body X, we have for the momenta $\mathbf{p}$ and kinetic energies T,

$$\mathbf{p}_X + \mathbf{p}_5 = \mathbf{p}_1 + \mathbf{p}_2 = \mathbf{p}_3 + \mathbf{p}_4 + \mathbf{p}_5, \tag{9.41}$$

and

$$T_X + T_5 = T_1 + T_2 = T_3 + T_4 + T_5. \tag{9.42}$$

The summed energy T_X of T_3 and T_4 has a fixed value for all momentum transfers $\mathbf{p}_X$. If T_3 is plotted against T_4 for different momentum transfers, the points lie along the straight line

$$T_3 + T_4 = T_X. \tag{9.42'}$$

In certain experiments it may be more convenient to plot different functions, but the experimental points will always lie on a curve C corresponding to (9.42'). If X has a finite lifetime τ for decay into two particles, there will be an energy spread of width $\delta = \hbar/\tau$. If it is not really a resonant state at all, but two noninteracting bodies, δ will be infinite and there will be no trace of the curve C in the phase space plot. If τ is finite, points in the phase space plot will be clustered round the curve C with a probability distribution whose width is δ.

Such particles may be called "particles," "resonances," or "final state interactions." Examples of interest in nuclear physics are the ρ- and ω-mesons which play an important part in the nuclear force.

Figure 9.4 shows the Dalitz plot for the reaction

$$\pi^- + p \rightarrow \pi^- + \pi^+ + n$$

for small values of the momentum transfer. The kinetic energies of the π^- and π^+ in the C.M. system are plotted against each other. If the π^- and π^+ are uncorrelated, we expect roughly an even distribution of points over the diagram. If they emerge from the reaction in a resonant state with a fairly definite mass m, then their relativistic energies must always add to $E_{\text{C.M.}}^{(0)}(\pi^-) + E_{\text{C.M.}}^{(0)}(p) - E_{\text{C.M.}}^{(f)}(n)$, where the superscript (0) indicates the entrance channel and (f) indicates the exit channel. For the incident π^- energy of Fig. 9.4, which is 3,000 MeV, the curve C is the straight line

$$E_{\text{C.M.}}(\pi^-) + E_{\text{C.M.}}(\pi^+) = (1860 - mc^2) \text{ MeV},$$

where the omission of the superscript indicates the final state kinetic energy rather than the total relativistic energy. Different points on the curve C represent different values of the momentum transfer, which is not measured in this experiment.

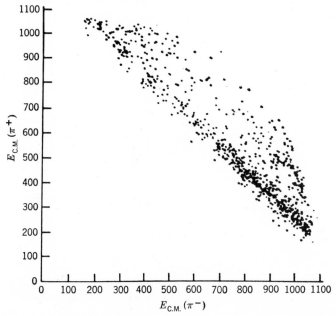

FIG. 9.4 Dalitz plot for the kinetic energies of the two pions in the final state of the reaction $\pi^- + p \rightarrow \pi^- + \pi^+ + n$ with 3000 MeV incident pions. (Adapted from Selove, 65.)

In Fig. 9.4 there are two straight lines C about which the points cluster. The strongest is the one for which the pion energies add to about 1100 MeV, corresponding to $mc^2 \simeq 760$ MeV, with a width of about 125 MeV. This resonance is the ρ-meson whose mass is 763 MeV (see Chapter 3A). There is a faint suggestion of a line at about 1450 MeV. This resonance is called the f^0.

Lifetimes of nuclear resonant states which last for a very short time may be observed in the same way. An example is the discovery of excited states of the α-particle in reactions of the form $1 + 2 \rightarrow 3 + 4 + 5$ with a three-body final state in which two of the bodies, $3 + 5$, constitute an α-particle. We shall consider the reaction

$$^3\text{He} + \text{d} \rightarrow {}^3\text{He} + \text{p} + \text{n},$$

where the following quantities are measured.

T_3 = energy of ^{3}He,

T_4 = energy of p,

θ_3 = angle of ^{3}He measured from the incident direction,

θ_4 = angle of p measured from the incident direction with the two counters and the incident beam coplanar.

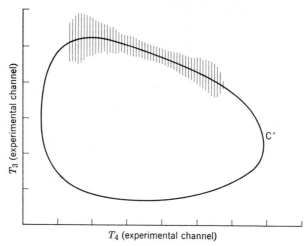

FIG. 9.5   The curve C' showing the values of T_3 and T_4 allowed by kinematics in the reaction ^{3}He + d → ^{3}He + p + n with the ^{3}He and p counters fixed at particular angles θ_3, θ_4. The length of the vertical lines is proportional to the differential cross section for the reaction. The cross section was not measured on the lower half of the curve. The axes represent channels in an experimental recording device which have approximately equal energy intervals between them. (Adapted from Donovan, 65.)

If the final state consisted of α + p, with the α-particle almost permanently bound, the plot of T_3 against T_4 would consist of a curve C on which different points corresponded to different sets of values of θ_3 and θ_4. If the counters are fixed at particular values of θ_3 and θ_4 (that is, if the momentum transfer is fixed), the values of T_3 and T_4 are restricted to be on another curve C'. Figure 9.5 shows the curve C' for 31.8 MeV ^{3}He incident on a deuterium target with $\theta_3 = 25°$, $\theta_4 = -45°$ (Donovan, 65). This curve is calculated from kinematics. A permanent α-particle is represented by a single point on C', namely the intersection of C and C'.

Figure 9.5 also shows an intensity plot of the differential cross section. There are two segments of C' populated by the reaction. The spread of the populated part gives the width of the resonance. In this particular example the populated segment on the right of the figure corresponds to a state of ^{4}He at 21.24 ± 0.20 MeV with a width of 1.2 MeV. The populated segment on the left of the figure corresponds to the intersection of the curves C and

C' for singlet deuterons ($T = 1$), where the neutron is bound to the proton rather than to the ^{3}He.

[vii] INTERFERENCE OF RESONANT AND POTENTIAL SCATTERING

In general, in the energy region occupied by a resonance there will be a potential scattering term $C_l(E)$ resulting from the coherent addition of the contributions to the scattering amplitude from the tails of distant resonances. We will consider the scattering amplitude as the sum of a resonant term from the single resonance, and a potential term. This will be legitimate for a wave packet whose width is no greater than the energy range for which $C_l(E)$ is sensibly constant.

We may think of the potential scattering as immediate scattering and resonant scattering as delayed, although we have seen that the delay is due to the stretching out of the trailing edge of the packet to a width comparable to the level width Γ_s, rather than to a delay in the propagation of the maximum point in the packet.

Many fallacious arguments about this interference appear in the literature and it is a good idea to work out in detail what happens. The extreme statement of the fallacy is as follows. "Poor energy resolution in the incident beam is equivalent to an incident wave packet of width δ. The resonantly scattered wave packet will be delayed in comparison with the immediate wave packet by the lifetime τ of the resonance. If $\hbar/\delta > \tau$ the potential and resonant wave packets will interfere. If $\hbar/\delta \ll \tau$, they will not interfere and potential scattering will be independent of resonant scattering. This will occur if there is sufficiently poor resolution in the beam."

The first fallacy is that poor energy resolution corresponds to a wave packet. We have proved in Section [i] that plane wave initial conditions apply unless there is time resolution in the experiment. Thus the incident wave packet has infinite time width, and the interference is complete. Equation (9.38) shows that the wave packet width is insignificant unless the experimental time resolution is comparable with the characteristic time of the reaction $\hbar/\Gamma_s$.

It may be argued that, even if there is no wave packet in an actual experiment, it is useful to consider a hypothetical experiment in which there is sufficient time resolution. In this case the interference term in the cross section is obtained by squaring the sum of the potential and resonant amplitudes given by using localized wave packets (9.35) in the scattering formalism. It is

$$
\frac{d\sigma_I}{d\Omega} = \frac{1}{2} \operatorname{Re} [R_{ls} C_l^*(E)] \frac{(E - \epsilon_s)[(E - \epsilon_s)^2 + (\Gamma_s + \delta)(\Gamma_s + 3\delta)/4]}{[(E - \epsilon_s)^2 + (\Gamma_s + \delta)^2/4]^2}
$$

$$
+ \frac{1}{2} \operatorname{Im} [R_{ls} C_l^*(E)] \frac{(E - \epsilon_s)^2 \Gamma_s/2 + (\Gamma_s + \delta)^2(\Gamma_s + 2\delta)/8}{[(E - \epsilon_s)^2 + (\Gamma_s + \delta)^2/4]^2} . \quad (9.43)
$$

Since comparison with the resonant differential cross section (9.38) shows that $d\sigma_I/d\Omega$ is of order $1/\delta$ as δ increases, the interference term does disappear. However, $d\sigma_R/d\Omega$ is also of this order, so that the interference term is always as important as the resonant term, even for wave packet initial conditions.

[viii] SCATTERING FROM OVERLAPPING RESONANCES

We have thus far considered the case where only one resonance is important at incident energies near ϵ_s except that the effect of distant resonances is called potential scattering. We shall now consider more explicitly the case where many resonances contribute to the scattering amplitude at the energy E. The scattering amplitude in this case is a sum of terms like (9.37). For a particular partial wave l, the trailing edge of the wave packet is

$$\xi(\mathbf{r}, t) = e^{iEX} \sum_s \frac{R_{ls}}{E - \epsilon_s + i(\Gamma_s + \delta)/2} \left\{ e^{\delta X/2} - \frac{i\delta e^{\Gamma_s X/2} e^{i(\epsilon_s - E)X}}{E - \epsilon_s + i(\Gamma_s + \delta)/2} \right\}.$$

$$(9.44)$$

For wave-packet scattering which is not integrated over the scattering direction, the probability of detection contains a coherent sum over l as well as s. The first term in the bracket describes properties of the wave packet, the second term is a wave packet tail containing properties of the scattering amplitude.

Each resonance contributes a tail to the amplitude with a decay constant $\hbar/\Gamma$. However, this contribution is multiplied by a phase factor $\exp[i(\epsilon_s - E)X]$ which gives a partial cancellation of the tails when the packets from different resonances are superposed.

If $\Gamma_s \gg D$ the factor $\epsilon_s - E$ can be large so that the phase factor oscillates rapidly. In this case, the phases of contributions from different resonances s, l may be considered as random so that the tails of the wave packets cancel on the average when summed over s and l. The average result is a scattered wave packet without time delay as in the case of potential scattering. Fluctuations about the average do have time delay. In the following section we shall consider the use of a potential to represent elastic scattering.

Further details of wave-packet scattering are given, for example, by Sasakawa (59), Dodd and McCarthy (64), and Rosenfeld (65).

B. DIRECT ELASTIC SCATTERING

We have shown in the case of elastic scattering that wave packets of high enough energy are propagated on the average without time delay. We could have performed the same calculation for off-diagonal S-matrix elements representing inelastic and rearrangement collisions with the same result. Another way of saying that wave packets are propagated without time delay is to say that the scattering amplitude is a slowly varying function of energy. Such a reaction will be defined to be a *direct reaction*.

The potential from which the direct reaction amplitude is derived in the case of elastic scattering is the optical model potential. The resonances in the scattering amplitude are given by poles in the complex E plane as shown in Fig. 9.6. Consider for simplicity the Kapur-Peierls formulation of the S-matrix. At lower energies the poles are near the real axis. It is possible for the incident energy to be at a point ϵ_1 very close to a certain eigenvalue E_s.

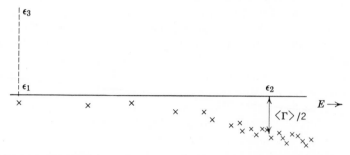

FIG. 9.6 Schematic diagram of poles in the lower-half energy plane for the Kapur-Peierls scattering amplitude.

In this case, E_s gives the principal contribution to the S-matrix. We have a well-determined level and the cross section looks like that for a well-separated resonance.

At higher energies the average width $\langle \Gamma \rangle$ can become much greater than the average level spacing $\langle D \rangle$. The appropriate energy interval for the average will be discussed shortly. The incident energy is now represented by a point such as ϵ_2, whose distance is the same order of magnitude from each of a number of poles E_s.

At lower energy the experimental resolution may be so bad that the cross sections for different resonances are not distinguished, even though the resonances may be separated. In this case we would be interested in the average cross section, the average being taken over an energy interval I given by the experimental resolution.

Feshbach, Porter, and Weisskopf (54) defined the optical model potential to be that potential which reproduces the average scattering amplitude $\langle S \rangle$. The average cross section $\langle \sigma \rangle$ may be written as follows

$$\langle \sigma \rangle = \langle |S - \langle S \rangle + \langle S \rangle|^2 \rangle$$
$$= \langle |S - \langle S \rangle|^2 + |\langle S \rangle|^2 + 2 \operatorname{Re} (S - \langle S \rangle)\langle S \rangle^* \rangle. \qquad (9.45)$$

The average scattering amplitude $\langle S \rangle$ is defined to be the one which makes the third term of (9.45) vanish. In this case we may write

$$\langle \sigma \rangle = \sigma_s + \sigma_c, \tag{9.46}$$

where

$$\sigma_s = |\langle S \rangle|^2, \qquad \sigma_c = \langle |S - \langle S \rangle|^2 \rangle. \tag{9.47}$$

The cross section σ_s is called the shape elastic cross section, since the average, smoothly varying, or instantaneous scattering amplitude [in the sense of our wave-packet description (9.33)] is reproduced by a potential which must have approximately the same space dimensions as the interaction region. This cross section exhibits fluctuations with a period of a few MeV due to single-particle or giant resonances in different partial waves at different energies. An example is shown in Fig. 9.1b. The resonances are due to interference of the incident wave with waves transmitted by the potential.

The cross section σ_c is called compound elastic or fluctuation scattering. It is large if the scattering amplitude in fact fluctuates widely, that is, if the incident energy is something like ϵ_1 in Fig. 9.6. Clearly, for wave packet initial conditions, we are not now in the situation where many resonances, which may be far away from the incident energy E, contribute to S with large phase factors $e^{i(\epsilon_s - E)X}$ whose random values cancel the delayed parts of the trailing edge of the wave packet on the average [see Equation (9.44)]. In fact the time dependence is much more like that for isolated resonances (9.37) where the trailing edge of the wave packet has a long tail of width $\hbar/\Gamma_s$. In this sense, σ_c represents delayed scattering. The word "compound" is sometimes used in a sense first developed by Bohr (36). The compound system is only called "compound" if it lasts for a time much longer than the time it takes the incident particle to cross a region of free space of the same dimensions as the nucleus. For isolated resonances the "delay time" is $\hbar/\Gamma_s$. In the usual experiment it is of course impossible to tell which particles are delayed. We prefer to describe the scattering amplitude as a function of energy and use the term "fluctuation scattering." This term can be applied also in the region where many resonances overlap. The fluctuations from the average situation for this region will be discussed in Section 1C of this chapter.

We shall now concern ourselves with the problem of finding the average scattering amplitude. This is done by means of a trick used by Wigner (51). The average amplitude is calculated by adding an imaginary part to the incident energy E.

To prove that this method gives the average scattering amplitude, we define the Kapur-Peierls amplitude in the resonance region to be

$$R(E) = \sum_s \frac{R_{ls}}{E_s - E}.$$ (9.48)

The average is given by $\int_I R(E)\,dE$ where I is the interval defined by the experimental resolution. This integral is zero if dE follows a contour lying wholly in the upper half plane. Such a contour is shown in Fig. 9.7.

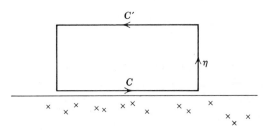

FIG. 9.7   The complex E plane for the Kapur-Peierls scattering amplitude showing the averaging process of Wigner. The crosses indicate poles in $R(E)$ given by (9.48).

Neglecting end effects, the integral of $R(E)$ along the strip C is equal to that along C', so that

$$\langle R(E) \rangle = \langle R(E + i\eta) \rangle.$$ (9.48)

If η is large enough to remove the rapid fluctuations, then the average value of $R(E + i\eta)$ is just $R(E + i\eta)$.

$$\langle R(E) \rangle = R(E + i\eta).$$ (9.49)

End effects were entirely avoided by Brown, de Dominicis, and Langer (59) by defining the average to be over a Lorentzian weight factor

$$W(E - E') = \frac{I/\pi}{(E - E')^2 + I^2}.$$ (9.50)

We can now perform the integration explicitly.

$$\begin{aligned}
\langle R(E) \rangle &= \frac{I}{\pi} \int_{-\infty}^{\infty} dE' \frac{R(E')}{(E - E')^2 + I^2} \\
&= \sum_s \frac{R_{ls}}{E_s - E - iI} \\
&= R(E + iI).
\end{aligned}$$ (9.51)

The experimental interval I is the imaginary part of the energy.

We shall now define the optical model potential $\tilde{V}$ to be the single-particle potential for which the average $\langle S - \langle S \rangle \rangle$ vanishes. $\langle S \rangle$ is the scattering amplitude for the optical model problem. The potential thus depends on the averaging procedure, in particular the interval I. The method used is that of Brown (59). We shall need several potential definitions.

V is the real potential describing the interaction of the projectile with all the target nucleons.

$\bar{V} = \langle 0| V |0\rangle$ is the average value of V for the ground state.

$\tilde{V} = U + iW$ is the optical model potential chosen so that $\langle S - \langle S\rangle\rangle = 0$.

$\mathscr{V} = V - \tilde{V}$ is the residual interaction.   (9.52)

The Hamiltonian H for the whole problem may be written

$$H = H_0 + \mathscr{V},   (9.53)$$

where H_0 is the Hamiltonian for the scattering of the projectile by the optical model potential. The situation is slightly more complicated if we introduce the antisymmetrization of the projectile with the target nucleons, but we can see the principle without doing this.

As in Chapter 8, we are interested in the modified Hamiltonian operator $\mathscr{H}$ corresponding to H with a boundary condition operator $\mathscr{L}$. In analogy with (9.53), we shall introduce the operator $\mathscr{H}_0$ for the optical model problem.

$$\mathscr{H} = \mathscr{H}_0 + \mathscr{V}.   (9.54)$$

We iterate the Green's function for the whole problem twice to obtain

$$\frac{1}{E - \mathscr{H}} = \frac{1}{E - \mathscr{H}_0} + \frac{1}{E - \mathscr{H}_0}\mathscr{V}\frac{1}{E - \mathscr{H}_0}$$
$$+ \frac{1}{E - \mathscr{H}_0}\mathscr{V}\frac{1}{E - \mathscr{H}}\mathscr{V}\frac{1}{E - \mathscr{H}_0}.   (9.55)$$

We may rewrite the definition of the optical model potential in terms of the Green's function operators. For the ground state $|0\rangle$ in the Kapur-Peierls representation, we choose the average over the interval I of the difference between the ground-state to ground-state S-matrix elements for $\mathscr{H}$ and $\mathscr{H}_0$ to vanish. The matrix element is

$$\langle 0| \frac{1}{E - \mathscr{H}} - \frac{1}{E - \mathscr{H}_0} |0\rangle$$
$$= \langle 0| \frac{1}{E - \mathscr{H}_0}\mathscr{V}\frac{1}{E - \mathscr{H}_0} + \frac{1}{E - \mathscr{H}_0}\mathscr{V}\frac{1}{E - \mathscr{H}}\mathscr{V}\frac{1}{E - \mathscr{H}_0} |0\rangle$$
$$= \langle 0| \left\{\sum_{ab} |a\rangle \frac{1}{E - E_a}\langle\tilde{a}| \left[\mathscr{V} + \mathscr{V}\frac{1}{E - \mathscr{H}}\mathscr{V}\right]|b\rangle \frac{1}{E - E_b}\langle\tilde{b}|\right\} |0\rangle$$
$$= \langle 0| \mathscr{V} + \mathscr{V}\frac{1}{E - \mathscr{H}}\mathscr{V} |0\rangle/(E - E_0)^2.   (9.56)$$

Here we have introduced complete sets of intermediate states $|a\rangle$, $|b\rangle$ and their time-reversed conjugates in the Kapur-Peierls representation, using (8.96).

The average will be performed according to the procedure (9.51) of Brown, de Dominicis, and Langer (59). The definition of the optical model potential becomes, in terms of the residual interaction $\mathscr{V}$,

$$\frac{1}{(E - E_0)^2} \langle 0| \mathscr{V} - \mathscr{V} \frac{1}{\mathscr{H} - E - iI} \mathscr{V} |0\rangle = 0. \qquad (9.57)$$

Since E_0 is a complex number, the first term can never become infinite.

We now have a formal definition of $\tilde{V}$ which depends on the interval I. We must show under what conditions it is useful. It will help us if we consider a modification of the picture developed by Lane, Thomas, and Wigner (55).

This picture discusses the giant resonances in neutron elastic scattering *amplitudes* at a few MeV (see Fig. 9.1b). These resonances have widths of the order of 1 MeV, and can be derived from the Kapur-Peierls theory of the scattering of a single neutron by a potential. Giant resonances for different partial waves overlap, so that they interfere in the cross section. The corresponding lifetime is of the order of magnitude of the nuclear crossing time by a particle that is immediately scattered. We shall consider the relationship of the compound nucleus resonances to the giant resonances, bearing in mind that we are discussing amplitudes, not cross sections. In this energy range the widths of the compound nucleus resonances are often larger than their spacings, so that a good resolution experiment does not reveal the resonances.

The giant resonances may be considered as the energy average of the resonances in the actual solution of the problem of the compound system. Following (8.100) we shall write the elastic scattering matrix elements of the S-matrix for the system in the Kapur-Peierls representation in the form

$$S_\alpha \equiv S_{\alpha\alpha}(E) = e^{2i\xi_\alpha} \left[1 + i \sum_s \frac{\Gamma_s^{(\alpha)}}{E_s - E} \right], \qquad (9.58)$$

where the entrance channel is α. The residues at the poles, denoted in (9.48) by R_{ls}, are here denoted by $\Gamma_s^{(\alpha)}$. They are the partial widths. It must be remembered that the imaginary part of E_s, or the total width Γ_s of a compound state [see Equation (8.87)], is approximately* the sum of the partial widths over all open channels. The physical interpretation is that the total

---

* Actually in the Kapur-Peierls theory the widths are defined so that this relationship does not hold. It holds for the Wigner-Eisenbud theory in the limit of isolated resonances (8.82) and for the Humblet-Rosenfeld theory.

decay probability of a state s is the sum of the decay probabilities for all possible channels α.

The compound partial width $\Gamma_s^{(\alpha)}$ is defined, following (8.65, 68, 100) and (9.58), as

$$\Gamma_s^{(\alpha)} = G_s^{(\alpha)} G_s^{(\alpha)}$$

$$= 2P_\alpha \gamma_s^{(\alpha)}$$

$$= 2k_\alpha R_\alpha v_\alpha \frac{\hbar^2 R_\alpha}{2\mu_\alpha} [\phi_s^{(\alpha)}(R_\alpha)]^2. \tag{9.59}$$

The compound reduced width is $\gamma_s^{(\alpha)}$ and the penetrability, defined by (8.7), is P_α.

The average scattering amplitude $\langle S_\alpha \rangle$ is given according to (9.52) by the scattering amplitude $\tilde{S}_\alpha$ for the optical model problem. The poles in the optical model solution are $\tilde{E}_m$, where

$$\tilde{E}_m = \epsilon_m - i\beta_m/2 - iW. \tag{9.60}$$

β_m is the width of the state in the real well U. ϵ_m is the position of the state. For a square well,

$$\beta_m \cong 2\hbar^2 k/\mu R. \tag{9.61}$$

The imaginary part W of the optical model potential just broadens the single-particle state, as is evident from (9.60). From the definition (9.52) of the optical model potential $\tilde{V}$, we have

$$S_\alpha - \langle S_\alpha \rangle = S_\alpha - \tilde{S}_\alpha$$

$$= ie^{2i\xi_\alpha}\left[\sum_s \frac{2P_\alpha \gamma_s^{(\alpha)}}{E_s - E} - \sum_m \frac{\Gamma_m}{\tilde{E}_m - E} \right]. \tag{9.62}$$

Choosing the interval I to be small enough so that $\tilde{S}_\alpha$ is sensibly constant, we define the real and imaginary parts of the single-particle resonant amplitude $R_\alpha(E)$ and $Q_\alpha(E)$ by

$$\left\langle \sum_s \frac{2P_\alpha \gamma_s^{(\alpha)}}{E_s - E} \right\rangle = R_\alpha(E) + iQ_\alpha(E)$$

$$= \sum_m \frac{\Gamma_m}{\tilde{E}_m - E}$$

$$= \sum_s \frac{2P_\alpha \gamma_s^{(\alpha)}}{E_s - E - iI}, \tag{9.63}$$

where

$$R_\alpha(E) = \sum_m \frac{(\epsilon_m - E)\Gamma_m}{(\epsilon_m - E)^2 + (W + \beta_m/2)^2},$$

$$Q_\alpha(E) = \sum_m \frac{\Gamma_m(W + \beta_m/2)}{(\epsilon_m - E)^2 + (W + \beta_m/2)^2}. \tag{9.64}$$

We shall assume that the residue at the single-particle pole, Γ_m, is real. This means specializing to the low-energy case where $W \ll E + U$ because there is not enough energy to excite many nonelastic channels. We cannot express $R_\alpha(E)$ more simply in terms of $\gamma_s^{(\alpha)}$, but $Q_\alpha(E)$ can be put into a more useful form. Using (9.63) we have

$$Q_\alpha(E) = \operatorname{Im} \sum_s \frac{2P_\alpha \gamma_s^{(\alpha)}}{E_s - E - iI}$$

$$\cong \frac{1}{\langle D \rangle} \int_{-\infty}^{\infty} \frac{2P_\alpha \bar{\gamma} I \, d\epsilon_s}{(\epsilon_s - E)^2 + I^2}$$

$$= 2\pi P_\alpha \bar{\gamma}/\langle D \rangle$$

$$= 2\pi P_\alpha s_\alpha. \tag{9.65}$$

Here we have converted the sum to an integral using the average reduced width $\bar{\gamma}$ and the average level density $1/\langle D \rangle$ for the channel α.

The function $s_\alpha \equiv \bar{\gamma}/\langle D \rangle$ is called the *Strength Function*. Its importance is that it links the resonance expansion to the optical model. It can be calculated from the optical model as follows. Using (9.58, 9.62, 9.63, 9.65) we have

$$\tilde{S}_\alpha = e^{2i\xi\alpha}[1 + i(R + i2\pi P_\alpha s_\alpha)]$$

$$|\tilde{S}_\alpha|^2 = 1 - 4\pi P_\alpha s_\alpha + [R^2 + 4\pi^2 P_\alpha^2 s_\alpha^2]. \tag{9.66}$$

For small strength functions, that is for nonoverlapping resonances and, particularly, away from a single-particle resonance, we may neglect the term in parentheses in (9.66). Defining the optical model transmission coefficient T_α by

$$T_\alpha = 1 - |\tilde{S}_\alpha|^2, \tag{9.67}$$

we have

$$T_\alpha \cong 4\pi P_\alpha s_\alpha. \tag{9.68}$$

The transmission coefficient is zero for a real potential since $\tilde{S}$ is then unitary, but for a complex potential it describes the absorption of particles into channels other than α. It will be discussed further in Section *C*[iv] of this chapter and in Chapter 11*B*. At present we shall consider the case where the nucleus is black, that is, it absorbs all the flux from the entrance channel.

T_α is then unity. The black nucleus strength function for s-wave neutrons is given by

$$s_0 = (\pi K r_0)^{-1}, \qquad (9.69)$$

where K is the internal wave number and r_0 is the matching radius.

For incident energies of a few MeV and for r_0 approximately 6 fm, the s-wave black nucleus strength function is approximately 0.03. Experimental

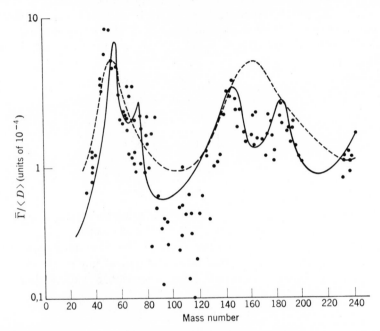

FIG. 9.8   Measured s-wave neutron strength functions plotted against mass number. The dotted curve is computed from the nonlocal optical model (Perey and Buck, 62). The solid curve is computed by Chase, Wilets, and Edmonds (58) from a generalized optical model including low-lying collective states. Experimental errors (ranging from about 10 per cent to 50 per cent) are not shown.

strength functions vary by nearly two orders of magnitude between different parts of the periodic table. A more detailed optical model is needed to predict the variation which occurs because of standing wave phenomena inside the nucleus dependent on Kr_0. Such a fit, using the nonlocal optical model of Perey and Buck (62) (see Chapter 11 D) is shown by the dotted line in Fig. 9.8. In this figure the ratio of partial width to spacing is plotted for an incident neutron energy of 1 eV.

$$\bar{\Gamma}/\langle D \rangle = 2P_\alpha s_\alpha = T_\alpha/2\pi. \qquad (9.70)$$

This ratio is calculated directly from the transmission coefficient and is independent of P_α and therefore of the arbitrary channel radius.

Experimental strength functions are obtained by measuring the properties of individual resonances at very low energies. At higher energies they are obtained by fitting elastic scattering and reaction cross section data with an optical model and calculating the strength functions.

$J\pi = 0+$ ϵ_s (KeV)	Γ_s (KeV)
4.34	0.0050
4.51	0.0013
4.94	0.0036
5.52	0.023
6.68	0.0105
8.51	0.038
9.80	0.0286
10.2	0.0465
11.7	0.018
13.1	0.062
15.4	0.0153
18.5	0.070
23.8	0.080
25.6	0.109
27.5	0.160
28.65	0.044
36.1	0.161
38.4	0.168

TABLE 9.1. The position and width parameters ϵ_s and Γ_s of all the resonances for *s*-state scattering of neutrons from ^{70}Ge between 4.34 KeV and 38.4 KeV. Note that widths are much less than spacings in this energy range (Goldberg, Mughabghab, Magurno, and May, 66).

For example, in the middle of the energy range of Table 9.1, the average level spacing is about 1 KeV while the average partial width is about 0.03 KeV. Here the partial width is the total width, since only the elastic channel is open. The quantity $\Gamma/\langle D \rangle$, which is proportional to the incident wave number k [see Equations (9.70), (8.7)], is 0.03 for 10 KeV. The strength function diagram is normalized to 1 eV. Hence the point on Fig. 9.8 for ^{70}Ge is

$$\Gamma/\langle D \rangle \simeq 3.10^{-4}.$$

The significance of the strength function is that it enables us to tell whether the resonances in a particular channel overlap. It is very important to know this since, if they do, the Breit-Wigner many-level formula no longer holds, and the consequent simplification in the understanding of the compound nucleus is lost. Clearly for 10 MeV in our example the ratio of elastic partial width to spacing is approaching 1. The total width is several times as large for most nuclei at 10 MeV since several channels are open.

We shall now consider the properties of the scattering amplitude in the neighborhood of the single-particle giant resonance (state) at energy ϵ_n. For compound states whose energies ϵ_s are near ϵ_n, the only large values of $G_s^{(\alpha)}$ occur when s labels basis vectors that represent the target in the ground state and the projectile in the scattering state n. In this case, (9.63), (9.64), and (9.65) reduce to the following equation for the average partial width.

$$\frac{\pi\Gamma}{\langle D\rangle} = 2\pi P_\alpha s_\alpha \simeq \frac{\Gamma_n(W + \beta_n/2)}{(\epsilon_n - E)^2 + (W + \beta_n/2)^2}. \tag{9.71}$$

Here we have assumed that single-particle resonances of the same angular momentum are far apart. This is a good assumption for a potential that has any resemblance to the shell-model potential. The condition $W \ll E + U$ is necessary for marked resonances. A large imaginary potential always damps the structure in momentum-transfer distributions for elastic scattering.

We can now show how the single-particle resonances in the optical-model problem are related to the actual compound-nucleus resonances.

The width Γ_m of the single-particle resonance is given by the single-particle equivalent of Equation (9.59).

$$\Gamma_m = \frac{\hbar^2}{\mu_\alpha} k_\alpha R_\alpha^2 v_\alpha [\tilde{\phi}_m^{(\alpha)}(R_\alpha)]^2. \tag{9.72}$$

The $\tilde{\phi}_m^{(\alpha)}(r)$ are the single-particle radial wave functions in the potential $\tilde{V}$.

The wave functions $\phi_s^{(\alpha)}(r)$ of the Kapur-Peierls basis for the actual compound nucleus problem may be expanded in terms of the single-particle radial wave functions $\tilde{\phi}_m^{(\alpha)}(r)$ as follows,

$$\phi_s^{(\alpha)}(r) = \sum_m a_{sm}^{(\alpha)}\tilde{\phi}_m^{(\alpha)}(r), \tag{9.73}$$

so that (9.59) becomes

$$\Gamma_s^{(\alpha)} = \frac{\hbar^2}{\mu_\alpha} k_\alpha R_\alpha^2 v_\alpha \sum_{mm'} a_{sm}^{(\alpha)}a_{sm'}^{(\alpha)}\tilde{\phi}_m^{(\alpha)}(R_\alpha)\tilde{\phi}_{m'}^{(\alpha)}(R_\alpha). \tag{9.74}$$

For compound states only in the neighborhood of ϵ_n (indicated by a prime on the sum over energies) we have from (9.71, 9.72, 9.74)

$$\Gamma_s^{(\alpha)} = [a_{sn}^{(\alpha)}]^2\Gamma_n, \qquad E \simeq \epsilon_n. \tag{9.75}$$

From the completeness of the representations connected by (9.73), we have for the single-particle amplitudes the following sum rule,

$$\sum_s [a_{sn}^{(\alpha)}]^2 = 1. \tag{9.76}$$

Hence

$$\sum_s' \Gamma_s^{(\alpha)} \cong \Gamma_n. \tag{9.77}$$

The energy diagram, Fig. 9.9, explains what this means. On the left are the states ϵ_n, $\epsilon_{n'}$ in the optical model potential $\tilde{V}$. We have used 4s and 5s states

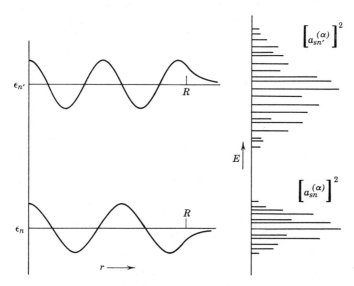

FIG. 9.9 Energy diagram showing how the widths of single-particle (optical-model) resonances are divided among the compound resonances.

for illustration. The average partial width $\bar{\Gamma}$ of a compound state varies like the strength function in the neighborhood of ϵ_n. Equation (9.71) shows that it has a Lorentzian shape with width $W + \beta_n/2$. The strength function is proportional to Γ_n. Thus the square of the expansion coefficient $|a_{sn}^{(\alpha)}|^2$ has an average energy variation like the average of $\gamma_s^{(\alpha)}$, that is, like $\bar{\gamma}$ or the strength function. The energy variation of $[a_{sn}^{(\alpha)}]^2$ is shown schematically on the right of Fig. 9.9.

The actual compound scattering problem is understood qualitatively by considering it as a perturbation on the optical-model problem caused by the residual potential $\mathscr{V}$. Each optical-model level is split into thousands or millions of compound states by $\mathscr{V}$. There is an appreciable probability of a compound state being excited only if ϵ_s is within a range approximately equal to W centered about ϵ_n. This is directly analogous to the situation in the shell model. The single-particle states are split by the residual interaction. With positive energies many more nucleons take part, so there are many more ways of coupling spins to produce the same partial wave quantum numbers l, j. Each mode of coupling gives a compound state. The density of states increases rapidly with energy because the number of coupling modes increases.

Thus, although $\mathscr{V}$ is strong enough to change the wave function so that the levels are split, it is not strong enough to mix the single-particle level $\phi_n^{(\alpha)}$, a distance $\epsilon_{n'} - \epsilon_n$ away in energy, into the compound state ϵ_s in the neighborhood of ϵ_n with large probability. The probability amplitude for mixing in $\phi_{sn'}^{(\alpha)}$ is $a_{sn'}^{(\alpha)}$, which is much smaller near ϵ_n than $a_{sn}^{(\alpha)}$.

We have also seen in (9.77) that the single-particle width is the sum of the compound widths.

In order to check the numbers we may consider the Feshbach, Porter, and Weisskopf (54) potential which fits low-energy neutron scattering as a function of energy.

$$V(r) = -(U + iW)f(r),$$
$$f(r) = 1; \qquad r \le R,$$
$$= 0; \qquad r > R,$$
$$U = 42 \text{ MeV}, \qquad W = 2 \text{ MeV}, \qquad R = 1.45A^{\frac{1}{3}} \text{ fm}. \qquad (9.78)$$

For $A = 160$, the $4s$ level is near zero energy. The $5s$ level is near 27 MeV. There is no doubt that $W \ll \epsilon_{5s} - \epsilon_{4s}$ and that $W \ll E + U$.

We may summarize our understanding of the excitation of compound states as follows. The actual wave function $|\Psi\rangle$ of the compound system is expanded in terms of Kapur-Peierls basis vectors, which are eigenstates of $\mathscr{H}$ corresponding to the energies of the compound states.

$$|\Psi\rangle = \sum_s |s\rangle\psi_s(r), \qquad (9.79)$$

where the compound state vectors $|s\rangle\psi_s(r)$ are expressed in terms of the wave functions of the target nucleus $\chi^{(j)}(\xi)$ and the optical model wave functions $\phi_m^{(j)}(\mathbf{r})$ as

$$|s\rangle\psi_s(r) = \sum_{mj} a_{smj}^{(j)}\chi^{(j)}(\xi)\phi_m^{(j)}(\mathbf{r}). \qquad (9.80)$$

From the normalization of $|s\rangle\psi_s(r)$, we have

$$\sum_{mj} [a_{sm}^{(j)}]^2 = 1. \qquad (9.81)$$

The residual interaction $\mathscr{V}$ is sufficient to mix many states $\chi^{(j)}\phi_m^{(j)}$ into $|s\rangle\psi_s$, so there are many terms which contribute to (9.81). Thus $[a_{sn}^{(\alpha)}]^2 \ll 1$ for any given s, so that the partial width of the compound resonance, given by (9.75), is very much less than Γ_n, the single-particle width. In practice, for neutron energies greater than a few MeV, the compound resonances are not separated, so that they are not revealed in an experiment with good resolution.

However, $\mathcal{V}$ is not strong enough to break down the underlying single-particle structure completely. It does not mix different single-particle levels n,n' into the same $|s\rangle\psi_s(r)$, but only spreads the single-particle resonance locally among compound states within a distance W of the energy of the single-particle state. Consequently, an experiment with a beam whose energy is ill-defined compared to $\langle D\rangle$ shows single-particle features in the energy dependence of the cross sections.

A slightly different point of view may further clarify the relationship between single-particle and many-body states. Initially the excitation is in the form of a single-particle state whose width is approximately W. As time evolves, this excitation spreads to the many-body states within the width W. Physically, the mechanism involves collisions between the single particle initially excited and the many other particles of the nucleus. This mechanism will now be formulated mathematically.

We have seen that the imaginary part of the optical-model potential W is related to the ratio of average widths to average level spacings. Knowing the statistical properties of the widths and spacings, we could calculate W at different energies.

We shall now discuss further the significance of the optical-model potential and the value of the energy-averaging interval I for which the optical model is valid. We start from the definition (9.57) of the optical model potential. Using the definitions of the potentials (9.52), we define $\mathcal{W}$ by

$$\mathcal{W} = \bar{V} - \tilde{V}. \tag{9.82}$$

$\mathcal{W}$ contains the entire imaginary part W of $\tilde{V}$. The residual interaction $\mathcal{V}$ is given by

$$\mathcal{V} = V - \bar{V} + \mathcal{W}. \tag{9.83}$$

Define the resolvents e and $\bar{e}$ by

$$\begin{aligned}
e &= \mathcal{K} - E - iI, \\
\bar{e} &= \overline{\mathcal{K}} - E - iI = e - (V - \bar{V}).
\end{aligned} \tag{9.84}$$

The defining equation (9.57) for $\tilde{V}$ becomes

$$\langle 0|\, (e - \bar{e} + \mathcal{W})\left[1 - \frac{1}{e}(e - \bar{e} + \mathcal{W}) \right] |0\rangle$$

$$= \langle 0|\, (e - \bar{e})\frac{1}{e}\bar{e}\,|0\rangle - \langle 0|\,(e - \bar{e})\frac{1}{e}|0\rangle\mathcal{W} + \mathcal{W}\langle 0|\frac{1}{e}(\bar{e} - \mathcal{W})\,|0\rangle$$

$$= 0.$$

Using the following identities,

$$\langle 0| \frac{1}{e} |0\rangle = \langle 0| \frac{1}{\bar{e} - \mathscr{W}} |0\rangle,$$

$$\langle 0| (e - \bar{e}) \frac{1}{e} \bar{e} |0\rangle = 0,$$

we have

$$\mathscr{W} = \frac{1}{1 - \langle 0| (V - \bar{V}) \frac{1}{e} |0\rangle} \langle 0| (V - \bar{V}) \frac{1}{e} (V - \bar{V}) |0\rangle$$

$$\equiv \langle 0| (V - \bar{V}) \frac{1}{e - \Lambda_0 (V - \bar{V})} (V - \bar{V}) |0\rangle. \tag{9.85}$$

We have defined Λ_0 to be the operator that projects out the ground state.

$$\Lambda_0 = |0\rangle\langle 0|. \tag{9.86}$$

Equation (9.85) can be checked by expanding in powers of $(V - \bar{V})/e$. $\mathscr{W}$ is more simply expressed in terms of the resolvent $\mathscr{K}'$ which is $\mathscr{K}$ with the ground state projected out.

$$\mathscr{K}' = \mathscr{K} - \Lambda_0 (V - \bar{V}). \tag{9.87}$$

$$\mathscr{W} = \langle 0| (V - \bar{V}) \frac{1}{\mathscr{K}' - E - iI} (V - \bar{V}) |0\rangle. \tag{9.88}$$

Define the eigenstates of $\mathscr{K}'$ to be $|s'\rangle$ for eigenvalues $E_{s'}$. Now we have

$$\frac{1}{\mathscr{K}' - E - iI} = \sum_{s'} |s'\rangle \frac{1}{E_{s'} - E - iI} \langle \tilde{s}'|. \tag{9.89}$$

We introduce intermediate states $|jm\rangle$ into (9.88).

$$\mathscr{W}(E) = \sum_{s'} \sum_{jm} \langle 0| V - \bar{V} |jm\rangle \frac{1}{E_{s'} - E - iI} \langle \widetilde{jm} | s'\rangle\langle \tilde{s}'| V - \bar{V} |0\rangle \tag{9.90a}$$

$$\cong \sum_{jm} \frac{\langle 0| V - \bar{V} |jm\rangle\langle \widetilde{jm}| V - V |0\rangle}{E_{jm} - E - iI}. \tag{9.90b}$$

We have further abbreviated the notation for the state vectors. The wave functions of the compound states are

$$|s\rangle \equiv |s)\psi_s(r). \tag{9.91a}$$

The Kapur-Peierls basis vectors are

$$|jm\rangle \equiv \chi^{(j)}(\xi)\tilde{\phi}_m^{(j)}(\mathbf{r}). \tag{9.91b}$$

The coefficients in the expansion of the compound states in basis vectors are

$$\langle \widetilde{jm} \mid s \rangle = a_{sm}^{(j)} = \int_0^R d\xi \, d^3r|s)\psi_s(r)\chi^{(j)}(\xi)\tilde{\phi}_m^{(j)}(\mathbf{r}). \qquad (9.91c)$$

In (9.90) we have approximated $E_{s'}$ by E_{jm} which are the eigenvalues in the complex potential. That this is justified for large I may be seen from Fig. 9.10.

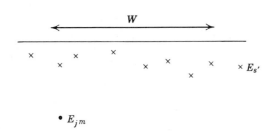

FIG. 9.10   The complex E plane showing the relationship between the eigenvalues $E_{s'}$, (crosses) of $\mathscr{H}$, and the eigenvalue E_{jm} of the optical-model Hamiltonian.

The average implies a sum over $E_{s'}$ in (9.90a). We replace the average distance $\langle |E + iI - E_{s'}| \rangle$ by the distance $|E + iI - E_{jm}|$. This is justified if $I \gg W$, which is the spread of the relevant $E_{s'}$.

Another way of deriving (9.90b) from (9.90a) is to observe that (9.90b) is the first-order term in the perturbation expansion

$$\mathscr{W}(E) = \langle 0| (V - \bar{V}) \frac{1}{\overline{\mathscr{H}} - E - iI} \sum_n (-1)^n$$

$$\times \left[(1 - \Lambda_0)(V - \bar{V}) \frac{1}{\overline{\mathscr{H}} - E - iI} \right]^n (V - \bar{V}) |0\rangle \qquad (9.92)$$

where $\overline{\mathscr{H}}$ is the scattering operator for the average potential $\bar{V}$. The approximation of taking the first term is clearly better, the larger $E - E_{jm}$. The same is true for larger I in $E + iI$. Thus we see that the larger I is, the faster (9.92) converges.

The series (9.92) can be interpreted as an expansion in the number of collisions that the incident particle makes in the nucleus. In analogy with the Born expansion for scattering from a potential (2.95), we may say that the particle moves under the influence of the average potential $\bar{V}$, except that it is scattered by $V - \bar{V}$ at certain points from which it propagates again according to the Green's function $(\mathcal{H} - E - iI)^{-1}$.

The physical interpretation of $\mathcal{W}$ is that it is related to the probability for the system to be excited out of the entrance channel into some intermediate compound state $|jm\rangle$. The entrance channel is not included in the intermediate states since the ground state of the target is projected out of $\mathcal{H}$ by the operator Λ_0.

Since we are dealing all the time with probability amplitudes, not probabilities, I is the width of a wave packet. We can relate the multicollision picture to time. The larger I is, the more quickly the wave packet passes over the nucleus and the fewer collisions it makes.

We must now discuss the experimental feasibility of having $I \gg W$. The appropriate value of W is W_m, the value for the state $|jm\rangle$ which corresponds to a target nucleus excited by an energy E_j and a single particle of energy roughly $E - E_j$. W is small for low energies because of the small number of open channels. $E - E_j$ is usually very small because the number of available states increases exponentially with energy (see Section C). Thus $W_m \ll W_0$, the value of W for the scattering of a particle of energy E from the ground state of the target.

In the case of easily deformable nuclei, there are low-lying collective states that are easily excited. These states should be taken with the ground state and treated preferentially. Thus we would have a generalized optical model representing the scattering of a particle, leaving the internal correlations of the nucleons in the nucleus largely undisturbed, but either translating the center of mass (elastic scattering) or exciting other collective degrees of freedom (collective inelastic scattering). This model was first calculated by Chase, Wilets, and Edmonds (58). It greatly improved the fit to the s-state strength function (see Fig. 9.8). It will be treated formally in Chapter 10D and in detail in Chapter 12A. We can see at this stage that if the low-lying collective states are projected out of the sum (9.90b) along with the ground state, the value of the imaginary potential W will be much smaller. It now describes the probability of removal of the incident particle from all of the low-lying channels instead of just the entrance channel.

In order to see the single-particle structure, we must of course have $I \ll W_0$. Thus the condition for the optical model to describe the observed cross section is

$$W_m \ll I \ll W_0. \tag{9.93}$$

We must remember that it is impossible in an actual scattering experiment to have a wave packet width I greater than about 10^{-5} eV. We must consider how a classical uncertainty I in the incident energy, which is not related to time resolution, can produce the same effect on the cross section as a wave packet of width I. We see this from (9.45). Averaging the amplitude is equivalent to averaging the cross section if the fluctuation scattering $\langle |S - \langle S \rangle|^2 \rangle$ is small. The fluctuation scattering will be discussed in Section C.

We now have an idea of the validity of the optical model and a physical interpretation of its potentials. We may summarize it by saying that the model is valid under two main conditions: first, that the energy-averaging interval I is very large compared to the imaginary potential W_m for the optical model for scattering of a projectile of very low energy from an excited state, and second, that the fluctuation or compound elastic scattering is small. These conditions are true for very high excitation energies where many resonances contribute to the scattering amplitude at a particular energy. The real part of the potential, U, is closely related to the average potential $\bar{V}$. The difference $\mathscr{W} = \bar{V} - V$ is largely imaginary if I is large. At least the real part of $\mathscr{W}$ is not comparable with $\bar{V}$. $\mathscr{W}$ is given by the probability of exciting channels other than the ones treated in the model. The model may be generalized so that collective excitations of the target are treated as well as the ground state.

In subsequent chapters, we shall consider the average interaction of a particle with a nucleus to be capable of description as scattering by a complex potential. The real part of the potential is given quite closely by the average potential which is closely related to the nucleon-nucleon forces. The imaginary part is related to the open channels which depend strongly on the details of nuclear structure and, therefore, very indirectly on the nucleon-nucleon force. For very high energies the expansion (9.92) for $\mathscr{W}$ may be used to describe the complex potential more simply in terms of nucleon-nucleon collisions. This approach has been taken by Watson and collaborators (Watson, 58). (See also Kerman, McManus, and Thaler, 59.) We shall not consider it further. The main point is that nuclear reactions are much more simply related to nucleon-nucleon forces at higher energies, although successful numerical predictions have not yet been made.

C. STATISTICAL THEORIES OF THE COMPOUND NUCLEUS

In the previous section we considered the conditions under which the average cross section for elastic scattering is given by the optical model, which involves the degrees of freedom of only a single particle. For inelastic and rearrangement collisions there are corresponding direct interaction models for the average cross section, which will be studied in the subsequent chapters. These models are applicable for the energy range in which resonances overlap so that their parameters cannot be extracted from cross sections.

It is important to distinguish between resonances for the same partial wave and those for different partial waves. If many resonances overlap, their partial wave quantum numbers of course cannot be identified experimentally. However, there is an important difference between differential cross sections where the sum over partial waves is coherent and cross sections integrated over angles where the partial wave sum is incoherent [see Equation (2.40)]. In the former case, contributions from all the overlapping resonances contribute coherently to the scattering amplitude for a particular energy. In the latter case, the coherent contributions come only from resonances with the same partial wave quantum numbers $J\pi$.

The existence and properties of resonances depend on the detailed properties of the compound nucleus. They are given by the eigenvalues and eigenvectors of the Hamiltonian for the whole system which, in general, is extremely complicated. There is an extremely large number of Hamiltonian matrix elements relevant to a particular situation. This fact alone can be used as the basis for a statistical approach to the problem, since statistical theorems are true in the limit of infinitely large populations. There are some basic statistical assumptions that can be verified by comparing the distributions to which they lead with experiment. The statistical assumptions can then be used in order to understand the distributions associated with fluctuations from the average cross sections. Statistical theories are associated largely with the names of Wigner, Thomas, and Porter. References will be given where appropriate.

The fundamental quantities associated with resonance theory are the eigenvalues E_s and the reduced width amplitudes $g_s^{(\lambda)}$. These quantities are closely related to the Hamiltonian matrix $\mathcal{H}$, defined by (8.52, 8.53), which has the boundary conditions built in so that nuclear properties may be discussed in terms of discrete resonances. The eigenvalues are obtained in principle by diagonalizing the matrix in a particular representation defined by the basis vectors $|s\rangle$.

$$\mathcal{H} X_s = E_s X_s. \tag{9.94}$$

The Hamiltonian matrix is composed of disjoint submatrices for each channel, labelled by the partition and $J\pi$. The eigenvectors X_s may be expressed in terms of their numerical components a_{st} in the representation.

$$|X_s\rangle = \sum_t a_{st}|t\rangle. \tag{9.95}$$

Multiplying on the left by the Hermitian conjugate of the channel wave function $|\lambda\rangle$ and integrating over the interior of the nucleus Ω, we have the following relation between the eigenvectors and the reduced width amplitudes $g_s^{(\lambda)}$.

$$\begin{aligned}
_{R_\lambda}\langle \lambda \mid X_s \rangle &= \sum_t a_{st\,R_\lambda}\langle \lambda \mid t \rangle \\
&= (2\mu_\lambda/\hbar^2 R_\lambda)^{1/2} \sum_t a_{st} g_t^{(\lambda)}.
\end{aligned} \tag{9.96}$$

In the Wigner-Eisenbud representation the basis $|s\rangle$ is chosen so that $\mathcal{H}$ is almost diagonal. It is diagonal in the approximation that resonances for the same channel do not overlap. The reduced width amplitudes are then directly related to the eigenvectors by

$$g_s^{(\lambda)} = (\hbar^2 R_\lambda/2\mu_\lambda)^{1/2} {}_{R_\lambda}(\lambda \mid X_s).$$ (9.97)

[i] PROPERTIES OF REDUCED-WIDTH AMPLITUDES

The Wigner-Eisenbud representation is chosen for considering statistical properties of nuclei because the reduced width amplitudes are real in this representation. We shall consider the properties of a single channel λ defined by a particular submatrix of $\mathcal{H}$.

The wave function X_s is very complex because of the strong nuclear interactions, and the wave functions for various states in the same channel are presumed to be essentially unrelated to each other. This is the assumption of nonoverlapping resonances. Each state is produced by a different interaction of the many nuclear degrees of freedom. We may regard the matrix elements as being composed of contributions from many cells of the $3A$-dimensional configuration space with the following statistical assumptions. The sign of the contribution from a particular cell is positive with the same probability that it is negative. The sign and magnitude of a particular contribution are random from state to state and independent of the signs and magnitudes of the contributions from the other cells. Since the overall size of each cell is such that its linear dimension is about 1 fm, there will be a very large number of independently contributing cells.

The central limit theorem of statistics states that, with the assumptions of the preceding paragraph, the matrix elements will be approximately normally distributed (that is, they will have a Gaussian distribution) and will be normally distributed in the limit $A \to \infty$.

We thus make the assumption for the reduced width amplitudes for levels of fairly high excitation that they are distributed approximately normally with zero means when sampled from level to level. The variances of these distributions are

$$\bar{\gamma} = \langle[g_s^{(\lambda)}]^2\rangle,$$ (9.98)

which are just the average reduced widths.

The distribution of

$$x = \frac{\gamma_s^{(\lambda)}}{\bar{\gamma}},$$ (9.99)

under the normality assumption for the distribution of matrix elements and reduced width amplitudes, is χ^2 with one degree of freedom. The distribution function $P_1(x)$ which gives the probability $P_1(x)\,dx$ of finding x in the interval

$(x, x + dx)$ is, for this distribution,

$$P_1(x) = x^{-\frac{1}{2}}e^{-x/2}. \tag{9.100}$$

The analysis of the distribution of experimental reduced widths by Porter and Thomas (56) confirmed the form (9.100), thus confirming the assumption of independent, normally distributed, and real reduced width amplitudes.

If the reduced width amplitudes were essentially complex with independent real and imaginary parts, the distribution of reduced widths would be that of the sum of the squares of two independent, normally distributed quantities, which is χ^2 with two degrees of freedom. The distribution function would then be

$$P_2(x) = e^{-x}, \tag{9.101}$$

which is easily distinguishable from $P_1(x)$ because it does not decrease towards small x.

This result obviously does not depend on the choice of representation. Although the reduced width amplitudes in the Kapur-Peierls representation are complex, their phases must be correlated.

[ii] Statistical Properties of Energy Levels

The different distributions related to the population of levels of definite spin and parity in complex quantum systems are discussed in a series of articles by Porter and collaborators (for example, Porter and Rosenzweig, 60). Properties of atomic as well as nuclear spectra are discussed.

A set of statistical assumptions about the matrix elements $\mathcal{K}_{rs}$ is made, which of course must reproduce the properties of the reduced width amplitudes already discussed.

$$\mathcal{K}_{rs} \equiv \langle r| \mathcal{K} |s\rangle \equiv \int d\tau \psi_r \mathcal{K} \psi_s, \tag{9.102}$$

where the integration is over the $3A$ coordinates of the nucleons. Porter and Rosenzweig represented the matrix $\mathcal{K}$ by matrices of finite dimension whose matrix elements were random except for the general assumptions which will be described below. A large number of random matrices were diagonalized numerically and the distributions of different properties of the eigenvalues extracted. Such distributions are for example nearest-neighbor spacings and nth-nearest-neighbor spacings. Comparison of these distributions with similar experimental distributions confirms the statistical hypothesis made originally for the matrix elements.

The ultimate justification for a statistical hypothesis about the matrix elements would be its derivation from an appropriate many-body Hamiltonian. No such derivation exists at present. Plausibility arguments are made.

The matrices considered by Porter and Rosenzweig were real, symmetric $N \times N$ matrices. The first two conditions are imposed by conservation of probability. The matrix is supposed to be representative of an ensemble of matrices, which is described by giving the differential probability P_N with which a matrix characterized by certain numbers $\mathscr{H}_{rs}$ occurs. The joint probability that $\mathscr{H}_{11}$ is in the interval $d\mathscr{H}_{11}$ *and* $\mathscr{H}_{12}$ is in the interval $d\mathscr{H}_{12}, \ldots$, etc. is

$$P_N(\mathscr{H}_{11}, \mathscr{H}_{12}, \ldots, \mathscr{H}_{NN}) \, d\mathscr{H}_{11} \, d\mathscr{H}_{12} \cdots d\mathscr{H}_{NN}.$$

The physical hypothesis is that the matrix of $\mathscr{H}$ for any sufficiently complex dynamical system will be a typical sample of the *same* multivariate distribution in *almost* any representation.

It is also assumed that P_N is made up of independent distributions for the separate matrix elements. This assumption is not so plausible, particularly if many levels are collective excitations. It is made for simplicity. It implies that there exists a representation in which the spin and the parity matrices of the system are diagonal and that $\mathscr{H}$ is typical of the distribution

$$P(\mathscr{H}_{11}, \mathscr{H}_{12}, \ldots, \mathscr{H}_{NN})$$
$$= f_{11}(\mathscr{H}_{11}) f_{12}(\mathscr{H}_{12}) \cdots f_{NN}(\mathscr{H}_{NN}), \qquad r < s. \quad (9.103)$$

It is assumed further that the distributions of off-diagonal matrix elements are *symmetric* about zero mean and that the distributions of diagonal matrix elements are symmetric but not about zero mean in general.

There is strong numerical evidence that, provided we do not choose an unfortunate representation in which $\mathscr{H}$ is almost diagonal, the large number $N(N - 1)/2$ of off-diagonal elements far outweighs the N diagonal elements in determining the spacing and width distributions. Thus the means of the diagonal elements are unimportant.

To infer the distribution of matrix elements of $\mathscr{H}$, the integral (9.102) is expressed as a sum over equal cells $\Delta\tau$ in configuration space.

$$\mathscr{H}_{rs} \cong \Delta\tau \sum_\alpha (\psi_r \mathscr{H} \psi_s)_\alpha. \quad (9.104)$$

In some representation the integrand $(\psi_r \mathscr{H} \psi_s)_\alpha$ evaluated in the αth cell is assumed to vary randomly with random sign independently of the integrand $(\psi_p \mathscr{H} \psi_q)_\alpha$ of another typical matrix element in the same representation. The central-limit theorem gives

$$P(\mathscr{H}_{rs}) = (2\pi \overline{\mathscr{H}_{rs}^2})^{-\frac{1}{2}} \exp(-\mathscr{H}_{rs}^2 / 2\overline{\mathscr{H}_{rs}^2}). \quad (9.105)$$

$\overline{\mathscr{H}_{rs}^2}$ is taken as a parameter of the distribution, with the same value for all off-diagonal elements and a different value for all diagonal elements.

The hypothesis of normally distributed matrix elements can be checked by examining the matrix elements which have been computed in the process of detailed energy level studies, or its consequences for level distributions can be predicted numerically by diagonalizing random matrices and compared with experiments. The former process, applied to the effective matrix elements derived by Kurath (56) as coefficients for mixing of single-particle wave functions to obtain the energy levels of p-shell nuclei, confirms the hypothesis. The comparison of Kurath's matrix elements with the normal distribution is shown in Fig. 9.11.

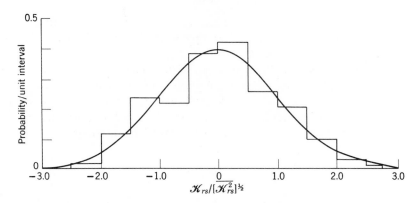

FIG. 9.11 Plot of the distribution of 675 off-diagonal matrix elements obtained in the work of Kurath (56). The solid curve is a normal distribution (9.105). The mean value of the off-diagonal elements is very close to zero. (Adapted from Porter and Rosenzweig, 60.)

The most simple distribution is that of nearest-neighbor spacings. This was surmised by Wigner (57) to be

$$P(x) = \left(\frac{\pi}{2}\right) x \exp\left(-\frac{\pi x^2}{4}\right), \qquad (9.106)$$

where x is the ratio of the spacing to the mean spacing. The mean spacing is measured from the curve of $T(E)$ against E, where $T(E)$ is the number of levels with energy less than or equal to E.

The correct mathematical distribution was determined on the basis of the normal-distribution hypothesis for the matrix elements by Mehta (60). It is close to (9.106). The interesting feature of the distribution is the repulsion of levels. Levels of the same spin and parity prefer to be spaced with the mean spacing and not to crowd together in clumps. This distribution fits histograms obtained from atomic and nuclear level data very well (see Fig. 9.12).

The numerical calculations of the distributions of eigenvalues of random matrices by Porter and Rosenzweig fitted the Wigner distribution (9.106) (see Fig. 9.13) and also the experimental distributions. Later calculations have

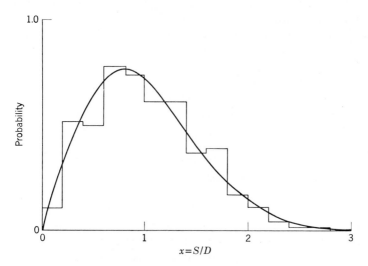

FIG. 9.12   Plot of the distribution of 230 nearest-neighbor spacings obtained from the eigenvalues of the matrices of Kurath (56). The solid curve is the Wigner surmise (9.106). (Adapted from Porter and Rosenzweig, 60.)

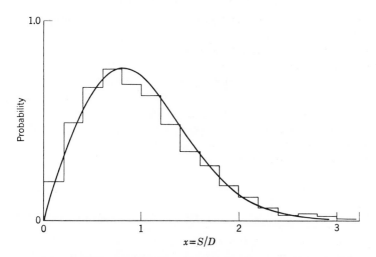

FIG. 9.13   Plot of the distribution of nearest-neighbor spacings obtained from the diagonalization of 180 random matrices of dimension 20. The solid curve is the Wigner surmise (9.106). (Adapted from Porter and Rosenzweig, 60.)

confirmed that the normal distribution hypothesis for matrix elements fits more complicated distributions like that of nth-nearest-neighbor spacings.

The basic statistical assumptions, which have been so strikingly confirmed by experiments closely related to the fundamental quantities, can also be applied to other experiments. We shall consider some examples in the region where resonances for different partial waves overlap, although they are still well separated for the same partial wave. Actually the statistical models give correct predictions in the region where resonances for the same partial wave overlap, but this is not understood.

[iii] THE STATISTICAL MODEL FOR AVERAGE CROSS SECTIONS

The average scattering cross sections of particles by a target of spin i, orbital angular momentum l and energy E leaving a residual nucleus characterized by i', l', E' has been discussed by Wolfenstein (51) and by Hauser and Feshbach (52). The spin of a level in the compound nucleus is denoted by J. The projectile and nuclear spins are combined to form the channel spins j_i, j_i' where $j_i = i \pm \frac{1}{2}, j_i' = i' \pm \frac{1}{2}$. We normally shall drop the subscripts on j, j'. The z-axis is taken along the incident direction. The z-component of j is m and is equal to that of J. That of the emergent particle is m', so that the z-component of j' is $m - m'$.

The statistical model is assumed for the compound nucleus. We assume that, at the excitation energy of the compound nucleus, there are many energy levels of all types. This means that the energy resolution of the incident beam is broad enough, so that many different levels are excited. The formation and decay of the compound nucleus are assumed to be independent for a particular channel. This implies well-separated resonances in each channel. The nucleus, however, "remembers" the incident beam direction and the channel quantum numbers $J\pi$. Particle emission only is considered. γ-ray widths are small.

The hypothesis of well-separated levels enables us to neglect the interference among the various values of l which contribute to the formation and those of l' which contribute to the decay of the compound nucleus in the channel labeled by $J\pi$. We may write

$$\sigma(i \mid i') = \sum_{ll'} \sigma(l, i \mid l', i'), \qquad (9.107)$$

where

$$\sigma(l, i \mid l', i') = [\tfrac{1}{2}(2i + 1)] \sum_{\alpha\beta} \sigma(l, j_\alpha \mid l', j_\beta'). \qquad (9.108)$$

Here $\sigma(l, i \mid l', i')$ is the cross section for the process involving the indicated initial and final values of the particles, orbital angular momenta, and spins of the target and residual nuclei. On the other hand, $\sigma(l, j_\alpha \mid l', j_\beta')$ is the cross section for the process labeled by the channel spins j_α, j_β'.

A certain fraction of the particles with orbital angular momentum l that strike the nucleus will stick, and will form a compound nucleus. In optical-model language we say that they will be absorbed from the entrance channel, and will excite a different compound state. The cross section for this process is the partial reaction cross section $\sigma_l{}^R$. It is calculated from the reflection coefficient or S-matrix element η_l of the optical model by (11.63).

$$\sigma_l{}^R = \frac{2\pi}{k^2}(2l + 1)e^{-2\,\mathrm{Im}\,\eta_l}\sinh 2\,\mathrm{Im}\,\eta_l. \tag{9.109}$$

For a black nucleus, where all particles are absorbed from the entrance channel, $\mathrm{Im}\,\eta_l = \infty$ and $\sigma_l{}^R = (2l + 1)\pi\lambda^2$ where $\lambda = 1/k$. The partial reaction cross section is often expressed in terms of the transmission coefficient $T_l(E)$, defined by (9.67), which is the probability of absorption compared with that of a black nucleus.

$$\sigma_l{}^R = (2l + 1)\pi\lambda^2 T_l(E). \tag{9.110}$$

The cross section for the formation of a compound state with spin J by particles with orbital angular momentum l is given by multiplying $\sigma_l{}^R$ by the probability that l and the channel spin j combine to form a system of spin J. This is

$$\sigma_l{}^R(C_{l\,j\,J}^{0\,m\,m})^2 = (2l + 1)\pi\lambda^2 T_l(E)(C_{l\,j\,J}^{0\,m\,m})^2. \tag{9.111}$$

To obtain the cross section for a particular process, we must multiply (9.111) by the relative probability of that process. The probability of the compound nucleus decaying in a particular channel is equal to the probability of its being formed in that channel. Thus we can use (9.111) also for the exit channel with the appropriate modification of indices. The assumption of independence of formation and decay means that we can multiply their respective probabilities.

The cross section for the production of a particle of orbital angular momentum l', channel spin j', energy E' in a direction θ is

$$\sigma(l, j \mid l', j'; \theta) = \pi\lambda^2(2l + 1)T_l(E)\sum_{J\pi}\frac{A_J(l, j \mid l', j'; \theta)}{1 + \sum_{pqr} T_p(E_q')/T_{l'}(E')} \tag{9.112}$$

The r index refers to possible channel spins, p to possible emergent particle angular momenta, E_q' to possible emergent particle energies. The factor A_J is defined as

$$A_J(l, j \mid l', j'; \theta) = \sum_{mm'} (C_{l\,j\,J}^{0\,m\,m})^2 (C_{l'\;\;j'\;\;J}^{m'\,m-m'\,m})^2 \,|Y_{l'}^m(\theta, \phi)|^2. \tag{9.113}$$

Equation (9.112) refers to the excitation of a single-level E' of the residual nucleus. If j and E are equal to j' and E' we have compound elastic scattering; otherwise we have compound inelastic scattering. Note that the angular distribution is symmetric about $90°$.

Experiments in which the levels of the residual nucleus are resolved are the most interesting. We shall not derive the theory for high excitation energies of the residual nucleus where its level density is high. In this case the level density of the residual nucleus is important.

The properties of the compound nucleus enter into Equation (9.112) only through the transmission coefficients T_l and the spins and parities $J\pi$ of the compound states. The statistical assumption involved in the theory is that the sum includes all values of J allowed by conservation of angular momentum. Thus a model for T_l is sufficient to calculate the average compound elastic or inelastic scattering, or other reactions with slight obvious modifications of the theory. The optical model calculates T_l, so it is capable of calculating compound elastic as well as direct elastic scattering with the addition of the assumptions involved in the Hauser-Feshbach theory.

In older statistical model work, it was necessary to make statistical assumptions about the level densities of the nuclei involved. So much information is now available, however, that it is possible, in many cases, to perform a complete Hauser-Feshbach calculation for the excitation of a particular low-lying nuclear state by a reaction with an entrance channel whose energy is so low that only channels with known quantum numbers can be excited.

In most cases, inelastic scattering is an unfortunate example, since most low-lying states result from collective excitations that are best coupled to the entrance channel in a generalized optical model, as discussed at the end of Section B. Equations (9.112, 9.113) are easily generalized to describe the situation where the exit channel has a different partition of the nucleons from the entrance channel. The modifications are the replacement of the intrinsic spin ½ of nucleons by the intrinsic spin I of the appropriate particles and the inclusion of possibly different partitions in the sum over pqr for unwanted channels in the denominator of (9.112). We shall quote the result for intrinsic spins I and i and entrance channel spin $\mathbf{j} = \mathbf{I} + \mathbf{i}$ (with corresponding primed quantities for the exit channel). We shall use λ to denote all the channel quantum numbers and α to denote a particular partition of nucleons in a particular energy state. The differential cross section summed over partial waves is

$$\sigma(\alpha \,|\, \alpha'; \theta) = \sum_L \frac{\hat\lambda^2}{4} \sum_{J\pi} \frac{1}{(2I+1)(2i+1)} \left\{ \sum_{lj} T_l(\alpha) \right\}$$

$$\times \sum_{l'j'} \left\{ \frac{T_{l'}(\alpha')}{\sum_{\lambda''} T_{l''}(\alpha'')} \right\} Z(lJlJ, jL) Z(l'Jl'J, j'L)$$

$$\times (-1)^{j-j'} P_L(\cos\theta). \tag{9.112'}$$

The angular momentum coefficients Z are related to the Racah coefficients W by (8.127).

A good example of such a calculation is that of Vogt, McPherson, Kuehner, and Almquist (64) for the reaction $^{12}C(^{12}C, \alpha)^{20}Ne$ at 25 MeV excitation in the compound nucleus, ^{24}Mg. The transmission coefficients are calculated from optical models fitted to the appropriate elastic scattering experiments. The overall quality of the theory is illustrated by the fit to the angular distribution of α-particles leaving the residual nucleus ^{20}Ne in its ground state. This is illustrated in Fig. 9.14.

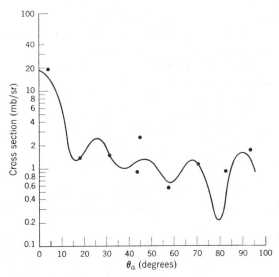

FIG. 9.14   The experimental and calculated values of the average differential cross section for the reaction $^{12}C(^{12}C, \alpha_0)^{20}Ne$ as a function of the C.M. angle θ_α of the emitted α-particles. Experimental error is ± 20 percent. Sample error in the theory is ± 15 percent at each angle. (Adapted from Vogt, McPherson, Kuehner, and Almquist, 64.)

The connection between the average compound elastic scattering of this theory and the fluctuation scattering of the optical model must be discussed. We have calculated the whole cross section here under the assumption that the resonances in particular channels are well separated. We could have calculated the average cross section with the optical model, but then the residual cross section would not be the same as the Hauser-Feshbach cross section. The condition of small fluctuation scattering was seen to be necessary for the optical model.

The chief experimental effect of the assumption of isolated resonances is the fact that Equation (9.112) predicts angular distributions which are symmetric about 90°. If we cannot neglect the interference between values of l and l', then the angular dependence is not given by $|Y_l^{m'}(\theta, \phi)|^2$, but by the square of a linear combination $\sum_{l'} C_{ll'} Y_{l'}^{m'}(\theta, \phi)$ which is not symmetric about 90°.

In subsequent theories of direct interactions, we shall calculate the coefficients $C_{ll'}$ with the help of direct interaction models. It should be noted that direct interaction models, particularly for low energies, often predict cross sections that are roughly symmetric about $90°$, so symmetry is not a safe criterion for isolated resonances.

[iv] DISTRIBUTIONS OF AVERAGE LEVEL SPACINGS

We can understand the rapid increase of the density of nuclear levels as a function of energy without a detailed model of nuclear structure. Consider the constituent nucleons as being independent of each other, and suppose each of them has a set of equally spaced single-particle energy levels. This would be true in the harmonic oscillator model. For a finite potential, the single-particle level spacing decreases with increasing excitation energy. The excited states of the system will have a spacing Δ, and will have greater statistical weight for greater excitation energy because of the increase of the spin j of the single-particle levels which gives more ways of dividing the energy among the particles. When an interaction among the particles is introduced, the levels will be split. The statistical weight of a single-particle level is a measure of the level density in the same energy region.

The level density $\rho(E)$ in the energy interval $(E, E + dE)$ is the reciprocal of the average level spacing $\langle D \rangle$. It is understood on the basis of the statistical model.

For a given entrance channel, the excitation energy E is considered as heat energy distributed over the many degrees of freedom of the excited nucleus. The heating of the compound system causes the evaporation of a particle. The process of evaporation is independent of the mode of formation of the compound nucleus and depends only on its energy. The energy distribution of evaporated particles is known from statistical mechanics to be a Maxwellian distribution.

$$P(E) = E \exp \frac{-E}{\mathscr{T}} . \tag{9.114}$$

$\mathscr{T}$ is the nuclear temperature. An experimental energy distribution is illustrated in Fig. 9.15.

The statistical mechanics of a system with many degrees of freedom can be discussed in terms of the entropy $\mathscr{S}$, where $\mathscr{S}$ is defined by

$$\mathscr{S}(E) = \ln \rho(E). \tag{9.115}$$

The level density $\rho(E)$ is the probability of finding the nucleus with energy in the interval $(E, E + dE)$. The entropy is related to the temperature by

$$\frac{1}{\mathscr{T}(E)} = \frac{d\mathscr{S}(E)}{dE} . \tag{9.116}$$

The temperature that determines the energy distribution of the emitted particles is the temperature of the residual nucleus after emission. The temperature can be determined by measuring the width of the energy distribution of emitted particles.

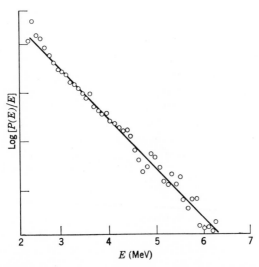

FIG. 9.15   The energy distribution of the final state in the reaction ^{64}Zn(p, p')^{64}Zn*. Log $[P(E)/E]$ is plotted against E on an arbitrary linear scale. The straight line corresponds to $\mathscr{T} = 0.933 \pm 0.018$ MeV. The parameter a of (9.118) has the value 5.61 ± 0.15 MeV^{-1}. (Adapted from Johnson and Hintz, 67.)

The level density can be estimated approximately by a thermodynamic argument. The average energy of a system $\bar{E}$ is a monotonically increasing function of temperature. The function $\bar{E}(\mathscr{T})$ has a vanishing derivative,

$$(d\bar{E}/d\mathscr{T})_{\mathscr{T}=0} = 0. \tag{9.117}$$

This is the same as saying that the specific heat is zero for $\mathscr{T} = 0$, according to the third law of thermodynamics. If an expansion of $E(\mathscr{T})$ near $\mathscr{T} = 0$ in powers of $\mathscr{T}$ is possible, it must start at least with the quadratic term. We shall assume that

$$\bar{E} = a\mathscr{T}^2. \tag{9.118}$$

This gives for the entropy

$$\mathscr{S} = \int \frac{dE}{\mathscr{T}(E)} = 2(a\bar{E})^{1/2} + \text{const.} \tag{9.119}$$

and for the level density

$$\rho(\bar{E}) = C \exp [2(a\bar{E})^{1/2}]. \tag{9.120}$$

The theory which enabled us to obtain the exponential form (9.120) for level densities is extremely rough. It simply gives us an idea of how rapidly the mean level spacing decreases with energy. It does not distinguish between levels with different quantum numbers. Typical values of a and C for nuclei with $A < 50$ are 1 MeV^{-1} and 0.5 MeV^{-1}, respectively. For $A > 100$, a is of the order of 10 MeV^{-1} and C of the order of 10^{-2} MeV^{-1}. Typical nuclear temperatures are of the order of 1 MeV.

[v] The Region Where a Large Number of Resonances Overlap

We have thus far discussed average cross sections in the region where many resonances overlap, where the optical model gives a good description of the scattering. Strength function considerations tell us that for incident energies of the order of 10 MeV the ratio of the average partial width to the spacing for a particular channel is of the order of 10 for elastic scattering from fairly light nuclei. Assuming that the total width Γ_s is the sum of a number of partial widths of the order of 10, we would have a few hundred resonances contributing to the scattering amplitude at a particular energy in a particular channel.

We can discuss the elastic scattering in terms of the scattering amplitude where, for a finite energy range, we introduce a potential scattering term $C_l(E)$ as in (9.25). We shall assume spinless particles at first in order to simplify the discussion.

$$f(E, \theta) = \frac{1}{2ik} \Sigma_l (2l + 1) P_l(\cos \theta) \left\{ C_l(E) + \Sigma_s \frac{R_{ls}}{E - \epsilon_s + i\Gamma_s/2} \right\}. \quad (9.121)$$

R_{ls} is proportional to the partial width. The average total width $\langle \Gamma \rangle$ is supposed to be many times greater than the average level spacing $\langle D \rangle$, so that many resonances overlap and contribute to the amplitude at any particular energy.

The variation of the individual resonance terms in (9.121) is now slow compared to the level spacing. Within an energy region of width $\pi \langle \Gamma \rangle$, mostly the same resonances interfere coherently, producing a slow variation of the cross section. The factor π comes from the shape of the resonances. Cross sections for two energies within a range $\pi \langle \Gamma \rangle$ are said to be correlated. At two energies spaced much further apart than $\pi \langle \Gamma \rangle$, the contributing resonances will be unrelated, so the cross sections will be uncorrelated. Since the reduced width amplitudes may be regarded as random, the resonance terms add very differently at intervals larger than $\pi \langle \Gamma \rangle$. The cross section exhibits random fluctuations characterized by a correlation energy $\pi \langle \Gamma \rangle$. This phenomenon was first noted by Porter and Thomas (56). It has been intensively studied by Ericson (63).

Similar considerations apply exactly to nonelastic reactions where the partial width now is a product of two partial width amplitudes having in general different values of the channel quantum numbers λ, since the exit and entrance channels are now different.

The correlation energy $\pi\langle\Gamma\rangle$ can be observed in experiments whose resolution is better than $\langle\Gamma\rangle$. It is sometimes used to define an average compound nucleus lifetime τ where

$$\tau = \hbar/\langle\Gamma\rangle. \tag{9.122}$$

Typical correlation energies are a few tens of kilovolts that correspond to about 10^{-19} sec. This means that, for compound elastic scattering, a particle would traverse the nucleus several thousand times. An example of cross section fluctuations is shown in Fig. 9.16. In this case the reaction is $^{12}C(^{12}C, \alpha_1)^{20}Ne$ between 10 MeV and 13 MeV incident energy. The correlation energy is about 250 KeV, so that $\langle\Gamma\rangle$ is of the order of 80 KeV.

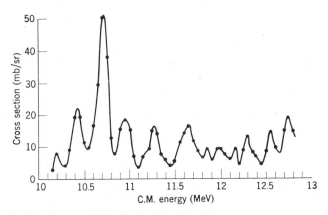

FIG. 9.16 Energy dependence of the differential cross section for the reaction $^{12}C(^{12}C, \alpha_1)^{20}Ne$ at 4.4°, leaving ^{20}Ne in its 2+ state at 1.63 MeV. (Adapted from Almquist, Kuehner, McPherson, and Vogt, 64.)

We can discuss the distribution of cross sections in terms of the random assumption for the reduced width amplitudes, which are real. The fluctuating part of the scattering amplitude (9.121) may be written for elastic scattering as

$$A_l \equiv (2l + 1)P_l(\cos\theta)\sum_s \frac{R_{ls}}{E - \epsilon_s + i\Gamma_s/2} = \xi_l + i\eta_l, \tag{9.123}$$

where R_{ls} is a real random number. If a large number of resonances contribute to the sum, ξ_l and η_l will be normally distributed with the same variance. If the sum of A_l over l is denoted by $\xi(\theta) + i\eta(\theta)$, the same property applies to $\xi(\theta)$ and $\eta(\theta)$. They are sums of random numbers, each with the same weight factor.

The differential cross section, excluding the direct scattering term, is

$$\sigma(\theta) = [\xi(\theta)]^2 + [\eta(\theta)]^2. \tag{9.124}$$

According to the theorem of statistics which says that the sum of the squares of n quantities, each normally distributed with the same variance, is distributed as χ^2 with n degrees of freedom, the differential cross section is distributed as χ^2 with two degrees of freedom. This distribution is given, for $x = \sigma(\theta)/\langle\sigma(\theta)\rangle$, by (9.101).

$$P_2(x) = e^{-x}. \tag{9.101}$$

Low cross sections are important in this distribution, and there is a long tail of high cross sections. Thus the ratio between the highest and lowest cross sections in the sample is large. In fact, it is of order $n \log n$ where n is the number in the sample.

For elastic or nonelastic reactions we can define a direct interaction amplitude S_D by analogy with the average amplitude $\langle S \rangle$ of (9.47) for elastic scattering. It is defined so that the average of the cross terms vanishes when the sum of direct and fluctuation (or compound) amplitudes are added and averaged. The average cross section is

$$\langle\sigma(\theta)\rangle = |S_D|^2 + \langle|S - S_D|\rangle^2 \equiv \sigma_D(\theta) + \langle\sigma_C(\theta)\rangle. \tag{9.125}$$

According to statistical theory, the corresponding probability distribution is

$$P(x) = \exp\{-(x - x_D)\}J_0(2ix^{1/2}x_D^{1/2}), \tag{9.126}$$

where x and x_D are $\sigma(\theta)$ and $\sigma_D(\theta)$ measured in units of $\langle\sigma_C(\theta)\rangle$. For $\sigma_D(\theta)$ smaller than $\langle\sigma_C(\theta)\rangle$, (9.126) does not differ much from the χ^2 distribution (9.101). On the other hand, it has a maximum for a nonzero value of $\sigma(\theta)$ if $\sigma_D(\theta)$ is larger than $\langle\sigma_C(\theta)\rangle$, so that this situation can easily be recognized experimentally.

In this way we have a chance of determining the direct and fluctuation contributions to the cross section separately, without making time measurements. We must find an angle at which the direct cross section is expected, on theoretical grounds, to be very small. At this angle the average cross section is $\langle\sigma_C(\theta)\rangle$. We can make assumptions for the angular distribution of $\sigma_C(\theta)$, the simplest of which is that it is isotropic. This assumption is also fairly realistic. We can then determine $\sigma_D(\theta)$ at different angles. In an actual case, it is hard to say at which angle the direct cross section is small on theoretical grounds. This will be discussed in subsequent chapters on direct interactions. At forward angles for small Q value, it is known to be small for inelastic scattering with a change of parity, while the fluctuation cross section is not necessarily small. Crude and often incorrect models for direct interactions predict that the cross section is small at backward angles.

We can make another generalization of Equation (9.101) to the case where all particles have spin, and the number of possible combinations of spin-projection numbers that can be measured is N. For an unpolarized beam in a single-scattering experiment, the cross section is averaged over initial spin projections and summed over final spin projections (see Chapter 8C). There

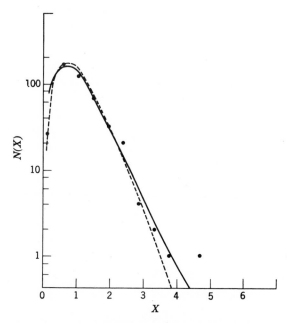

FIG. 9.17   Comparison of the observed and calculated probability distributions of the differential cross section for the reaction $^{12}C(^{12}C, \alpha_1)^{12}Ne$ leaving ^{20}Ne in its 2+ state at 1.63 MeV. The curves are explained in the text. (Adapted from Almquist, Kuehner, McPherson, and Vogt, 64.)

are N effective incoherent channels. The probability distribution is now χ^2 with $2N$ degrees of freedom

$$P_{2N}(x) = \frac{N}{(N-1)!}(Nx)^{N-1}e^{-Nx}. \qquad (9.127)$$

For total cross sections, the sum over partial waves is also incoherent, so the number N is increased appropriately.

This form requires all N channels to have the same variance for the normal distributions of ξ and η. A further discussion of these effects has been given by Brink and Stephen (63).

An example of the distribution of a differential cross section is shown in Fig. 9.17. The reaction is $^{12}C(^{12}C, \alpha_1)^{20}Ne$ where the final nucleus ^{20}Ne is left in its first excited 2+ state. In this case, there are three possible final magnetic substates, $m = +2, 0, -2$ and, of course, only one possible initial magnetic substate because the spins of ^{12}C are zero. If the three incoherent contributions to the cross section are added with equal weights, the distribution function, putting $N = 3$ in (9.127), is proportional to

$$x^2 e^{-3x}.$$

This is the dashed curve in Fig. 9.17. The solid curve is obtained by weighting the magnetic substates according to the results of a Hauser-Feshbach type calculation, using optical model transmission coefficients determined from elastic scattering (Almquist, Kuehner, McPherson, and Vogt, 64).

FURTHER READING

1. N. Bohr, *Nature*, **137**, 344 (1936).
   N. Bohr and F. Kalckar, *Kgl.Danske Videnskab. Selskab, Mat-fys. Medd.* **14**, No. 10 (1937).
   R. Serber, *Phys. Rev.* **72**, 1114 (1947).
   E. P. Wigner, *Am. J. Phys.*, **23**, 371 (1955).
   F. L. Friedman and V. F. Weisskopf, *Niels Bohr and the Development of Physics*, Pergamon Press, Ltd., London, 1955.
   Qualitative discussions of reactions.

2. V. F. Weisskopf and D. H. Ewing, *Phys. Rev.*, **57**, 472, 935 (1940).
   W. Hauser and H. Feshbach, *Phys. Rev.*, **87**, 366 (1952).
   H. Feshbach, D. C. Peaslee, and V. F. Weisskopf, *Phys. Rev.*, **71**, 145 (1947).
   Statistical models.

3. R. G. Thomas, *Phys. Rev.*, **97**, 224 (1955).
   General discussion of the compound nucleus.

4. H. Feshbach, C. E. Porter, and V. F. Weisskopf, *Phys. Rev.*, **96**, 448 (1954).
   G. E. Brown, *Rev. Mod. Phys.*, **31**, 893 (1959).
   M. Sano, S. Yoshida, and T. Terasawa, *Nucl. Phys.*, **6**, 20 (1959).
   Reactions averaged over an energy interval.

5. L. R. Dodd and I. E. McCarthy, *Phys. Rev.*, **134**, A1136 (1964).
   K. F. Ratcliff and N. Austern, *Ann. Phys. (N.Y.)*, **42**, 185 (1967).
   Interference of direct and compound nucleus reactions.

6. C. E. Porter and R. G. Thomas, *Phys. Rev.*, **104,** 483 (1956).
   C. E. Porter and N. Rosenzweig, *Suomalaisen Tiedeakatemian Toimituksia*, **AVI,** No. 44 (1960).
   C. E. Porter, *Nucl. Phys.*, **40,** 167 (1963).
   Statistical properties of energy levels and reduced width amplitudes.

7. T. Ericson, *Ann. Phys. (N. Y.)*, **23,** 390 (1963).
   D. M. Brink and R. O. Stephen, *Phys. Letters*, **5,** 77 (1963).
   Fluctuations in cross sections.

8. S. Fernbach, R. Serber, and T. B. Taylor, *Phys. Rev.*, **75,** 1352 (1949).
   K. M. Watson, *Rev. Mod. Phys.*, **30,** 565 (1958) (and references therein).
   A. K. Kerman, H. McManus, and R. M. Thaler, *Ann. Phys.*, **8,** 558 (1959).
   Derivation of the optical model from two-body scattering at high energies.

PROBLEMS

1. A gamma ray is emitted from the first excited state of ^{57}Fe, whose lifetime is 10^{-7} sec, at time t_0. It is resonantly scattered by an ^{57}Fe scatterer and then detected at time t_1. What is the distribution of the detection probability as a function of the time $t = t_1 - t_0$? What is this time distribution if the source and scatterer are moving apart at a speed such that the incident γ-ray has an energy relative to the scatterer which is 10^{-7} eV less than the resonant energy?

2. Calculate and plot the s- and p-wave strength functions as functions of the well radius for 0.1 MeV neutrons incident on square wells of radii between 3 fm and 6 fm, depth $(50 + 2i)$ MeV.

3. Verify that the curve C in the Dalitz plot of Fig. 9.4 is the straight line $E_{\text{C.M.}}(\pi^-) + E_{\text{C.M.}}(\pi^+) = 1100$ MeV for the ρ-meson. The incident π^- energy is 3,000 MeV.

4. Plot the curve C' for the reaction ^{3}He $+$ d $\rightarrow$ ^{3}He $+$ p $+$ n when the counters are fixed at $\theta_3 = 30°$, $\theta_4 = -30°$. Let the axes be T_3 and T_4 as in Fig. 9.5. Plot the curves C' for the 21 MeV state of the α-particle and for the singlet deuteron.

5. Verify the formula (9.69) for the black nucleus s-state strength function. At what energy is the average partial width equal to $1/10$ of the average spacing according to this formula?

6. Plot the distribution of $\gamma_s^{(0)}/\bar{\gamma}$ for the resonances of Table 9.1 as a suitable histogram and compare the distribution with the Porter-Thomas distribution (9.100).

7. Compare the distribution of nearest-neighbor spacings for the resonances of Table 9.1 with the Wigner surmise (9.106).

8. Use the WKB approximation to calculate the s-state transmission coefficient for 100 MeV neutrons incident on a square well potential $V = -20$ MeV, $W = -15$ MeV, $R = 4$ fm.

9. What is the average number of effective open channels for a resonance in the experiment $^{12}C(^{12}C, \alpha_1)^{20}Ne$ described by Fig. 9.16?

10

FORMAL SCATTERING THEORY

We now have a knowledge of two-nucleon scattering and of the role of the two-nucleon interaction in bound nuclei. We have seen that two-nucleon scattering experiments are insufficient to provide all the data needed for understanding many-body bound states in principle because, in many-body theories, the two-nucleon interaction appears off the energy shell. In Chapter 9 it was shown, without actually evaluating many-body quantities such as reduced width amplitudes, that the interaction of particles with nuclei at high energies may be described to a good approximation as scattering by a complex potential if we fix attention on only one or a few channels. This enables us to use single-particle models for scattering, at least as a first approximation, and thereby to greatly reduce the number of degrees of freedom required to describe certain reactions. Part of the nucleus may be regarded as an inert core.

At least three bodies are required to give us any knowledge of properties of interactions off the energy shell. Even if our present understanding of nuclear physics enables us to have some confidence in few-body models of reactions, we must still calculate the models. This requires a knowledge of the formal structure of scattering theory so that we can make reliable approximations.

The case of two-body scattering, which has been discussed in Chapter 2, will provide a concrete example as an aid to understanding the quantities involved in the formal theory.

Consider a physical system that consists of two or more colliding parts. The Hamiltonian H is split into two parts, K and V, so that if K were the entire Hamiltonian the parts would have the same internal structure but would not scatter. At times $t = -\infty$ and $+\infty$, the parts are regarded as being so far apart that they do not feel the interaction V. The asymptotic wave functions $\Phi(\pm\infty)$ are eigenstates of K. They are plane waves or Coulomb waves in the two-body example.

The S-matrix is defined to be the operator that acts on $\Phi(-\infty)$ to produce $\Phi(+\infty)$ (when the correct representation is used).

$$\Phi(+\infty) = S\Phi(-\infty). \tag{10.1}$$

Heisenberg and Wheeler are responsible for the idea that the S-matrix tells us all we can know about a system. Knowledge of the S-matrix means a knowledge of the asymptotic part of the wave function. The wave function in the interior region, that is, the region where V acts significantly on the colliding parts, is obtained by solving the Schrödinger equation. It cannot be measured in principle because, if the measuring equipment is put into the interior region, there is no way of distinguishing it from V.

The Schrödinger equation has never been verified and, in fact, contains information that is inherently unverifiable. It is sometimes possible to relate measurements of cross sections (asymptotic information) in one reaction to measurements of cross sections in other reactions by using properties of the S-matrix. Thus far this has only been done for two bodies in each of the initial and final channels. The relations are known as dispersion relations. These relations must exist for all possible combinations of initial and final particles in a many-body reaction, but it has thus far proved more profitable to describe much of the many-body information by wave functions from model Schrödinger equations, where the effective potentials can be determined quite well phenomenologically. The object of phenomenological reaction calculations is to use models for few-body reactions in order to predict effects observed in slightly more complicated reactions. One of the bodies may be a many-body core regarded for the purpose of the model as inert.

A. THE PHYSICAL PICTURE OF GELL-MANN AND GOLDBERGER

A physical description of the scattering process has been given by Gell-Mann and Goldberger (53). The wave function $\Psi(t)$ for the system is defined by the Schrödinger equation

$$i\hbar \frac{\partial \Psi(t)}{\partial t} = (K + V)\Psi(t). \tag{10.2}$$

The asymptotic Schrödinger equation is

$$i\hbar \frac{\partial \Phi(t)}{\partial t} = K\Phi(t). \tag{10.3}$$

The stationary states of this equation ϕ_i and the corresponding energy eigenvalues E_i are given by

$$\Phi_i(t) = \phi_i e^{-iE_i t}. \tag{10.4}$$

From now on we shall use units such that $\hbar = c = 1$ until the units are needed. We shall discuss the scattering from initial state Φ_j to final state Φ_i. The initial state Φ_j determines the actual state Ψ_j and may be used to characterize it. The probability that the system whose state vector is Ψ_j will be found in a particular state Φ_i at time t is given, according to the basic definition of probability amplitudes in quantum mechanics, by

$$w_{ij}(t) = |f_{ij}(t)|^2 N_j^{-1}, \qquad (10.5)$$

where

$$f_{ij}(t) = \langle \Phi_i(t) | \Psi_j(t) \rangle. \qquad (10.6)$$

An explicit normalizing factor N_j, given by

$$N_j = \langle \Psi_j(t) | \Psi_j(t) \rangle, \qquad (10.7)$$

has been included since the normalization of continuum states requires discussion. As in the discussion of the Fermi gas in Chapter 1B, we approximate the continuum states by bound states in a cubic box of side L with perfectly reflecting walls, whose normalization is proportional to $L^{-3/2}$. L will be allowed to tend to infinity when convenient.

We shall examine the transition rates at time $t = 0$. We have to describe the physical development of the state $\Psi_j(t)$ with time from some time T in the distant past when the system was in the asymptotic state $\Phi_j(T)$, which is equivalent to $\Psi_j(T)$. Since $\Psi_j(t)$ is an eigenstate of H, the time development of it is given by

$$\Psi_j(t) = e^{-iH(t-T)}\Phi_j(T). \qquad (10.8)$$

Equation (10.8), however, does not describe an actual physical situation. The beam is always turned on over a finite (even though long) time as we have discussed for wave packets representing two-body scattering in Chapter 9. A complete physical description includes a description of the wave packet. The actual shape of the wave-packet weight factor is immaterial to the discussion as long as it builds up from nothing to its full value over a finite time τ. However, as we have seen in Chapter 9A, it is convenient for integration to use an exponential distribution in time, which corresponds to a function with a single pole in the complex energy plane. The absolute square of the energy function is a Lorentzian of width $\epsilon = \hbar/\tau$.

Since we are interested in steady-state cross sections by the nature of most scattering experiments, we shall be interested in the limit $\tau \to +\infty$ or $\epsilon \to 0+$. However, we have seen in Chapter 9A that there are some cases in which the time-dependent transients can be measured, confirming our understanding of the energy-time superposition principle that is used in writing the wave-packet description of the scattering process. This description is given by a superposition of energy eigenstates (10.8) with an exponential weight factor.

$$\Psi_j(t) = \epsilon \int_{-\infty}^{0} dT e^{\epsilon T} e^{-iH(t-T)} \Phi_j(T). \tag{10.9}$$

We shall now find expressions for the scattering amplitude $f_{ij}(0)$ and the normalization N_j by formal manipulation of equation (10.9). The aim is to express these quantities as matrix elements of V, in which the space integrations are restricted to the interaction region.

Using (10.4), we can write (10.9) as

$$\Psi_j(t) = e^{-iHt} \epsilon \int_{-\infty}^{0} dT e^{[\epsilon + i(H - E_j)]T} \phi_j. \tag{10.10}$$

A very convenient notation, which is used throughout the formal theory, is to formally integrate (10.10) in order to write it as the operation on ϕ_j of an integral operator.

$$\Psi_j(t) = e^{-iHt} \frac{\epsilon}{\epsilon + i(H - E_j)} \phi_j. \tag{10.11}$$

We were introduced to this technique in Chapter 2C, and have also used it in Chapters 6 and 8. Equation (10.11) is a formal solution of the Schrödinger equation (10.2) with ingoing boundary conditions built in. The integral operator

$$G(s \pm i\epsilon) = (H - s \mp i\epsilon)^{-1} \tag{10.12}$$

is a Green's function operator for the total scattering problem with ingoing and outgoing boundary conditions, respectively; s is an energy variable.

Since ϕ_j is an eigenfunction of K it satisfies

$$(H - E_j)\phi_j = V\phi_j. \tag{10.13}$$

We may substitute (10.13) in (10.11) to obtain both an explicit and an implicit relation for the state vector at $t = 0$.

$$\Psi_j(0) = \phi_j - \frac{1}{H - E_j - i\epsilon} V\phi_j = \phi_j - G(E_j + i\epsilon)V\phi_j, \tag{10.14}$$

$$\Psi_j(0) = \phi_j - \frac{1}{K - E_j - i\epsilon} V\Psi_j(0) = \phi_j - G_0(E_j + i\epsilon)V\Psi_j(0). \tag{10.15}$$

$G_0(s)$ is the Green's function for the noninteracting system with ingoing boundary conditions. That the two relations (10.14, 10.15) are identical may

be seen by the fact that they have the same power-series expansion for small
V.

$$\Psi'_j(0) = \phi_j - G_0(E_j + i\epsilon)V\phi_j + G_0(E_j + i\epsilon)VG_0(E_j + i\epsilon)V\phi_j + \cdots.$$
$$(10.16)$$

This series is the Born series. For a two-body problem, it is convergent for all
values of V at high enough energy. We shall discuss it for three-body problems in Section 10E.

Using the integral equation (10.15) for $\Psi'_j(0)$ in (10.6), we may express the
scattering amplitude $f_{ij}(0)$ as

$$f_{ij}(0) = \delta_{ij} + \frac{1}{E_j - E_i + i\epsilon} R_{ij}(\epsilon), \qquad (10.17)$$

where

$$R_{ij}(\epsilon) = \langle \phi_i | V | \Psi'_j(0) \rangle. \qquad (10.18)$$

The analogous equation for two-body scattering is (2.91).

$R_{ij}(\epsilon)$ has no singularities in the limit $\epsilon \to 0+$ because, if we subtitute the
series (10.16) for $\Psi'_j(0)$ in (10.18), we see that the integral operator

$$\lim_{\epsilon \to 0+} \frac{1}{K - E_j - i\epsilon}$$

never operates on ϕ_j, an eigenfunction of K, but only on $V\phi_j$.

We must now see what happens to Equation (10.17) for the scattering amplitude in the double limit $L \to \infty$, $\epsilon \to 0+$. We must also discuss the normalization in this limit. The limiting operation must be performed in a special
way because we must ensure that no part of the system is ever outside the box.
This means that, as τ and L both tend to infinity, we must keep $v\tau < L$ where
v is the group velocity of the wave packet. When τ and L both tend to $+\infty$,
quantities proportional to $\epsilon^{-1}L^{-3}$ tend to zero.

We shall discuss first the normalization N_j. We write

$$f_{ij}(t) = \langle \Phi_i | e^{i(E_i - H)t} | \Psi'_j(0) \rangle. \qquad (10.19)$$

Differentiating (10.19) we have, from (10.13, 18),

$$\dot{f}_{ij}(0) = -iR_{ij}(\epsilon). \qquad (10.20)$$

By means of some complex number arithmetic using (10.17, 10.18, 10.20) we
have, for the transition rate at $t = 0$,

$$\left[\frac{d}{dt} |f_{ij}(t)|^2 \right]_{t=0} = 2\delta_{ij} \operatorname{Im} R_{jj}(\epsilon) + \frac{2\epsilon}{(E_j - E_i)^2 + \epsilon^2} |R_{ij}(\epsilon)|^2. \qquad (10.21)$$

By expanding Ψ_j in the complete set ϕ_i, we can see that N_j is given by

$$N_j = \sum_i |f_{ij}(t)|^2. \tag{10.22}$$

If probability is conserved in the scattering process, the normalization N_j is constant in time. Hence, if we sum both sides of (10.21) over i, the left-hand side vanishes, and we have the identity

$$2 \operatorname{Im} R_{jj}(\epsilon) + \sum_i \frac{2\epsilon}{(E_j - E_i)^2 + \epsilon^2} |R_{ij}(\epsilon)|^2 = 0. \tag{10.23}$$

Substituting (10.18) for $f_{ij}(0)$ in (10.22) and expanding, we have

$$N_j = 1 + \frac{2}{\epsilon} \operatorname{Im} R_{jj}(\epsilon) + \sum_i \frac{1}{(E_j - E_i)^2 + \epsilon^2} |R_{ij}(\epsilon)|^2. \tag{10.22a}$$

On using the identity (10.23), (10.22a) becomes

$$N_j = 1 + \epsilon^{-1} \operatorname{Im} R_{jj}(\epsilon). \tag{10.24}$$

Since each wave function in $R_{jj}(\epsilon)$ contains a normalization $L^{-3/2}$, the second term in (10.24) is of order $\epsilon^{-1}L^{-3}$ in the double limit $\epsilon \to 0+$, $L \to \infty$. It therefore vanishes in the limit and $N_j \to 1$.

For practical purposes we do not include the double limit in the notation. The limit $\epsilon \to 0+$ is sometimes explicitly indicated to define whether the boundary conditions are ingoing or outgoing. The limit of the state vector $\Psi_j(0)$ is denoted by

$$\lim_{\substack{\epsilon \to 0+ \\ L \to \infty}} \Psi_j(0) = \psi_j^{(+)}. \tag{10.25}$$

The integral equation (10.15) for the scattering becomes

$$\psi_j^{(+)} = \phi_j - \lim_{\epsilon \to 0+} \frac{1}{K - E_j - i\epsilon} V \psi_j^{(+)}, \tag{10.26a}$$

$$= \phi_j - G_0(E_j + i\epsilon)V\psi_j^{(+)}. \tag{10.26b}$$

Both forms of (10.26) are known as the Lippmann-Schwinger (50) equation. The limit $\epsilon \to 0+$ has been omitted in the notation for (10.26b).

The scattering amplitude in the limit is

$$f_{ij} = \delta_{ij} + \lim_{\epsilon \to 0+} \frac{1}{E_j - E_i + i\epsilon} T_{ij}. \tag{10.27}$$

The limit of $R_{ij}(\epsilon)$ is the t-matrix. Its matrix elements are

$$T_{ij} \equiv \langle \phi_i| T |\phi_j \rangle = \langle \phi_i| V |\psi_j^{(+)} \rangle, \tag{10.28}$$

which is the type of expression we set out to find. The t-matrix is related to the Green's function by

$$G_0(s)T(s) = G(s)V. \tag{10.29}$$

This may be seen by multiplying (10.26) on the left by V, leaving the following equations for the operators that multiply ϕ_j.

$$T(s) = V - VG_0(s)T(s) \tag{10.30a}$$

$$= V - VG(s)V. \tag{10.30b}$$

Equation (10.30a) is the operator form of the Lippmann-Schwinger equation, and (10.30b) corresponds to the explicit Lippmann-Schwinger relation (10.14). These equations are in convenient form for further operator manipulation in special cases such as the three-body problem.

B THE S-MATRIX

The S-matrix, according to (10.1), is a time development operator for infinite times. It is convenient to discuss it in the interaction representation rather than the Schrödinger representation which was used in Section A of this chapter. In the Schrödinger representation the state vectors are time-dependent, but the operators are time-independent. The time dependence of the noninteracting states, which are eigenstates of K, is removed by a unitary transformation to the interaction representation, denoted by primed quantities.

$$\Psi''(t) = e^{iKt}\Psi(t). \tag{10.31}$$

The interaction representation state vector satisfies the Schrödinger equation

$$i\hbar \frac{\partial \Psi''(t)}{\partial t} = V(t)\Psi''(t), \tag{10.32}$$

where

$$V(t) = e^{iKt}Ve^{-iKt}. \tag{10.33}$$

The interaction representation reduces to the Schrödinger representation at $t = 0$.

Unitary operators are especially important in quantum mechanics because a unitary transformation of an operator preserves its eigenvalues. The time-development operator for the whole system is unitary. It is defined as follows.

$$\Psi''(t) = U(t, t_0)\Psi''(t_0). \tag{10.34}$$

In the interaction representation the S-matrix is $U(\infty, -\infty)$. It is necessary to prove that it is unitary in the limit of infinite times.

[i] THE TIME-DEVELOPMENT OPERATOR

We shall first discuss some explicit formulas for $U(t, t_0)$. Since

$$\Psi(t) = e^{-iH(t-t_0)}\Psi(t_0),$$ (10.35)

we have

$$U(t, t_0) = e^{iKt}e^{-i(K+V)(t-t_0)}e^{-iKt_0}.$$ (10.36)

To express U in terms of interaction-representation quantities, we differentiate (10.36) with respect to t, obtaining by the use of (10.33)

$$i\hbar \frac{\partial U(t, t_0)}{\partial t} = V(t)U(t, t_o).$$ (10.37)

Integrating (10.37), we have

$$U(t, t_0) = 1 - i\int_{t_0}^{t} dt' V(t')U(t', t_0).$$ (10.38)

Iterating (10.38) gives

$$U(t, t_0) = \mathcal{T} \exp\left[-i\int_{t_0}^{t} dt' V(t')\right],$$ (10.39)

where the time-ordering operator $\mathcal{T}$ signifies that terms in the power series are ordered with earliest times standing to the right. We now allow t and t_0 to go to zero or infinity. The limiting process is defined in exactly the same way as it was for the wave function in (10.9).

$$U(t, -\infty) = \lim_{\epsilon \to 0+} \epsilon \int_{-\infty}^{0} dT e^{\epsilon T} U(t, T).$$ (10.40)

We find the limit of Equation (10.36) for $U(t, t_0)$ as $t_0 \to \infty$ by using the definition (10.34) of U in the wave packet expansion (10.9) of $\Psi_j(t)$, which must be transformed into the interaction representation:

$$\Psi'_j(t) = e^{iKt}e^{-iHt}\epsilon \int_{-\infty}^{0} dT e^{\epsilon T}e^{iHt}e^{-iKt}\phi_j.$$ (10.41)

We now substitute (10.41) into the definition (10.34) of U, multiply on the right by $\langle\phi_j|$, and sum over j.

$$\sum_j U(t, -\infty) |\Psi_j(-\infty)\rangle\langle\phi_j|$$

$$= e^{iKt}e^{-iHt}\lim_{\epsilon\to 0+}\sum_j \frac{\epsilon}{\epsilon + i(H - E_j)} |\phi_j\rangle\langle\phi_j|. \quad (10.42)$$

For large negative times T, we use (10.4, 10.31) to obtain

$$\Psi'_j(T) = e^{iKT}\Psi_j(T) = e^{iKT}\Phi_j(T) = \phi_j.$$ (10.43)

Therefore, the left-hand side of (10.42) is $U(t, -\infty)$ by the completeness relation $\sum_j |\phi_j\rangle\langle\phi_j| = 1$.

We now recall the discussion at the end of Section 10A where we pointed out that $\Psi_j(t)$ could be replaced for $t = 0$ by $\psi_j^{(+)}$, defined by the limit of the Green's function operator in (10.42). Thus we have

$$U(0, -\infty) = \sum_j |\psi_j^{(+)}\rangle\langle\phi_j|, \tag{10.44}$$

or

$$U(0, -\infty)\phi_j = \psi_j^{(+)}. \tag{10.45}$$

[ii]   THE DISTORTION OPERATORS

$U(0, -\infty)$ is generally called $\Omega^{(+)}$. It is the distortion operator which produces the corresponding eigesntate of the Hamiltonian with ingoing boundary conditions when acting on one of the free states ϕ_j.

Using similar arguments with ϵ replaced everywhere by $-\epsilon$ we find that $U(0, +\infty)$ produces the eigenstate with outgoing boundary conditions from ϕ_j. In terms of two-body scattering, the distortion operators produce distorted waves from plane waves.

The distortion operators are defined by

$$\Omega^{(\pm)} = U(0, \pm\infty), \tag{10.46}$$

$$\Omega^{(\pm)}\phi_j = \psi_j^{(\pm)}. \tag{10.47}$$

If we had differentiated (10.36) with respect to t_0 instead of t, and had carried through exactly the same arguments, we would have arrived at

$$U(\infty, t) = \lim_{\epsilon \to 0+} \int_0^\infty dT e^{-\epsilon T} U(T, t). \tag{10.48}$$

Equations (10.36) and (10.48) give

$$U(\infty, t) = U(\infty, 0)U(0, t). \tag{10.49}$$

U is unitary for finite times by definition, that is,

$$U(t, t_0) = U^\dagger(t_0, t). \tag{10.50}$$

The application of the limiting processes to (10.50) does not change it for infinite times; hence

$$U(\pm\infty, 0) = U^\dagger(0, \pm\infty) = \Omega^{(\mp)}. \tag{10.51}$$

[iii]   THE S-MATRIX ELEMENTS

From Equation (10.49) and the definition of the S-matrix we have, for the interaction representation,

$$S = U(\infty, -\infty) = U(\infty, 0)U(0, -\infty) = \Omega^{(-)\dagger}\Omega^{(+)}. \tag{10.52}$$

The S-matrix elements may be worked out as follows. Equations (10.42) and (10.44) give

$$U(t, -\infty) = e^{iKt} \sum_j e^{-iE_j t} |\psi_j^{(+)}\rangle\langle\phi_j|. \tag{10.53}$$

Multiplying (10.53) by $V(t)$ and introducing the complete set of intermediate states ϕ_j, we have

$$V(t)U(t, -\infty) = \sum_{ij} |\phi_i\rangle\langle\phi_i| e^{i(E_i - E_j)t} V |\psi_j^{(+)}\rangle\langle\phi_j|. \tag{10.54}$$

Equation (10.8) gives, in the limit of infinite arguments,

$$S = U(\infty, -\infty) = 1 - i\int_{-\infty}^{\infty} dt' V(t')U(t', -\infty). \tag{10.55}$$

Substituting (10.54) into (10.55) and integrating, we have

$$S = 1 - \sum_{ij} |\phi_i\rangle 2\pi i\delta(E_i - E_j)T_{ij} \langle\phi_j|. \tag{10.56}$$

The matrix elements S_{ij} are

$$S_{ij} \equiv \langle\phi_i| S |\phi_j\rangle = \delta_{ij} - 2\pi i\delta(E_i - E_j)T_{ij}. \tag{10.57}$$

Another form for S_{ij} follows from (10.52).

$$\begin{aligned}
S_{ij} &= \langle\phi_i| \Omega^{(-)\dagger}\Omega^{(+)} |\phi_j\rangle \\
&= \langle\Omega^{(-)}\phi_i | \Omega^{(+)}\phi_j\rangle \\
&= \langle\psi_i^{(-)} | \psi_j^{(+)}\rangle. \tag{10.58}
\end{aligned}$$

[iv] UNITARITY OF THE S-MATRIX

The unitarity of S is its most important property. It is used to relate S-matrices for different processes by means of dispersion relations. Physically it means that the eigenvalues of all the dynamical variables of the system are preserved by the interaction. Probability is conserved.

To prove that S is unitary, we expand $S^\dagger S$ and $SS^\dagger$ in terms of distortion operators. For the case of $S^\dagger S$, we have

$$S^\dagger S = \Omega^{(+)\dagger}\Omega^{(-)}\Omega^{(-)\dagger}\Omega^{(+)}. \tag{10.59}$$

$\Omega^{(\pm)\dagger}\Omega^{(\pm)}$ is the unit operator, as can be seen by introducing expansions in terms of complete sets ϕ_i, ϕ_j and by using the orthonormality of the eigenstates $\psi_j^{(\pm)}$.

$$\begin{aligned}
\Omega^{(\pm)\dagger}\Omega^{(\pm)} &= \sum_{ij} |\phi_i\rangle\langle\phi_i| \Omega^{(\pm)\dagger}\Omega^{(\pm)} |\phi_j\rangle\langle\phi_j| \\
&= \sum_{ij} |\phi_i\rangle\langle\psi_i^{(\pm)} | \psi_j^{(\pm)}\rangle\langle\phi_j| \\
&= 1.
\end{aligned}$$

However, $\Omega^{(\pm)}$ are not necessarily unitary, since

$$\Omega^{(\pm)}\Omega^{(\pm)\dagger} = \sum_i \Omega^{(\pm)} |\phi_i\rangle\langle\phi_i| \,\Omega^{(\pm)\dagger}$$
$$= \sum_i |\psi_i^{(\pm)}\rangle\langle\psi_i^{(\pm)}|$$

is not the unit operator if there are bound states ψ_α, so that the scattering states $\psi_i^{(\pm)}$ do not form a complete set. We may write

$$\Omega^{(\pm)}\Omega^{(\pm)\dagger} = 1 - \sum_\alpha |\psi_\alpha\rangle\langle\psi_\alpha|. \tag{10.60}$$

ψ_α are discrete bound states satisfying

$$H\psi_\alpha = E\psi_\alpha. \tag{10.61}$$

We may now show that $S^\dagger S$ and $SS^\dagger$ are the unit operator.

$$S^\dagger S = \Omega^{(+)\dagger}\Omega^{(-)}\Omega^{(-)\dagger}\Omega^{(+)}$$
$$= \Omega^{(+)\dagger}[1 - \sum_\alpha |\psi_\alpha\rangle\langle\psi_\alpha|]\Omega^{(+)}$$
$$= 1 - \Omega^{(+)\dagger} \sum_\alpha |\psi_\alpha\rangle\langle\psi_\alpha| \,\Omega^{(+)}$$
$$= 1 - \Omega^{(+)\dagger} \sum_{\alpha j} |\psi_\alpha\rangle\langle\psi_\alpha| \,\Omega^{(+)} \,|\phi_j\rangle\langle\phi_j|$$
$$= 1 - \Omega^{(+)\dagger} \sum_{\alpha j} |\psi_\alpha\rangle\langle\psi_\alpha| \,\psi_j^{(+)}\rangle\langle\phi_j|.$$

The second term is zero, since the scattering states $\psi_j^{(+)}$ are orthogonal to the bound states ψ_α. Similarly

$$SS^\dagger = \Omega^{(-)\dagger}\Omega^{(+)}\Omega^{(+)\dagger}\Omega^{(-)} = 1.$$

[v] Cross Sections and the Optical Theorem

The differential cross section for the transition $j \rightarrow i$ is the transition rate divided by the incident flux vL^{-3}, where v is the velocity of the colliding systems and L^3 is the normalization volume. Using Equation (10.21) for the transition rate, the differential cross section, apart from forward scattering $(j \rightarrow j)$ which will be treated separately, is

$$\sigma_{ij} = \lim_{\substack{\epsilon \to 0+ \\ L \to \infty}} \left\{ \frac{2\epsilon}{(E_j - E_i)^2 + \epsilon^2} \right\} |R_{ij}(\epsilon)|^2 L^3 v^{-1}. \tag{10.62}$$

In the limit $L \rightarrow \infty$ there is a continuum of final states. We are really interested in the transition probability to one of a group of final states G whose density is given by saying that the number of final states in the interval dE_i about E_i is $\rho(E_i)\,dE_i$. For an exponential initial wave packet the weight factor of the group of final states G is $2\epsilon/[(E_j - E_i)^2 + \epsilon^2]$.

The transition probability to the group of final states in the double limit is the sum of transition probabilities to the members of the group.

$$\dot{w}_{Gj} = \lim_{\epsilon \to 0+} \int dE_i \hbar^{-1} |R_{ij}(\epsilon)|^2 \frac{2\epsilon}{(E_j - E_i)^2 + \epsilon^2} \rho(E_i)$$

$$= \frac{2\pi}{\hbar} |T_{ij}|^2 \rho(E_j). \tag{10.63}$$

Using Equation (10.57) for the S-matrix elements, we can write the unitarity relation as

$$(S^\dagger S)_{ij} = \delta_{ij} = \delta_{ij} + 2\pi i \delta(E_i - E_j) T_{ij}{}^\dagger - 2\pi i \delta(E_i - E_j) T_{ij}$$
$$- (2\pi i)^2 \sum_k \delta(E_i - E_k) T_{ik}{}^\dagger \delta(E_k - E_j) T_{kj}. \tag{10.64}$$

Noting that

$$\delta(E_i - E_k)\delta(E_k - E_j) = \delta(E_i - E_j)\delta(E_k - E_j),$$

we can factor out $2\pi i \delta(E_i - E_j)$.

On the energy shell, that is, for $E_i = E_j = E$, we have for (10.64)

$$(T - T^\dagger)_{ij} = -2\pi i \sum_k T_{ik}{}^\dagger \delta(E_k - E_i) T_{kj}. \tag{10.65}$$

The diagonal matrix element of this equation is

$$\text{Im } T_{ii} = -\pi \sum_k |T_{ki}|^2 \delta(E_k - E_i). \tag{10.66}$$

The left-hand side of (10.66) is the imaginary part of the forward scattering amplitude. The right-hand side is proportional to the total cross section for all possible transitions. The equation is known as the *optical theorem*. It is a dispersion relation.

[vi] DISPERSION RELATIONS

We now have considered enough properties of the S-matrix to formulate relationships between S-matrix elements for different systems known as dispersion relations. The S-matrix will be written in a matrix notation for (10.57),

$$S = 1 + iR, \tag{10.67}$$

where

$$R_{ij} = -2\pi \delta(E_i - E_j) T_{ij}. \tag{10.67a}$$

The necessary physical ideas and mathematical entities will be treated in turn.

Causality. We showed in Chapter 9A that causality requires the S-matrix to be analytic in the upper half energy plane. Cauchy's integral theorem states that, if $R_{ij}(E) \to 0$ rapidly enough for large imaginary energies, then

$$R_{ij}(E) = \frac{1}{2\pi i} \lim_{\epsilon \to 0+} \int_\Gamma \frac{dE' R_{ij}(E')}{E' - E - i\epsilon}. \tag{10.68}$$

The contour of integration Γ is an infinite semicircle in the upper half plane enclosing the pole $E + i\epsilon$.

Dispersion Relation. A dispersion relation is obtained by subtracting from (10.68) the corresponding relation for $R_{ij}{}^*$. It takes the form

$$\lim_{\epsilon \to 0+} R_{ij}(E + i\epsilon) = \frac{1}{\pi} \int_{-\infty}^{\infty} dE' \frac{\text{Im } R_{ij}(E')}{E' - E - i\epsilon}. \tag{10.69}$$

Unitarity. Using (10.67) the unitarity relation may be written as

$$2 \text{ Im } R = R^\dagger R. \tag{10.70}$$

Taking matrix elements between states i and j and introducing a complete set labeled by k, we have

$$i \langle i| R^\dagger - R |j\rangle = \langle i| R^\dagger R |j\rangle$$
$$= i \langle i| R^\dagger |j\rangle - i \langle i| R |j\rangle = \sum_k \langle i| R^\dagger |k\rangle\langle k| R |j\rangle$$
$$= i \langle j| R |i\rangle^* - i \langle i| R |j\rangle = \sum_k \langle k| R |i\rangle^*\langle k| R |j\rangle. \tag{10.71}$$

Time Reversal Invariance. Invariance of the S-matrix under time reversal implies

$$\langle j| R |i\rangle = \langle i| R |j\rangle. \tag{10.72}$$

Substituting the complex conjugate of (10.72) in (10.71) we have

$$i \langle i| R |j\rangle^* - i \langle i| R |j\rangle = \sum_k \langle k| R |i\rangle^*\langle k| R |j\rangle,$$

or, in abbreviated notation,

$$2 \text{ Im } R_{ij} = \sum_k R_{ki}{}^* R_{kj}. \tag{10.73}$$

Writing (10.73) in the notation of (10.65), using our original t-matrix, we have

$$2 \text{ Im } T_{ij} = -2\pi i \sum_k T_{ik}{}^\dagger \delta(E_k - E_i) T_{kj}. \tag{10.74}$$

The similarity of (10.74) and (10.65) is obvious. We have used time reversal invariance to simplify (10.65) slightly.

Relationships between Scattering Amplitudes. The dispersion relation (10.69) is conventionally written, with the limiting process understood, as

$$R_{ij}(E) = \frac{1}{\pi} \int_\Gamma dE' \frac{\text{Im } R_{ij}(E')}{E' - E}. \tag{10.75}$$

Using the relationship (10.73) for intermediate states we may write

$$R_{ij}(E) = \frac{1}{2\pi} \int_\Gamma dE' \frac{\sum_k R_{ki}{}^* R_{kj}}{E' - E}. \tag{10.76}$$

Equation (10.76) relates the scattering amplitude for the problem to scattering amplitudes for different problems, namely the transition of the initial state to an intermediate state and the transition of the intermediate state to the final state. This equation is exact only if a complete set of intermediate states is considered. Clearly, if we choose intermediate states so that either R_{ki} or R_{kj} are amplitudes for the same process as R_{ij}, then (10.76) is a set of coupled integral equations, and there is some chance of solving it or at least using it as a basis for an approximation. An example of this will be given in Chapter 12*D*[iii].

C. THE TWO-BODY PROBLEM

In Chapter 2 we considered elastic scattering, which is the single-channel two-body problem on the energy shell. For three-body and more-body problems it is intuitively obvious that the two-body amplitudes occur off the energy shell because a third body can absorb momentum from the two-body collision. All the information about the two-body problem is contained in the two-body Green's function operator $G(s)$. We shall therefore include a brief discussion of the properties of this Green's function operator and related operators. The problem is reviewed in detail by Newton (60).

From the explicit form (10.14) of the Lippmann-Schwinger equation and the definition (10.47) of the distortion operators $\Omega^{(\pm)}$, it is clear that

$$\Omega^{(\pm)}(s) = \lim_{\epsilon \to 0+} [1 - G(s \pm i\epsilon)V]$$

$$\equiv 1 - G^{(\pm)}(s)V. \tag{10.77}$$

Equation (10.77) serves also as a definition of the notation $G^{(\pm)}(s)$. The total energy of the two-body system is s.

The t-matrix is obtained from the Green's function by the use of the Lippmann-Schwinger equation.

$$T(s) = \lim_{\epsilon \to 0+} T(s + i\epsilon) = V - VG^{(+)}(s)V \tag{10.30c}$$

$$= V\Omega^{(+)}(s). \tag{10.30d}$$

If $\Omega^{(+)}(s)$ acts on a plane wave whose energy is not s, we have a wave function off the energy shell. The matrix element of T between plane waves whose energies are unequal and not equal to s is also said to be off the energy shell.

We shall discuss the matrix element of the Green's function operator in the coordinate representation. In order to discuss functions of a single variable, it is convenient to make a partial wave expansion of the Schrödinger equation (2.18). For a local potential we have, expressing V in units of $\hbar^2/2\mu$,

$$\left[-\frac{d^2}{dr^2} + V(r) + \frac{l(l+1)}{r^2} - k^2 \right] u_l(k, r) = 0. \tag{2.18}$$

The complete Green's function or resolvent for the scattering problem satisfies

$$\left[-\frac{d^2}{dr^2} + V(r) + \frac{l(l+1)}{r^2} - k^2\right] G_l(k; r, r') = \delta(r - r'). \quad (10.78)$$

For $r \neq r'$, G_l is a solution of (2.18). At $r = r'$, its derivative has a discontinuity of unity. This follows from the definition of the δ function.

$$\left[\frac{d}{dr} G_l(k; r, r')\right]_{r=r'-\epsilon}^{r=r'+\epsilon} = -1. \quad (10.79)$$

The Green's function for ingoing boundary conditions occurs in the integrand of the partial wave expansion of the explicit Lippmann-Schwinger equation corresponding to (10.14).

$$u_l(k, r) = U_l(kr) - \int_0^\infty dr' G_l(k; r, r') V(r') U_l(kr'). \quad (10.80)$$

In this equation, U_l is the Riccatti-Bessel function defined by (2.19). It represents an ingoing wave at infinity. G_l contains no ingoing waves at infinity. Therefore it must be proportional to the solution of the Schrödinger equation (2.18) which represents outgoing waves for $r > r'$. This solution is $f_l(-k, r)$, defined by the boundary condition

$$\lim_{r \to \infty} e^{ikr} f_l(k, r) = i^l. \quad (10.81)$$

The Green's function G_l must of course be regular at the origin, so for $r < r'$ it is proportional to the regular solution $\phi_l(k, r)$ of (2.18), defined by the boundary condition

$$\lim_{r \to 0} (2l + 1)!! \, r^{-l-1} \phi_l(k, r) = 1. \quad (10.82)$$

Thus

$$G_l(k; r, r') = \phi_l(k, r) a(k, r'), \quad r < r',$$
$$= f_l(-k, r) b(k, r'), \quad r > r', \quad (10.83)$$

where a and b are proportionality factors. They are determined within a constant $C(k)$ by the requirement that $G_l(k; r, r')$ be continuous for $r = r'$.

$$a(k, r) = C(k) f_l(-k, r)$$
$$b(k, r) = C(k) \phi_l(k, r). \quad (10.84)$$

The derivative property (10.79) then fixes $C(k)$. It gives

$$C(k) W[\phi_l(k, r), f_l(-k, r)] = -1. \quad (10.85)$$

The Wronskian in (10.85) can be determined from the properties of the solutions of the Schrödinger equation (2.18). The ingoing and outgoing solutions $f_l(k, r)$ and $f_l(-k, r)$ are independent solutions (for $k \neq 0$) of (2.18).

The regular solution $\phi_l(k, r)$, which is an even function of k, can be expressed as a linear combination of these solutions with coefficients $f_l(\mp k)$.

$$\phi_l(k, r) = \tfrac{1}{2}ik^{-l-1}[f_l(-k)f_l(k, r) - (-1)^l f_l(k)f_l(-k, r)]. \quad (10.86)$$

Using the fact that the Wronskian of two solutions of the same linear second-order differential equation is independent of r, we may evaluate it at $r \to \infty$ and use the boundary condition (10.81) to obtain

$$W[f_l(k, r), f_l(-k, r)] = (-1)^l 2ik. \quad (10.87)$$

Making use of (10.86, 10.87), we find the Wronskian required for (10.85).

$$f_l(k) = k^l W[f_l(k, r), \phi_l(k, r)]. \quad (10.88)$$

The functions $f_l(\pm k)$ are Jost functions. We can understand their significance best by considering their relationship to the S-matrix. We recall the asymptotic form of the physical wave function $u_l(k, r)$, given in the external region by a linear combination (2.25) of ingoing and outgoing waves where the S-matrix element η_l is the relative amplitude of the outgoing wave. The asymptotic form of (2.25) is

$$u_l(k, r) \sim \tfrac{1}{2}i^{l+1}[e^{-ikr} - (-1)^l \eta_l e^{ikr}]. \quad (10.89)$$

Using (10.86) and the boundary condition (10.81), we may write the asymptotic form for large r of the regular solution $\phi_l(k, r)$.

$$\phi_l(k, r) \sim \tfrac{1}{2}i^{l+1}k^{-l-1}[f_l(-k)e^{-ikr} - (-1)^l f_l(k)e^{ikr}]. \quad (10.90)$$

By comparison of (10.89, 10.90), it follows that the physical solution $u_l(k, r)$ is proportional to the regular solution $\phi_l(k, r)$,

$$u_l(k, r) = \frac{k^{l+1}}{f_l(-k)} \phi_l(k, r) \quad (10.91)$$

and the S-matrix element is

$$\eta_l(k) = \frac{f_l(k)}{f_l(-k)}. \quad (10.92)$$

More insight into the physical significance of $f_l(k)$ is obtained by writing it in a way that shows that its phase is the phase shift.

$$f_l(k) = |f_l(k)| \, e^{i\delta_l(k)}. \quad (10.93)$$

Another very useful relation is

$$f_l^*(-k) = f_l(k), \quad (10.94)$$

which follows from (10.88), the fact that the $\phi_l(k, r)$ is real, and the reality of the Schrödinger equation (2.18) which leads, with the boundary condition (10.81), to

$$f_l^*(-k, r) = (-1)^l f_l(k, r). \tag{10.95}$$

With the help of (10.94) we can immediately prove two facts that we already know. First, since (10.92) gives

$$\eta_l(k) = \frac{1}{\eta_l(-k)}, \tag{10.96}$$

(10.94) implies that

$$|\eta_l|^2 = 1. \tag{10.97}$$

That is, the S-matrix is unitary.

Second, since $\phi_l(k, r)$ is real, (10.91) shows with the help of (10.94) that the phase of the physical wave function $u_l(k, r)$ is the phase shift $\delta_l(k)$, apart from changes of sign in $\phi_l(k, r)$. This was first proved in Chapter 2B.

We now have some understanding of the Jost functions in relation to the S-matrix. We can obtain the analytic form of the Green's function from (10.83) by using the form (10.88) of the Wronskian appearing in (10.85). The Green's function becomes

$$G_l(k; r, r') = \frac{(-1)^l k^l \phi_l(k, r_<) f_l(-k, r_>)}{f_l(-k)}, \tag{10.98a}$$

or, in terms of the physical partial wave $u_l(k, r)$,

$$G_l(k; r, r') = (-1)^l k^{-1} u_l(k, r_<) f_l(-k, r_>). \tag{10.98b}$$

It is necessary also to discuss the chief analytic properties of the Green's function. These are easily seen from its spectral representation.

The spectral representation is obtained by introducing a complete set of eigenstates $|k, l\rangle$ of H and l into the matrix element of $G_l(s)$.

$$\langle r| G_l(s) |r'\rangle = \int k'^2 \, dk' \frac{\langle r | k', l\rangle\langle k', l | r'\rangle}{H - s}. \tag{10.99}$$

The integral here is defined to include a sum over discrete bound states $\psi_{nl}(r)$ with eigenvalues E_n, and an integral over the physical continuum states $u_l(k, r)$. We may write (10.99) explicitly in terms of bound and continuum states.

$$\begin{aligned} G_l(k; r, r') &= \langle r| G_l(s) |r'\rangle \\ &= \frac{2}{\pi} \int_0^\infty dk' \frac{u_l(k', r)u_l^*(k', r')}{k'^2 - k^2} \\ &\quad + \sum_n \frac{\psi_{nl}(r)\psi_{nl}(r')}{(\hbar^2/2\mu)E_n - k^2}. \end{aligned} \tag{10.100}$$

In the energy plane, $G_l(s)$ has poles on the negative real axis for the bound states and a branch cut on the positive real axis for the continuum of positive eigenvalues. We have the Green's function $G_l^{(+)}(s)$ for ingoing boundary conditions (that is, $G_l^{(+)}(s)$ contains only outgoing waves at infinity) on the upper rim of the branch cut and the Green's function for outgoing boundary conditions $G_l^{(-)}(s)$ on the lower rim of the branch cut. It is interesting and useful to note that the residues at the bound-state poles are separable in r and r'.

The properties of the two-body scattering operators that we have discussed in this section are useful for the discussion of three-body problems in terms of two-body quantities.

D. THE MULTI-CHANNEL TWO-BODY PROBLEM

A generalized two-body problem is the scattering of a particle from a nucleus that has degrees of freedom other than just those of translation of the center of mass. It may be, for example, a deformed nucleus that has rotational degrees of freedom or a deformable nucleus with vibrational degrees of freedom. In this case, particles may not only scatter elastically, but may excite the collective degrees of freedom and scatter inelastically. We shall discuss the problem by a method due to Feshbach (58).

For the purpose of the formal theory of this section, we shall assume that only the collective degrees of freedom are capable of being excited and that there is no limit to the number of excitation quanta (sometimes called phonons) that can occur. This means, for example, that we assume that the nucleus will never fly apart, no matter how fast it is rotating.

The wave functions of the nucleus will be denoted by solutions of the Schrödinger equation

$$H_N \psi_i(\xi) = \epsilon_i \psi_i(\xi), \qquad (10.101)$$

where the ξ are generalized coordinates describing collective degrees of freedom (for example, quadrupole vibrations). The ψ_i form a complete orthonormal set.

We expand the total scattering wave function $\Psi^{(+)}$ in terms of the set ψ_i as follows.

$$\Psi^{(+)}(\mathbf{k}, \mathbf{r}, \xi) = \sum_i \psi_i(\xi) u_i^{(+)}(\mathbf{r}), \qquad (10.102)$$

where $\mathbf{k}$ is the incident wave vector and $\mathbf{r}$ is the position vector of the incident particle in the center of mass system. The superscript $(+)$ indicates ingoing boundary conditions. It will be dropped temporarily from $u_i^{(+)}$ for convenience. The $i = 0$ term in this sum describes the target nucleus in its ground state plus a projectile of energy E in the entrance channel. The other values of i correspond to possible exit channels in which the projectile has a different energy. For simplicity we shall ignore possible spin flip.

The expansion (10.102) of $\Psi'^{(+)}$ is now inserted into the Schrödinger equation for the scattering problem

$$(H - E - i\epsilon)\Psi'^{(+)} = 0, \qquad (10.103)$$

where

$$H = H_N(\xi) + K(\mathbf{r}) + V(\mathbf{r}, \xi). \qquad (10.104)$$

K is the kinetic energy operator of the projectile, V is the potential felt by the projectile. The small positive energy ϵ will be dropped in the formalism. Its significance will be explained when the scattering amplitude is considered.

Employing the orthonormality of the ψ_i, (10.103) is equivalent to a set of coupled differential equations for the amplitudes u_i.

$$(K + V_{ii} + \epsilon_i - E)u_i = -\sum_{j \neq i} V_{ij} u_j. \qquad (10.105)$$

In order to see this, we substitute (10.102) (with i replaced by j) into (10.103, 10.104), multiply on the left by $\psi_i^\dagger$, and integrate over ξ using (10.101). The matrix elements V_{ij} of the potential matrix V are

$$V_{ij}(\mathbf{r}) = \langle \psi_i | V | \psi_j \rangle, \qquad (10.106)$$

where V is Hermitian, that is,

$$V_{ij} = V_{ji}. \qquad (10.107)$$

The collective degrees of freedom are integrated out in (10.106), so that V_{ij} is a function only of $\mathbf{r}$.

It is useful to introduce a matrix notation for the set of coupled equations (10.105). The kinetic energy matrix K is given by

$$K_{ij} = K\delta_{ij}. \qquad (10.108)$$

The coupling matrix U is given by

$$U_{ij} = V_{ij} + \epsilon_i \delta_{ij}. \qquad (10.109)$$

These matrices operate on a column vector χ given by

$$\chi = \begin{bmatrix} u_0 \\ u_1 \\ . \\ . \\ . \end{bmatrix}. \qquad (10.110)$$

In this notation the coupled equations (10.105) are written

$$(K + U - E)\chi = 0. \qquad (10.111)$$

In practice we do not observe all the channels i. We shall first derive equations for the individual channels, assuming that only one channel is observed.

[i] The Optical Model for Elastic Scattering

First, we shall consider only the entrance channel $i = 0$. We have seen in our general discussion of the optical model in Chapter 9B that the possible excitation of the other channels is taken into account by a complex potential. We shall derive this potential for the collective case considered here.

We eliminate all channels but the entrance channel by splitting off the entrance channel wave function from χ, leaving χ_I.

$$\chi = \begin{bmatrix} u_0 \\ \chi_I \end{bmatrix}. \tag{10.112}$$

Equation (10.111) becomes

$$(K + U_{00} - E)u_0 = -U_{0I}\chi_I, \tag{10.113a}$$

$$(K + U_{II} - E)\chi_I = -U_{I0}u_0, \tag{10.113b}$$

where U_{IJ} are defined by

$$U = \begin{bmatrix} U_{00} & U_{0I} \\ U_{I0} & U_{II} \end{bmatrix}. \tag{10.114}$$

To obtain an equation for u_0 we must eliminate χ_I. Solving (10.113b) formally for χ_I, we obtain

$$\chi_I = -\frac{1}{K + U_{II} - E - i\epsilon} U_{I0}u_0. \tag{10.115}$$

For the sake of explicitness we have reintroduced the small imaginary part ϵ to the energy, with the implied limit $\epsilon \to 0+$, in order to ensure ingoing boundary conditions. All open exit channels contain only outgoing waves. Closed channels have standing wave boundary conditions as in the general theory (8.46).

Substituting (10.115) into (10.113a) gives

$$\left(K + U_{00} - U_{0I}\frac{1}{K + U_{II} - E - i\epsilon}U_{I0} - E\right)u_0 = 0. \tag{10.116}$$

The optical model potential is (recalling that $U_{00} = V_{00}$ since $\epsilon_0 = 0$)

$$\tilde{V} = V_{00} - U_{0I}\frac{1}{K + U_{II} - E - i\epsilon}U_{I0}. \tag{10.117}$$

Its two important properties are that it is complex and nonlocal. The $i\epsilon$ term in the Green's function for open channels makes $\tilde{V}$ complex. Physically, the complex term comes from processes in which the particles leave the entrance channel u_0 because of the coupling U_{I0} and are emitted in one of the exit channels u_i contained in χ_I. Of course this does not happen unless at least u_1

is an open channel, $E > \epsilon_1$. Compare (10.117) with the equation for the general case (9.86). The same discussion holds, as for the general case, if we do not wish to consider the excited channels. However, the present case is one where we have a model for the excited channels. They can be considered in more detail.

We obtain valuable insight into the problem by considering the spectral representation of the Green's function in (10.117). We may write it as

$$\tilde{V} = U_{00} - \sum_n \frac{U_{0I}|\chi_I^{(n)}\rangle\langle\chi_I^{(n)}|\,U_{I0}}{E^{(n)} - E} - \int_{\epsilon_1}^{\infty} dE' \frac{U_{0I}|\chi_I(E')\rangle\langle\chi_I(E')|\,U_{I0}}{E' - E - i\epsilon}.$$
(10.118)

The bound states $\chi_I^{(n)}$ are solutions of the set of coupled equations

$$(K + U_{II} - E^{(n)})\chi_I^{(n)} = 0.$$
(10.119)

They represent a particle bound to an excited nucleus. The continuum states are solutions of the set

$$(K + U_{II} - E')\chi_I(E') = 0.$$
(10.120)

The nonlocal character of $\tilde{V}$ becomes obvious when we let it operate on u_0. Consider, for example, the discrete sum over n. It may be written in terms of a nonlocal operator $\mathscr{K}(\mathbf{r}, \mathbf{r}')$.

$$\sum_n \frac{U_{0I}(\mathbf{r})|\chi_I^{(n)}(\mathbf{r})\rangle\langle\chi_I^{(n)}(\mathbf{r}')|\,U_{I0}(\mathbf{r}')\,|u_0(\mathbf{r}')\rangle}{E^{(n)} - E} \equiv \int d^3r'\,\mathscr{K}(\mathbf{r}, \mathbf{r}')u_0(\mathbf{r}').$$
(10.121)

The real and imaginary parts of $\tilde{V}$ are, from (10.118),

$$\operatorname{Re}\tilde{V} = V_{00} - \sum_n \frac{U_{0I}|\chi_I^{(n)}\rangle\langle\chi_I^{(n)}|\,U_{I0}}{E^{(n)} - E} - P\int \frac{dE'}{E' - E}\,U_{0I}|\chi_I(E')\rangle\langle\chi_I(E')|U_I^0,$$
(10.122a)

$$\operatorname{Im}\tilde{V} = -\pi U_{0I}|\chi_I(E)\rangle\langle\chi_I(E)|\,U_{I0}, \qquad E = \epsilon_1,$$

$$= 0, \qquad\qquad E < \epsilon_1.$$
(10.122b)

P denotes the Cauchy principle value. Since the numerators of (10.118) are both positive definite, $\operatorname{Im}\tilde{V}$ is negative definite, as it must be for absorption.

The configuration space representation of $\operatorname{Im}\tilde{V}$ is

$$\langle\mathbf{r}'|\operatorname{Im}\tilde{V}|\mathbf{r}\rangle = -\pi\langle\mathbf{r}'|\,U_{0I}|\chi_I(E)\rangle\langle\chi_I(E)|\,U_{0I}|\mathbf{r}\rangle.$$
(10.123)

The set $\chi_I(E)$ is the set of wave functions for the inelastic channels; U_{0I} and U_{I0} are the sets of potentials coupling the entrance channel to each of the inelastic channels. The right-hand side of (10.123) is the sum of products of matrix elements (on the energy shell), each product representing the excitation of an inelastic channel. Hence we can see explicitly in this model that the imaginary part of the optical-model potential gives the probability of inelastic scattering.

The real part of $\tilde{V}$ contains off-shell matrix elements for inelastic scattering. It includes the virtual excitation of closed channels.

[ii] INELASTIC SCATTERING TO ONE CHANNEL: THE DISTORTED WAVE BORN APPROXIMATION

In Section [i] we concentrated on elastic scattering. We shall now concentrate on the inelastic scattering to the ath channel assuming that the couplings are weak. Instead of eliminating all channels but the entrance channel, as for Equations (10.113), we shall eliminate all but the entrance channel and the ath channel obtaining the equations

$$(K + U_{00} - E)u_0 = -U_{0a}u_a - U_{0J}\chi_J \qquad (10.124a)$$

$$(K + U_{aa} - E)u_a = -U_{a0}u_0 - U_{aJ}\chi_J \qquad (10.124b)$$

$$(K + U_{JJ}^{(1)} - E)\chi_J = -U_{J0}u_0 - U_{Ja}u_a. \qquad (10.124c)$$

The coupling matrix U is now split by analogy with (10.114) as follows:

$$U = \begin{bmatrix} U_{00} & U_{0a} & U_{0J} \\ U_{a0} & U_{aa} & U_{aJ} \\ U_{J0} & U_{Ja} & U_{JJ}^{(1)} \end{bmatrix}. \qquad (10.125)$$

Here the vector χ_J represents the wave functions of all the channels except the entrance channel and the ath channel. The superscript (1) means that one inelastic channel is being explicitly included in the theory.

We shall eliminate the unwanted channels by solving (10.124) formally for χ_J, yielding the following equations for u_0 and u_a.

$$\left(K + U_{00} - U_{0J} \frac{1}{K - E + U_{JJ}^{(1)}} U_{J0} - E\right)u_0$$

$$= -U_{0a}u_a + U_{0J} \frac{1}{K - E + U_{JJ}^{(1)}} U_{Ja}u_a, \qquad (10.126a)$$

$$\left(K + U_{aa} - U_{aJ} \frac{1}{K - E + U_{JJ}^{(1)}} U_{Ja} - E\right)u_a$$

$$= -U_{a0}u_0 + U_{aJ} \frac{1}{K - E + U_{JJ}^{(1)}} U_{J0}u_0. \qquad (10.126b)$$

We shall define optical-model potentials for the homogeneous equations by analogy with (10.117).

$$\tilde{V}_0^{(1)} = V_{00} - U_{0J} \frac{1}{K - E + U_{JJ}^{(1)}} U_{J0}, \qquad (10.127a)$$

$$\tilde{V}_a^{(1)} = V_{aa} - U_{aJ} \frac{1}{K - E + U_{JJ}^{(1)}} U_{Ja}. \qquad (10.127b)$$

$\tilde{V}_0^{(1)}$ differs from the elastic scattering optical potential $\tilde{V} \equiv \tilde{V}_0^{(0)}$ in that the imaginary part does not include the probability of exciting the ath channel. $\tilde{V}_a^{(1)}$ is the optical-model potential for elastic scattering from the nucleus in the excited state ψ_a. Its imaginary part excludes the probability of exciting the entrance channel.

It is convenient also to define off-diagonal optical-model potentials for the coupling in the homogeneous terms of (10.126), using $U_{ij} = V_{ij}, i \neq j$.

$$\tilde{V}_{0a}^{(1)} = V_{0a} - U_{0J} \frac{1}{K - E + U_{JJ}^{(1)}} U_{Ja}, \qquad (10.128a)$$

$$\tilde{V}_{a0}^{(1)} = V_{a0} - U_{aJ} \frac{1}{K - E + U_{JJ}^{(1)}} U_{J0}. \qquad (10.128b)$$

By analogy with (10.122) it is seen that the spectral representation of the off-diagonal optical model potential gives an imaginary part which is the sum of products of two amplitudes, one for exciting one of the channels J starting from the entrance channel, and one for exciting one of the channels J starting from the ath channel.

We now have two coupled equations for the two channels under consideration.

$$(K + \tilde{V}_0^{(1)} - E)u_0 = -\tilde{V}_{0a}^{(1)}u_a, \qquad (10.129a)$$

$$(K + \epsilon_a + \tilde{V}_a^{(1)} - E)u_a = -\tilde{V}_{a0}^{(1)}u_0. \qquad (10.129b)$$

To determine the inelastic scattering amplitude, we consider Equation (10.129b), which gives the wave function for channel a in the form of an integral

$$u_a = -\frac{1}{K + \epsilon_a + \tilde{V}_a^{(1)} - E} \tilde{V}_{a0}^{(1)}u_0. \qquad (10.130)$$

The amplitude is given by (10.28), where ϕ_i is the wave function of the system in its final asymptotic state, defined by the asymptotic Hamiltonian, which we will here denote by H_0. The interaction Hamiltonian H_{int} [called V in (10.28)] is that part of the total Hamiltonian H (10.103), which is not acting in the asymptotic state.

$$H = H_0 + H_{\text{int}}. \qquad (10.131)$$

The formalism that we shall now introduce is the distorted wave formalism. It has proved extremely useful for calculating scattering problems. Instead of a plane wave, we consider the wave function of the scattered particle in the asymptotic state to be a distorted wave $\chi_a^{(-)}(\mathbf{k}_a, \mathbf{r})$ computed in an auxiliary potential $\mathscr{V}_a(r)$, which will be chosen for greatest computational convenience. Using the definition (10.104) of K, we have

$$(K + \mathscr{V}_a - E + \epsilon_a + i\epsilon)\chi_a^{(-)}(\mathbf{k}_a, \mathbf{r}) = 0. \tag{10.132}$$

The energy E_a of the outgoing particle is $E + \epsilon_a$. We have included the small positive energy ϵ temporarily in (10.132) to indicate that $\chi_a^{(-)}$ has outgoing boundary conditions (outgoing plane wave and ingoing spherical wave) and to emphasize the fact that $\chi_a^{(-)}$ is computed with a different Hamiltonian from that for wave functions such as $\Psi^{(+)}$ with ingoing boundary conditions, where we have $-i\epsilon$. This is important because it means that operators α in a matrix element such as

$$\langle \chi^{(-)}| \, \alpha \, |\Psi^{(+)}\rangle$$

must operate consistently to the right or left. We shall choose the right.

The inelastic scattering amplitude is, for final state a,

$$f_{a0} = \langle \chi_a^{(-)}\psi_a| \, V - \mathscr{V}_a \, |\Psi^{(+)}\rangle, \tag{10.133}$$

where $\Psi^{(+)}$ is the total wave function given by (10.103). Since $\mathscr{V}_a$ is now included in H_0 by definition, we have

$$H_{\text{int}} = V - \mathscr{V}_a. \tag{10.134}$$

We now use the following identity, proved from Equations (10.101, 10.103, 10.104, 10.132, 10.133).

$$f_{a0} = \langle (H_N + K + \mathscr{V}_a)\chi_a^{(-)}\psi_a| \, \Psi^{(+)}\rangle - \langle \chi_a^{(-)}\psi_a| \, H_N + K + \mathscr{V}_a \, |\Psi^{(+)}\rangle$$

$$= \langle \chi_a^{(-)}\psi_a| \, E - (H_N + K + \mathscr{V}_a) \, |\Psi^{(+)}\rangle. \tag{10.135}$$

The expansion (10.102) of $\Psi^{(+)}$ will be considered, using the form (10.130) for each of the u_i except u_0. Any of the channels $i \neq 0$ could have replaced a in the derivation of (10.130).

$$\Psi^{(+)} = \sum_{i \neq 0} \psi_i \frac{-1}{K + \epsilon_i + \tilde{V}_i^{(1)} - E} \tilde{V}_{i0}^{(1)} u_0 + \psi_0 u_0. \tag{10.136}$$

This expression is substituted into (10.135) to obtain the scattering amplitude.

$$f_{a0} = \sum_i \langle \chi_a^{(-)}\psi_a| \, -(H_N + K + \mathscr{V}_a - E) \, |\psi_i \frac{-1}{K + \epsilon_i + \tilde{V}_i^{(1)} - E} \tilde{V}_{i0} u_0\rangle. \tag{10.137}$$

Equation (10.137) may be simplified greatly. H_N, operating on ψ_i, is equivalent to ϵ_i from (10.101). The operator in (10.137) now contains no functions of the internal coordinates of the nucleus. Hence it commutes with ψ_i. Since the ψ_i are orthonormal, we are left with only the $i = a$ term of the sum. The operator cancels the Green's function in the ket vector if we make the following choice of the auxiliary distorting potential $\mathscr{V}_a$.

$$\mathscr{V}_a = \tilde{V}_a^{(1)}. \tag{10.138}$$

The inelastic scattering amplitude is, reintroducing the superscript $(+)$ on u_0,

$$f_{a0} = \langle \chi_a^{(-)} | \tilde{V}_{a0}^{(1)} | u_0^{(+)} \rangle. \tag{10.139}$$

It now remains to calculate $u_0^{(+)}$. This may be done by solving the equations (10.129) as a set of coupled differential equations. Because of the necessary partial-wave expansions to obtain equations for functions of one variable, there are actually several sets of more than two coupled equations to be solved. This will be discussed in detail in Chapter 12A.

A useful approximation may be made if the coupling between channels 0 and a is weak. The inhomogeneous term of (10.129a) is then neglected, so that $u_0^{(+)}$ is the wave function for elastic scattering computed in the optical model potential $\tilde{V}_0^{(1)}$, which describes the excitation of all possible channels except channel a.

$$u_0^{(+)} \cong \chi_0^{(+)}(\mathbf{k}_0, \mathbf{r}). \tag{10.140}$$

This is the *distorted wave Born approximation* (DWBA).

The DWBA is valid under the condition of weak coupling. This will be discussed for a specific case in Chapter 12. It provides a way of calculating the inelastic scattering amplitude from elastic scattering information. For computation the following approximation is made

$$\tilde{V}_0^{(1)} \cong \tilde{V}_a^{(1)} \cong \tilde{V}. \tag{10.141}$$

This involves the assumption that the optical-model potential for elastic scattering $\tilde{V}$, which describes the possibility of exciting all inelastic channels, is very similar to $V_0^{(1)}$ and $\tilde{V}_a^{(1)}$, both of which exclude the possibility of exciting the ath channel. The assumption that the optical-model potential $\tilde{V}_a^{(1)}$ for the nucleus in state a is the same as that for the ground state is plausible if the energy difference ϵ_a is not large. We understand the dependence of the optical-model potential on the excitation by considering a single highly excited particle in a Fermi gas. The more degenerate the Fermi gas, the less absorptive it is.

[iii] THE COUPLED-CHANNELS MODEL

If the coupling between the entrance channel and a certain finite number M of inelastic channels cannot be considered as weak, but the remainder of the couplings can, then we must solve coupled optical-model equations for the $M + 1$ channels. The coupled equations (10.126) have already been derived for the case $M = 1$.

Instead of splitting off the equations for only two channels for special consideration, as in (10.124), we must do the same for the $M + 1$ strongly coupled channels.

The coupled equations become

$$(K + \epsilon_i + V_{ii} - E)u_i = -\sum_{j=0}^{M} U_{ij}u_j - U_{iJ}\chi_J, \qquad j \neq i, \quad (10.142a)$$

$$(K + U_{JJ}^{(M)} - E)\chi_J = -\sum_{j=0}^{M} U_{Jj}u_j. \qquad (10.142b)$$

We again define the optical-model potentials by formally solving for χ_J. The diagonal potential for the ith channel is

$$\tilde{V}_i^{(M)} = V_{ii} - U_{iJ}\frac{1}{K - E + U_{JJ}^{(M)}}U_{Ji}. \qquad (10.143a)$$

The off-diagonal potentials are

$$\tilde{V}_{ij}^{(M)} = V_{ij} - U_{iJ}\frac{1}{K - E + U_{JJ}^{(M)}}U_{Jj}. \qquad (10.143b)$$

With these definitions of the optical-model potentials, the system reduces to the $M + 1$ coupled equations,

$$(K + \epsilon_i + \tilde{V}_i^{(M)} - E)u_i = -\sum_{j=0}^{M}\tilde{V}_{ij}^{(M)}u_j, \qquad j \neq i, \qquad i = 0, \dots, M.$$
$$(10.144)$$

Again the superscript M denotes that M inelastic channels are being explicitly included in the theory. The imaginary parts of the optical potentials (10.143) are sums of products of pairs of amplitudes for transitions from the channels i, j to each of the open inelastic channels *NOT* included among the M. If all the channels with strong coupling are included among the M, the imaginary parts of the $\tilde{V}_{ij}^{(M)}$ and $\tilde{V}_i^{(M)}$ are much less than the imaginary part of the elastic scattering optical-model potential $\tilde{V} = \tilde{V}_0^{(0)}$.

The coupled channels model improves on the distorted wave Born approximation because the terms of first order in $\tilde{V}_{ij}^{(M)}$ are not neglected on the right-hand sides of (10.144). In the DWBA, only the term in $\tilde{V}_{0a}^{(1)}$ is included, where the transition $0 \to a$ is the one under consideration.

E.   THE THREE-BODY PROBLEM

It involves only a simple coordinate transformation to obtain two-body scattering amplitudes from one-body quantities. However, it was not until 1960 that it was shown in principle by Faddeev (60) how to obtain three-body amplitudes from two-body quantities. The two-body quantities are not merely the scattering amplitudes because they contain only information about the two-body problem on the energy shell. The complete solution of the two-body problem is involved. It may be expressed in terms of the Green's function operator or related operators. We shall assume that three-body forces are unimportant in nuclear problems. The forces acting between the bodies 1, 2, and 3 are the potentials $V_i, i = 0, \ldots, 3$. V_i is the force between the two bodies labeled by j and $k, j \neq k \neq i$. $V_0 = 0$.

We shall use mainly the formalism of Lovelace (64). The three-body system is much more complicated than the two-body system. This is reflected in the coordinates. A set of coordinates with cyclic symmetry is given by certain transformations of the momenta of the three particles $\mathbf{k}_i$, where we use units such that $\hbar = 1$. The masses of the particles are $m_i, i = 1, 2, 3$.

The momentum of the center of mass of the three bodies is set equal to zero, so that we work in the three-body center of mass system.

$$\mathbf{P} = [2(m_1 + m_2 + m_3)]^{-\frac{1}{2}}(\mathbf{k}_1 + \mathbf{k}_2 + \mathbf{k}_3) = 0. \qquad (10.145)$$

The coordinates used for describing the problem are

$$\mathbf{p}_1 = [2m_2 m_3(m_2 + m_3)]^{-\frac{1}{2}}(m_3\mathbf{k}_2 - m_2\mathbf{k}_3),$$

$$\mathbf{q}_1 = [2m_1(m_2 + m_3)(m_1 + m_2 + m_3)]^{-\frac{1}{2}}[m_1(\mathbf{k}_2 + \mathbf{k}_3) - (m_2 + m_3)\mathbf{k}_1].$$

$$(10.146)$$

Two other sets of momenta are described by cyclic permutations of the indices 1, 2, 3. The reason for choosing these coordinates is that the kinetic energy operator separates as in (10.147) below. $\mathbf{p}_1$ is the momentum of particles 2 and 3 in their two-body center of mass system. $\mathbf{q}_1$ is the momentum of particle 1 relative to the center of mass of the (23) system.

The noninteracting Hamiltonian K is given by

$$K = k_1^2/2m_1 + k_2^2/2m_2 + k_3^2/2m_3 = P^2 + p_i^2 + q_i^2, \qquad i = 1, 2, 3. \qquad (10.147)$$

In the three-body center of mass system the Hilbert space for the state vectors $|\mathbf{p}, \mathbf{q}\rangle$ of the three-body problem is the space of square integrable functions of two momentum vectors $\mathbf{p}, \mathbf{q}$. The problem of the normalization of continuum states has been treated in the general formal scattering theory of Section A.

The resolvent or three-body Green's function operator for three noninteracting particles is $G_0(s)$, given by

$$G_0(s) = [K - s]^{-1}. \qquad (10.148)$$

The resolvent or three-body Green's function operator for the complete problem is

$$G(s) = [H - s]^{-1} = [K + V - s]^{-1}, \tag{10.149}$$

where

$$V = \sum_{i=0}^{3} V_i. \tag{10.150}$$

[i] THE THREE-BODY LIPPMANN-SCHWINGER EQUATION

The operator form of the Lippmann-Schwinger equation was derived in Section 10A on general scattering theory. It is

$$G(s) = G_0(s) - G_0(s)VG(s). \tag{10.151}$$

The operators act on asymptotic three-body channel wave functions Φ_x, which will be described for the case of nonidentical uncharged particles. The subscript $x = 0, \ldots, 3$ describes different asymptotic situations. The wave function for three free bodies is

$$\Phi_0 = \exp i \, (\mathbf{k}_1 \cdot \mathbf{r}_1 + \mathbf{k}_2 \cdot \mathbf{r}_2 + \mathbf{k}_3 \cdot \mathbf{r}_3). \tag{10.152}$$

The wave function for the case where particles j and k are in their nth bound state and particle i is free is

$$\Phi_{in} = e^{i\mathbf{q}_i \cdot \mathbf{s}_i} \psi_{in}(\mathbf{t}_i), \tag{10.153}$$

where $\mathbf{s}_i$ and $\mathbf{t}_i$ are the coordinates conjugate to $\mathbf{q}_i$ and $\mathbf{p}_i$. These wave functions are the channel wave functions. The Lippmann-Schwinger equation for the exact three-body wave function Ψ_x for the asymptotic situation is obtained in more explicit language by multiplying both sides of (10.151) by $-i\epsilon$, applying it to Φ_x and taking the limit.

We find the result of this process for $G(s)$ by considering the explicit form of the Lippmann-Schwinger equation for particles in channel x interacting by means of the potential V_x.

$$\begin{aligned}
\Psi_x &= \Phi_x - \lim_{\epsilon \to 0+} \frac{1}{H - E_x - i\epsilon} V_x \Phi_x \\
&= \lim_{\epsilon \to 0+} \frac{H - E_x - i\epsilon - V_x}{H - E_x - i\epsilon} \Phi_x \\
&= \lim_{\epsilon \to 0+} \frac{-i\epsilon}{H - E_x - i\epsilon} \Phi_x \\
&= \lim_{\epsilon \to 0+} -i\epsilon G(E_x + i\epsilon)\Phi_x.
\end{aligned} \tag{10.154}$$

In deriving (10.154) we have used the Schrödinger equation for the asymptotic state Φ_x, which also defines the total energy of the system E_x.

$$(H - V_x - E_x)\Phi_x = 0. \tag{10.155}$$

The result for $G_0(s)$ is obtained as follows for the separate cases Φ_0, Φ_{1n}.

$$\lim_{\epsilon \to 0+} -i\epsilon G_0(E_0 + i\epsilon)\Phi_0$$

$$= \lim_{\epsilon \to 0+} \frac{-i\epsilon}{K - E_0 - i\epsilon} \exp i(\mathbf{k}_1 \cdot \mathbf{r}_1 + \mathbf{k}_2 \cdot \mathbf{r}_2 + \mathbf{k}_3 \cdot \mathbf{r}_3)$$

$$= \lim_{\epsilon \to 0+} \frac{-i\epsilon}{(k_1^2 + k_2^2 + k_3^2)/2m - E_0 - i\epsilon} \Phi_0$$

$$= \Phi_0 \tag{10.156}$$

$$\lim_{\epsilon \to 0+} -i\epsilon G_0(E_{1n} + i\epsilon)\Phi_{1n}$$

$$= \lim_{\epsilon \to 0+} \frac{-i\epsilon}{-i(\nabla_{p_1}^2 + \nabla_{q_1}^2) - E_{1n} - i\epsilon} e^{i\mathbf{q}_1 \cdot \mathbf{s}_1} \psi_{1n}(t_1). \tag{10.157}$$

When the operators in (10.157), which act on eigenstates, are replaced by their eigenvalues, the denominator does not vanish. Therefore,

$$\lim_{\epsilon \to 0+} -i\epsilon G_0(E_{1n} + i\epsilon)\Phi_{1n} = 0. \tag{10.158}$$

The same is true for Φ_{2n} and Φ_{3n}.

The three-body Lippmann-Schwinger equation may now be applied independently to the different Φ_x representing different asymptotic channels. We have the set of independent equations.

$$\Psi_0^{(+)} = \Phi_0 - G_0^{(+)}(E_0)V\Psi_0^{(+)},$$

$$\Psi_{1n}^{(+)} = -G_0^{(+)}(E_{1n})V\Psi_{1n}^{(+)},$$

etc. $\tag{10.159}$

The set of independent integral equations (10.159) does not specify unique solutions to the three-body problem because the equations for the situations where there is an asymptotic bound state are homogeneous. Not all the boundary conditions are incorporated.

Further insight into the problem can be gained by considering the solution formed by iterating the form (10.30a) for the three-body Lippmann-Schwinger equation.

$$T(s) = V - VG_0(s)T(s)$$

$$= V_1 + V_2 + V_3 \tag{10.30a}$$

$$- (V_1 + V_2 + V_3)G_0(s)(V_1 + V_2 + V_3)$$

$$+ \text{etc.} \tag{10.160}$$

The series is rearranged in the following way.

$$T(s) = [V_1 - V_1 G_0(s) V_1 + V_1 G_0(s) V_1 G_0(s) V_1 - \cdots]$$
$$+ [V_2 - V_2 G_0(s) V_2 + \cdots]$$
$$+ [V_3 - V_3 G_0(s) V_3 + \cdots]$$
$$+ [V_1 - V_1 G_0(s) V_1 + \cdots] G_0(s) [V_2 - V_2 G_0(s) V_2 + \cdots]$$
$$+ \cdots$$
$$+ \cdots . \tag{10.161}$$

In the rearranged series (10.161) the potentials all appear in the infinite series expressions in square brackets, each of which is a three-body t-matrix representing the interaction of two particles while the third is free. This type of three-body t-matrix will be denoted by $T_i(s)$.

$$T_i(s) = V_i - V_i G_0(s) V_i + V_i G_0(s) V_i G_0(s) V_i - \cdots$$
$$\equiv V_i - V_i G_0(s) T_i(s). \tag{10.162}$$

It acts on the three-body state vectors $|\mathbf{p}_i, \mathbf{q}_i\rangle$, and must be distinguished from the two-body t-matrix, denoted $\hat{T}_i(s)$ for the purpose of this section, which acts on two-body state vectors such as $|\mathbf{p}_i\rangle$. The t-matrix $T_i(s)$ is derived from the three-body Green's function $G_i(s)$ which is defined by

$$G_i(s) = (K + V_i - s)^{-1} \equiv (H_i - s)^{-1}. \tag{10.163}$$

K is the three-body kinetic energy operator. This equation serves to define the channel Hamiltonian H_i. The matrix element of the three-body t-matrix is related, for the interacting pair i, to the matrix element of the two-body t-matrix by

$$\langle \mathbf{p}_i', \mathbf{q}_i' | T_i(s) | \mathbf{p}_i, \mathbf{q}_i \rangle = \delta(\mathbf{q}_i' - \mathbf{q}_i) \langle \mathbf{p}_i' | \hat{T}_i(s - q_i^2) | \mathbf{p}_i \rangle. \tag{10.164}$$

This is seen by realizing that V_i is independent of $\mathbf{q}_i$, so the dependence of the Green's function (10.163) on $\mathbf{q}_i$ is merely in the kinetic energy part K, which acts on the plane wave eigenstate $|\mathbf{p}_i, \mathbf{q}_i\rangle$ to give q_i^2.

The three-body t-matrices $T_i(s)$ have singularities for bound states of the pair i [see for example (10.30c, 10.100)]. These singularities are concealed in the iteration series (10.160). Rearranging the series to the form (10.161) makes the singularities explicit and puts them in a form in which they are understood in the two-body problem. We can use the scattering diagrams introduced in Chapter 2C to characterize the problem. Singularities are associated with the kernel $V_i G_0(s)$ of the integral equation (10.162), as shown in (10.161), which gives rise to the "dangerous diagrams" (disconnected diagrams) of Fig. 10.1. The sum of all the dangerous diagrams in which i is free is the t-matrix $T_i(s)$.

The form (10.164) of $T_i(s)$ makes explicit the type of singularity characteristic of the disconnected diagrams, which occurs irrespective of the existence of two-body bound states. The δ-function for the motion of the undisturbed particle does not appear under an appropriate momentum integration. The Faddeev formulation collects all the disconnected diagrams into expressions consisting of a δ-function multiplied by a two-body t-matrix.

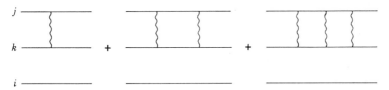

FIG. 10.1   The kernel $V_i G_0$ introduces diagrams like these, which represent the first three terms of $T_i(s)$, into the three-body scattering amplitude.

The singularities are thus made easier to handle. The bound state singularities give no more trouble than they do in the two-body problem. We shall next consider the method of handling the δ-function singularities.

[ii] THE FADDEEV EQUATIONS

The Faddeev equations remove the two difficulties associated with the three-body Lippmann-Schwinger equation. The problem of homogeneous integral equations for the cases where two of the bodies are asymptotically bound is removed by having coupled integral equations. The problem of the dangerous diagrams is removed by having the potentials appear only in three-body t-matrices for two interacting particles and one free particle, which are equivalent to t-matrices for the interaction of two-body pairs.

Instead of representing the different asymptotic channels by wave functions Φ_{in}, we shall define transition operators whose matrix elements in a plane-wave representation give the amplitudes for all possible transitions. These operators are

$$U_{ij}^{(+)}(s) = \sum_{k \neq i} V_k - \sum_{k \neq i} \sum_{l \neq j} V_k G(s) V_l,$$
$$U_{ij}^{(-)}(s) = \sum_{l \neq j} V_l - \sum_{k \neq i} \sum_{l \neq j} V_k G(s) V_l, \qquad i, j, k, l = 0, \ldots, 3.$$
$$(10.165)$$

We can understand the reason for defining the transition operators by considering their use in expressing the S-matrix elements (10.58) for typical transitions. For example, the S-matrix element for a rearrangement collision where j is free initially and i is free finally is

$$S_{in,jm}(\mathbf{q}_i', \mathbf{q}_j) = \delta_{ij}\delta_{nm}\delta(\mathbf{q}_i' - \mathbf{q}_j) - 2\pi i \delta(q_i'^2 - E_{in} - q_j^2 + E_{jm})$$

$$\times \int d^3p_i' \int d^3p_j \psi_{in}*(\mathbf{p}_i')U_{ij}^{(+)}(\mathbf{p}_i', \mathbf{q}_i', \mathbf{p}_j, \mathbf{q}_j; q_i^2 - E_{in} + i\epsilon)\psi_{jm}(\mathbf{p}_j). \quad (10.166)$$

In this case the pair j are bound initially in their nth bound state, the pair i are bound finally in their mth bound state. The primed coordinates are for the final state. The plus and minus forms of the transition operators can be used interchangeably, since the bound-state wave functions are solutions of the homogeneous Schrödinger equation.

The matrix element of $U_{ij}^{(\pm)}(s)$ in a plane-wave representation is represented by the notation

$$U_{ij}^{(\pm)}(\mathbf{p}', \mathbf{q}_i', \mathbf{p}_j, \mathbf{q}_j; s) = \langle \mathbf{p}_i', \mathbf{q}_i'|\, U_{ij}^{(+)}(s)\, |\mathbf{p}_j, \mathbf{q}_j\rangle. \quad (10.167)$$

In Equation (10.166) the amplitude $U_{ij}^{(\pm)}(s)$ appears for the case where two of the momentum variables $\mathbf{q}_i'$, $\mathbf{q}_j$ are measured. They represent the momenta of the initial and final particles. The other two variables $\mathbf{p}_i'$, $\mathbf{p}_j$ are not measured. They represent the relative motion of particles in the initial and final bound states and occur for all values with amplitudes $\psi_{in}*(\mathbf{p}_i')$ and $\psi_{jm}(\mathbf{p}_j)$, respectively. These amplitudes are the Fourier coefficients or Fourier transforms of the space wave functions and give the amplitudes with which the respective plane waves $\exp i(\mathbf{p}_i' \cdot \mathbf{t}_i')$ and $\exp i(\mathbf{p}_j \cdot \mathbf{t}_j)$ occur in the matrix element. The total energy of the system is $q_i^2 - E_{in}$.

For a breakup collision, where the incident particle breaks up a bound state leaving three particles free finally, the S-matrix element is

$$S_{0,jn}(\mathbf{p}_0', \mathbf{q}_0', \mathbf{q}_j) = -2\pi i \delta(q_j^2 - E_{jn} - p_0'^2 - q_0'^2)$$

$$\times \int d^3p_j U_{0j}^{(\pm)}(\mathbf{p}_0', \mathbf{q}_0', \mathbf{p}_j, \mathbf{q}_j; q_j^2 - E_{jn} + i\epsilon)\psi_{jn}(\mathbf{p}_j). \quad (10.168)$$

In this case the momentum of the incident particle $\mathbf{q}_j$ is measured, together with all the final state momenta, which are sufficiently specified by $\mathbf{p}_0'$, $\mathbf{q}_0'$. Only one momentum variable in the plane-wave matrix element of $U_{0j}^{(\pm)}$ is not measured. The Fourier coefficient of the plane wave $\exp i(\mathbf{p}_j \cdot \mathbf{t}_j)$ is the momentum-space wave function $\psi_{jn}(\mathbf{p}_j)$. The total energy of the system is $q_j^2 - E_{jn}$.

To derive the Faddeev equations in terms of the transition operators, we use the Green's function operators $G_i(s)$ of Equation (10.163), corresponding to the t-matrices T_i for the case where only the ith pair interact.

From (10.163) and the definition (10.149) of the complete three-body Green's function operator $G(s)$, we obtain the Green's function operator form of the Faddeev equations

$$G(s) = G_j(s) - \sum_{l \neq j} G(s)V_l G_j(s)$$
$$= G_i(s) - \sum_{k \neq i} G_i(s)V_k G(s), \qquad i, j, k, l = 0, \dots, 3. \quad (10.169)$$

The transition operator form of the Faddeev equations is obtained by substituting (10.169) into (10.165).

$$U_{ij}^{(+)}(s) = \sum_{k \neq i} V_k - \sum_{l \neq j} U_{il}^{(+)}(s)G_0(s)T_l(s),$$
$$U_{ij}^{(-)}(s) = \sum_{l \neq j} V_l - \sum_{k \neq i} T_k(s)G_0(s)U_{kj}^{(-)}(s), \qquad i, j, k, l = 0, \dots, 3.$$

$$(10.170)$$

Here we have used the relationship

$$G_i(s)V_i = G_0(s)T_i(s) \qquad (10.171)$$

and the fact that $T_0(s) \equiv 0$.

The form (10.170) of the Faddeev equations has just as many amplitudes as physically different transitions that can take place. For different asymptotic conditions, we have three coupled integral equations.

Consider, for example, the case where particles 1 and 2 are bound initially. The three coupled integral equations for the $U_{i3}^{(-)}$ operators are

$$U_{13}^{(-)}(s) = V_1 + V_2 - T_2(s)G_0(s)U_{23}^{(-)}(s) - T_3(s)G_0(s)U_{33}^{(-)}(s)$$
$$U_{23}^{(-)}(s) = V_1 + V_2 - T_3(s)G_0(s)U_{33}^{(-)}(s) - T_1(s)G_0(s)U_{13}^{(-)}(s)$$
$$U_{33}^{(-)}(s) = V_1 + V_2 - T_1(s)G_0(s)U_{13}^{(-)}(s) - T_2(s)G_0(s)U_{23}^{(-)}(s). \quad (10.172)$$

The amplitudes for the three possible processes involving the required initial state are connected. These processes are the rearrangement collisions 1,3 and 2,3 and the elastic scattering of particle 3 by the pair 3. For the breakup case the equations are

$$U_{01}^{(+)}(s) = V_1 + V_2 + V_3 - U_{02}^{(+)}(s)G_0(s)T_2(s) - U_{03}^{(+)}(s)G_0(s)T_3(s)$$
$$U_{02}^{(+)}(s) = V_1 + V_2 + V_3 - U_{01}^{(+)}(s)G_0(s)T_1(s) - U_{03}^{(+)}(s)G_0(s)T_3(s)$$
$$U_{03}^{(+)}(s) = V_1 + V_2 + V_3 - U_{01}^{(+)}(s)G_0(s)T_1(s) - U_{02}^{(+)}(s)G_0(s)T_2(s). \quad (10.173)$$

The amplitudes related by the Faddeev equations are in this case those for the breakup of each pair, in turn, by the third particle.

Note that, in the Faddeev equations, the three-body t-matrices $T_i(s)$, which contain the δ-function singularities according to (10.164), always appear under a momentum integration which removes the singularity.

It is useful to consider what is involved in solving a three-body problem by means of the Faddeev equations. Because of the relationships between the $\mathbf{p}_i$ and $\mathbf{q}_i$ for different i and the fact (10.164) that the energy argument of the two-body t-matrix $\hat{T}_i$ corresponding to $T_i(s)$ is $(s - q_i^2)$ rather than s, it is clear that, in at least some of the integral expressions on the right-hand sides of the equations, the integration will be over positive and negative values of the energy argument. Thus it is essential to know the two-body Green's functions for all values of the energy, including the singularities for bound states. The two-body t-matrices are completely off the energy shell in that the energy variable and both momentum variables in the momentum representation may be integrated over. This complete knowledge of the two-body Green's function may be derived from the potential, but it certainly cannot be derived from the scattering amplitude. Thus the three-body problem cannot be solved in terms of physical knowledge of two-body phenomena. It can only be solved in terms of an underlying theory, such as a potential, for the two-body interactions. The Faddeev kernels each contain a three-body t-matrix and a G_0 operator, which is equivalent to an energy denominator when the equations are written in a matrix representation. This involves a six-dimensional integration which can be reduced to two dimensions of energy by expanding the amplitudes in rotation functions (Omnes, 64).

The preceding discussion is intended to warn the reader against optimism with regard to the use of the Faddeev equations for the solution of problems in nuclear physics where complicated local potentials are generally used to describe two-body phenomena. However, there is a special case where the Faddeev equations can be reduced to manageable proportions. This is the case of separable potentials where the integral equations reduce to a single one-dimensional integral equation. A separable potential, which gives a separable two-body Green's function and t-matrix, arises from the inter-action of two bodies by means of a single bound state [see Equation (10.100)]. For nucleon-nucleon collisions at very low energy, this model is not completely unrealistic.

Extremely good fits to experimental data for different three-nucleon situations have been achieved by Aaron, Amado, and Yam (65) who solved the Faddeev equations numerically, using a single separable potential. Examples will be given in Chapter 14. It must be noted that the good fit obtained by using a crude model makes the enormous computing problem involved in using a better model hardly worthwhile, because of the insensitivity of the data to the model. Of course, the good fits emphasize the value of taking all three-body effects into account. It is evidently more important to have a correct three-body theory than a detailed two-body model. The use by Moszkowski (65) of a pseudopotential in the Faddeev equations for three nucleons in nuclear matter has already been noted in Chapter 4.

[iii]   The Static Limit: Distorted Waves

The case where one of the three bodies is so much heavier than the other two that momentum can be transferred to it with a negligible energy transfer is very useful in the study of nuclear reactions. It is called the static limit. Most of the single-particle model phenomena we have discussed up to this stage involve the assumption of an infinitely massive core, although in two-body cases we of course can remove this assumption by using the reduced mass in conjunction with quantities in the center of mass system.

Nuclear models are described in terms of a basis set of independent particle wave functions, so that many nuclear reactions can be described as a linear combination of three-body matrix elements involving the interaction of the projectile with a single nucleon in the presence of a heavy core.

In the static limit, the coordinates $\mathbf{p}_i$ and $\mathbf{q}_i$ of (10.146) are considerably simplified. Consider the case where particle 3 is infinitely heavy and is taken as the origin of coordinates, $\mathbf{r}_3 = \mathbf{k}_3 = 0$.

$$
\begin{aligned}
\mathbf{q}_1 &= -(2m)^{-\frac{1}{2}}\mathbf{k}_1, & \mathbf{p}_1 &= (2m)^{-\frac{1}{2}}\mathbf{k}_2, \\
\mathbf{q}_2 &= -(2m)^{-\frac{1}{2}}\mathbf{k}_2, & \mathbf{p}_2 &= -(2m)^{-\frac{1}{2}}\mathbf{k}_1, \\
\mathbf{q}_3 &= (4m)^{-\frac{1}{2}}(\mathbf{k}_1 + \mathbf{k}_2), & \mathbf{p}_3 &= (4m)^{-\frac{1}{2}}(\mathbf{k}_1 - \mathbf{k}_2).
\end{aligned}
\tag{10.174}
$$

The conjugate variables are

$$
\begin{aligned}
\mathbf{s}_1 &= -(2m)^{\frac{1}{2}}\mathbf{r}_1, & \mathbf{t}_1 &= (2m)^{\frac{1}{2}}\mathbf{r}_2, \\
\mathbf{s}_2 &= -(2m)^{\frac{1}{2}}\mathbf{r}_2, & \mathbf{t}_2 &= -(2m)^{\frac{1}{2}}\mathbf{r}_1, \\
\mathbf{s}_3 &= m^{\frac{1}{2}}(\mathbf{r}_1 + \mathbf{r}_2), & \mathbf{t}_3 &= m^{\frac{1}{2}}(\mathbf{r}_1 - \mathbf{r}_2).
\end{aligned}
\tag{10.175}
$$

The use of the static limit simplifies the coordinates so that the Faddeev equations can be uncoupled yielding a single integral equation. We shall not be concerned explicitly with this equation.

We shall first consider the formal transformation of the expression for the transition operators $U_{ij}^{(\pm)}(s)$ into a representation involving distorted waves computed in arbitrary auxiliary potentials (Greider and Dodd, 66). This transformation is very useful for understanding transition amplitudes in approximations to be used later.

We define the channel interactions v_i, v_j, v_k as follows.

$$
v_i = V_j + V_k, \qquad j, k \neq i.
\tag{10.176}
$$

The channel Hamiltonian of (10.163) is

$$
H_i = K + V_i = H - v_i.
\tag{10.177}
$$

We shall choose particle k to be infinitely heavy.

Corresponding to the channel interactions v_i, we introduce channel distortion operators $\Omega_i^{(\pm)}(s)$ defined in terms of the complete Green's function (10.149) by

$$\Omega_i^{(\pm)}(s) = 1 - G^{(\pm)}(s)v_i. \qquad (10.178a)$$

These operators, when acting on the channel states Φ_i, yield eigenstates of the complete system with ingoing and outgoing boundary conditions, respectively, in all channels. The channel wave functions Φ_i were introduced in (10.152, 10.153). For brevity we omit the quantum number n representing the bound state.

$$\Omega_i^{(\pm)}(s)|\Phi_i\rangle = \Psi_i^{(\pm)}. \qquad (10.178b)$$

The channel distortion operators of Equation (10.178) may be used to rewrite the transition operators $U_{ij}^{(\pm)}(s)$ in a form different from Equations (10.165).

$$U_{ij}^{(+)}(s) = v_i\Omega_j^{(+)}(s),$$
$$U_{ij}^{(-)}(s) = \Omega_i^{(-)\dagger}(s)v_j. \qquad (10.179)$$

It is possible to simplify the form of the transition operators considerably. We introduce distorted waves by means of the auxiliary potentials w_i. Convenient choices for the w_i will be found to effect the simplification. The Green's functions corresponding to the potentials w_i are

$$g_i^{(\pm)}(s) = [H_i + w_i - s \mp i\epsilon]^{-1}. \qquad (10.180)$$

The corresponding distortion operators are

$$\omega_i^{(\pm)}(s) = 1 - g_i^{(\pm)}(s)w_i. \qquad (10.181)$$

These distortion operators act on the channel wave functions Φ_i to give distorted waves $\chi_i^{(\pm)}$.

$$\omega_i^{(\pm)}(s)\Phi_i = \chi_i^{(\pm)}. \qquad (10.182)$$

We shall now discuss the simplification of the $U_{ij}^{(\pm)}(s)$ by the proper choice of the distorting potential w_j. Using the definitions (10.180, 10.181) we expand the transition operator in the following way, choosing $U_{ij}^{(-)}(s)$ as an example.

$$\begin{aligned}
U_{ij}^{(-)}(s) &= \Omega_i^{(-)\dagger}(s)v_j \\
&= \Omega_i^{(-)\dagger}(s)(v_j - w_j)\omega_j^{(+)}(s) \\
&\quad + \Omega_i^{(-)\dagger}(s)[1 + (v_j - w_j)g_j^{(+)}(s)]w_j. \qquad (10.183)
\end{aligned}$$

After some algebra involving the simplification of the second term in the square brackets by the use of the operator identity.

$$\frac{1}{A} - \frac{1}{B} = \frac{1}{A}(B - A)\frac{1}{B}, \qquad (10.184)$$

with $G^{(+)} = 1/A$ and $g_j^{(+)} = 1/B$, the second term of (10.183) reduces to $(H_i - s - i\epsilon)[\omega_j^{(+)}(s) - 1]$.

In an actual problem we are concerned with the matrix elements of the transition operators for the channel states Φ_i. The second term of (10.183) operating on $\langle\Phi_i|$ gives $i\epsilon[\omega_j^{(+)}(s) - 1]$, since Φ_i is an eigenfunction of H_i.

Equation (10.183) reduces to

$$U_{ij}^{(-)}(s) = \Omega_i^{(-)\dagger}(s)(v_j - w_j)\omega_j^{(+)}(s), \qquad (10.185)$$

if w_j is chosen so that

$$\lim_{\epsilon \to 0+} i\epsilon \langle\Phi_i| \omega_j^{(+)}(s) |\Phi_j\rangle = 0. \qquad (10.186)$$

It is seen that the introduction of the auxiliary potentials enables the transition operator to be written in a comparatively simple form, provided w_j is chosen so that the matrix element in (10.186) is finite. With this choice, the left-hand side of (10.186) vanishes in the limit.

The expression (10.185) is simplified as far as the entrance channel is concerned if w_j is chosen so that it produces only elastic scattering in this channel.* This is true, for example, if w_j depends only on the relative coordinate s_j, which is conjugate to q_j. In the static limit this is $-(2m)^{1/2}r_j$. With this choice, only the plane wave $\exp i(q_j \cdot s_j)$ for relative motion is distorted and the bound state $\psi_j(p_j)$ is unaffected.

A similar transformation is made for the exit channel by writing

$$\Omega_i^{(-)}(s) = [1 - G^{(-)}(s)(v_i - w_i)]\omega_i^{(-)}(s), \qquad (10.187)$$

with the help of the identity (10.184). Substituting (10.187) in (10.185), the transition operator becomes in the distorted wave representation

$$U_{ij}^{(-)}(s) = \omega_i^{(-)\dagger}[(v_j - w_j) - (v_i - w_i^\dagger)G^{(+)}(s)(v_j - w_j)]\omega_j^{(+)}(s). \quad (10.188a)$$

The corresponding transition amplitude is $T_{ij}^{(-)}(s)$, given by

$$T_{ij}^{(-)}(s) = \langle\chi_i^{(-)}| (v_j - w_j) - (v_i - w_i^\dagger)G^{(+)}(s)(v_j - w_j) |\chi_j^{(+)}\rangle. \quad (10.189a)$$

The corresponding equations for the $U_{ij}^{(+)}$ form of the transition operator are derived with the condition that the matrix element of $\omega_i(s)$ for channel wave functions is finite. They are

$$U_{ij}^{(+)}(s) = \omega_i^{(-)\dagger}[(v_i - w_i^\dagger) - (v_i - w_i^\dagger)G^{(+)}(s)(v_j - w_j)]\omega_j^{(+)}(s), \quad (10.188b)$$

$$T_{ij}^{(+)}(s) = \langle\chi_i^{(-)}| (v_i - w_i^\dagger) - (v_i - w_i^\dagger)G^{(+)}(s)(v_j - w_j) |\chi_j^{(+)}\rangle. \quad (10.189b)$$

* The matrix element in (10.186) can only be infinite if there is a pole in the Green's function $g_j^{(+)}$ of (10.180) representing a three-body bound state. If w_j depends only on s_j, the particle j must scatter from the fixed core k. It cannot interact also with the particle i losing enough energy to become bound.

We have thus expressed the exact three-body transition amplitudes in a distorted wave representation. The distorting potential for the entrance channel in (10.189a) and the exit channel in (10.189b) is defined with the weak restriction that it produces only elastic scattering in these channels. The other distorting potential is quite arbitrary. Each expression involves a knowledge of the complete Green's function. Equation (10.189a) is known as the post form of the expression, and Equation (10.189b) is the prior form.

Instead of deriving an integral equation for the static three-body problem from the Faddeev equations, we shall use a method that starts from the distorted wave amplitudes (10.188, 10.189). The method is due to Dodd and Greider (66). The integral equation is formulated by means of an intermediate potential v_x which is chosen for a specific reaction so that the kernel satisfies the same properties as the Faddeev kernels. It must contain no repeated potentials $V_v G_0^{(+)}(s) V_v$, where v is one of the i, j, k. [Remember that the first term of any Green's function $G_v^{(+)}(s)$ is $G_0^{(+)}(s)$.] Such a factor would be represented by a disconnected diagram. The potential v_x may or may not be one of the v_i, v_j, v_k. The Green's function corresponding to v_x is

$$g_x^{(\pm)}(s) = [H - v_x - s \mp i\epsilon]^{-1}. \qquad (10.190)$$

Using the operator identity

$$G^{(+)}(s) \equiv g_x^{(+)}(s)[1 - v_x G^{(+)}(s)] \qquad (10.191)$$

in (10.188a) we obtain the first of two coupled integral equations.

$$U_{ij}^{(-)}(s) = \omega_i^{(-)\dagger}(s)(v_j - w_j)\omega_j^{(+)}(s) - \omega_i^{(-)\dagger}(s)(v_i - w_i^\dagger)g_x^{(+)}(s)U_{xj}^{(-)}(s), \qquad (10.192)$$

where $U_{xj}^{(-)}(s)$ is defined by

$$U_{xj}^{(-)}(s) = (v_j - w_j)\omega_j^{(+)}(s) - v_x G^{(+)}(s)(v_j - w_j)\omega_j^{(+)}(s). \qquad (10.193)$$

Repeating the same procedure with (10.193) instead of (10.188a), we obtain $U_{xj}^{(-)}(s)$ in terms of $U_{ij}^{(-)}(s)$.

$$\begin{aligned}
U_{xj}^{(-)}(s) &= (v_j - w_j)\omega_j^{(+)}(s) - v_x g_i^{(+)}(s)[1 - (v_i - w_i^\dagger)G^{(+)}(s)](v_j - w_j)\omega_j^{(+)}(s) \\
&= (v_j - w_j)\omega_j^{(+)}(s) - v_x G_i^{(+)}(s)\omega_i^{(-)\dagger}(s)[1 - (v_i - w_i^\dagger)G^{(+)}(s)] \\
&\qquad\qquad\qquad\qquad\qquad\qquad\qquad\qquad \times (v_j - w_j)\omega_j^{(+)}(s). \qquad (10.194)
\end{aligned}$$

Comparison of (10.194) with (10.188a) yields the second integral equation.

$$U_{xj}^{(-)}(s) = (v_j - w_j)\omega_j^{(+)}(s) - v_x G_i^{(+)}(s)U_{ij}^{(-)}(s). \qquad (10.195)$$

The two equations (10.192, 10.195) are combined to form a single integral equation that will form the basis of our discussion.

$$\begin{aligned}
U_{ij}^{(-)}(s) &= \omega_i^{(-)\dagger}(s)[(v_j - w_j) - (v_i - w_i^\dagger)g_x^{(+)}(s)(v_j - w_j)]\omega_j^{(+)}(s) \\
&\quad + \omega_i^{(-)\dagger}(s)(v_i - w_i^\dagger)g_x^{(+)}(s)v_x G^{(+)}(s)U_{ij}^{(-)}(s). \qquad (10.196a)
\end{aligned}$$

The inhomogeneous term of this equation is the DWBA term with an additional term which resembles the second term of a t-matrix, but which is specified when a particular reaction is considered. It represents virtual excitations of the two-body intermediate states in the spectrum of the Green's function $g_x^{(+)}(s)$.

The prior form of Equation (10.196a) is

$$U_{ij}^{(+)}(s) = \omega_i^{(-)\dagger}(s)[(v_i - w_i^\dagger) - (v_i - w_i^\dagger)g_x^{(+)}(s)(v_j - w_j)]\omega_j^{(+)}(s)$$
$$+ U_{ij}^{(+)}(s)G_j^{(+)}(s)v_x g_x^{(+)}(s)(v_j - w_j)\omega_j^{(+)}(s). \quad (10.196b)$$

By a suitable choice of w_i and v_x, each of which is arbitrary, the kernel can be chosen to have no term consisting of a power of $V_v G_0^{(+)}(s)$, so that the inhomogeneous term is the first approximation to a series whose terms do not have disconnected diagram singularities.

The Green's function $G_i^{(+)}(s)$ has previously been discussed in (10.163, 10.164). It depends only on the potential V_i, so its matrix elements can be calculated from the two-body Green's function for the pair i. The Green's function $g_x^{(+)}(s)$ can be calculated if the potentials are functions of coordinates in which the kinetic energy operator separates; for example, if it contains the potentials $V_i(\mathbf{r}_j)$ and $V_j(\mathbf{r}_i)$,

$$g_x^{(+)}(s) = [K + V_i + V_j - s - i\epsilon]^{-1}. \quad (10.197a)$$

Under the condition that particle k is infinitely heavy, K separates exactly into K_i, depending only on $\mathbf{r}_i$, and K_j, depending only on $\mathbf{r}_j$.

We shall now consider the same two examples as we did for the Faddeev equations. For rearrangement from the j channel to the i channel, w_j must be chosen to depend only on $\mathbf{r}_j$ if the post form of the equation is used. Thus w_j is $V_i(\mathbf{r}_j)$. The choice $v_x = V_i + V_j$ gives a kernel which does not contain a term like $V_i G_0^{(+)}(s)$. The corresponding Green's function is, from (10.177, 10.190),

$$g_x^{(+)}(s) = [K + V_k - s - i\epsilon]^{-1}. \quad (10.197b)$$

The distorting potential w_i is arbitrary and can be chosen to give quickest convergence. Physical intuition leads us to choose $w_i = V_j(\mathbf{r}_i)$. It has not been shown that this is the best choice.

The integral equation is

$$U_{ij}^{(-)}(s) = \omega_i^{(-)\dagger}(s)[V_k - V_k G_k^{(+)}(s)V_k]\omega_j^{(+)}(s)$$
$$+ \omega_i^{(-)\dagger}(s)V_k G_k^{(+)}(s)(V_i + V_j)G_i^{(+)}(s)U_{ij}^{(-)}(s)$$
$$= \omega_i^{(-)\dagger}(s)T_k(s)\omega_j^{(+)}(s) + \omega_i^{(-)\dagger}(s)V_k G_k^{(+)}(s)(V_i + V_j)G_i^{(+)}(s)U_{ij}^{(-)}(s).$$
$$\quad (10.198)$$

The inhomogeneous term of this equation contains the t-matrix for the interaction of the pair k, that is, the two light particles. The kernel contains no terms $V_v G_0^{(+)}(s)$.

The transition amplitude corresponding to the inhomogeneous term is

$$T_{ij}^{(-)}(s) = \langle \chi_i^{(-)} | T_k(s) | \chi_j^{(+)} \rangle. \tag{10.199}$$

This is the *distorted wave t-matrix approximation* (*DWTA*).

For the breakup reaction, the exit channel is the channel 0. w_j is again chosen to be V_i. The final state distortion operator is $\omega_0^{(-)}$, given by $w_0^\dagger = V_i + V_j$.

$$\omega_0^{(-)}(s) = 1 - (K + V_i + V_j - s - i\epsilon)^{-1}(V_i + V_j). \tag{10.200}$$

This operator factors into the product of two operators depending only on $\mathbf{r}_i$ and $\mathbf{r}_j$.

$$1 - \frac{1}{K + V_i + V_j - s - i\epsilon}(V_i + V_j)$$

$$= \left[1 - \frac{1}{K_i + K_j + V_i + V_j - s - i\epsilon} V_i \right]$$

$$\left[1 - \frac{1}{K_i + K_j + V_j - s - i\epsilon} V_j \right]. \tag{10.201}$$

Operating on the final state wave function $|\mathbf{p}_0', \mathbf{q}_0'\rangle \equiv |\mathbf{k}_i', \mathbf{k}_j'\rangle$, this operator gives a product of distorted waves for each particle,

$$\left[1 - \frac{1}{K + V_i + V_j - s - i\epsilon}(V_i + V_j) \right] |\mathbf{k}_i', \mathbf{k}_j'\rangle$$

$$= \lambda_i^{(+)}(s - E_j)|\mathbf{k}_i'\rangle \lambda_j^{(+)}(s - E_i)|\mathbf{k}_j'\rangle, \tag{10.202}$$

where $(s - E_i) = E_j$, $(s - E_j) = E_i$, and

$$\lambda_i^{(+)}(s) = 1 - \frac{1}{K_i + V_i - s - i\epsilon}. \tag{10.203}$$

The choice $v_x = V_i + V_j$ permits the Green's function $g_x^{(+)}(s)$ to factorize. The integral equation becomes

$$U_{0j}^{(-)}(s) = \omega_0^{(-)\dagger}(s)[V_k - V_k G_k^{(+)}(s)V_k]\omega_j^{(+)}(s)$$

$$+ \omega_0^{(-)\dagger}(s)V_k G_k^{(+)}(s)(V_i + V_j)G_0^{(+)}(s)U_{0j}^{(-)}(s)$$

$$= \omega_0^{(-)\dagger}(s)T_k(s)\omega_j^{(+)}(s) + \omega_0^{(-)\dagger}(s)V_k G_k^{(+)}(s)(V_i + V_j)G_0^{(+)}(s)U_{0j}^{(-)}(s). \tag{10.204}$$

The inhomogeneous term is again the *distorted wave t-matrix approximation* and the kernel contains no $V_\nu G_0^{(+)}(s)$ terms.

In both the rearrangement and breakup reactions that we have discussed, the DWTA terms contain distorted waves on the energy shell, although the reduction of the three-body t-matrix T_k to the two-body expression $\hat{T}_k$ involves a knowledge of it off the energy shell. This will be discussed more fully when specific reactions are treated in detail.

The static limit is much simpler than the more general problem. However, from the point of view of calculation, it has a serious drawback. The kernels of Equations (10.198, 10.204) consist of products of five operators, each of which must be expressed as a matrix element in a three-body representation and integrated over the coordinates. The Faddeev kernels contain only two operators. At present, computers have not reached a sufficient state of development to make numerical solutions of either set of equations feasible except for extremely simplified models.

It is interesting to consider the corrections to the DWTA. This will be done for a breakup collision. It is easiest to use the prior form of (10.204).

$$U_{0j}^{(+)}(s) = \omega_0^{(-)\dagger}(s)T_k(s)\omega_j^{(+)}(s) + U_{0j}^{(+)}(s)G_j^{(+)}(s)(V_i + V_j)G_0^{(+)}(s)T_k(s)\omega_j^{(+)}(s).$$

(10.205)

This form for the transition operator may be rewritten as an explicit expression, dropping explicit reference to the energy argument s,

$$U_{0j}^{(+)} = \left\{\omega_0^{(-)\dagger}\,\frac{1}{1 - T_k\omega_j^{(+)}G_j^{(+)}(V_i + V_j)G_0^{(+)}}\right\}T_k\omega_j^{(+)}.$$ (10.206)

We have the DWTA except for a correction operator Q which modifies the final state distortion operator $\omega_0^{(-)\dagger}$.

$$Q = [1 - T_k\omega_j^{(+)}G_j^{(+)}(V_i + V_j)G_0^{(+)}]^{-1}.$$ (10.207)

The correction operator introduces three-body effects that are defined to be ones resulting from departures from the DWTA with the free two-body values of the distorting potentials. While Q is extremely difficult to evaluate, it has one interesting property that is immediately obvious. It is not symmetrical in i and j. We shall see in Chapter 14 that three-body effects in the (p, 2p) reaction are described by changing the final state-distorting potentials (which is the only available means in the computation for modifying $\omega_0^{(-)}$). They should not be modified symmetrically. The identity of the two emergent protons is of course taken care of by antisymmetrizing the matrix element.

FURTHER READING

1. M. Gell-Mann and M. L. Goldberger, *Phys. Rev.*, **91**, 398 (1953).
   B. Lippmann and J. Schwinger, *Phys. Rev.*, **79**, 469 (1950).
   Discussions of basic scattering theory.

2. R. G. Newton, *J. Math. Phys.*, **1**, 319 (1960).
   Potential scattering.

3. N. F. Mott and H. S. W. Massey, *The Theory of Atomic Collisions* (third edition), Oxford University Press, London, 1965.
   R. G. Newton, *Scattering Theory of Waves and Particles*, McGraw-Hill Book Co. Inc., New York, 1966.
   M. L. Goldberger and K. M. Watson, *Collision Theory*, John Wiley and Sons, Inc., New York, 1964.
   Comprehensive reviews of scattering theory.

4. H. Feshbach, *Ann. Phys.* (*N. Y.*), **5**, 357 (1958).
   Multichannel scattering.

5. A. N. Mitra, *Nucl. Phys.*, **32**, 529 (1962).
   L. D. Faddeev, *Zh. Eksperim. i Teor. Fiz.*, **39**, 1459 (1960) (English translation; *Soviet Phys. JETP*, **12**, 1014 (1961)).
   C. A. Lovelace, *Phys. Rev.*, **135**, 1225 (1964).
   R. Aaron, R. D. Amado, and Y. Y. Yam, *Phys. Rev.*, **136**, B650 (1964); **140**, B1291 (1965); *Rev. Mod. Phys.*, **37**, 516 (1965).
   L. R. Dodd and K. R. Greider, *Phys. Rev.*, **146**, 765 (1966).
   The three-body problem.

PROBLEMS

1. Derive expressions for the matrix elements in coordinate representation of the Green's function operators $G_0^{\pm}(s)$ for a free particle of energy s from the definitions (10.12, 10.77).

2. How would you compute the t-matrix element $\langle \mathbf{k}' | T(s) | \mathbf{k} \rangle$ from the wave function for the scattering of an uncharged particle by a central potential in the case $s = \hbar^2 k^2 / 2m$, $k \neq k'$?

3. Write the partial wave expansion of $\langle \mathbf{k}' | T(s) | \mathbf{k} \rangle$ in terms of the lth multipole component of the t-matrix $T_l(s; r, r')$.

4. Describe in detail how you would compute the lth multipole component of the Green's function for scattering by an arbitrary local potential.

5. Plot the Green's function $G_l(k; r, R)$ of (10.98b) against r for $l = 0$ in the case of 20.75 MeV neutron scattering from the square well $V = -40$ MeV, $R = 4$ fm.

6. Consider the following separable potential in momentum space for the lth partial wave:

$$V_l(p, q) = \lambda_l g_l(p) g_l(q).$$

show that the lth multipole component of the t-matrix is given by

$$T_l(s; p, q) = g_l(p) t_l(s) g_l(q),$$

where

$$t_l(s) = \left[\frac{1}{\lambda_l} + 4\pi \int_0^\infty dq \, \frac{q^2 \, |g_l(q)|^2}{q^2 - s - i\epsilon} \right]^{-1}.$$

7. Set up an integral equation with a connected kernel for direct inelastic scattering starting from (10.196a).

8. Reduce the Faddeev equations for the interaction of particle 1 with a bound state of 2 and 3 to a single integral equation for the case of three nonidentical particles of equal mass with equal two-body potentials.

11

ENTRANCE CHANNEL
PHENOMENA

In this chapter we shall discuss specific optical models used to represent differential cross sections for elastic scattering, total reaction cross sections, and angular distributions of polarization, where appropriate, for scattering mainly of nucleons, but also for scattering of very light nuclei, on larger nuclei. We have seen that the optical-model potential defined by formal theory is quite close to the average potential for the ground state of the target, so that its extension in space is approximately the same as that of the nucleus. The remainder of the potential is complex and nonlocal. The diagonal part of the nonlocal imaginary potential is the sum of the probabilities of exciting open channels other than the entrance channel.

Fernbach, Serber, and Taylor (49) used a local complex potential model to discuss the elastic scattering of 90 MeV neutrons on nuclei. Feshbach, Porter, and Weisskopf (54) showed the reason why a complex potential model represents the single-particle resonance structure observed in low-energy neutron scattering when poor energy resolution is used. The potential shown by these authors to give approximately correct fits to the data was a complex square well (9.74).

Woods and Saxon (54) showed that a model with a diffuse surface gave much better fits to angular distributions than a square well. The original Woods-Saxon optical model potential had four parameters and was defined by

$$V(r) = -(V + iW)[1 + \exp\{(r - R)/a\}]^{-1}, \qquad (11.1)$$

where the parameters are

V: real well depth

W: imaginary well depth

$R = r_0 A^{\frac{1}{3}}$: Woods-Saxon radius

a: surface diffuseness parameter.

Calculations of proton elastic scattering with this model, generally at energies from 10 MeV to about 100 MeV showed that good fits to the data could be obtained for momentum transfers less than about 1 fm^{-1} (forward angles), but that at backward angles magnitudes of cross sections were often predicted quite badly. Some examples are shown in Fig. 11.1.

Since many nuclear reaction experiments involve momentum transfers not much larger than 1 fm^{-1}, it is regarded as significant that the four-parameter model provides good fits in this range. The model is presumably a good first approximation for calculating distorted waves to be used in calculations of more complicated reactions, where only momentum transfers and not polarizations are measured. The four parameters already provide a

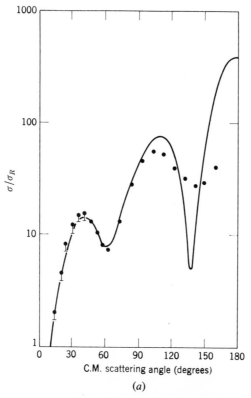

(*a*)

FIG. 11.1   Proton elastic scattering fitted by the Woods-Saxon four-parameter optical model. (*a*) 17 MeV protons scattered by ^{11}B. $V = 50$, $W = 8$, $r_0 = 1.3$, $a = 0.5$. (Adapted from Lim and McCarthy, 67.) (*b*) 95 MeV protons scattered by ^{27}Al. $V = 26$, $W = 10$, $r_0 = 1.30$, $a = 0.81$. (Adapted from Glassgold and Kellogg, 58.) (*c*) 40 MeV protons scattered by ^{27}Al showing two indistinguishable fits for each of which $Vr_0{}^2$ is similar. $V = 41.7$, $W = 11.1$, $r_0 = 1.20$, $a = 0.97$ (full line). $V = 34.2$, $W = 10.0$, $r_0 = 1.31$, $a = 0.91$ (dashed line). (Adapted from Glassgold and Kellogg, 58.)

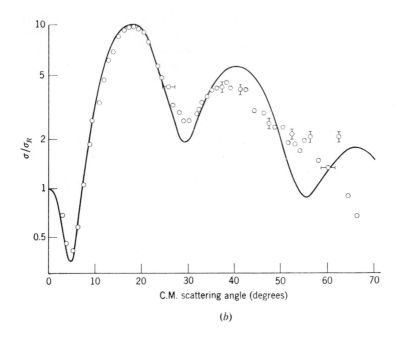

(b)

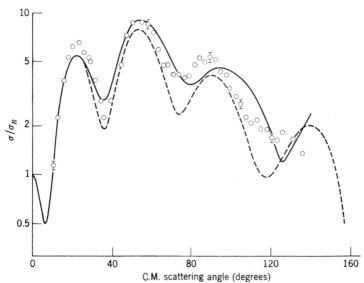

FIG. 11.1 (*continued*).

(c)

large parameter space in which to search for the best fit. This model is generally not unique, the most important ambiguity being that VR^n acts like a single parameter, rather than V and R separately, over a range of r_0 from about 1.15 fm to 1.35 fm. The power n is approximately 2. It is also significant that angular distributions are largely independent of the shape of the potential in the interior region. The parameters V and W are energy-dependent but, to a first approximation, they do not depend strongly on A.

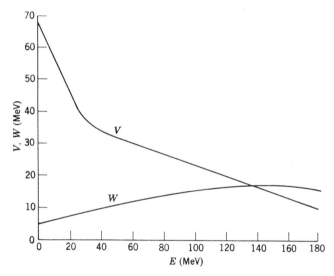

FIG. 11.2   Energy dependence of V and W in the four-parameter model averaged over A. The curves represent an average obtained from a survey of the literature.

Figure 11.2 shows the approximate energy dependence of V and W obtained from a survey of the literature. The ambiguity is considered to be VR^2, and the values of V are corrected to a standard value of r_0 equal to 1.30 fm.

The value of a in the Woods-Saxon model varies from about 0.5 fm to 0.7 fm. If no other facts are known about a nucleus, 0.65 fm is a good value to try first.

It is found that it is always possible to obtain better fits to angular distribution data by including more parameters in the model. This is of course expected from elementary principles of curve fitting. For example, there is no a priori reason why the real and imaginary form factors should have the same shape parameters r_0 and a. Two more parameters could be introduced by relaxing this restriction. Nuclear matter calculations (see, for example, Fig. 6.3) predict a "wine bottle" shape for the real potential. Several more parameters could be introduced describing this. There is some a priori justification for expecting the imaginary form factor to be peaked on the surface, since the probability for interaction in the interior is reduced by the Pauli principal. Yennie has pointed out that this effect is not spherically symmetric because, on the far side of the target nucleus (that is, the side away from the source), reaction products can leave the nucleus. A spherical form factor with surface peaking is often used for the imaginary potential.

The number of parameters used is largely an aesthetic decision. However, the law of diminishing returns sets in very rapidly after four. Since angular distributions for momentum transfers below about $1 \, fm^{-1}$ are quite well-fitted, the four-parameter model will be taken seriously.

Spin-orbit coupling has not yet been mentioned. It is absolutely necessary on physical grounds to include it because large polarizations are observed for nucleons. If we do not measure polarization and are content to average over spins in the theory then, as we have seen, momentum-transfer predictions are quite good. Inclusion of a spin-orbit coupling potential that produces correct polarization considerably improves differential cross-section fits at larger momentum transfers. As we shall see, the computational difficulties are considerably increased with spin-orbit coupling. This increase is magnified when the model is used to describe wave functions for reactions. Hence it is usual, unless polarizations are specifically being discussed, to omit spin-orbit coupling.

The theory of scattering by a real potential was discussed in Chapter 2. It is essentially the same for a complex potential except that the phase shifts are complex numbers. The reflection amplitudes η_l have magnitudes less than unity, so that particles are absorbed. In Section B of this chapter the formalism including spin-orbit coupling will be presented. Details of scattering by a local complex potential may be understood by setting the spin-orbit potential equal to zero in this formalism.

A. WAVE FUNCTIONS FOR THE LOCAL OPTICAL MODEL

Wave functions for potential scattering have already been discussed in Chapter 2. However, there are some properties that are very important for an understanding of reactions that require detailed discussion. In order to fit angular distributions, the optical model needs only to predict the correct phase shifts at a particular energy. It may be regarded as a method of predicting phase shifts. Knowledge of the phase shifts at a particular energy does not imply a unique knowledge of the wave function in the interior region. It is the wave function that is needed to describe reactions in distorted wave models. If we choose to regard the optical model as a physical description of the scattering process, rather than as a formula for generating phase shifts, we must use quantities derived from the wave function to furnish the description.

[i] PROBABILITY FLUX

We may first ask what happens to particles as they travel through the nucleus, remembering of course that this is loose language for the question of the probability of something happening to one particle. The intensity of the incident beam in a scattering experiment is never so large that two particles may hit the same nucleus with finite probability.

The probability flux is defined to be

$$\mathbf{j}(\mathbf{r}) = \frac{\hbar}{2i\mu} [\psi^*(\mathbf{r})\nabla\psi(\mathbf{r}) - \psi(\mathbf{r})\nabla\psi^*(\mathbf{r})]. \qquad (11.2)$$

The divergence of the flux at a point $\mathbf{r}$ gives the probability of losing a particle from the entrance channel at $\mathbf{r}$, that is, of a reaction being initiated at $\mathbf{r}$. This is given by

$$
\begin{aligned}
\nabla \cdot \mathbf{j}(\mathbf{r}) &= \frac{\hbar}{2i\mu} \nabla \cdot [\psi^*(\mathbf{r})\nabla\psi(\mathbf{r}) - \psi(\mathbf{r})\nabla\psi^*(\mathbf{r})] \\
&= \frac{\hbar}{2i\mu} [\psi^*(\mathbf{r}) \nabla^2\psi(\mathbf{r}) - \psi(\mathbf{r}) \nabla^2\psi^*(\mathbf{r})] \\
&= \frac{\hbar}{2i\mu} \left\{ \frac{2\mu}{\hbar^2} [V(r) + iW(r) - E] - \frac{2\mu}{\hbar^2} [V(r) - iW(r) - E] \right\} \\
&\quad \times \psi^*(\mathbf{r})\psi(\mathbf{r}) \\
&= \frac{2}{\hbar} W(r)\rho(\mathbf{r}), \qquad (11.3)
\end{aligned}
$$

where $\rho(\mathbf{r}) = \psi^*(\mathbf{r})\psi(\mathbf{r})$ is the probability density at $\mathbf{r}$. Figure 11.3 shows the flux and its divergence for 18 MeV α-particles on ^{40}Ar using a typical set of parameters.

The probability flux picture is easily understood. Particles are deflected by the Coulomb potential so that they can be scattered without substantially feeling the nuclear potential, except in the tail. Particles which impinge on the nucleus are absorbed with high probability at the surface. The intensity of the flux becomes smaller towards the far side of the nucleus. The divergence of the flux is large on the near surface, and decreases towards the far side because there are fewer particles left to be absorbed. The flux lines focus on the far side. There the divergence is again large because, although it is unlikely that a particle will arrive at the focus on a particular orbit (in a classical picture), there are many orbits, all meeting in approximately the same place. The significance of the classical orbits has been discussed with reference to the WKB approximation in Chapter 2. The position uncertainty for a particular orbit is a few de Broglie wavelengths. For 20 MeV protons, the de Broglie wave length λ is about 1 fm. For 20 MeV α-particles, it is about 0.5 fm. For a medium nucleus, about 10 and 18 partial waves, respectively, contribute at this energy.

The relative insensitivity of the cross section to the interior value of the potential is understood from the fact that nearly all particles that hit

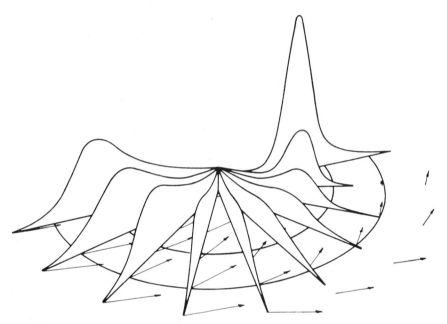

FIG. 11.3   The probability flux $\mathbf{j}(\mathbf{r})$ (indicated by arrows drawn to a logarithmic scale starting from $\mathbf{r}$) and its divergence (plotted vertically) for 18 MeV α-particles scattered by ^{40}Ar. The semicircles represent the distances for which $V(r) = 0.1V(0)$ and $0.9V(0)$.

the nucleus are absorbed. The relative insensitivity of the cross section to the shape of the imaginary potential is understood by the fact that most of the absorption occurs near the surface, even if a Woods-Saxon form factor is used. In the interior, there are few particles left to be absorbed.

In a reaction theory the solution $\psi(\mathbf{r})$ of an elastic scattering problem is used for the distorted wave $\chi^{(+)}(\mathbf{r})$ with ingoing boundary conditions. It is interesting to discuss the flux for the time-reversed wave function $\chi^{(-)}(\mathbf{r})$ which is used for the outgoing particle. The flux pictures for $\chi^{(-)}$ and $\chi^{(+)}$ are identical except that the arrows point in the opposite direction. The flux for $\chi^{(-)}$ is large on the side of the nucleus nearest the detector. The focal region is on the side of the nucleus away from the detector. It moves with the scattering angle so that it is always opposite the detector. The divergence of the flux vector **j**(**r**) represents the probability of a reaction product particle being generated at **r**. Reaction products that start on the side near the detector are more likely to escape from the nucleus in the direction of the detector. Reaction products that start in the focal region also are likely to reach the detector because, although any one particle is fairly certain to be absorbed, many particles that start in different directions finish in the detector direction.

[ii]   SPACE LOCALIZATION AND APPROXIMATE WAVE FUNCTIONS

Since reactions are more likely to be initiated in some regions of the nucleus (the near surface and the focus) than others, it is clear that momentum-transfer distributions will depend on more detailed properties of the reaction than just the volume of the nucleus weighted by the relevant bound state factors. The uncertainty principle helps us to understand that momentum-transfer distributions reflect space localization.

There is no difficulty in understanding that the magnitude of the wave function, or the divergence of the flux, is large on the near surface and becomes smaller towards the far surface. However, some properties of the focal region should be mentioned.

The intensity of the focus depends on the nature of the projectile. Heavier particles have a wave number **k** with a larger imaginary part than lighter particles, even if the imaginary parts of the potentials are similar, because of the factor $(2\mu)^{\frac{1}{2}}$. Thus heavier particles are more strongly absorbed. The maximum value of $|\psi(\mathbf{r})|$ in the focal region for α-particles is about 1, for unit incident flux, whereas for protons or neutrons it is about 3 or 4, particularly at incident energies less than 50 MeV. The focus is on the scattering axis. It occupies a small volume because of the factor $r^2 \sin \theta$ in the volume element. The proportion of the total reaction cross section (which is the flux divergence integrated over all space) that comes from the focus can be 15 per cent for protons at fairly low energies, whereas for α-particles it is of the order of 1 per cent. Thus the focal contribution to α-particle reactions is negligible, whereas the contribution for nucleon reactions is important.

At lower energies (<10 MeV) the focus is nearer the center of the nucleus, so the wave function is large not only at the surface, but also in the focal part of the interior region It is possible to find reactions for which this effect has an influence on the shape of angular distributions, thus leading to a method of obtaining information about the interior. At higher energies (>100 MeV) the particles are less affected by the real potential. The trajectories are more like plane wave trajectories, and the absorption occurs more uniformly over the nucleus. Again, reactions at these energies are more sensitive to the interior.

The dependence of the focus on the energy and the nature of the projectile is illustrated in Fig. 11.4, where the magnitude of the wave function $|\psi(\mathbf{r})|$ on the scattering axis is plotted. One other interesting effect is observed in Fig. 11.4. For lighter particles at lower energy the wave function becomes

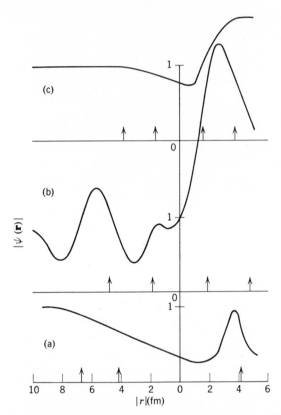

FIG. 11.4 The magnitude $|\psi(\mathbf{r})|$ of the optical-model wave function plotted on the scattering axis. The radii for which $V(r) = 0.1V(0)$ and $0.9V(0)$ are indicated by arrows. (a) 18 MeV α-particles scattered by ^{40}Ar, (b) 10 MeV protons scattered by ^{19}F, (c) 68.5 MeV protons scattered by ^{12}C. The particles are incident from the left.

less "classical." The WKB approximation, which does not describe reflection from changing potentials, is better for heavier particles and higher energy. The wave function for 10 MeV protons oscillates sharply in the exterior region on the near side. This is a standing wave effect due to reflections from the rapidly changing potential at the near surface. The effect is much less pronounced for 60 MeV protons and almost absent for α-particles.

Guided by the uncertainty principle, which is an approximate reaction theory, we may hope that a simple parametrization of the space localization in an optical-model wave function would enable us to predict effects in reactions that are not present if localization is neglected, that is, if the optical model wave functions are approximated by plane waves. We may be even more ambitious and hope to find a useful parametrization of the phase of an optical-model wave function. For a description of a reaction, we need only find a useful parametrization of the wave function in the region of space where reactions mainly occur, that is, near the nuclear surface. Angular localization for a given radius is thus important.

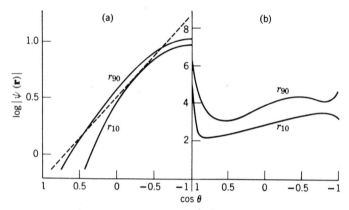

FIG. 11.5   Plot of $\log |\psi(\mathbf{r})|$ against $\cos \theta = \hat{\mathbf{k}} \cdot \hat{\mathbf{r}}$ for (a) 18 MeV α-particles scattered by ^{40}Ar (the dotted line is $\gamma' = 0.9$), (b) 30 MeV neutrons scattered by ^{88}Sr. The curves labeled r_{90}, r_{10} are computed for the radii where $Z(r) = 0.9V(0)$ and $0.1V(0)$, respectively. The zeros for both vertical scales are chosen arbitrarily.

We notice that the intensity falls off as θ gets further away from 180°, except for the sharp focal increase from 15° to 0°. This suggests that we try the localization factor $\exp(\gamma' \cos \theta)$. This expression gives a straight line when $\log |\psi(\mathbf{r})|$ is plotted against $\cos \theta$. The slope of the line is γ'. In Fig. 11.5 $\log |\psi(\mathbf{r})|$ is plotted against $\cos \theta$ at two different radii for 18 MeV α-particles scattered by ^{40}Ar and 30 MeV neutrons scattered by ^{88}Sr.

From Fig. 11.5 it is clear that the localization factor is a good approximation at least from about 60° to 120° where the factor $r^2 \sin \theta$ ensures the greatest contribution to the reaction. For nucleons it becomes a rapidly worse approximation below 30 MeV for smaller nuclei. It is better for larger nuclei. In the focal region for nucleons this localization factor is significantly unrealistic. Since integrations over space are required for reaction matrix elements, it is possibly a good first approximation to represent the focus by a delta function whose strength a gives the integrated intensity of the wave function over the focal region.

We must now attempt to understand the phase of an optical model wave function. A qualitative understanding in terms of the WKB approximation was developed in Chapter 2. In Fig. 11.6 the lines of equal phase are shown for 24 MeV neutrons scattered by ^{118}Sn along with the value of $|\psi(\mathbf{r})|$ on the scattering axis. First, it is obvious how the change of local wave number from the external region to the internal region produces focusing. Second, the projection on the scattering axis of the lines of equal phase is roughly

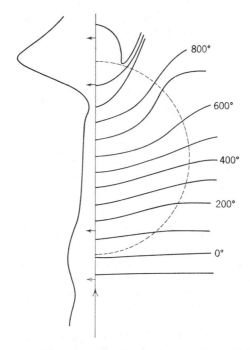

FIG. 11.6   The optical-model wave function for the scattering of 24 MeV neutrons by ^{118}Sn. The magnitude of the wave function is plotted to the left of the scattering axis. The lines of equal phase are plotted on the right at intervals of 100°. The surface region is indicated by arrows. Particles are incident from the bottom.

independent of angle for a given radius. To test this observation, the phase of $\psi(\mathbf{r})$ is plotted against $\cos\theta$ for different radii in Fig. 11.7. If the curve is a straight line, the phase of $\psi(\mathbf{r})$ is given by $\beta(r)\mathbf{k}\cdot\mathbf{r}$, where $\beta(r)k$ is the slope of the line for each r. In fact, $\beta(r)$ is not strongly dependent on r in the surface, which is where reactions take place. It is given to within about 5 per cent by the local wave number:

$$\beta(r)k = \frac{2\mu}{\hbar^2}\,[E - V(r) - iW(r)]^{1/2}. \tag{11.4}$$

This approximation improves as the energy increases.

The average phase of $\psi(\mathbf{r})$ in the focal region is not so closely related to the phase in the surface. It is necessary to introduce a fourth parameter for it, ϕ. The variation of the phase across the focal region is strikingly smaller than elsewhere. This encourages the use of one parameter.

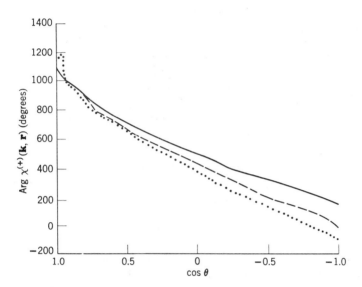

FIG. 11.7   The phase of the optical-model wave function as a function of $\cos \theta$ for radii where $V(r) = 0.9V(0)$ (solid line), $0.5V(0)$ (dashed line), $0.1V(0)$ (dotted line), for 24 MeV neutrons scattered by ^{118}Sn. (Adapted from Amos, 66.)

The parametrization of the optical-model wave function, which was therefore suggested by McCarthy and Pursey (61) for energies greater than 30 MeV, is

$$\psi(\mathbf{r}) \cong e^{i(\beta - i\gamma)\mathbf{k}\cdot\mathbf{r}}[1 + ae^{i\phi}\delta(\hat{\mathbf{k}}R - \mathbf{r})], \qquad (11.5)$$

where

$$\gamma = \gamma'/kR. \qquad (11.6)$$

The five parameters are γ, a, β, ϕ, R.

Clearly this parametrization of the wave function is almost as simple to calculate with as plane waves. There is only one more parameter than the original potential uses. It gives an extremely good description of the wave function in the surface, but an extremely poor description in the asymptotic region, so that it is of no use for elastic scattering. In subsequent chapters on reactions we shall see how intuition derived from this simple form for the wave function enables us to predict important features of differential cross sections.

[iii] ANGULAR MOMENTUM SPACE PROPERTIES OF WAVE FUNCTIONS

We shall now consider the partial waves $u_l(r)$ in the expansion (2.17) of $\psi(\mathbf{r})$. It is possible to develop an intuitive feeling for the partial waves by plotting their magnitude and phase as a function of r. This is done in Fig. 11.8 for 30 MeV neutrons scattered by ^{12}C (actually $u_l(r)/r$ is plotted).

The partial waves for large l are solutions of (2.18) for very small values of the potentials in comparison with $l(l + 1)/r^2$. They look like the Riccatti-Bessel function $U_l(r)$. Their phase is almost zero except for changes of $180°$ at the zeros of $U_l(r)$, where the function reverses in sign. The phase curve in Fig. 11.8b has almost a rectangular form.

For smaller values of l the potential is important. For small r, the wave function is the solution of the radial Schrödinger equation in a uniform complex potential, namely a Riccatti-Bessel function of a complex argument. For a real potential the phase of $u_l(r)$ at the origin is the phase shift δ_l. The imaginary part of the potential is responsible for the rectangular corners of the curve in Fig. 11.8b being rounded off. In fact, for very small l the phase has small oscillations about the straight line $-Cr + A$. For small l, we may say that

$$u_l(r) \cong |u_l(r)| \, e^{-i(Cr-A)}. \tag{11.7}$$

In a reaction matrix element the product of at least two partial waves $u_l(r)$ and $u_{l'}(r')$ is important. The phase of the product is $A + B - (Cr + Dr')$ if both l and l' are small. The integrand of the radial integral fluctuates rapidly from positive to negative values, so that the integral is small. This effect was noticed by Austern (61) and is known as phase averaging. It means that the contributions to a reaction matrix element from low partial waves are relatively small. It is due to the imaginary part of the potential and is the angular momentum space analogue of the space localization of the reaction to the surface. Note that the smoothness of the phase curve in Fig. 11.8b is the key to this explanation. The oscillation of the integrand occurs also for plane waves, for which there is obviously no localization in angular momentum or configuration space.

We have already seen in Chapter 2B how the large phase differences between partial waves for large and small (that is, exterior and interior) values of l are responsible for the focus. The focus is thus a property of the real part of the potential. This is because the nucleus has a surface.

It is interesting to examine the S-matrix elements $\eta_l = \exp(2i\delta_l)$ more closely as a function of l. Figure 11.9 shows a typical situation for strongly absorbed particles, in this case 18 MeV α-particles scattered by ^{40}Ar. The phase, arg η_l, is the real part of the nuclear phase shift. Its value for $l = 0$ is given roughly by the WKB approximation, and it decreases rapidly as l increases. The magnitude $|\eta_l|$ is small where the imaginary part of δ_l is

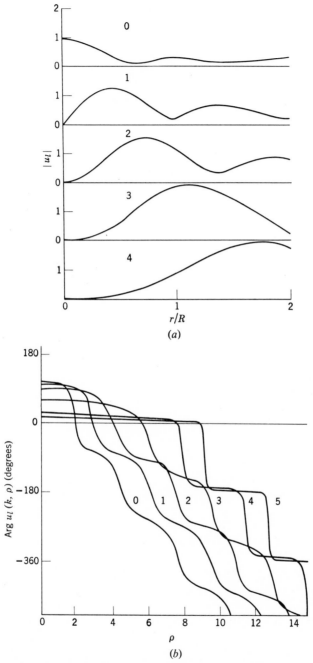

FIG. 11.8 (a) The magnitude and (b) the phase of the partial waves for the scattering of 30 MeV neutrons from ^{12}C, $V = 40$, $W = 8$, $r_0 = 1.2$, $a = 0.5$. The values of l are indicated on the curves.

large. In Fig. 11.9 the reflection coefficient for the first eight partial waves is
very small. It becomes unity after $l = 12$. Therefore, only the partial waves
for $l = 9,10,11$ distinguish the scattering from that for a black disc. It was
found by Blair that a good first approximation to α-particle elastic scattering
was obtained by a sharp cutoff diffraction model in which all the partial
waves inside a cutoff value l_c were eliminated.

$$\eta_l = 1, \qquad l \geqslant l_c,$$
$$\eta_l = 0, \qquad l < l_c. \qquad\qquad (11.8)$$

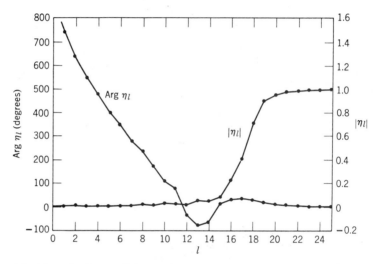

FIG. 11.9   The reflection coefficient η_l for 43 MeV α-particles scattered by ^{58}Ni, plotted
against l. (Adapted from Rost, 62.)

Marginal improvements to the Blair model could be effected by giving real
values less than 1 to a few surface reflection coefficients. A very good fit to
α-particle elastic scattering may be obtained by the model of Austern and
Blair (65), which uses a parametrization of η_l. $|\eta_l|$ is fitted by a Woods-Saxon
form factor, while arg η_l is fitted by successive derivatives. This simple
model is also useful for inelastic scattering and will be further discussed in
the next chapter.

B.   THE OPTICAL MODEL WITH SPIN-ORBIT COUPLING

For fitting all entrance channel data, it is necessary to include spin-orbit
coupling in the potential for nucleon scattering. This produces polarization.
In order to introduce the theory of polarization, we shall give the formalism

of the optical model in the form in which it is used for computation (Mel-kanoff, Nodvik, Saxon, and Cantor, 61).

The Schrödinger equation is

$$\left[-\frac{\hbar^2}{2\mu} \nabla^2 + V_C(r) + V_S(r)\mathbf{S} \cdot \mathbf{L} \right]\Psi = E\Psi, \qquad (11.9)$$

where, in terms of the Pauli spin operator $\boldsymbol{\sigma}$,

$$\mathbf{S} = \tfrac{1}{2}\hbar\boldsymbol{\sigma}$$

$$\mathbf{L} = \mathbf{r} \times \frac{\hbar}{i} \nabla. \qquad (11.10)$$

The formalism for uncharged particles will be presented first and then generalized to the case of charged particles. The incident wave function, normalized to unit flux, is the wave function in the absence of the potential. It is

$$\Psi_{\text{inc}} = v^{-\frac{1}{2}} e^{ikz} \chi_{\text{inc}}, \qquad (11.11)$$

where v is the velocity of the incident particle and the incident spin function is

$$\chi_{\text{inc}} = a_{\frac{1}{2}}\alpha + a_{-\frac{1}{2}}\beta. \qquad (11.12)$$

α and β are normalized eigenfunctions of S_z, and $a_{\frac{1}{2}}, a_{-\frac{1}{2}}$ are the corresponding amplitudes.

The partial wave expansion of the free incident wave is

$$\Psi_{\text{inc}} = v^{-\frac{1}{2}} \sum_l [4\pi(2l + 1)]^{\frac{1}{2}} i^l \frac{U_l(kr)}{kr} Y_l^0(\theta, \phi) [a_{\frac{1}{2}}\alpha + a_{-\frac{1}{2}}\beta]. \quad (11.13)$$

The normalized spherical harmonics are defined as

$$Y_l^m(\theta, \phi) = (-1)^m \left[\frac{2l + 1}{4\pi}\right]^{\frac{1}{2}} \left[\frac{(l - m)!}{(l + m)!}\right]^{\frac{1}{2}} P_l^m(\cos\theta)e^{im\phi} \quad (11.14)$$

where $P_l^m(\cos\theta)$ are the associated Legendre polynomials.

The product functions $Y_l^0\alpha$ and $Y_l^0\beta$ of (11.13) are simultaneous eigenfunctions of the operators L^2, L_z, S^2, S_z, but not of $\mathbf{L} \cdot \mathbf{S}$. This is remedied by introducing the *jj* coupling functions $\mathcal{Y}_{jls}^{m_j}$ defined in Equation (5.5).

The total wave function is simply the incident wave function with the function $j_l(kr)$ replaced by $u_l^{\pm}(kr)/kr$, where $u_l^{\pm}$ are the solutions of the radial wave equation for spin parallel to $\mathbf{L}$ and antiparallel to $\mathbf{L}$, respectively. The total wave function is

$$\Psi_{\text{total}} = \Psi_{\text{inc}} + \Psi_{\text{scat}}$$

$$= \left(\frac{4\pi}{v}\right)^{\frac{1}{2}} \sum_l (l+1)^{\frac{1}{2}} i^l \frac{u_l^+(k,r)}{kr} [a_{\frac{1}{2}} \mathcal{Y}_{l+\frac{1}{2},l,\frac{1}{2}}^{\frac{1}{2}} + a_{-\frac{1}{2}} \mathcal{Y}_{l+\frac{1}{2},l,\frac{1}{2}}^{-\frac{1}{2}}]$$

$$+ \left(\frac{4\pi}{v}\right)^{\frac{1}{2}} \sum_l l^{\frac{1}{2}} i^l \frac{u_l^-(k,r)}{kr} [-a_{\frac{1}{2}} \mathcal{Y}_{l-\frac{1}{2},l,\frac{1}{2}}^{\frac{1}{2}} + a_{-\frac{1}{2}} \mathcal{Y}_{l-\frac{1}{2},l,\frac{1}{2}}^{-\frac{1}{2}}]. \quad (11.15)$$

The radial equation separates because the two terms of (11.15) are not coupled by **S · L**. The independent equations are

$$\frac{d^2 u_l^{\pm}}{dr^2} + \left\{ k^2 - \frac{2\mu}{\hbar^2} \left[V_C + \frac{\hbar^2}{2} \begin{pmatrix} l \\ -l-1 \end{pmatrix} V_S \right] - \frac{l(l+1)}{r^2} \right\} u_l^{\pm} = 0. \quad (11.16)$$

The radial wave function must reduce to the incident wave $krj_l(kr)$ [$= U_l(kr)$] when there is no interaction and must be such that only the scattered wave is modified by the interaction. These conditions are satisfied in the exterior region by the expression

$$u_l^{\pm} = kr\{j_l(kr) + C_l^{\pm}[-n_l(kr) + ij_l(kr)]\}. \quad (11.17)$$

The form of the scattered part of (11.17) is the outgoing Hankel function $h_l^{(1)}$ defined by (2.24). For large kr, (11.17) becomes

$$u_l^{\pm} \sim krj_l(kr) + C_l^{\pm} e^{i(kr - l\pi/2)}, \quad (11.18)$$

or equivalently

$$u_l^{\pm} \sim \sin\left(kr - \frac{l\pi}{2}\right) + C_l^{\pm} e^{i(kr - l\pi/2)}. \quad (11.19)$$

In terms of the complex phase shifts $\delta_l^{\pm}$, (11.19) must be of the form

$$u_l^{\pm} \sim A_l^{\pm} \sin\left(kr - \frac{l\pi}{2} + \delta_l^{\pm}\right). \quad (11.20)$$

Comparison of the coefficients of $e^{\pm ikr}$ in (11.19, 20) yields

$$C_l^{\pm} = (2i)^{-1}(e^{2i\delta_l^{\pm}} - 1), \quad (11.21)$$

$$A_l^{\pm} = e^{i\delta_l^{\pm}}. \quad (11.22)$$

Substituting (11.18) into (11.15) and subtracting Ψ_{inc}, as given by (11.15) with $u_l^{\pm}$ set equal to U_l, we have the asymptotic form for Ψ_{scat}.

$$\Psi_{\text{scat}} \sim v^{-\frac{1}{2}} \frac{e^{ikr}}{r} A(\theta)[a_{\frac{1}{2}}\alpha + a_{-\frac{1}{2}}\beta] + iB(\theta)[a_{-\frac{1}{2}} e^{i\phi}\alpha - a_{\frac{1}{2}} e^{i\phi}\beta], \quad (11.23)$$

where

$$A(\theta) = k^{-1} \sum_l [(l+1)C_l^+ + lC_l^-]P_l(\cos\theta),$$
$$B(\theta) = (ik)^{-1} \sum_l [C_l^+ - C_l^-]P_l^1(\cos\theta). \tag{11.24}$$

The wave function of the scattered wave can more conveniently be expressed in terms of $\boldsymbol{\sigma}$ and $\mathbf{n}$, the unit vector normal to the scattering plane defined by

$$\mathbf{n}\sin\theta = \mathbf{k}' \times \mathbf{k}, \tag{11.25}$$

where $\mathbf{k}$ and $\mathbf{k}'$ are unit vectors in the direction of propagation before and after scattering. In this notation we have

$$\Psi_{\text{scat}} \sim v^{-\frac{1}{2}} \frac{e^{ikr}}{r} [A(\theta) + B(\theta)\boldsymbol{\sigma}\cdot\mathbf{n}]\chi_{\text{inc}}$$

$$\equiv v^{-\frac{1}{2}} \frac{e^{ikr}}{r} f(\theta)\chi_{\text{inc}}. \tag{11.26}$$

The differential cross section is

$$\sigma(\theta) = [f(\theta)\chi_{\text{inc}}]^\dagger [f(\theta)\chi_{\text{inc}}]. \tag{11.27}$$

The polarization vector is defined by

$$\mathbf{P}(\theta) = \frac{[f(\theta)\chi_{\text{inc}}]^\dagger \boldsymbol{\sigma}[f(\theta)\chi_{\text{inc}}]}{\sigma(\theta)}. \tag{11.28}$$

These quantities are given by (11.26) as

$$\sigma(\theta) = |A|^2 + |B|^2 + (A^*B + AB^*)\mathbf{n}\cdot\mathbf{P}_0, \tag{11.29}$$

$$\mathbf{P}(\theta)$$
$$= \frac{(|A|^2 - |B|^2)\mathbf{P}_0 + [A^*B + AB^* + 2|B|^2\mathbf{P}_0\cdot\mathbf{n}]\mathbf{n} + i(A^*B - AB^*)\mathbf{n}\times\mathbf{P}_0}{|A|^2 + |B|^2 + (A^*B + AB^*)\mathbf{P}_0\cdot\mathbf{n}}.$$
$$\tag{11.30}$$

The incident polarization vector is given by

$$\mathbf{P}_0 = \chi_{\text{inc}}^\dagger \boldsymbol{\sigma}\chi_{\text{inc}}. \tag{11.31}$$

If the incident beam is unpolarized, $\mathbf{P}_0 = 0$, the scattered beam is polarized along the direction $\mathbf{n}$ perpendicular to the scattering plane.

$$\sigma(\theta) = |A|^2 + |B|^2, \tag{11.32}$$

$$\mathbf{P}(\theta) = P(\theta)\mathbf{n} = \frac{A^*B + AB^*}{|A|^2 + |B|^2}\mathbf{n}. \tag{11.33}$$

$P(\theta)$ is called the polarization. It is often measured by a double scattering experiment as illustrated in Fig. 11.10, which serves to define the symbols. The quantities defining the first and second scattering are denoted by

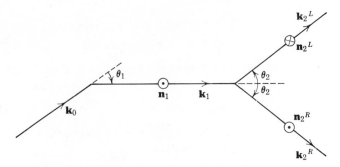

FIG. 11.10   Definition of the symbols used in the discussion of a double scattering experiment.

subscripts 1 and 2. The differential cross section for the second scattering is given, when the polarization $P_1(\theta_1)$ is known, by combining Equations (11.29, 11.33).

$$\sigma_2(\theta_2) = |A_2|^2 + |B_2|^2 + (A_2{}^*B_2 + A_2B_2{}^*)\mathbf{n}_2 \cdot \mathbf{P}_1(\theta_1)$$

$$= (|A_2|^2 + |B_2|^2)(1 + \mathbf{P}_2 \cdot \mathbf{P}_1). \tag{11.34}$$

From Fig. 11.10 it is clear that

$$\mathbf{n}_1 = \mathbf{n}_2{}^R = -\mathbf{n}_2{}^L, \tag{11.35}$$

so that the differential cross sections for the right and left beams are

$$\sigma_2{}^R(\theta_2) = (|A_2|^2 + |B_2|^2)(1 + P_2P_1),$$

$$\sigma_2{}^L(\theta_2) = (|A_2|^2 + |B_2|^2)(1 - P_2P_1). \tag{11.36}$$

The ratio of left and right intensities is

$$\frac{\sigma_2{}^L(\theta_2)}{\sigma_2{}^R(\theta_2)} = \frac{1 - P_2P_1}{1 + P_2P_1}, \tag{11.37}$$

or

$$P_2(\theta_2) = \frac{1}{P_1(\theta_1)} \frac{\sigma_2{}^L - \sigma_2{}^R}{\sigma_2{}^L + \sigma_2{}^R}. \tag{11.38}$$

We shall now generalize our formalism to the case of charged incident particles where the asymptotic wave function in the absence of the nuclear potential is, for a point charge with Coulomb parameter η,

$$\Psi_C \sim v^{-\frac{1}{2}} \left\{ e^{i[kz - \eta \ln k(r-z)]} \left[1 - \frac{\eta^2}{ik(r-z)} \right] \right.$$

$$\left. + \frac{1}{r} f_C(\theta) e^{i(kr - \eta \ln 2kr)} \right\}, \tag{11.39}$$

where

$$\eta = \frac{\mu ZZ'e^2}{\hbar^2 k}, \tag{11.40}$$

and the Rutherford scattering amplitude $f_C(\theta)$ is

$$f_C(\theta) = -\frac{\eta}{2k \sin^2 \theta/2} e^{-i\eta \ln (\sin^2\theta/2)+2i\sigma_0}. \tag{11.41}$$

The Coulomb phase shift σ_l is given by

$$\sigma_l = \arg \Gamma(l + 1 + i\eta). \tag{11.42}$$

The partial wave expansion of Ψ_C is

$$\Psi_C = v^{-\frac{1}{2}} \sum_l [4\pi(2l + 1)]^{\frac{1}{2}} i^l \frac{F_l(kr)}{kr} Y_l^0(\theta, \phi), \tag{11.43}$$

where F_l is the regular Coulomb function of Equation (2.28).

The analogue of (11.15) for charged particles is

$$\Psi_{\text{total}} = \Psi_{\text{inc}} + \Psi_{\text{scat}}$$

$$= \left(\frac{4\pi}{v}\right)^{\frac{1}{2}} \sum_l (l + 1)^{\frac{1}{2}} i^l e^{i\sigma_l} \frac{u_l^+(k, r)}{kr} [a_{\frac{1}{2}} \mathscr{Y}_{l+\frac{1}{2},l,\frac{1}{2}}^{\frac{1}{2}} + a_{-\frac{1}{2}} \mathscr{Y}_{l+\frac{1}{2},l,\frac{1}{2}}^{-\frac{1}{2}}$$

$$+ \left(\frac{4\pi}{v}\right)^{\frac{1}{2}} \sum_l l^{\frac{1}{2}} i^l e^{i\sigma_l} \frac{u_l^-(k, r)}{kr} [-a_{\frac{1}{2}} \mathscr{Y}_{l-\frac{1}{2},l,\frac{1}{2}}^{\frac{1}{2}} + a_{-\frac{1}{2}} \mathscr{Y}_{l-\frac{1}{2},l,\frac{1}{2}}^{-\frac{1}{2}}]. \tag{11.44}$$

Equation (11.44) is formally identical to (11.15) except for the appearance of the Coulomb phase factor $e^{i\sigma_l}$. The radial wave function is computed in a central potential $V_C(r)$, which includes a term for the effect of the nucleon charges inside the nucleus. It is sufficiently accurate to use the Coulomb potential inside a uniformly charged sphere of radius R up to the Woods-Saxon radius R, and the point charge potential for $r > R$.

$$[V_C(r)]_{\text{Coulomb}} = \frac{ZZ'e^2}{2R} \left(3 - \frac{r^2}{R^2}\right), \qquad r \leq R,$$

$$= ZZ'e^2/r, \qquad r \geq R. \tag{11.45}$$

$u_l^\pm(k, r)$ are matched to Coulomb functions beyond the matching radius. The expression in the external region is

$$u_l^\pm(k, r) = F_l(kr) + C_l^\pm [G_l(kr) + iF_l(kr)], \tag{11.46}$$

which reduces in the limit of large r to the equivalent forms

$$u_l^\pm(k, r) \sim F_l(kr) + C_l^\pm e^{i(kr-\eta \ln 2kr - l\pi/2 + \sigma_l)} \tag{11.47}$$

$$= \sin (kr - \eta \ln 2kr - l\pi/2 + \sigma_l) + C_l^\pm e^{i(kr-\eta \ln 2kr - l\pi/2 + \sigma_l)}. \tag{11.48}$$

In this case the phase shifts $\delta_l{}^\pm$ are defined by the following asymptotic form for $u_l{}^\pm$.

$$u_l{}^\pm(k, r) \sim A_l{}^\pm \sin\left(kr - \eta \ln 2kr - \frac{l\pi}{2} + \sigma_l + \delta_l{}^\pm\right). \qquad (11.49)$$

The phase shifts defined in this way exclude the Coulomb phase shift σ_l. Comparison of the coefficients of $e^{i(kr-\eta \ln 2kr - \pi/2 + \sigma_l)}$ and $e^{-i(kr-\eta \ln 2kr - l\pi/2 + \sigma_l)}$ in (11.48, 11.49) yields

$$C_l{}^\pm = (2i)^{-1}[e^{2i\delta_l{}^\pm} - 1], \qquad (11.50)$$

$$A_l{}^\pm = e^{i\delta_l{}^\pm}. \qquad (11.51)$$

Substituting (11.46) into (11.44) and making use of (11.39) and the form of (11.44) for a point charge potential, we obtain for the asymptotic form of the total wave function

$$\Psi_{\text{total}} \sim v^{-\frac12}\left\{ e^{i[kz - \eta \ln k(r-z)]}\left[1 - \frac{\eta^2}{ik(r-z)}\right]\chi_{\text{inc}} \right.$$
$$+ \frac{v^{-\frac12}e^{i(kr-\eta \ln 2kr)}}{r}\left\{A(\theta)[a_{\frac12}\alpha + a_{-\frac12}\beta] + iB(\theta)\right.$$
$$\left. \times [a_{-\frac12}e^{i\phi}\alpha - a_{\frac12}e^{i\phi}\beta]\right\}, \qquad (11.52)$$

where

$$A(\theta) = f_C(\theta) + k^{-1}\sum_l e^{2i\sigma_l}[(l + 1)C_l{}^+ + lC_l{}^-]P_l(\cos\theta)$$

$$B(\theta) = (ik)^{-1}\sum_l e^{2i\sigma_l}[C_l{}^+ - C_l{}^-]P_l{}^1(\cos\theta). \qquad (11.53)$$

From this point the formalism follows the formalism for uncharged particles exactly.

We now have the complete formalism for the solution of the optical-model equation in the asymptotic region. To compute the asymptotic quantities $A(\theta)$ and $B(\theta)$, we must obtain the $C_l{}^\pm$ by matching the internal wave functions $u_l{}^\pm$ and their derivatives $u_l{}^{\pm\prime}$ to the values and derivatives of the form (11.46) for the external region. The matching equations, where all quantities are evaluated at the matching radius or channel radius r_0, are

$$\frac{u_l{}^{\pm\prime}}{u_l{}^\pm} = \frac{F_l' + C_l{}^\pm(G_l' + iF_l')}{F_l + C_l{}^\pm(G_l + iF_l)}, \qquad (11.54)$$

which yield for $C_l{}^\pm$

$$C_l{}^\pm = \frac{u_l{}^\pm F_l' - u_l{}^{\pm\prime}F_l}{u_l{}^{\pm\prime}G_l - u_l{}^\pm G_l' + i(u_l{}^{\pm\prime}F_l - u_l{}^\pm F_l')}. \qquad (11.55)$$

Knowing $C_l{}^\pm$ we can calculate the phase shifts $\delta_l{}^\pm$ or the reflection coefficients $\eta_l{}^\pm$, which are generally defined to be $\exp 2i(\delta_l{}^\pm + \sigma_l)$.

The internal wave functions are usually computed by numerical integration, starting very near the origin with an arbitrary complex normalization. It is not necessary to know the normalization in order to compute $C_l^\pm$ because it is divided out in Equation (11.54). Of course, for computing wave functions and their associated quantities, the normalization must be known. If $\tilde{u}_l^\pm$ and $\tilde{u}_l^{\pm\prime}$ are the unnormalized values, the normalized wave functions are

$$u_l^\pm(k, r) = \tilde{u}_l^\pm(k, r)\left[\frac{F_l + C_l^\pm(G_l + iF_l)}{\tilde{u}_l^\pm}\right]_{r=r_0}. \qquad (11.56)$$

The experimentally measurable entrance channel quantities are the differential cross section (11.32), the polarization (11.33), and the total reaction cross section.

The total reaction cross section is obtained from the optical model as follows.

$$\sigma^R = \frac{\text{absorbed flux}}{\text{incident flux}}. \qquad (11.57)$$

The absorbed flux is the integral over all space of the divergence of the flux or, equivalently, the integral of the flux over the surface of a sphere outside the nucleus, say of radius r_0. The incident flux is defined to be unity. The absorbed flux is

$$-\frac{\hbar}{2i\mu}\int r_0^2 \sin\theta \, d\theta \, d\phi\left[\Psi_\text{total}^\dagger \frac{\partial\Psi_\text{total}}{\partial r} - \Psi_\text{total}\frac{\partial\Psi_\text{total}^\dagger}{\partial r}\right]. \qquad (11.58)$$

Substituting (11.44) for Ψ_total and making use of the orthonormality of the $\mathcal{Y}_{jls}^{m_j}$ and the relation

$$|a_{1/2}|^2 + |a_{-1/2}|^2 = 1, \qquad (11.59)$$

we have after performing the integration in (11.58)

$$\sigma^R = \frac{4\pi}{v}\sum_l (l+1)\left\{r^2\left(-\frac{\hbar}{2i\mu}\right)\left[\frac{u_l^{+*}}{kr}\frac{\partial}{\partial r}\frac{u_l^+}{kr} - \frac{u_l^+}{kr}\frac{\partial}{\partial r}\frac{u_l^{+*}}{kr}\right]_{r=r_0}\right\}$$
$$-\frac{4\pi}{v}\sum_l l\left\{r^2\left(-\frac{\hbar}{2i\mu}\right)\left[\frac{u_l^{-*}}{kr}\frac{\partial}{\partial r}\frac{u_l^-}{kr} - \frac{u_l^-}{kr}\frac{\partial}{\partial r}\frac{u_l^{-*}}{kr}\right]_{r=r_0}\right\}. \qquad (11.60)$$

Using the asymptotic form (11.46) for $u_l^\pm$ and the Wronskian relation

$$G_l F_l' - F_l G_l' = 1, \qquad (11.61)$$

we have

$$\frac{4\pi}{v}\left\{r^2\left(\frac{-\hbar}{2i\mu}\right)\left[\frac{u_l^{\pm*}}{kr}\frac{\partial}{\partial r}\frac{u_l^\pm}{kr} - \frac{u_l^\pm}{kr}\frac{\partial}{\partial r}\frac{u_l^{\pm*}}{kr}\right]_{r=r_0}\right\} = \frac{4\pi}{k^2}[\text{Im } C_l^\pm - |C_l^\pm|^2]. \qquad (11.62)$$

Substituting (11.62) into (11.60) we have

$$\sigma^R = \sum_l \sigma_l^R$$

$$= \frac{4\pi}{k^2} \sum_l \{(l+1)[\text{Im } C_l^+ - (\text{Im } C_l^+)^2 - (\text{Re } C_l^+)^2]$$

$$+ l[\text{Im } C_l^- - (\text{Im } C_l^-)^2 - (\text{Re } C_l^-)^2] . \qquad (11.63)$$

Equation (11.63) also defines the partial reaction cross sections σ_l^R or transmission coefficients T_l used in the statistical model (see Chapter 9(C)[iv]), so that the optical model may be used to predict compound elastic scattering with the statistical assumption made by Hauser and Feshbach (52) that all terms with angular momentum quantum numbers allowed by the selection rules are equally weighted.

C. FITTING OF ENTRANCE CHANNEL DATA BY THE OPTICAL MODEL

The optical model may be taken seriously as a representation of entrance channel data if a smooth variation of its parameters with energy and mass number can be found which reproduces all data within experimental error. Finding the best form for the potential and determining the parameters involves a large program of work, which has been undertaken by several laboratories for many years.

Search codes are available for computers that minimize the value of χ^2 for fits to data by adjusting parameters automatically.

$$\chi^2 = \sum_i \frac{(T_i - E_i)^2}{E_i^2}, \qquad (11.64)$$

where T_i and E_i are the theoretical and experimental estimates of the ith piece of data.

There are several ways of attacking the problem. For a particular target at a particular energy it is usual to fit the experiment for which most data are available first and then try the parameters on the other two types of experiment. Usually the differential cross section is fitted and the parameters checked by comparison with polarization and total reaction cross section measurements. However, some have tried the reverse procedure by fitting polarization and checking the parameters by comparison with differential cross sections and the total reaction cross section. Good fits and consistent parameters are found for protons although work is still going on to improve the fits and the uniqueness of the parameter determination. For heavier particles it may be shown that the parameters are not unique.

[i] Protons

In order to illustrate the quality of the information available from optical-model fitting, we shall consider a calculation performed by Perey (63) for energies ranging from 9.4 MeV to 22.2 MeV.

The potentials used were

$$V_C(r) = V_S f(r, r_{0S}, a_S) + i W_S f(r, r_{0I}, a_I)$$

$$+ 4 i a_I W_D \frac{d}{dr} f(r, r_{0I}, a_I) + [V_C(r)]_{\text{Coulomb}},$$

$$V_S(r) = \boldsymbol{\sigma} \cdot \mathbf{l} \left(\frac{\hbar}{m_\pi c} \right)^2 V_{SO} \frac{1}{r} \frac{d}{dr} f(r, r_{0S}, a_S). \qquad (11.65)$$

The function $f(r, r_0, a)$ is the Woods-Saxon form factor (11.1), $[V_C(r)]_{\text{Coulomb}}$ is given by (11.45), and m_π is the pion mass.

In this potential there are eight parameters. The spin-orbit potential is real and is constrained to have the shape of the derivative of the real central form factor. The Woods-Saxon term in the imaginary potential may have different shape parameters from those for the real potential, and surface absorption may be included with a shape that is the derivative of the first term in the imaginary potential.

The average quality of the fits obtained is illustrated for 17 MeV protons on Cu in Fig. 11.11.

The geometrical parameters and the spin-orbit strength were given by

$$r_{0S} = 1.25 \, \text{fm}$$
$$a_S = 0.65 \, \text{fm}$$
$$r_{0I} = 1.25 \, \text{fm}$$
$$a_I = 0.47 \, \text{fm}$$
$$V_{SO} = 7.5 \, \text{MeV} \ (E < 17 \, \text{MeV}), \ 8.5 \, \text{MeV} \ (E > 17 \, \text{MeV})$$

It was found that surface and volume imaginary form factors were almost indistinguishable as far as differential cross sections were concerned. However, the polarization was fitted better by a surface absorption. Reaction cross sections came within experimental error for both models. Therefore the strength W_S of the central absorption term was set equal to zero.

An automatic search was conducted to obtain the best values of V_S and W_D for fitting differential cross sections, and a systematic variation of V_S with energy and target was discovered.

$$V_S = \left\{ 53.3 - 0.55E + \left(0.4 \frac{Z}{A^{1/3}} + 27 \frac{N-Z}{A} \right) \right\} \, \text{MeV}. \qquad (11.66)$$

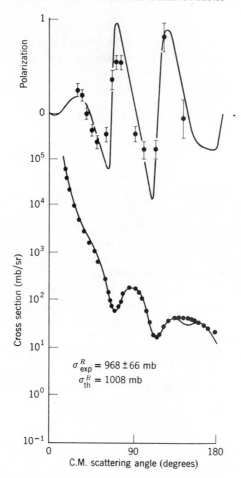

FIG. 11.11 Differential cross section, polarization, and total reaction cross section for 17 MeV protons scattered by Cu, all calculated in the potential of Perey (63). (Adapted from Perey, 63.)

The nuclear symmetry term $(N - Z)/A$ reflects an isospin dependence of the optical-model potential.

No systematic variation of W_D was found. There were wide fluctuations from nucleus to nucleus; for example, at 17 MeV the minimum value was 10.4 MeV for Ni, the maximum was 18.7 MeV for Pt. There was also no systematic increase of W_D with energy. The different values represent the strong dependence of W_D on the details of nuclear structure. The probability of exciting nonelastic channels varies widely with the exact structure of the nucleus.

An attempt to improve the fit slightly by adding a volume imaginary potential W_S and allowing the search code to readjust V_S and W_D for each value of W_S resulted in a decrease of W_D by approximately the amount of W_S. The best fits were obtained with, at most, 5 MeV addition of W_S. The values of W_S for best fit with $W_D = 0$ ranged at 17 MeV from 4.06 MeV for Au to 7.67 MeV for Ni.

[ii] NEUTRONS

Optical-model fits for neutrons are well illustrated by the work of Bjorklund and Fernbach (58). Neutron scattering experiments at 4.1 MeV, 7 MeV, and 14 MeV were analyzed with a form factor that was the same as (11.65) except that the central imaginary potential was a surface Gaussian $Wg(r, r_0, b)$ with form factor given by

$$g(r, r_0, b) = \exp\left[\frac{-(r - r_0 A^{1/3})^2}{b^2}\right]. \tag{11.67}$$

In this case polarization data are not available. However, accurate data are available for total neutron cross sections (which are finite because there is no Coulomb scattering) and total reaction cross sections.

E (MeV)	V_S (MeV)	W (MeV)	V_{S0} (MeV)	a (fm)	b (fm)	r_0 (fm)
4.1	50	7	9.5	0.65	0.98	1.25
7	45.5	9.5	8.6	0.65	0.98	1.25
14	44	11	8.3	0.65	0.98	1.24

TABLE 11.1. Neutron optical-model parameters determined by Bjorklund and Fernbach (58).

At each energy a set of parameters independent of A and Z was found, which gave the best overall fit to the data. The parameters are given in Table 11.1. They compare quite closely with those determined by Perey for protons.

[iii] DEUTERONS

The most striking fact about attempts to fit deuteron elastic scattering is that not only is the VR^n ambiguity present, but a discrete set of V with the same R may be found, which gives equally good fits.

The effect has been thoroughly examined by Perey and Perey (63). Values of the parameters defined by (11.65) for 11.8 MeV deuterons scattered by Cu are given in Table 11.2. The magnitudes of relevant partial waves were

Potential No.	1	2	3	4	5
V_S (MeV)	36.8	58.5	90.7	128.2	167.8
W_D (MeV)	10.07	13.32	18.34	24.3	31.9
r_{0S} (fm)	1.070	1.153	1.172	1.193	1.232
a_S (fm)	0.987	0.879	0.822	0.775	0.716
r_{0I} (fm)	1.444	1.434	1.410	1.403	1.394
a_I (fm)	0.739	0.708	0.661	0.608	0.560
σ^R (mb)	1440	1476	1468	1460	1451
χ^2	1.4	0.65	0.78	0.84	0.96

TABLE 11.2.   Ambiguous potentials for fitting the differential cross sections for 11.8 MeV deuterons scattered by Cu.   (Perey and Perey, 63.)

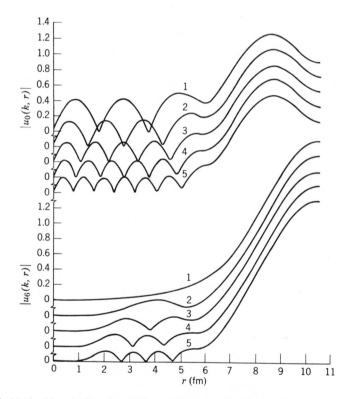

FIG. 11.12   Magnitudes of partial waves calculated in the ambiguous deuteron optical-model potentials of Table 11.2 for 11.8 MeV deuterons scattered by copper. (Adapted from Perey and Perey, 63.)

plotted against r for each potential. Such a plot is shown in Fig. 11.12. The external values are almost identical for all the potentials, but the number of internal nodes increases by one for each successive potential. The wave functions are identical in the near-surface region, but the focus becomes progressively sharper, more intense, and nearer the center as V_S increases. The local maxima are, for unit incident flux, 1.65 and 0.90, situated at 1.8 fm and 3.5 fm for potentials 5 and 1, respectively. These focal intensities cause large effects in reaction calculations. It is possible to distinguish the parameter sets, for example, in stripping calculations (see Chapter 13A). Polarization was not included in the calculation.

[iv] α-Particles

The same type of parameter multiplicity has been discovered for α-particles as for deuterons; hence it is not meaningful to give detailed potential values. However, some general comparisons with proton parameter sets can be made. An analysis by Satchler (65) at 28 MeV showed that elastic scattering for various nuclei was well fitted by a Woods-Saxon four-parameter potential with ranges of parameters given below.

$$
\begin{array}{ll}
V(\text{MeV}) & 46\text{–}54 \\
W(\text{MeV}) & 8.6\text{–}15.4 \\
R(\text{fm}) & [1.2 + 1.5\,A^{\frac{1}{3}}] \\
a(\text{fm}) & 0.53\text{–}0.58
\end{array}
$$

The real part of this particular set of potentials is comparable with that for protons, the imaginary part is about twice as large. r_0 is explained roughly by adding the radius of the α-particle to the radius of the nucleus, which is still larger than that for protons; a is about 0.1 fm less than for protons.

[v] Summary of Phenomenological Information

For protons and neutrons the optical model gives a good and unique fit to entrance channel data at energies above about 10 MeV and possibly lower. For composite particles a good fit can be obtained, but it is not unique. The difference between potentials that are equivalent for entrance channel data is in the internal wave functions.

Fairly definite statements can be made about at least eight parameters for protons. The most noticeable feature is the energy dependence of the real part of the potential for both protons and neutrons. The form (11.66) compares closely with (5.40) for the bound single-particle model. The discrepancy between the energy-independent parts can be resolved by considering the VR^2 ambiguity. The radii are 1.25 fm and about 1.4 fm for the respective cases, and the potentials are 53.3 MeV and 39 MeV. The imaginary part of the potential rises as the exclusion principle relaxes with increasing energy, and ultimately falls slowly with decreasing nucleon-nucleon cross section.

Parameter studies have indicated that varying certain parameters has a consistent effect on the angular distributions. In terms of the four-parameter model we can state these effects.

Increasing V or R causes the maxima and minima to shift towards smaller angles. Increasing W damps the oscillations of the cross sections. Increasing a lowers some maxima relative to others. The last two rules are not invariable and the effects of increasing W and a are sometimes similar. Spin-orbit coupling affects back angles more than forward angles and is capable of correcting the back angle discrepancies found in the four-parameter model.

It is noticeable in all cases that the polarization angular distribution has the shape of the derivative of the differential cross section angular distribution. This effect was explained by Rodberg (63). The scattering amplitude $X(\theta)$ for spin-up particles is computed in a deeper potential than the scattering amplitude $Y(\theta)$ for spin-down particles,

$$X(\theta) = A(\theta) + B(\theta)$$
$$Y(\theta) = A(\theta) - B(\theta). \tag{11.68}$$

According to the phenomenological fitting rules above, for a small angular displacement $\delta\theta$, X and Y compare with the scattering amplitude M for $V_{SO} = 0$ as follows:

$$X(\theta) = M(\theta + \delta\theta) \cong M(\theta) + \frac{\partial M}{\partial\theta}\,\delta\theta,$$

$$Y(\theta) = M(\theta - \delta\theta) \cong M(\theta) - \frac{\partial M}{\partial\theta}\,\delta\theta. \tag{11.69}$$

The polarization $P(\theta)$ is given to order $(\delta\theta)^2$ by

$$P(\theta) = \frac{|X(\theta)|^2 - |Y(\theta)|^2}{|X(\theta)|^2 + |Y(\theta)|^2} \cong \delta\theta\,\frac{\partial\sigma(\theta)}{\partial\theta}\,\sigma(\theta), \tag{11.70}$$

where

$$\sigma(\theta) = |M(\theta)|^2, \text{ apart from a constant.} \tag{11.71}$$

Besides the projectiles considered here, the optical model has been used for fitting scattering data for heavier ions. However, the absorption for these particles is even stronger than for α-particles and the interior of the wave function less important, so that the real potential ambiguity is present. The optical model cannot be considered as a serious description of the interaction of a particle with a nucleus, except for proton or neutron projectiles, without further information from reactions.

D. THE NONLOCAL OPTICAL MODEL

The optical-model potentials usually used for fitting entrance channel data and calculating distorted waves are local except for the spin-orbit coupling term. Computation is simpler for local potentials. We have seen, however, that the optical-model potential is nonlocal. In our simple example (10.118) the matrix element of V contains sums over products of two matrix elements for the virtual excitation of intermediate states, which have been shown in (10.121) to be equivalent to the single matrix element of a nonlocal potential operator.

Local potentials which are equivalent to nonlocal ones, in the sense that they reproduce the same cross sections at a given energy, vary with the energy. This is illustrated in (11.66). It is certain that the energy dependence of the local potential for protons and neutrons contains this effect. The optical model also is basically different for high and low energy. The optical model describes an average over fluctuations resulting from overlapping resonances. Therefore there is some intrinsic energy dependence because of differences in average widths at different energies.

In the coordinate representation a nonlocal potential operating on a wave function has the form

$$V\Psi(\mathbf{r}) = \int d^3r' V(\mathbf{r}, \mathbf{r}')\Psi(\mathbf{r}'). \qquad (11.72)$$

The function $V(\mathbf{r}, \mathbf{r}')$ is symmetric. This may be seen in the example (10.121). It follows from the fact that the potential matrix V_{ij} is hermitian. The generalization of this example is straightforward.

To facilitate numerical calculations, the nonlocal potential is chosen to have the form

$$V(\mathbf{r}, \mathbf{r}') = U\left(\frac{|\mathbf{r} + \mathbf{r}'|}{2}\right) H(|\mathbf{r} - \mathbf{r}'|). \qquad (11.73)$$

An extensive investigation of the use of this model for neutron scattering was made by Perey and Buck (62). The factor H is $\delta(\mathbf{r} - \mathbf{r}')$ in a local potential. Hence the factor U was chosen to have the same form as used in local models as a function of the average radial variable p, where

$$p = \frac{1}{2}|\mathbf{r} + \mathbf{r}'|. \qquad (11.74)$$

$$U(p) = -(V + iW_I)f_S(p) + iW_D f_D(p), \qquad (11.75)$$

where f_S, f_D are the Woods-Saxon form factor and its derivative, respectively. The nonlocality was chosen to have the Gaussian form with width parameter β.

$$H(|\mathbf{r} - \mathbf{r}'|) = \exp\left[-\left|\frac{\mathbf{r} - \mathbf{r}'}{\beta}\right|^2\right]\Big/\pi^{3/2}\beta^3. \qquad (11.76)$$

A spin-orbit coupling term was used. It had the form

$$V_S(r) = V_{SO}\left(\frac{\hbar}{2Mc}\right)^2 \frac{1}{a_S r} \frac{\exp\left[(r - R)/a_S\right]}{\{1 + \exp\left[(r - R)/a_S\right]\}^2}, \qquad (11.77)$$

where M is the nucleon mass, rather than the pion mass which was used in (11.65).

The Schrödinger equation to be solved on the computer is an integro-differential equation with the same angular factors and external radial wave functions as the local calculation. Only the calculation of the radial partial waves $u_l^\pm(r)$ is different. The Schrödinger equation is

$$\left(\frac{\hbar^2}{2\mu}\nabla^2 + E\right)\Psi(\mathbf{r}) = -V_S(r)\boldsymbol{\sigma}\cdot\mathbf{l}\Psi(\mathbf{r}) + \int d^3r' V(\mathbf{r}, \mathbf{r}')\Psi(\mathbf{r}'). \quad (11.78)$$

Perey and Buck found an energy-independent set of parameters, which fitted all neutron entrance channel data in the range 7 MeV to 24 MeV.

V (MeV)	R (fm)/$A^{1/3}$	a_S (fm)	W_D (MeV)	a_D (fm)	V_{SO} (MeV)	β (fm)
71	1.22	0.65	15	0.47	1300	0.85

TABLE 11.3.   Parameters of the nonlocal neutron optical-model potential of Perey and Buck (62).

At 4.1 MeV the total cross sections agree well with experiment, but the differential cross sections are too small. The total cross section in the optical model describes all types of absorption including compound elastic scattering. Differential cross sections were well fitted by adding on an isotropic compound elastic cross section derived by subtracting the observed nonelastic cross section from the theoretically predicted reaction cross section σ^R.

The parameters used in the potentials (11.75, 11.76, 11.77) are given in Table 11.3.

Since local potentials are much easier to calculate with, the equivalence of nonlocal and local potentials at the same energy was investigated by Perey and Buck (62). It is possible to find an approximate expression for the equivalent local potential.

The nonlocal wave equation is written

$$\left(\frac{\hbar}{2\mu}\nabla^2 + E\right)\Psi_N(\mathbf{r}) = \int d^3r' U_N\left(\frac{\mathbf{r} + \mathbf{r}'}{2}\right)\left\{\exp\left[-\left|\frac{\mathbf{r} - \mathbf{r}'}{\beta}\right|^2\right]\right/ \pi^{3/2}\beta^3\right\}\Psi_N(\mathbf{r}').$$

$$(11\ 79)$$

Making the coordinate transformation

$$\mathbf{r} - \mathbf{r}' = \beta\mathbf{s}, \qquad (11.80)$$

substitution in the integral I of (11.79) gives

$$I = \int d^3s\, U_N(\mathbf{r} + \tfrac{1}{2}\beta\mathbf{s})[\exp{(-s^2)}/\pi^{3/2}]\Psi_N(\mathbf{r} + \beta\mathbf{s}). \tag{11.81}$$

Using the operator form of the Taylor expansion we write

$$I = \left[\int d^3s\, \exp{\{\beta\mathbf{s} \cdot (\tfrac{1}{2}\boldsymbol{\nabla}_1 + \boldsymbol{\nabla}_2)\}}\, \exp{(-s^2)}/\pi^{3/2}\right] U_N(\mathbf{r})\Psi_N(\mathbf{r}), \tag{11.82}$$

where $\boldsymbol{\nabla}_1$ operates only on $U_N(\mathbf{r})$, $\boldsymbol{\nabla}_2$ operates only on $\Psi_N(\mathbf{r})$. Formally integrating (11.82), we have

$$\left(\frac{\hbar^2}{2\mu}\nabla^2 + E\right)\Psi_N(\mathbf{r}) = \exp{\left[\frac{\beta^2}{4}|\tfrac{1}{2}\boldsymbol{\nabla}_1 + \boldsymbol{\nabla}_2|^2\right]} U_N(\mathbf{r})\Psi_N(\mathbf{r}). \tag{11.83}$$

We can thus see that the nonlocal potential is equivalent to a momentum-dependent potential. The first term in the expansion of the exponential is the effective mass approximation. Well inside the potential, the function $U_N(r)$ is almost constant. The effects of $\boldsymbol{\nabla}_1$ are neglected, thus neglecting the diffuseness of the surface. This approximation yields

$$\left(\frac{\hbar^2}{2\mu}\nabla^2 + E\right)\Psi_N(\mathbf{r}) = U_N \exp{[\tfrac{1}{4}\beta^2\,\nabla^2]}\Psi_N(\mathbf{r}). \tag{11.84}$$

The local wave equation is

$$\left(\frac{\hbar^2}{2\mu}\nabla^2 + E\right)\Psi_L(\mathbf{r}) = U_L\Psi_L(\mathbf{r}). \tag{11.85}$$

It was empirically determined by Perey and Buck that local potentials could be found, which were almost perfectly equivalent to the nonlocal potential at a particular energy, in the sense that they reproduced the nonlocal angular distribution. This suggests that for equivalent potentials,

$$\Psi_L(\mathbf{r}) \simeq \Psi_N(\mathbf{r}). \tag{11.86}$$

Assuming that U_L is also constant inside the surface, and using (11.85, 11.86) we see that $\Psi_N(\mathbf{r})$ is an approximate eigenfunction of ∇^2.

$$\nabla^2\Psi_N(\mathbf{r}) = -\frac{2\mu}{\hbar^2}[E - U_L]\Psi_N(\mathbf{r}). \tag{11.87}$$

Thus for equivalent potentials U_L and U_N we have, from (11.84, 11.87),

$$\left(\frac{\hbar^2}{2\mu}\nabla^2 + E\right)\Psi_N(\mathbf{r}) = U_N \exp{\left[-\frac{\mu\beta^2}{2\hbar^2}(E - U_L)\right]}\Psi_N(\mathbf{r})$$

$$= U_L\Psi_N(\mathbf{r}). \tag{11.88}$$

Equation (11.88) yields an approximate relationship between U_L and U_N, which was found empirically to hold even for the full radial dependence, giving

$$U_N(r) = U_L(r) \exp \left\{ \frac{\mu \beta^2}{2\hbar^2} [E - U_L(r)] \right\}. \tag{11.89}$$

It is thus empirically established that both nonlocal and local optical models can be found, which give the same entrance channel results at a particular energy. If the optical-model wave functions are to be taken seriously and used in distorted wave reaction theories, the wave functions must also be equivalent inside the nucleus. In fact they are not. The focal part of the wave function computed in a nonlocal potential is about 15 per cent less than that computed in the equivalent local potential. This is called the Perey effect.

In more general language the Perey effect is an example of the fact that potentials having different forms of nonlocality or momentum dependence can be found, which are equivalent on the energy shell, so that they give the same scattering data. They are inequivalent off the energy shell, which means that they have different wave functions. Only experiments that involve off-shell matrix elements of the potentials can distinguish them.

FURTHER READING

1. H. Feshbach, C. E. Porter, and V. F. Weisskopf, *Phys. Rev.*, **96**, 448 (1954).
   Original paper linking the optical model to resonance theory.

2. S. Fernbach, R. Serber, and T. B. Taylor, *Phys. Rev.*, **75**, 1352 (1949).
   Simple derivation of the optical model parameters for 90 MeV neutron scattering.

3. K. A. Amos, Nucl. Phys., **77**, 225 (1966).
   N. Austern, *Ann. Phys.* (*N.Y.*), **15**, 299 (1961).
   R. M. Eisberg, I. E. McCarthy, and R. A. Spurrier, *Nucl. Phys.*, **10**, 571 (1959).
   I. E. McCarthy, *Nucl. Phys.*, **10**, 583 (1959); **11**, 574 (1959).
   Optical-model wave functions and probability flux.

4. M. A. Melkanoff, J. S. Nodvik, D. S. Saxon, and D. G. Cantor. *A FORTRAN Program for Elastic Scattering Analyses with the Nuclear Optical Model*, University of California Press, Berkeley and Los Angeles, 1961.
   Details of the mathematics and computation of the optical model.

5. *Proceedings of the International Conference on the Nuclear Optical Model*, edited by A. E. S. Green, C. E. Porter, and D. S. Saxon, Florida State University Press, Tallahassee, 1959.

   Reviews of the optical model and related work.

6. P. E. Hodgson, *The Optical Model of Elastic Scattering*, Clarendon Press, Oxford, 1963.

   Review of phenomenological fitting.

7. P. J. Wyatt, J. G. Wills, and A. E. S. Green, *Phys. Rev.*, **119**, 1031 (1960).
   F. G. Perey and B. Buck, *Nucl. Phys.*, **32**, 353 (1962).

   The nonlocal optical model.

8. A. M. Lane, *Nucl. Phys.*, **35**, 676 (1962).

   Isospin-dependent optical model.

PROBLEMS

1. Calculate the mean free paths of the following different particles in nuclei.

   (a) 20 MeV protons.
   (b) 80 MeV protons.
   (c) 20 MeV α-particles.

   For protons use the curves of Fig. 11.2. For α-particles use the lowest values of the parameters given in Chapter 11C[iv].

2. Use the WKB approximation to calculate rough values of the parameters β and γ' in the analytic form (11.5) for the optical-model wave function in the cases (a) and (c) of Problem 1.

3. Calculate the s-state phase shift for the scattering of 20 MeV neutrons from the square well $V = 50$ MeV, $W = 5$ MeV, $R = 4$ fm. Compare it with the phase of the s-state partial wave $u_0(k, r)$ at the origin.

4. Find another square well potential that gives the same asymptotic form of the s-state partial wave for 40 MeV α-particles as the square well $V = 50$ MeV, $W = 0$, $R = 5$ fm. Ignore the Coulomb potential.

5. Show that the normalizing factor (11.56) is $e^{i\delta_l{}^{\pm}}$, where $\delta_l{}^{\pm}$ is defined to exclude the Coulomb phase shift.

6. Calculate the s-state transmission coefficient T_0 for the square well potential of Problem 3.

7. The parameters used for computing the curves of Fig. 11.7 for 24 MeV neutrons scattered by ^{118}Sn were $V = 40$ MeV, $W = 11$ MeV, $r_0 = 1.25$ fm, $a = 0.7$ fm. Use the figure to verify the local WKB approximation (11.4) for the wave number k.

8. For the approximate wave function $\chi^{(+)}$ of (11.5) define a wave function $\chi^{(-)}$ by

$$\chi^{(-)*}(\mathbf{k}, \mathbf{r}) = \chi^{(+)}(-\mathbf{k}, \mathbf{r}).$$

Draw a diagram to show that $\chi^{(-)}$ is the time-reversed wave function corresponding to $\chi^{(+)}$.

9. Find the time-reversed wave function corresponding to (11.44) with the help of Appendix 4J.

12

INELASTIC SCATTERING

In this chapter, theoretical models for inelastic scattering will be discussed. It will always be assumed that the projectile acts as an entity throughout the process. This is an obvious approximation for nucleons. It will also be made for more complicated projectiles such as α-particles. Inelastic scattering is caused by the excitation of the nucleus to a state of higher energy than the ground state. The basic interaction causing it is the interaction between the projectile and the individual nucleons in the nucleus.

For infinite nuclear matter, the approximation that nucleons interact in pairs has proved to work very well. For inelastic scattering this means that a nucleon projectile interacts with one nucleon. In this approximation the matrix element is the element for a three-body problem involving the projectile, the struck nucleon, and the core of the nucleus. Since the particular inelastic channel of interest is not the only channel that can be excited, the problem is called a quasi-three-body problem, if the assumption is made that it is sufficient to consider this channel without its coupling to other channels. The possibility of exciting other channels is taken into account by using a complex optical model potential for the projectile-core interaction which is almost the same as the elastic scattering optical-model potential if the channel is weakly excited.

In general the ground state Ψ_j and an excited state Ψ_i of a nucleus are represented by linear combinations of independent particle wave functions, which are antisymmetrized products of single-particle wave functions such as $\phi_{\mu\alpha}^{(j)}(x_\beta)$ where j indicates the eigenstate of the nucleus, μ indicates the particular independent particle basis state, α indicates the particular single-particle state in the basis and x_β is the set of coordinates of the single particle.

$$\Psi_j = \sum_\mu a_\mu^{(j)} \det \phi_{\mu\alpha}^{(j)}(x_\beta),$$
$$\Psi_i = \sum_\nu a_\nu^{(i)} \det \phi_{\nu\gamma}^{(i)}(x_\delta).$$

$$(12.1)$$

If the projectile interacts with one nucleon, the wave function Ψ'_i is formed from Ψ'_j by promoting a single nucleon into a higher single-particle state in at least one of the basis states so that all the necessary conservation laws are satisfied. The matrix element for the single nucleon process is a quasi-three-body matrix element. The matrix element for the whole inelastic scattering is a linear combination of such matrix elements with coefficients determined by a detailed knowledge of the nuclear structure symbolized by (12.1).

In some cases the amplitude for a particular independent particle wave function dominates the eigenstates Ψ'_j, Ψ'_i. Even if this is not the case, the transition may be dominated by a single quasi-three-body matrix element because of selection rules. This is verified by comparing experimental and single-particle values for the γ-ray transition rate. One such process is the excitation of the $\frac{9}{2}+$ first excited state of ^{89}Y from the $\frac{1}{2}-$ ground state.

Such inelastic scattering reactions are called single-particle or quasi-three-body reactions. They are rare, but they are interesting because they afford some chance of studying the two-nucleon interaction in nuclei.

Many more reactions may be capable of description by a manageably small number of quasi-three-body matrix elements with coefficients derived from the eigenfunctions found in nuclear structure calculations (see Chapter 7). Haybron and McManus (65) have successfully described several transitions, using the particle-hole eigenfunctions found by Gillet and Vinh Mau (64) by fitting energy levels. These transitions are interesting because they are of the type that would be described better by a simple collective model than a simple shell model.

A large number of nuclear states are collective in the sense that many coefficients $a_\mu^{(j)}$ have approximately equal magnitude, but their phases add up in a way that allows an eigenstate of the many-body Schrödinger equation. The inelastic scattering could be described by a large number of quasi-three-body matrix elements; however, it is more economical to use collective degrees of freedom to describe the excitation, just as it is to describe the states themselves. Collective inelastic scattering reactions have larger cross sections than single-particle ones because of the phase enhancements. This is analogous to the enhanced γ-ray transition rates for collective modes.

Another mechanism for collective excitations could perhaps be the interaction of the projectile with more than one nucleon at a time, resulting in quasi-n-body terms. Haybron and McManus compared their quasi-three-body calculation to a calculation involving collective coordinates, and found that the methods gave approximately equivalent results. This provides some evidence for the two-body collision mechanism for nucleon projectiles. Since the incident energy was 156 MeV, and the incident wavelength therefore about 0.35 fm, the predominance of two-body collisions in this case is perhaps not surprising.

We have already discussed inelastic scattering involving the excitation of collective degrees of freedom in Chapter 10. We shall now give details of the models and compare their predictions with experiment.

A. COLLECTIVE EXCITATIONS

We have seen in Chapter 7C that many nuclear states are described either as rotational excitations of a permanently deformed nucleus or as vibrational deformations of a nucleus whose surface is almost spherical in its ground state.

In Chapter 10D we considered the formal theory of scattering of a particle by a nucleus described only by collective coordinates. We shall use this theory to describe scattering in terms of the collective model. Denoting the collective coordinates of the target nucleus by ξ and the coordinates of the projectile by $\mathbf{r}$, we expand the total wave function for the problem $\Psi(\mathbf{r}, \xi)$ in eigenstates of the total angular momentum J and its projection K.

$$\Psi(\mathbf{r}, \xi) = \sum_{JK} a_{JK} \psi_J{}^K(\mathbf{r}, \xi). \tag{12.2}$$

We shall derive a set of coupled equations by substituting the expansions (12.2, 12.3) in the original Schrödinger equation in analogy with Chapter 10D. The complete orthonormal basis for expanding $\psi_J{}^K$ will be taken to be the angular wave function of the particle coupled to the wave function $\Psi_I{}^k$ of the target nucleus. The angular wave function of the particle is a jj coupling function $\mathscr{Y}_{jls}^m$, defined by (5.5).

The basis functions are defined by

$$\phi_{Ijl}^{JK}(\Omega_r, \xi) = \sum_{mk} C_{jIJ}^{mkK} i^l \mathscr{Y}_{jls}^m \Psi_I{}^k. \tag{12.3}$$

The expansion of $\psi_J{}^K$ is

$$\psi_J{}^K(\mathbf{r}, \xi) = r^{-1} \sum_{jl} f_{ijl}^J(r) \phi_{Ijl}^{JK}(\Omega_r, \xi). \tag{12.4}$$

The expansion coefficients f are the solutions of the sets of coupled equations,

$$[K_l + V_{Ijl,Ijl}^J(r) - E] f_{Ijl}^J(r) + \sum_{j'l'} V_{Ijl,I'j'l'}^J(r) f_{I'j'l'}^J(r) = 0$$

$$[K_{l'} + V_{I'j'l',I'j'l'}^J(r) - E'] f_{I'j'l'}^J(r) + \sum_{j''l''} V_{I'j'l',I'j''l''}^J(r)$$

$$\times f_{I'j''l''}^J(r) + V_{I'j'l',Ijl}^J(r) f_{Ijl}^J(r) = 0. \tag{12.5}$$

where

$$K_l = \frac{\hbar^2}{2\mu} \left[\frac{l(l+1)}{r^2} - \frac{d^2}{dr^2} \right], \tag{12.6}$$

$$V_{I'j'l',Ijl}^J(r) = (\phi_{I'j'l'}^{JK}(\Omega_r, \xi)| V(\mathbf{r}, \xi) |\phi_{Ijl}^{JK}(\Omega_r, \xi)). \tag{12.7}$$

The round brackets indicate integration over ξ and Ω_r but not r.

These equations are solved numerically. The elastic radial wave functions $f_{I j l}^{J}(r)$ are matched to the usual linear combination (2.25) of ingoing and outgoing spherical waves in the exterior region, while the inelastic radial wave functions $f_{I' j' l'}^{J}(r)$ are matched to purely outgoing spherical waves.

The generalized optical-model potential includes collective coordinates. The nonspherical potential operator for the off-diagonal interaction matrix elements (12.7) is one which excites rotational or vibrational degrees of freedom. It is assumed to be restricted to the nuclear surface and to depend only on the distance from the surface $R(\Omega')$, whose angular dependence is expressed in terms of the body-fixed coordinates Ω' by different collective models for the rotational and vibrational cases.

$$\tilde{V}(\mathbf{r}, \xi) = U(r) + V[r - R(\Omega')]. \tag{12.8}$$

For the rotational case we consider a permanently deformed surface with axial symmetry. We express it in the space-fixed system by means of a rotational transformation.

$$R(\theta') = R_0[1 + \sum_L \beta_L Y_L^0(\theta', 0)]$$
$$= R_0[1 + \sum_L \beta_L \sum_p Y_L^{p*}(\Omega_r) D_{p0}^L(\hat{S})]. \tag{12.9}$$

The direction $\hat{S}$ specifies the orientation in space of the nuclear symmetry axis. The deformation parameters β_2 were introduced for the case of quadrupole deformation, $L = 2$, in (6.68, 6.69). The ground-state rotational band represents quadrupole deformation. We shall restrict ourselves to this case.

The radial form of the off-diagonal potential is taken to be the derivative of $U(r)$, which is normally a Woods-Saxon potential. For quadrupole deformation the generalized optical-model potential is

$$\tilde{V}(\mathbf{r}, \xi) = U(r) + \beta_2 \sum_p Y_2^{p*}(\Omega_r) D_{p0}^2(\hat{S}) R_0 \frac{dU}{dr}. \tag{12.10}$$

The nuclear wave functions for the ground-state rotational band are

$$\Psi_I^{'k} = \left[\frac{2I + 1}{8\pi^2}\right]^{\frac{1}{2}} D_{k0}^I(\hat{S}),$$

$$\Psi_{I'}^{'k'} = \left[\frac{2I' + 1}{8\pi^2}\right]^{\frac{1}{2}} D_{k'0}^{I'}(\hat{S}). \tag{12.11}$$

The potential matrix elements (12.7) are given from (12.3, 12.7, 12.10, 12.11) by performing the angular integrations over $\hat{S}$ and Ω_r by means of the Wigner-Eckart theorem and its extension for rotation functions. They reduce to sums over projection quantum numbers of products of four

Clebsch-Gordan coefficients. The sums may be performed by means of the rules described in Appendix 4.

The final form for the case of quadrupole deformation is very simple.

$$V_{II'}^{(2)} = (4\pi)^{-\frac{1}{2}}\beta_2 R_0 V_S (-1)^I (2I+1)^{\frac{1}{2}} C_{I'2I}^{0\,00} F_{II'}^{(2)}(r), \qquad (12.12)$$

where $F_{II'}^{(2)}$ is the derivative of the Woods-Saxon potential. The strength of the coupling is proportional to the deformation parameter β_2.

Vibrational excitations were studied in Chapter 7C[iii]. In this case the shape of the nuclear surface is

$$R(\Omega) = R_0[1 + \sum_{LM} \alpha_{LM} Y_L^M(\Omega_r)]. \qquad (12.13)$$

Since no rotations are involved, we may now use the space-fixed coordinates Ω_r. The α_{LM} are the collective coordinates, which describe surface oscillations. $V[r - R(\Omega_r)]$ is expanded in powers of $\alpha_{LM} Y_L^M(\Omega_r)$ by means of the Taylor expansion

$$V[r - R(\Omega_r)] = U(r) + r\frac{dU}{dr}\sum_{LM}\alpha_{LM}Y_L^M(\Omega_r)$$

$$+ \tfrac{1}{2}r^2\frac{d^2U}{dr^2}\sum_{LML'M'}\alpha_{LM}\alpha_{L'M'}Y_L^M(\Omega_r)Y_{L'}^{M'}(\Omega_r) + \cdots. \qquad (12.14)$$

The first term of (12.14) is the central optical-model potential. The second term represents single-phonon excitations of multipolarity L. The third term represents two-phonon excitations. Further terms possibly stretch the credibility of the collective model too far.

In analogy to the permanent deformation parameter β_L used in the rotational case, a dynamical or rms deformation parameter is defined by

$$\beta_L^2 = \langle 0| \sum_M |\alpha_{LM}|^2 |0\rangle, \qquad (12.15)$$

where $|0\rangle$ is the ground state.

Using the definition (7.54) and the properties (7.56) of the phonon creation and annihilation operators b_{LM}^* and b_{LM} we have for the simple harmonic vibration model,

$$\beta_L^2/(2L+1) = \hbar\omega/2B_L. \qquad (12.16)$$

To obtain the potential matrix elements (12.7) we perform one angular integration over Ω_r. The result for the $L = 2$ case is

$$V_{02}^{(2)} = (4\pi)^{-\frac{1}{2}}\beta_2 R_0 V_S F_{02}^{(2)}(r), \qquad V_{22}^{(2)} = 0. \qquad (12.17)$$

$F_{02}^{(2)}$ is the derivative of the optical-model form factor. For $L = 2$ the coupling strengths are the same for both vibrational and rotational excitations.

[i] The Distorted Wave Born Approximation

It is useful first to consider the distorted wave Born approximation, which is simply evaluated and leads to some interesting relationships between the differential cross sections for excitations of different multipolarity L as well as to some other properties that enable angular distributions to be used to measure spins and parities of nuclear states. The DWBA must be justified in terms of a coupled channels calculation. This has been examined in a few cases, as will be described briefly later. The essential result is that the DWBA is justified for small deformation parameters β_L and improves as the energy increases. The DWBA for collective excitations has been discussed generally in Chapter 10D[ii].

The differential cross section is given by

$$\frac{d\sigma}{d\Omega} = \left(\frac{\mu}{2\pi\hbar^2}\right)^2 \frac{k'}{k} \sum_{\text{av}} |f_{a0}|^2, \tag{12.18}$$

where only the ground state and the excited state a are considered in the theory. $\sum_{\text{av}}$ means an average over initial quantum numbers that could in principle be measured but are not, and a sum over similar quantum numbers for the final state. Such quantum numbers are angular momentum projections, which could be measured by using aligned nuclei and measuring polarization. $\mathbf{k}$ and $\mathbf{k}'$ are the propagation vectors of the incident and outgoing waves.

For both rotational and vibrational excitations, the DWBA matrix element f_{a0} reduces, for zero-spin initial states, to the form

$$f_{a0}{}^M = \int d^3r \chi^{(-)*}(\mathbf{k}', \mathbf{r}) \langle \Psi_L{}^M | V_{\text{int}} | \Psi_0{}^0 \rangle \chi^{(+)}(\mathbf{k}, \mathbf{r})$$

$$\equiv A_L R_0 \int d^3r \chi^{(-)*}(\mathbf{k}', \mathbf{r}) \frac{dU}{dr} Y_L{}^M(\Omega_r) \chi^{(+)}(\mathbf{k}, \mathbf{r}). \tag{12.19}$$

The interaction potential V_{int} is the first-order difference between $\tilde{V}(\mathbf{r}, \xi)$ and the central potential $U(r)$. The constant A_L depends on the mechanism (12.12, 12.17) and the deformation parameter β_L. The factor $Y_L{}^M(\Omega_r)$ appears explicitly in the interaction (12.14) in the vibrational case, and is produced by the rotational transformation leading to (12.9) in the rotational case.

We shall not take the spin of the projectile into account. For nucleons this involves the neglect of spin-orbit coupling, which is a fairly small perturbation on the optical-model potential for momentum-transfer calculations. Inelastic polarization will not be discussed. For α-particles there is no spin.

The distorted waves in (12.19) are expanded in partial waves as follows

$$\chi^{(+)}(\mathbf{k}, \mathbf{r}) = (kr)^{-1} \sum_l [4\pi(2l + 1)]^{\frac{1}{2}} i^l e^{i\sigma_l} u_l(k, r) Y_l^{\,0}(\Omega_r),$$

$$\chi^{(-)*}(\mathbf{k}', \mathbf{r}) = (k'r)^{-1} \sum_{l'm'} 4\pi i^{-l'} e^{i\sigma_{l'}} u_{l'}(k', r) Y_{l'}^{\,m'}{}^{*}(\Omega_r) Y_{l'}^{\,m'}(\Omega_{k'}).$$

(12.20)

In Equation (12.20) we have chosen the direction of **k** to be the z-axis. The scattering angles $\Omega_{k'}$ may be reduced to $(\theta, 0)$ because of axial symmetry. The distorted waves obey the time-reversal relation

$$\chi^{(-)*}(\mathbf{k}, \mathbf{r}) = \chi^{(+)}(-\mathbf{k}, \mathbf{r}).$$

(12.21)

It is interesting to note that the property of the spherical harmonics

$$Y_l^{\,m}(\Omega) = (-1)^l Y_l^{\,m}(-\Omega)$$

(12.22)

gives the parity relation

$$\chi^{(-)*}(\mathbf{k}, \mathbf{r}) = \chi^{(+)}(\mathbf{k}, -\mathbf{r}).$$

(12.23)

When the relations (12.20) are substituted into (12.19) the angular integration is performed by means of the Wigner-Eckart theorem (A4.51). The resulting expression for the scattering amplitude is

$$f_{a0}{}^M = A_L R_0 \frac{4\pi}{kk'} \sum_{ll'} (2l + 1) \left[\frac{2L + 1}{2l' + 1} \right]^{\frac{1}{2}} i^{l-l'} e^{i(\sigma_l + \sigma_{l'})}$$

$$\times C_{lL\,l'}^{0\,M\,M} C_{lLl'}^{000} R_{ll'} Y_{l'}^{\,M}(\theta, 0). \quad (12.24)$$

The radial integral $R_{ll'}$ is

$$R_{ll'} = \int dr \frac{dU}{dr} u_l(k, r) u_{l'}(k', r).$$

(12.25)

The projection M can be measured in principle and is summed over after squaring $f_{a0}{}^M$ to obtain the cross section according to (12.18).

There are some general properties of the matrix element (12.24, 12.25) which lead to an understanding of the DWBA in this case. (Rost and Austern, 60; Austern, 63.) One is the phase averaging property of the partial waves $u_l(k, r)$ discussed in Chapter 11A[iii]. Due essentially to the presence of the imaginary potential, the radial integral $R_{ll'}$ is smaller for small values of l, l' than for values in the vicinity of kR_0, that is, surface values. It is a reasonable first approximation to consider that surface values of $R_{ll'}$ dominate the matrix element, just as we have seen that surface partial waves dominate the elastic scattering matrix element. Note that the Clebsch-Gordan coefficients in (12.24) imply that l, l', L obey the triangle inequalities so that $|l - l'|$ is never larger than L.

For simplicity we shall first consider the $M = 0$ part of the cross section.

The amplitude $f_{a0}{}^0$ may be considered as an average of Legendre polynomial contributions for l' near the surface value l_0.

$$\frac{d\sigma}{d\Omega} \propto |\langle P_{l'}(\cos\theta)\rangle_{l'\cong l_0}|^2. \tag{12.26}$$

Successive P_l functions resemble each other closely at small values of θ, but gradually drift out of phase as θ becomes larger. In the angular distribution,

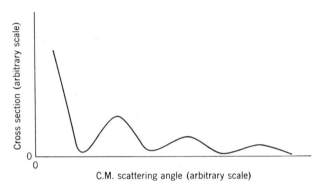

FIG. 12.1 Schematic diagram showing the general shape of the angular distribution at angles less than about $90°$ for survace inelastic scattering.

the different terms in the average interfere constructively at small angles, and destructively at larger angles, so that the angular distribution looks like $P_{l_0}(\cos\theta)$ multiplied by an envelope factor that decreases for larger θ. This is illustrated in Fig. 12.1. $P_{l_0}(\cos\theta)$ may be approximated by a Bessel function for small θ.

$$P_{l_0}(\cos\theta) \cong J_0\left[(2l_0 + 1)\sin\frac{\theta}{2}\right]. \tag{12.27}$$

If $l - l' \ll l_0$, only the Clebsch-Gordan coefficients are rapidly varying functions of l' in (12.24). The properties of the Clebsch-Gordan coefficients lead to a simple relationship that considerably elucidates angular distributions.

$$\sum_{l'} i^{l-l'-L} C_{l\ L\ l'}^{0MM} C_{lLl'}^{000} \cong \frac{[(L-M)!\,(L+M)!]^{1/2}}{(L-M)!!\,(L+M)!!}, \qquad L+M \text{ even,}$$

$$= 0, \qquad\qquad\qquad L+M \text{ odd.} \tag{12.28}$$

Thus only the terms having $|M| = L, L-2, \ldots$, etc. contribute to the inelastic scattering.

The $Y_L{}^M$ functions for successive M's are obtained from each other by differentiation. For $M \geq 0$,

$$Y_{l'}{}^M(\theta, 0) = \left[\frac{2l' + 1}{4\pi} \frac{(l' - M)!}{(l' + M)!}\right]^{\frac{1}{2}} (\sin \theta)^M \frac{d^M}{d(\cos \theta)^M} P_{l'}(\cos \theta). \quad (12.29)$$

Each differentiation reverses the phase of oscillation in the angular distribution. Since only all odd or all even values of M appear according to whether L is odd or even, angular distributions for successive L have opposite phases. This rule is part of the *Blair phase rule* (Blair, 60). The rule states that angular distributions for even L are out of phase with elastic scattering, while angular distributions for odd L are in phase with elastic scattering. The rule was discovered in the study of inelastic scattering by the Fraunhofer approximation. It will be discussed in this context in Section 12D[ii].

The phase rule is valid if the contribution to the angular distribution from a single surface partial wave l_0 is much greater than that from interior partial waves. It requires strong absorption. The conditions are ideally fulfilled for α-particle inelastic scattering.

For nucleon inelastic scattering the absorption is not so strong. Several values of l' interfere in the DWBA matrix element. Their contributions, considered as complex numbers, differ in phase by as much as 180°. We have seen that the large phase differences between the partial waves of an elastic scattering wave function produce the focusing effect. It is therefore important to consider the phases of the partial matrix elements in the DWBA amplitude.

The equation (12.24) for the scattering amplitude is abbreviated as follows,

$$f_{a0}{}^M = \sum_{ll'} I_{ll',L}^M Y_{l'}{}^M(\theta, 0). \quad (12.30)$$

The coefficients $I_{ll',L}^M$ are the partial matrix elements. Since the phase of the partial wave u_l is approximately the real part δ_l of the elastic scattering phase shift for r less than the value for the first minimum where u_l has its greatest contribution to the radial integral (12.25), the phase of $I_{ll'}$ is very closely approximated by

$$\arg I_{ll',L}^M \cong \frac{(l - l')\pi}{2} + \delta_l + \delta_{l'} + \sigma_l + \sigma_{l'}. \quad (12.31)$$

Successive phase shifts can differ by as much as 70 or 80 degrees for intermediate energy protons. Thus the angular oscillations for $l' = l_0 - 1$ and $l_0 + 1$ can reinforce in certain angular regions, cancelling the angular oscillation for $l = l_0$. This effect depends on the phase shifts and thus on the energy. It is too complicated to lead to a clear-cut rule, but it obviously invalidates the phase rule. Since the invalidity of the phase rule for nucleons is related to the large phase differences of successive surface partial waves, it is also related to the focusing in the optical-model wave functions.

The parity relation (12.23) gives a more general way of identifying parity changes in a nuclear reaction. This is the *parity rule* of Kromminga and McCarthy (61) and Glendenning (59). It states that angular distributions decrease as θ approaches zero if the parity changes in the reaction, provided the Q-value is not too large in comparison with the incident energy.

For $\mathbf{k} = \mathbf{k}'$, that is, for forward scattering with zero Q-value (the adiabatic limit), the DWBA amplitude (12.18) may be written

$$[f_{a0}{}^M(0)]_{Q=0} = A_L R_0 \int d^3r [\chi^{(+)}(\mathbf{k}, \mathbf{r})\chi^{(+)}(\mathbf{k}, -\mathbf{r})] \frac{dU}{dr} Y_L{}^M(\Omega_r). \quad (12.32)$$

The term in square brackets has even parity. Thus if L is odd (parity change), $f_{a0}{}^M(0)$ vanishes.

The parity rule has a second part which is understood by arguments closely related to those for the phase rule. The forward differential cross section is large if the parity does not change in the reaction. This enables parities to be distinguished by inelastic scattering experiments at small angles.

For forward scattering, $Y_{l'}{}^M(\theta, 0)$ is zero for $M = 0$. This is easily seen from (12.29). $Y_{l'}{}^M(\theta, 0)$ increases as θ increases. Thus, for $\theta = 0$,

$$[f_{a0}{}^M(0)]_{Q=0} = \sum_{ll'} [I_{ll',L}^M]_{Q=0} \left[\frac{2l'+1}{4\pi}\right]^{1/2} \equiv \sum_{ll'} J_{ll',L}^M. \quad (12.33)$$

We have redefined the partial matrix element to be $J_{ll',L}^M$ in this particular argument in order to simplify the notation.

It follows from properties of the Clebsch-Gordan coefficients in (12.24) that

$$J_{ll',L}^M = (-1)^L J_{l'l,L}^M. \quad (12.34)$$

This is a selection rule which implies the exact cancellation of all partial matrix elements $J_{ll'}$ so that the cross section is zero for $\theta = 0$. The physical content of (12.34) is exactly the same as that of (12.32).

For $\theta = 0$, the argument for the general shape of the angular distribution illustrated in Fig. 12.1 still holds. Contributions for different l' tend to add constructively for forward angles. It is only very close to $\theta = 0$ and for L odd that the selection rule (12.34) overrides this argument. Hence the surface character of the reaction leads to large forward cross sections for L even and rapidly decreasing forward cross sections as $\theta \to 0$ for L odd.

We have seen that the DWBA predicts two general rules for identifying spectroscopic information from angular distributions. In detail it leads to different shapes for different values of L. The fits to experimental angular distributions for sufficiently small momentum transfers are so good that it is a reliable method of identifying L. DWBA angular distributions for similar energies and nuclei of similar sizes have characteristic shapes for each L value. Some such shapes are illustrated in Fig. 12.2.

If the parameters which fit elastic scattering are used in the DWBA for inelastic scattering, the only free parameter in the theory is the deformation parameter β_L. This is obtained as a multiplying factor for the whole angular distribution. Its values are well-determined and generally agree with values obtained by electromagnetic methods.

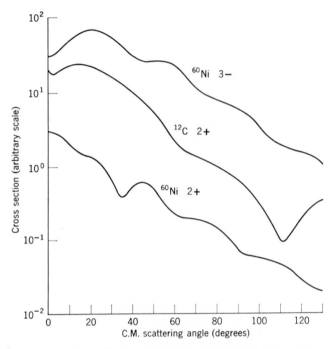

FIG. 12.2   Shapes of DWBA angular distributions for 40 MeV inelastic scattering of protons from even nuclei. The spin and parity of the excited state are identified with each curve.

[ii]   THE COUPLED CHANNELS APPROXIMATION

The coupled channels approximation has already been explained in this chapter and in Chapter $10D$[iii]. A calculation in which 0+ and 2+ states were coupled was performed by Buck (63). Later calculations by Tamura (65) couple many more channels. For momentum transfers less than about 1 fm^{-1}, it is possible to fit experimental angular distributions well for several channels both in magnitude and shape. In the case of 14.5 MeV proton inelastic scattering by ^{48}Ti, it was found by Buck that the DWBA gives the same shape for inelastic angular distributions as the coupled channels approximation, but the magnitude is larger for $\beta_2 > 0.2$. Thus the DWBA

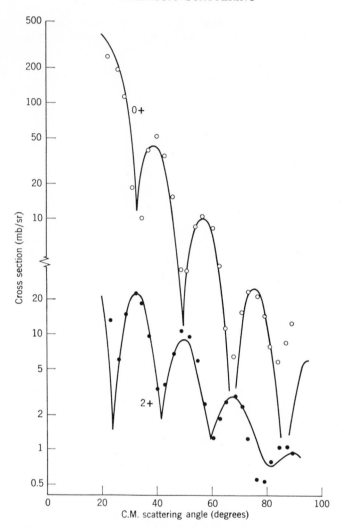

FIG. 12.3   Scattering of 28.5 MeV α-particles from the first collective states of ^{24}Mg using the collective model in the coupled channels approximation. (Adapted from Tamura, 65.)

underestimates β_2 in this case. For very low energies where shape resonance effects make the optical-model wave functions very large in the nucleus, the DWBA may overestimate the cross section by nearly an order of magnitude in the regions of resonance for $\beta_2 > 0.2$ (Chase, Wilets, and Edmonds, 58). The DWBA improves as the energy increases.

Fits to data are illustrated in Figs. 12.3 and 12.4 for 28.5 MeV α-particles

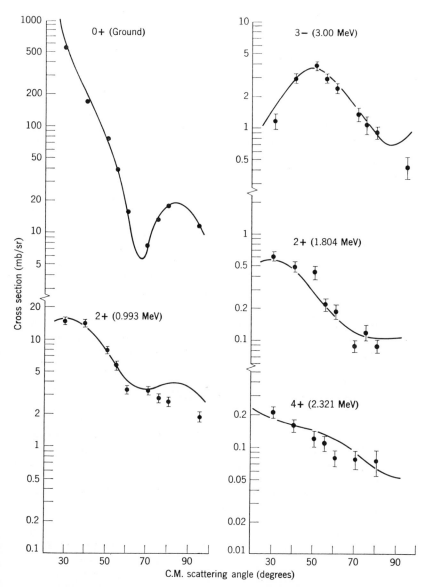

FIG. 12.4   Scattering of 17.5 MeV protons from various states of ^{64}Zn using the collective model in the coupled channels approximation. (Adapted from Tamura, 65.)

scattered by ^{24}Mg and 17.5 MeV protons scattered by ^{64}Zn. The phase rule for the 0+ and 2+ states is illustrated well for α-particles in Fig. 12.3. In Fig. 12.4 the breakdown of the phase rule for protons is obvious. The first 0+, 2+, and 3− states are almost in phase. The parity rule is also illustrated in Fig. 12.4. Cross sections at forward angles are large for even L, while the cross section for the 3− state falls rapidly from 50° towards $\theta = 0$.

Besides determining values of β_L for low-lying states, the coupled channels approximation is useful for investigating the nature of the collective excitations involved. The phase rule may break down already for 4+ excitations which must be described as a coherent linear combination of the direct excitation of a two-phonon state and successive single-phonon excitations [see Equation (12.109)], where the phonons concerned have spin and parity 2+.

B. QUASI-THREE-BODY EXCITATIONS

Inelastic scattering may be described by a linear combination of matrix elements in which a single nucleon in one of the ground-state configurations is excited into one of the possible configurations in the excited state. In this process the remainder of the nucleus plays the part of an inert core or third body. Since the particular inelastic channel is not the only one that can be excited, the matrix element is called a quasi-three-body matrix element. Other channels are taken into account by imaginary potentials in the interaction between the projectile and the core. These potentials are nearly the same as the elastic scattering optical-model potential if the channel is sufficiently weakly excited.

We saw in Chapter 10E[iii] that the quasi-three-body matrix element can be written in a distorted wave representation leading to the *distorted wave t-matrix approximation*. This was derived without considering antisymmetry. Generalizing to the antisymmetric matrix element we have

$$f_{a0} = \langle 2^{-\frac{1}{2}}[\Psi_1{}' \, \Phi_2{}' - \Phi_1{}'\Psi_2{}']| \, t_{12} \, |2^{-\frac{1}{2}}[\Psi_1\Phi_2 - \Phi_1\Psi_2]\rangle. \quad (12.35)$$

We use the convention that the wave function on the left of a pair has the coordinates $\mathbf{r}_1$. We have labeled the nucleons with the subscripts 1 and 2. Ψ is the wave function of a particle with positive energy; Φ is the wave function of a bound particle. The primes indicate the final state.

The nucleon-nucleon t-matrix is related to the t-matrix for the scattering of two nucleons in the presence of a noninteracting core by (10.164). If we use the coordinate space representation, the t-matrix is easily expressed in terms of the relative coordinates of particles 1 and 2 and the coordinates of their center of mass. The distorted waves are expressed in terms of the coordinates of the particles relative to the center of mass of the core. The coordinate transformation between these two systems is formally easy, but results in a matrix element that cannot be computed with today's machines because of the multiplicity of the integrations.

There are two ways out of this difficulty. The first is to use the distorted wave Born approximation that replaces the *t*-matrix by the nucleon-nucleon potential. This is theoretically unsatisfactory, since the limit of the differential cross section in the absence of the core is the Born approximation, not the correct result. Use of a pseudopotential such as the one defined in Equation (3.102) ensures that the cross section is correct in the absence of the core, at least for the limited range of nucleon-nucleon data fitted by the pseudopotential. We shall use the local pseudopotential approach.

The two-nucleon *t*-matrix is approximated by

$$t_{12} = t_{12}(r)(W + BP^\sigma + MP^r + HP^\sigma P^r). \tag{12.36}$$

This pseudopotential is central, but spin- and isospin-dependent. Since there is no spin-orbit coupling in the approximation, a singlet state remains a singlet state throughout the interaction, and a triplet state remains a triplet state.

The spin and isospin exchange operators P^σ, P^r are related to $\sigma(1) \cdot \sigma(2)$ and $\tau(1) \cdot \tau(2)$ by

$$P^\sigma = \tfrac{1}{2}[1 + \sigma(1) \cdot \sigma(2)], \tag{3.30}$$

$$P^r = \tfrac{1}{2}[1 + \tau(1) \cdot \tau(2)]. \tag{3.38}$$

We recall that the space, spin, and isospin exchange operators, when operating on an antisymmetric wave function, are related by

$$P^r P^\sigma P^r = -1. \tag{3.41}$$

Hence an antisymmetric two-body wave function $|A\rangle$ is written

$$|A\rangle = 2^{-\frac{1}{2}} |\Psi_1 \Phi_2 - \Phi_1 \Psi_2\rangle = 2^{-\frac{1}{2}}(1 - P^r P^\sigma P^r)|\Psi_1 \Phi_2\rangle. \tag{12.37}$$

We shall now express the antisymmetric matrix element (12.35) as a sum of matrix elements, which can be computed. We use the orthogonality of the spin and isospin wave functions involved in Ψ and Φ just as we did in the argument leading up to Equation (3.101) for singlet and triplet scattering in the p-p system.

It is convenient to denote the spin up and down space wave functions in Ψ by X, Y and in Φ by ϕ, ψ. Spin functions for spin up and down are α, β. Isospin functions for up (proton) and down (neutron) are p, n.

We may now write Ψ and Φ in terms of space, spin, and isospin wave functions. For example, if Ψ, Φ represent a proton and a neutron, respectively

$$\begin{aligned}\Psi_1 &= (X_1\alpha_1 + Y_1\beta_1)p_1, \\ \Phi_2 &= (\phi_2\alpha_2 + \psi_2\beta_2)n_2.\end{aligned} \tag{12.38}$$

Spin-orbit coupling in the optical-model wave functions will be neglected. This means that we can, in principle, identify spin up and down particles experimentally. It also means that X and Y are the same function. Spin-orbit coupling in the shell model cannot be neglected. Therefore ϕ and ψ are not the same function.

We may write the antisymmetric wave function $|A\rangle$ of (12.37) as

$$|A\rangle = 2^{-\frac{1}{2}} |(A_a + B_a)T_a + (A_s + B_s)T_s\rangle, \qquad (12.39)$$

where the antisymmetric and symmetric isospin functions are

$$\begin{aligned} T_a &= p_1 n_2 - n_1 p_2, \\ T_s &= p_1 n_2 + n_1 p_2. \end{aligned} \qquad (12.40)$$

The coefficients in (12.39) are

$$\begin{aligned} A_a &= \tfrac{1}{2}\{X_1\phi_2\}\alpha_1\alpha_2 + \tfrac{1}{4}[X_1\psi_2][\alpha_1\beta_2] + \tfrac{1}{4}\{X_1\psi_2\}\{\alpha_1\beta_2\} \\ B_a &= \tfrac{1}{2}\{Y_1\psi_2\}\beta_1\beta_2 - \tfrac{1}{4}[Y_1\phi_2][\alpha_1\beta_2] + \tfrac{1}{4}\{Y_1\phi_2\}\{\alpha_1\beta_2\}, \end{aligned} \qquad (12.41a)$$

$$\begin{aligned} A_s &= \tfrac{1}{2}[X_1\phi_2]\alpha_1\alpha_2 + \tfrac{1}{4}[X_1\psi_2]\{\alpha_1\beta_2\} + \tfrac{1}{4}\{X_1\psi_2\}[\alpha_1\beta_2], \\ B_s &= \tfrac{1}{2}[Y_1\psi_2]\beta_1\beta_2 + \tfrac{1}{4}[Y_1\phi_2]\{\alpha_1\beta_2\} - \tfrac{1}{4}\{Y_1\phi_2\}[\alpha_1\beta_2]. \end{aligned} \qquad (12.41b)$$

The bracket notation is defined by

$$\begin{aligned} [MN] &= MN - NM, \\ \{MN\} &= MN + NM. \end{aligned} \qquad (12.42)$$

The reason for separating the wave function in coefficients of symmetric and antisymmetric isospin functions is that the cases of like and unlike particles are easily distinguished. The third component of isospin is 0 for T_a and ± 1 for T_s. For like particles only the T_s term contributes to the matrix element. For unlike particles both are required. The A and B terms in (12.41) involve only X and Y, respectively, so the incoherent sum over polarizations, which must be performed to obtain the cross section, is simplified by keeping A and B terms distinct.

It is convenient also to antisymmetrize the final state in the matrix element.

$$|A'\rangle = 2^{-\frac{1}{2}} |(A_a' + B_a')T_a' + (A_s' + B_s')T_s'\rangle. \qquad (12.43)$$

The differential cross section is now written

$$\frac{d\sigma}{d\Omega} = \frac{k'}{k}\left(\frac{\mu}{2\pi\hbar^2}\right)^2 \frac{4}{2j+1} \sum_{m_j m_{j'}} \{|A'A|^2 + |B'A|^2 + |A'B|^2 + |B'B|^2\}, \qquad (12.44)$$

where the squares of space-spin matrix elements are defined by

$$|M'N|^2 = |\langle M'| t_{12} |N\rangle|^2 \equiv |f_{M'N}|^2. \qquad (12.45)$$

The quantum numbers j, j' are the total spins of the initial and final bound states, m_j and m_j' are their projections. The factor $\frac{1}{4}$ coming from the $2^{-\frac{1}{2}}$ factors in (12.39, 12.43) is removed by using the orthogonality of the isospin functions in squaring the matrix elements. In (12.44) A refers to A_s if like particles collide and $A_a + A_s$ if unlike particles are involved. Similar identification is made for A', B, and B'.

The exchange operators (12.36) are now allowed to operate on the initial state giving wave functions $|F\rangle$. We use the fact that, for any exchange operator P,

$$
\begin{aligned}
P\{MN\} &= \{MN\}, \\
P[MN] &= -[MN].
\end{aligned}
\tag{12.46}
$$

Defining the coefficients A_{TS} for isospin T and spin S in the two-nucleon system by (3.99), we can derive all the functions $|F\rangle$ where, for example,

$$
\begin{aligned}
|F(A_s)\rangle &= [W + BP^\sigma + MP^r + HP^\sigma P^r]\,|A_s\rangle \\
&= \tfrac{1}{2}A_{11}[X_1\phi_2]\alpha_1\alpha_2 + \tfrac{1}{4}A_{11}[X_1\psi_2]\{\alpha_1\beta_2\} + \tfrac{1}{4}A_{10}\{X_1\psi_2\}[\alpha_1\beta_2].
\end{aligned}
\tag{12.47}
$$

The orthonormality of the spin functions is now used as in (3.97) to obtain the squares of the space-spin matrix elements in the form

$$
\begin{aligned}
|A'A|^2 &= |\tfrac{1}{2}C_1 M_1{}^D + \tfrac{1}{2}C_2 M_1{}^E + \tfrac{1}{4}C_3 M_2{}^D + \tfrac{1}{4}C_4 M_2{}^E|^2, \\
|B'B|^2 &= |\tfrac{1}{2}C_1 M_{11}{}^D + \tfrac{1}{2}C_2 M_{11}{}^E + \tfrac{1}{4}C_3 M_{12}{}^D + \tfrac{1}{4}C_4 M_{12}{}^E|^2, \\
|B'A|^2 &= |\tfrac{1}{4}C_5 M_3{}^D + \tfrac{1}{4}C_6 M_3{}^E|^2, \\
|A'B|^2 &= |\tfrac{1}{4}C_5 M_4{}^D + \tfrac{1}{4}C_6 M_4{}^E|^2.
\end{aligned}
\tag{12.48}
$$

The definitions of the C coefficients and the matrix elements are given in Table 12.1.

Since we are neglecting spin-orbit coupling for the unbound particles, the optical-model wave functions X and Y are identical. We have kept them separate until this stage for clarity. We shall now identify them, setting for both direct and space-exchange cases

$$
\begin{aligned}
M_1 &= M_{12}, \\
M_2 &= M_{11}.
\end{aligned}
\tag{12.49}
$$

The wave functions of the bound particles, however, are not alike because we cannot ignore spin-orbit coupling in the shell model. In fact the inelastic scattering computation is easiest when the jj coupling scheme is nearly accurate.

The total spins j, j' and parities π, π' of initial and final nuclear states are input information in the inelastic scattering calculation. The single-particle wave functions for these states are

$$\phi(\mathbf{r}) = R_{np}(r) C_{p\;\frac{1}{2}\;j}^{m_p\;\frac{1}{2}\;m_j} Y_p^{m_p}(\Omega_r),$$
$$\psi(\mathbf{r}) = R_{np}(r) C_{p\;\frac{1}{2}\;j}^{m_p\;-\frac{1}{2}\;m_j} Y_p^{m_p}(\Omega_r), \tag{12.50}$$

where ϕ and ψ represent space wave functions for spin up and down, respectively. Since the spin and parity are both known, only one of the terms

	Like Particles		Unlike Particles
C_1	A_{11}		$A_{11} + A_{01}$
C_2	$-A_{11}$		$A_{01} - A_{11}$
C_3	$A_{11} + A_{10}$		$A_{01} + A_{00} + A_{11} + A_{10}$
C_4	$-A_{11} + A_{10}$		$A_{01} - A_{00} - A_{11} + A_{10}$
C_5	$A_{11} - A_{10}$		$A_{01} - A_{00} + A_{11} - A_{10}$
C_6	$-A_{11} - A_{10}$		$A_{01} + A_{00} - A_{11} - A_{10}$

	Direct M_i^D	Space Exchange M_i^E
M_1	$\langle X_1'\phi_2' \mid t_{12} \mid X_1\phi_2 \rangle$	$\langle X_1'\phi_2' \mid t_{12} \mid \phi_1 X_2 \rangle$
M_2	$\langle X_1'\psi_2' \mid t_{12} \mid X_1\psi_2 \rangle$	$\langle X_1'\psi_2' \mid t_{12} \mid \psi_1 X_2 \rangle$
$M_{11} = M_2$	$\langle Y_1'\psi_2' \mid t_{12} \mid Y_1\psi_2 \rangle$	$\langle Y_1'\psi_2' \mid t_{12} \mid \psi_1 Y_2 \rangle$
$M_{12} = M_1$	$\langle Y_1'\phi_2' \mid t_{12} \mid Y_1\phi_2 \rangle$	$\langle Y_1'\phi_2' \mid t_{12} \mid \phi_1 Y_2 \rangle$
M_3	$\langle Y_1'\phi_2' \mid t_{12} \mid X_1\psi_2 \rangle$	$\langle Y_1'\psi_2' \mid t_{12} \mid \psi_1 X_2 \rangle$
M_4	$\langle X_1'\psi_2' \mid t_{12} \mid Y_1\phi_2 \rangle$	$\langle X_1'\psi_2' \mid t_{12} \mid \phi_1 Y_2 \rangle$

TABLE 12.1.   Definition of the coefficients and matrix elements
in Equation (12.48).

multiplying α in the explicit form (5.5) applies, and only one of the terms multiplying β. The orbital angular momentum quantum numbers p, p' define the parity.

The radial wave functions $R_{np}^{\pm}(r)$ are solutions of the radial equation (5.7). The plus and minus apply to states with $j = p \pm \frac{1}{2}$, respectively.

The optical-model wave functions X and Y are given explicitly by Equation (11.44). Since there is no difference between u_l^+ and u_l^-, we may combine the coefficients of α, that is, the terms in $\mathscr{Y}_{l-\frac{1}{2},l,\frac{1}{2}}^{\frac{1}{2}}$ and $\mathscr{Y}_{l+\frac{1}{2},l,\frac{1}{2}}^{\frac{1}{2}}$ and the coefficients of β, that is, the terms in

$\mathscr{Y}_{l-\frac{1}{2},l,\frac{1}{2}}^{-\frac{1}{2}}$ and $\mathscr{Y}_{l+\frac{1}{2},l,\frac{1}{2}}^{-\frac{1}{2}}$, giving

$$|X\rangle = (kr)^{-1} \sum_{lm} 4\pi i^l e^{i\sigma_l} u_l(k,r) a_{\frac{1}{2}} Y_l^m(\Omega_r) Y_l^{m*}(\Omega_k),$$
$$|Y\rangle = (kr)^{-1} \sum_{lm} 4\pi i^l e^{i\sigma_l} u_l(k,r) a_{-\frac{1}{2}} Y_l^m(\Omega_r) Y_l^{m*}(\Omega_k). \tag{12.51}$$

For an unpolarized beam $|a_{1/2}|^2 = |a_{-1/2}|^2 = 1$, so that

$$|X\rangle = |Y\rangle = \chi^{(+)}(\mathbf{k}, \mathbf{r}) = (kr)^{-1} \sum_{lm} 4\pi i^l e^{i\sigma_l} u_l(k, r) Y_l^m(\Omega_r) Y_l^{m*}(\Omega_k),$$

$$\langle X'| = \langle Y'| = \chi^{(-)*}(\mathbf{k}', \mathbf{r}) = (k'r)^{-1} \sum_{l'm'} 4\pi i^{-l'} e^{i\sigma_{l'}} u_{l'}(k', r) Y_{l'}^{m'}(\Omega_r) Y_{l'}^{m'*}(\Omega_{k'}).$$
$$(12.52)$$

Choosing the z-axis in exactly the same way as we did for the collective case, we may use the optical-model wave functions (12.20) for the distorted waves.

The space part of the pseudopotential t_{12} is expanded in multipoles (see Appendix 4*G*).

$$t_{12}(|\mathbf{r}_1 - \mathbf{r}_2|) = 4\pi \sum_{\lambda\mu} t_\lambda(r_1, r_2) Y_\lambda^{\mu*}(\Omega_1) Y_\lambda^{\mu}(\Omega_2). \qquad (12.53)$$

The multipole component t_λ for a Yukawa pseudopotential $e^{-\mu_v r}/\mu_v r$ is

$$t_\lambda(r_1, r_2) = -j_\lambda(i\mu_v r_<) h_\lambda^{(1)}(i\mu_v r_>), \qquad (12.54)$$

where $r_>$ and $r_<$ are the greater and lesser, respectively, of r_1 and r_2. This form is used, for example, in the three-Yukawa pseudopotential (3.102).

We must now multiply the unbound wave functions (12.20) for initial and final states, the bound wave functions (12.50) for initial and final states, and the pseudopotential (12.53), and integrate over the coordinates $\mathbf{r}_1$ and $\mathbf{r}_2$ to obtain matrix elements. A typical pair of direct and exchange matrix elements are M_1^D and M_1^E. We shall illustrate the reduction of these to a sum over angular momentum coefficients and radial integrals.

$$
\begin{aligned}
M_1^D = \iint & r_1^2 \, dr_1 r_2^2 \, dr_2 \, d\Omega_1 \, d\Omega_2 \\
\times \ & (kr_1)^{-1} \sum_l [4\pi(2l+1)]^{1/2} i^l e^{i\sigma_l} u_l(k, r_1) Y_l^0(\Omega_1) \\
\times \ & (k'r_1)^{-1} \sum_{l'm'} 4\pi i^{-l'} e^{i\sigma_{l'}} u_{l'}(k', r_1) Y_{l'}^{m'*}(\Omega_1) Y_{l'}^{m'}(\theta, 0) \\
\times \ & R_{np}(r_2) C_{p\ \frac12\ j}^{m_p\ \frac12 m_j} Y_p^{m_p}(\Omega_2) \\
\times \ & R_{n'p'}(r_2) C_{p'\ \frac12\ j'}^{m_{p'}\ \frac12 m_{j'}} Y_{p'}^{m_{p'}*}(\Omega_2) \\
\times \ & \sum_{\mu\lambda} 4\pi t_\lambda(r_1, r_2) Y_\lambda^{\mu}(\Omega_1) Y_\lambda^{\mu*}(\Omega_2),
\end{aligned}
$$
$$(12.55D)$$

$$
\begin{aligned}
M_1^E = \iint & r_1^2 \, dr_1 r_2^2 \, dr_2 \, d\Omega_1 \, d\Omega_2 \\
\times \ & (kr_1)^{-1} \sum_l [4\pi(2l+1)]^{1/2} i^l e^{i\sigma_l} u_l(k, r_1) Y_l^0(\Omega_1) \\
\times \ & (k'r_2)^{-1} \sum_{l'm'} 4\pi i^{-l'} e^{i\sigma_{l'}} u_{l'}(k', r_2) Y_{l'}^{m'*}(\Omega_2) Y_{l'}^{m'}(\theta, 0) \\
\times \ & R_{np}(r_2) C_{p\ \frac12\ j}^{m_p\ \frac12 m_j} Y_p^{m_p}(\Omega_2) \\
\times \ & R_{n'p'}(r_1) C_{p'\ \frac12\ j'}^{m_{p'}\ \frac12 m_{j'}} Y_{p'}^{m_{p'}*}(\Omega_1) \\
\times \ & \sum_{\lambda\mu} 4\pi t_\lambda(r_1\ r_2) Y_\lambda^{\mu}(\Omega_1) Y_\lambda^{\mu*}(\Omega_2).
\end{aligned}
$$
$$(12.55E)$$

The angular integrations are performed by means of the Wigner-Eckart theorem (A4.51), the principal difference between direct and exchange terms being that quantum numbers of unbound and bound particles separately are coupled by the multipole quantum number λ of t_{12} in the direct term, whereas quantum numbers of bound particles are coupled to quantum numbers of unbound particles in the exchange term.

In general the matrix elements are given for $i = 1, \ldots, 4$ by

$$M_i^D(m_j, m_{j'}', \theta) = \sum_{l\lambda l'\mu} C_{i,l\lambda l'} G_{l\lambda l'}^D Y_{l'}^{\mu *}(\theta, 0), \tag{12.56D}$$

$$M_i^E(m_j, m_{j'}', \theta) = \sum_{l\lambda l'\mu} C_{i,l\lambda l'} G_{l\lambda l'}^E Y_{l'}^{m_p - \mu *}(\theta, 0). \tag{12.56E}$$

The coefficients are

$$C_{i,l\lambda l'} = (4\pi)^{3/2} i^{l-l'} e^{i(\sigma_l + \sigma_{l'})} (2\lambda + 1)(2l + 1) \left[\frac{2p + 1}{(2p' + 1)(2l' + 1)} \right]^{1/2}$$
$$\times C_{p \; \frac{1}{2} \; j}^{m_p \rho_i m_j} C_{p' \; \frac{1}{2} \; j'}^{m_{p'} \rho_i' m_j'}, \tag{12.57}$$

$$G_{l\lambda l'}^D = R_{l\lambda l'}^D C_{l\lambda l'}^{000} C_{l \; \lambda \; l'}^{0 - \mu - \mu} C_{p\lambda p'}^{000} C_{p \; \lambda \; p'}^{m_p \mu m_{p'}}, \tag{12.58D}$$

$$G_{l\lambda l'}^E = R_{l\lambda l'}^E C_{l\lambda p'}^{000} C_{l\lambda p'}^{0\mu\mu} C_{p\lambda l'}^{000} C_{p \; \lambda \; l'}^{m_p - \mu m'}. \tag{12.58E}$$

The radial integrals are

$$R_{l\lambda l'}^D = (kk')^{-1} \iint dr_1 \, dr_2 u_{l'}(k', r_1) R_{n'p'}(r_2) t_\lambda(r_1, r_2) u_l(k, r_1) R_{np}(r_2), \tag{12.59D}$$

$$R_{l\lambda l'}^E = (kk')^{-1} \iint dr_1 \, dr_2 u_{l'}(k', r_2) R_{n'p'}(r_1) t_\lambda(r_1, r_2) u_l(k, r_1) R_{np}(r_2). \tag{12.59E}$$

The quantum numbers ρ_i, ρ_i' are defined by

$$\rho_i = \frac{1}{2} \quad \text{for} \quad i = 1, 4 \quad \text{and} \quad -\frac{1}{2} \quad \text{for} \quad i = 2, 3,$$

$$\rho_i' = \frac{1}{2} \quad \text{for} \quad i = 1, 3 \quad \text{and} \quad -\frac{1}{2} \quad \text{for} \quad i = 2, 4. \tag{12.60}$$

[i]   GENERAL PROPERTIES OF DIRECT AND EXCHANGE MATRIX ELEMENTS

There are several general facts about the matrix elements, which can be seen by inspection of Equations (12.56) through (12.60). First, the direct matrix element may be written, suppressing the index i, as

$$M^D = \sum_L \int d^3 r_1 \chi^{(-)*}(\mathbf{k'}, \mathbf{r}_1) \chi^{(+)}(\mathbf{k}, \mathbf{r}_1) F_L(\mathbf{r}_1), \tag{12.61}$$

where

$$F_L(\mathbf{r}_1) = \int d^3 r_2 \Phi'^*(\mathbf{r}_2) t_{12}(|\mathbf{r}_1 - \mathbf{r}_2|) \Phi(\mathbf{r}_2). \tag{12.62}$$

The selection rules in (12.58D) state that λ is the angular momentum transfer L involved in the reaction, where

$$\mathbf{p} + \mathbf{L} = \mathbf{p}'. \tag{12.63}$$

Very often only one value of L is allowed by the selection rule. In any case only a few values of L contribute. Each term of the form (12.61) is formally analogous to the matrix element (12.19) for collective excitations. The radial form factor dU/dr is replaced by a more complicated radial integral over r_2.

l	l'	$|I^D|$	$\arg I^D$	l	l'	$|I^D|$	$\arg I^D$
0	1	0.1772	235°	1	0	0.2995	56°
1	2	0.5700	9°	2	1	0.7448	189°
2	3	0.9603	323°	3	2	1.1470	143°
3	4	0.7546	223°	4	3	0.8746	43°
4	5	0.3648	164°	5	4	0.4061	344°
5	6	0.1586	158°	6	5	0.1739	338°
6	7	0.0744	161°	7	6	0.0805	341°
7	8	0.0350	166°	8	7	0.0376	346°

TABLE 12.2. Partial matrix elements defined by (12.64) for a $2s_{1/2}$ to $1p_{1/2}$ proton-hole transition in ^{19}F caused by 20 MeV protons. (From Amos, Madsen, and McCarthy, 67.)

This integral is generally localized to the surface region to a large extent, since bound-state wave functions for all except s states are small in the interior. All the considerations of section A apply to the direct term. Phase averaging reduces the value of the partial matrix elements for interior values of l, l'. The parity rule is verified in exactly the same way. In particular, Equation (12.34) for the partial matrix elements remains true.

The partial matrix elements $I_{ll'}^D$, defined by

$$M^D = \sum_{ll'} I_{ll'}^D Y_{l'}^{\mu *}(\theta, 0), \tag{12.64}$$

are illustrated in Table 12.2 for 20 MeV protons causing a $2s_{1/2}$ to $1p_{1/2}$ proton-hole transition in ^{19}F. In this case, only $L = 1$ contributes. Only the $\mu = 0$ terms are shown. The triangle selection rule in (12.58D) means that $l' = l \pm 1$.

This table illustrates several points. First, the surface partial matrix elements, where $l \simeq kR$, are dominant. In this case l and l' are 2, 3, and 4. The interior contribution is much smaller. Thus phase averaging reduces the interior partial matrix elements, but the wave length is longer than for α-particles, so that it is harder to distinguish the interior from the surface.

Second, the parity rule is illustrated. The contribution to the matrix element at $\theta = 0$ is obtained by multiplying each column by $[(2l' + 1)/4\pi]^{\frac{1}{2}}$. Equation (12.34) is verified, since the phases of contributions from the left and right columns are opposite and the magnitudes are equal.

The situation is entirely different for the exchange term. The multipole quantum number λ is coupled by the selection rules (12.58E) to a bound-state quantum number and an unbound-state quantum number, which takes all values. Therefore, λ takes all values and is unrelated to L. (In the particular case used for illustration, $p' = 0$, so $\lambda = l$. This introduces a simplification into the discussion of the partial matrix elements, but the principles that will be illustrated are more general.)

The most important fact about the exchange term is that it is almost in phase with the direct term. The only factors in the partial matrix elements that are different for direct and exchange terms are the G factors of Equations (12.58). They are real except for the radial integrals R. In our discussion of optical model wave functions in Chapter 11A[iii], we saw that the phase of a partial wave was almost equal to the real part of the phase shift δ_l for values of r less than the first minimum. The dominant contribution to the integrand comes from this range of r (see Fig. 11.8 for an example). Therefore the phases of the exchange partial matrix elements are given very closely by (12.31), exactly like those for the direct partial matrix elements.

The parity rule does not hold for the exchange terms. The exchange integral cannot be factorized into an $\mathbf{r}_1$ integral that depends on the properties of the distorted waves and an $\mathbf{r}_2$ integral whose parity is fixed, since each integral includes a distorted wave. However, calculations of angular distributions show that pure exchange cross sections do, in fact, decrease toward forward angles for a parity-changing reaction. There is an approximate parity rule which may be illustrated in the ^{19}F case already discussed.

In this case

$$\lambda = l = l' \pm 1. \tag{12.65}$$

The properties of the Clebsch-Gordan coefficients in (12.58E) give

$$G^E_{\lambda+1,\lambda+1,\lambda} \cong -G^E_{\lambda,\lambda,\lambda+1}\left[\frac{2\lambda + 3}{2\lambda + 1}\right]^{\frac{1}{2}}, \tag{12.66}$$

under the condition that

$$R^E_{\lambda+1,\lambda+1,\lambda} \cong R^E_{\lambda,\lambda,\lambda+1}. \tag{12.67}$$

The condition (12.67) becomes more and more valid for higher values of λ. There are similar rules for larger values of p'.

The phase properties and the approximate parity rule for partial matrix elements are illustrated in Table 12.3 for the exchange partial matrix elements in our example.

This table, in comparison with the direct table, first shows the approximate phase equality of $I^D_{ll'}$ and $I^E_{ll'}$. Except for the second row, the phases correspond within a few degrees. The approximate parity rule (12.66, 12.67) is very closely obeyed. The magnitudes of the contributions in the left and right columns are almost identical except for the first two rows, and their phases are almost opposite.

$\lambda = l$	l'	$|I^E|$	arg I^E	$\lambda = l$	l'	$|I^E|$	arg I^E
0	1	1.0350	223°	1	0	0.4423	47°
1	2	0.5935	314°	2	1	0.5433	183°
2	3	0.8352	325°	3	2	0.8259	146°
3	4	0.2362	239°	4	3	0.2329	59°
4	5	0.0140	176°	5	4	0.0137	356°
5	6	0.0006	165°	6	5	0.0006	345°
6	7	0	166°	7	6	0	346°
7	8	0	169°	8	7	0	349°

TABLE 12.3.   Exchange partial matrix elements for a $2s_{1/2}$ to $1p_{1/2}$ proton-hole transition in ^{19}F caused by 20 MeV protons. (From Amos, Madsen, and McCarthy, 67.)

The table also illustrates the important difference between direct and exchange matrix elements. For exchange matrix elements, phase averaging competes with another effect. The terms $I^E_{ll'}$ for successively higher l, l' are computed with successive values of λ. The magnitude of the multipole component $t_\lambda(r_1, r_2)$ decreases rapidly with successive λ. This effect weights the interior partial waves strongly.

The exchange term therefore is more sensitive to the interior of the nucleus than the direct term.

[ii] ANGULAR DISTRIBUTIONS

Angular distributions for our ^{19}F example are illustrated in Fig. 12.5. Cross sections calculated with pure direct, pure exchange, and Serber exchange matrix elements (3.91) are denoted σ_D, σ_E and σ_S. The properties of angular distributions that have been discussed are illustrated. The phase correspondence of direct and exchange terms makes the angular distributions very similar. Maxima and minima occur in roughly the same places. The cross section for Serber exchange looks like the average of the other two for the same reason. The approximate parity rule for the exchange term is seen in the forward direction.

One point that cannot be illustrated without a detailed discussion is the relative magnitude of σ_D and σ_E. In this case they are comparable. This is not

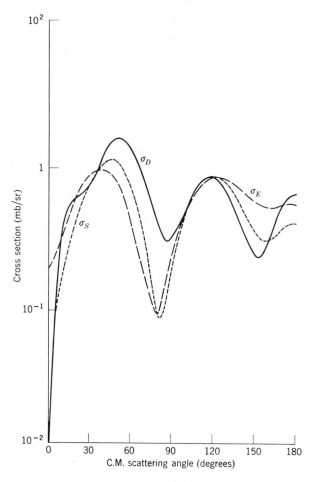

FIG. 12.5 Angular distributions in the DWTA for the excitation of a $1p_{1/2}$ proton to a $2s_{1/2}$ state in ^{19}F by 20 MeV proton inelastic scattering. σ_D, σ_E, and σ_S represent cross sections calculated with a pure direct term, a pure exchange term, and a Serber exchange mixture, respectively. (Adapted from Amos, Madsen, and McCarthy, 67.)

invariably true. In some cases σ_E is larger than σ_D. In the limit $t(|\mathbf{r}_1 - \mathbf{r}_2|) \rightarrow \delta(\mathbf{r}_1 - \mathbf{r}_2)$, they are identical.

There is certainly no case for omitting σ_E on the ground that it is much smaller than σ_D, as has sometimes been suggested in early literature on the subject. However, the phase correspondence makes σ_D a rough approximation to σ_E, so that calculations which omit σ_D are capable of giving very similar results to those that include spin dependence and antisymmetry, provided that an appropriate normalizing factor is included.

At this time there has been very little work done in comparing quasi-three-body type inelastic scattering with experiment at lower energies ($<$50 MeV). Rough correspondence with angular distributions for the excitation of different states in ^{90}Zr has been achieved by Gray, Kenefick, Kraushaar, and Satchler (66), using only the direct term. Fits obtained with such a model are typified by this work. The effective interaction was found to be of shorter range and much stronger than the free p-p interaction.

Using the free p-p pseudopotential (3.102) in the full theory of this chapter, Amos, Madsen, and McCarthy (67) and Amos (67) have obtained fair agreement with the magnitudes of cross sections in the reaction ^{89}Y(p, p′)^{89}Y* at 18.9 MeV and 24.5 MeV. For this transition, the model of the excitation of a $2p_{1/2}$ proton to the $1g_{9/2}$ state is extremely good. Thus far experiments on this reaction have not yielded sufficient detail for comparison of angular distributions. The fit is illustrated in Fig. 12.6. In this case, σ_E is greater than σ_D by a factor of about 2.

For the ^{28}Si(p, n) reaction, which is also described by the present formalism, Agodi and Schiffrer (64) have obtained angular distributions which again correspond roughly to experiment, but which require a very strong p-n force. Exchange matrix elements were calculated in this case.

One interesting fact about angular distributions is that they are capable of yielding information about the relative strength of the effective nucleon-nucleon force in the surface and the interior of nuclei. There is some a priori justification for believing that the effective force is weaker internally because the Pauli principle inhibits interactions. Amos and McCarthy (63) have shown that calculations with weaker effective forces in the interior produce different angular distributions from those with uniform interaction. They also produce smaller total cross sections, but this is meaningless since many-body effects have been introduced, which are not explicitly described by the model. The preliminary indication from the angular distribution shapes is that there is no sign of weaker interior forces in the ^{89}Y(p, p′)^{89}Y* reaction.

[iii] THE DISTORTED WAVE IMPULSE APPROXIMATION

The high-energy limit of the theory of this section is the distorted wave impulse approximation (DWIA). Writing the full p-p t-matrix and the wave functions in the momentum representation, we have for the direct matrix element in the DWTA, for a particular value of L,

$$M^D = \int d^3k_1 \int d^3k_2 \int d^3k_1{}' \int d^3k_2{}' \chi^{(-)*}(\mathbf{k}', \mathbf{k}_1)\Phi'^*(\mathbf{k}_2)$$

$$\times t_{12}(E; \mathbf{k}_1, \mathbf{k}_2, \mathbf{k}_1{}', \mathbf{k}_2{}')\Phi(\mathbf{k}_2{}')\chi^{(+)}(\mathbf{k}, \mathbf{k}_1{}'). \quad (12.68)$$

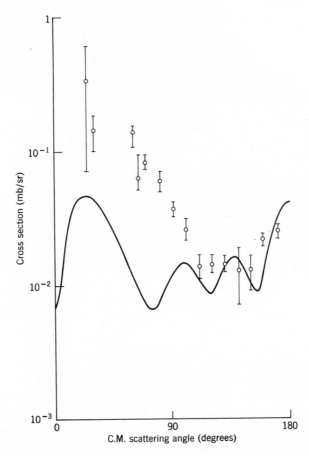

FIG. 12.6   The DWTA with no free parameters and a Serber exchange mixture compared with experimental data for the excitation of the $\frac{9}{2}+$ first excited state of ^{89}Y by 24.5 MeV proton inelastic scattering. (Amos, 67).

For sufficiently high energy the wave functions vary much more rapidly with the momentum variables over the range that contributes to the integral than do the t-matrix elements. The t-matrix may be taken outside the integral where, on squaring the matrix element, it becomes the differential cross section for p-p scattering at the energy E.

In the pseudopotential approximation the DWIA may be understood in another way. At high energies the optical-model wave functions are not far from plane waves. We have seen that refraction and absorption may be included to a good approximation simply by adding a complex part to the wave number of a plane wave.

The direct matrix element (12.68) may be written

$$M^D = \int d^3r_1 e^{-ik'\cdot\mathbf{r}_1} e^{ik\cdot\mathbf{r}_1} \int d^3r_2 \Phi'^*(\mathbf{r}_2) t_{12}(|\mathbf{r}_1 - \mathbf{r}_2|) \Phi(\mathbf{r}_2). \qquad (12.69)$$

The substitution

$$\mathbf{r} = \mathbf{r}_1 - \mathbf{r}_2$$

$$\mathbf{r}' = \mathbf{r}_2$$

yields

$$M^D = \int d^3r\, e^{i(k-k')\cdot\mathbf{r}} t_{12}(r) \int d^3r'\, e^{i(k-k')\cdot\mathbf{r}'} \Phi'^*(\mathbf{r}')\Phi(\mathbf{r}'), \qquad (12.70)$$

where the first factor is simply the Fourier transform of the nucleon-nucleon interaction. The square of the first factor is the nucleon-nucleon collision cross section if the Q value is neglected. The distorted wave impulse approximation consists of replacing the plane waves by distorted waves in the second factor of (12.70).

This argument is not correct for the exchange term. However, we shall rely on the general similarity of the two terms discussed in the previous section. Exchange effects are of course included in the p-p cross section. The matrix element in the DWIA becomes

$$f_{a0} = \left(\frac{d}{d\Omega}\, \sigma_{N\text{-}N}\right) \int d^3r\, \chi^{(-)*}(\mathbf{k}', \mathbf{r})\chi^{(+)}(\mathbf{k}, \mathbf{r})\Phi'^*(\mathbf{r})\Phi(\mathbf{r}). \qquad (12.71)$$

The energy region where this approximation is valid has an enormous advantage over the lower-energy region. The two-nucleon interaction is known in great detail, including spin dependence and polarization effects. The optical-model wave functions may be computed from elastic scattering data. They are insensitive to small potential changes at this energy. The reaction becomes a probe for the model used for the nuclear bound states.

Using bound-state wave functions computed in the particle-hole model by Gillet and Vinh Mau (64), Haybron and McManus (65) have computed cross sections and polarizations for (p, p') inelastic scattering at 156 MeV on ^{12}C, ^{16}O, and ^{40}Ca. The bound-state wave functions are linear combinations of single-particle wave functions, so the matrix element is a linear combination of transition matrix elements (12.71).

The quality of the fits is illustrated by the ^{12}C results in Fig. 12.7. The fact that the theory fits well indicates that the bound-state description is good and that the description of the reaction mechanism, including the optical model and the quasi-three-body assumption, is good. Only the off-energy-shell matrix elements of the p-p interaction are not tested. The only other example of an equally detailed reaction calculation with corresponding experimental results is the (p, 2p) reaction, which will be discussed in Chapter 14.

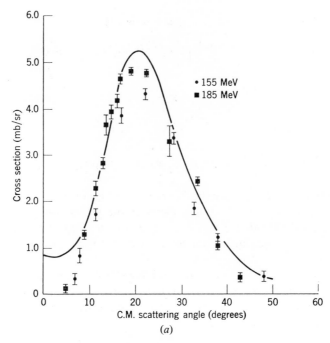

FIG. 12.7   Inelastic scattering of 156 MeV protons from the 4.43 MeV 2+ level of ^{12}C. The theory (solid line) is the DWIA. (*a*) Differential cross section, (*b*) polarization. (Adapted from Haybron and McManus, 65.)

This is an even more sensitive test of the reaction mechanism than inelastic scattering because one of the final state momentum variables is measured, rather than integrated out.   Integrations always throw away information.

C. CALCULATIONS WITH APPROXIMATE DISTORTED WAVES

In Chapter 11*A*[ii] it was seen that, in the nuclear surface region, the phase of a distorted wave may be approximated by that of a plane wave $\exp{(i\beta \mathbf{k} \cdot \mathbf{r})}$ where βk is the effective wave number.   To quite a good approximation the effective wave number is the wave number in the local nuclear matter approximation.   This approximation is sometmes known as the eikonal approximation.   The amplitude of the distorted wave is given by an appropriate space weighting factor.

[i]   THE MODEL OF McCARTHY AND PURSEY

This model will be treated in some detail because of the understanding it provides of the shapes of angular distributions.

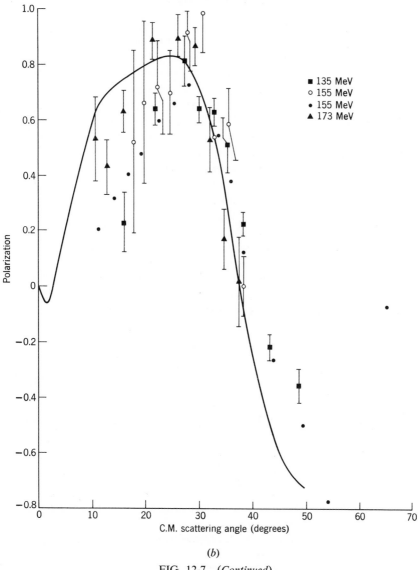

(b)

FIG. 12-7 (Continued)

Before the availability of high-speed computers, direct interaction calculations were performed using plane waves instead of distorted waves in the DWBA. The Butler (51) approximation introduced distortion with a single parameter R, the Butler radius. The radial integral was simply cut off for $r < R$, simulating the effects of absorption, phase averaging, and possible reduction of the effective interaction strength in the interior. In order to predict angular distributions, which are momentum-transfer distributions when the energy differences of the initial and final states are fixed by the experiment, the uncertainty principle tells us that we must have the correct weighting of space. The plane-wave theory or the Butler theory assume that only space weighting is important. Phase distortion of the wave functions of the unbound particles is disregarded. The radial space weighting in the Butler theory came from the cutoff R and the falling-off of the nuclear wave function for large r. The angular space weighting came from the spherical harmonic $Y_L{}^M(\theta, 0)$ in the DWBA matrix element. This localization, as we shall see below, produced maxima and minima in the angular distribution, one or two of which could be fitted to experiment in ideal cases by adjusting the angular momentum transfer L and the radius R. The theory was used to determine L.

McCarthy and Pursey (61) noticed that the analytic wave function (11.5) was much more realistic than plane waves, and almost as easy to compute, particularly for α-particle inelastic scattering where the focus term may be disregarded. The wave function retains the eikonal approximation for the phase, but weights the angular dimensions of space much more realistically.

For α-particle inelastic scattering from collective states of even nuclei whose ground state is always $0+$, the approximation takes the form

$$f_{a0} = \int d^3r R(r) Y_L{}^M(\theta, \phi) \exp\left[i\mathbf{K} \cdot \mathbf{r} - \gamma'(\hat{\mathbf{k}} - \hat{\mathbf{k}}') \cdot \mathbf{r}\right]. \qquad (12.72)$$

The radial localization factor $R(r)$, which usually is dU/dr, was taken to be a gaussian of width λ.

$$R(r) = \exp\left[-\frac{(r - R)^2}{\lambda^2}\right]. \qquad (12.73)$$

The real phase factor β is absorbed into K. In fitting data, $\mathbf{K}$ was taken to be the momentum transfer,

$$\mathbf{K} = \mathbf{k} - \mathbf{k}'. \qquad (12.74)$$

The factor β thus results in the empirical value of R being somewhat larger than the average nuclear radius.

The angular integration in (12.72) is performed, yielding

$$f_{a0} = \int r^2 \, dr R(r)\{4\pi i^L j_L(\xi r) Y_L{}^M(\theta_\xi, \phi_\xi)\}, \qquad (12.75)$$

where

$$\xi = (\boldsymbol{\xi} \cdot \boldsymbol{\xi})^{1/2},$$

$$\boldsymbol{\xi} = \mathbf{K} + i\left(\frac{\gamma'}{r}\right)(\hat{\mathbf{k}} - \hat{\mathbf{k}}'), \qquad (12.76)$$

and θ_ξ, ϕ_ξ are the polar angles of the complex vector $\boldsymbol{\xi}$.

To obtain the differential cross section, $|f_{a0}|^2$ is summed over M. The angular part of the sum is

$$\sum_M Y_L^M(\theta_\xi, \phi_\xi) Y_L^{M*}(\theta_{\xi'}^*, \phi_{\xi'}^*) = \frac{2L+1}{4\pi} P_L(\cos \Theta), \quad (12.77)$$

where $\boldsymbol{\xi}' = \mathbf{K} + (i\gamma'/r')(\hat{\mathbf{k}} - \hat{\mathbf{k}}')$ and r' is the radial integration variable in f_{a0}^*.

$$\cos \Theta = \frac{\boldsymbol{\xi} \cdot \boldsymbol{\xi}'^*}{\xi \xi'^*}. \quad (12.78)$$

In the adiabatic limit, $k = k'$, $\cos \Theta = 1$. Using this approximation and setting $r = R$ in (12.76), the differential cross section is

$$\frac{d\sigma}{d\Omega} \propto \left| \int r^2 \, dR(r) j_L(\xi r) \right|^2$$

$$= \left| \int r^2 \, dr \exp\left[-\frac{(r - R)^2}{\lambda^2} \right] j_L\left[2(kr + i\gamma') \sin \frac{\theta}{2} \right] \right|^2. \quad (12.79)$$

This expression may be compared with the plane-wave theory by simply setting $\gamma' = 0$. The angular distribution in the plane-wave theory is very like $|j_L(KR)|^2$. The radial integration is confined quite closely to R by the factor $R(r)$. In particular, the radial integration does not prevent the differential cross section having zeros at approximately the zeros of $j_L(KR)$. This is a serious disadvantage of the plane-wave theory.

The inclusion of the parameter γ' gives the cross section a finite value at the minima without altering their angular positions. This is explained in terms of the uncertainty principle. A spherical space distribution means a perfect absence of definition in angle, therefore perfect definition of angular momentum, so that only one spherical Bessel function contributes. Inclusion of the angular space weighting brings in spherical Bessel functions for other values of L, whose zeros are at different angles.

Fits to α-particle inelastic scattering at 40 MeV with this model are remarkably good in shape. It has not yet been used to predict absolute magnitudes, but there is no reason why it should not at least predict relative magnitudes for excitation of different states. Figure 12.8 shows the fit to the excitation of the first 2+ state of ^{32}S by 40 MeV α-particles. The fit is equally good for neighboring nuclei, and the parameters are consistent. $\gamma' = 0.9$, $\lambda = 0.88$ fm, and $R = 2.2A^{1/3}$ fm. The value $\gamma' = 0.9$ is checked very closely by plotting optical-model wave functions against angle as in Fig. 11.5. $\lambda = 0.88$ fm is quite reasonable for the width of the surface in comparison with dU/dr for the Woods-Saxon potential. $R = 2.2A^{1/3}$ fm is approximately 7 fm for ^{32}S, whereas the formula of Satchler (65) for the optical-model radius for α-particles (Chapter 11C[iv]) gives $R_0 = 6$ fm. Thus $\beta = \frac{7}{6}$, which is again quite reasonable on the basis of the local nuclear matter approximation for the phase of the optical-model wave function.

One important feature of the angular distributions of Equation (12.79) is that the minimum for small momentum transfers ($\theta \to 0$) remains, even for 2+ excitations, in contrast to the parity rule. For α-particle scattering there

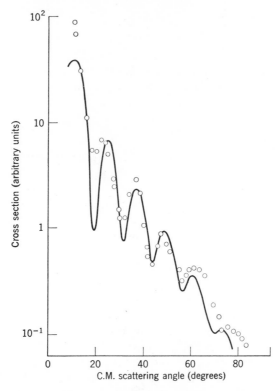

FIG. 12.8   Inelastic scattering of 41.7 MeV α-particles from the first 2+ state of ^{32}S, fitted by the model of McCarthy and Pursey. (Adapted from McCarthy and Pursey, 61.)

is a forward angle correction for Coulomb excitation, which may obscure this fact. However, even DWBA curves computed with the full optical model show a small maximum only for $\theta < 5^0$ in the α-particle case (see Fig. 12.11).

Figure 12.9 demonstrates the effect of distortion on forward scattering very clearly for the excitation of the first 2+ state of ^{12}C by 40 MeV protons. In this calculation the correct Q value of 4.43 MeV was used. The dashed line represents the McCarthy-Pursey approximation with the term γ' included in the argument of the spherical Bessel function. The curve still follows the oscillatory pattern of the plane-ware theory shown by the dotted line. The full line is computed by using a focus term in the form (11.5) for the distorted waves. This term completely alters the shape of the angular distribution, putting maxima where there were minima in some cases, particularly at $\theta = 0$.

The full line, in fact, fits the experiment extremely well. It may be compared with the DWBA curve for the same reaction in Fig. 12.2.

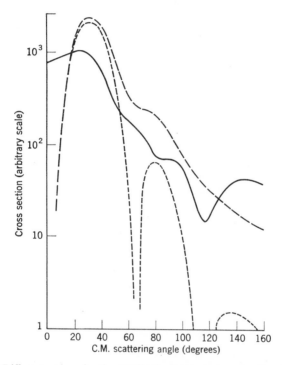

FIG. 12.9 Different stages in the McCarthy-Pursey approximation for the inelastic scattering of 40 MeV protons from the 4.43 MeV 2+ state of ^{12}C. The curves are explained in the text. (Adapted from Kromminga and McCarthy, 62.)

The success of the approximate wave function in fitting even quite complicated curves like that of Fig. 12.9 gives great insight into the shapes of angular distributions as well as confirming the usefulness of the approximations.

The replacement of the forward minimum in the plane-wave theory by a maximum is seen to be due to the focus. In our discussion of angular distributions in terms of partial waves, we saw that the forward maximum is due to constructive interference of surface partial matrix elements in the forward direction. These partial matrix elements come from surface partial waves whose constructive interference in the wave function is responsible for focusing.

Interferences of the focal and surface contributions clearly are responsible for the large departures of nucleon inelastic scattering from the shape characteristic of plane waves. The shape persists in α-particle scattering, where the focus effect is negligible, except at extreme forward angles.

The model of course obeys the parity rule for parity-changing reactions.

At least one further fact about inelastic scattering can be understood on the basis of the model. This is the failure of the phase rule for proton inelastic scattering resulting again from focus-surface interference, as described in Section 12A.

The model is useful for fitting data in order to obtain spectroscopic information. Above about 30 MeV for protons, and at lower energies for α-particles, it closely parallels the results of more accurate DWBA calculations. Since accurate calculations are relatively simple for inelastic scattering, this is not an important advantage. However, the simplicity of the approximate wave function makes many calculations possible that would be impossible for partial wave expansions because of the computing time involved. In the next chapter we shall see that its application to the (p, 2p) reaction predicted effects that were not observed in accurate distorted wave treatments for several years.

In application to quasi-three-body problems, the inclusion of the focus makes off-energy-shell elements of the two-nucleon t-matrix important in the distorted wave integral. Calculations with a much more general t-matrix than the local pseudopotential approximation used so far are possible with the analytic approximation to the wave function, although too long for computation with partial wave expansions.

[ii] THE SEMICLASSICAL APPROXIMATION

At energies greater than about 150 MeV, the distorted wave impulse approximation gives extremely good results for inelastic scattering. This approximation is semiclassical in the sense that the probability of the two-nucleon collision on the energy shell, rather than the probability amplitude with weighting factors for off-shell amplitudes, is used. However, at high energies the eikonal approximation for the distorted waves is also extremely good, and may be used in conjunction with the approximation that particle trajectories do not change direction in the nucleus. This approximation is discussed in detail by Glauber (59).

The phase of the distorted wave at a point $\mathbf{r}$ is found by the local WKB approximation. An additional advantage of this approximation at high energy is that relativistic kinematics may be used without further complication. The distorted wave is written

$$\chi^{(+)}(\mathbf{k}, \mathbf{r}) = D(\mathbf{r})e^{i\mathbf{k}\cdot\mathbf{r}}. \tag{12.80}$$

The distortion factor $D(\mathbf{r})$ is given by

$$D(\mathbf{r}) = \exp\left[-i\frac{E}{\hbar^2 c^2 k}\int_{\mathbf{r}} ds(\boldsymbol{\rho})\tilde{V}(\boldsymbol{\rho})\right]. \qquad (12.81)$$

The optical model potential is $\tilde{V}(\boldsymbol{\rho})$. The integrations are taken over straight line classical trajectories $s(\boldsymbol{\rho})$ for the projectile $-\infty$ to $\mathbf{r}$. The energy E is now the total relativistic energy of the particle.

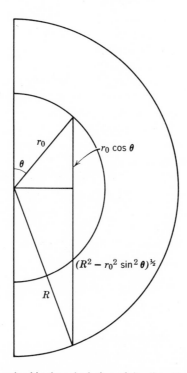

FIG. 12.10   Geometry involved in the calculation of the distortion factor for a square well.

To illustrate the calculation of a distortion factor, consider the case of a square well of radius R, depth $V + iW$. The distortion factor will be calculated on a spherical shell of radius r_0. The distance traveled in the potential is given by

$$s = (R^2 - r_0^2 \sin^2 \theta)^{1/2} + r_0 \cos \theta. \qquad (12.82)$$

This is seen in Fig. 12.10.

For r_0 not too close to R, the first term in (12.82) varies quite slowly with

θ. We shall set it equal to C. $D(\mathbf{r})$ becomes

$$D(\mathbf{r}) = \exp\left[-i\frac{E}{\hbar^2 c^2 k} C(V + iW)\right]$$

$$\times \exp\left[-i\frac{EV}{\hbar^2 c^2 k} r_0 \cos\theta + \frac{EW}{\hbar^2 c^2 k} r_0 \cos\theta\right]. \quad (12.83)$$

The angular dependence of (12.83) is the same as that of the McCarthy-Pursey wave function (11.5) with the focus term omitted. Hence, to a good approximation, the semiclassical theory gives the same answer as the McCarthy-Pursey theory. It gives a means of computing the parameters β and γ, knowing the optical-model potentials. For 40 MeV α-particles with $V = 40$ MeV, $W = 10$ MeV, Equation (12.83) gives $\beta = 1.6$, $\gamma = 0.13$. The values determined by curve fitting with Equation (12.79) are $\beta = 1.17$ and $\gamma = 0.046$. The fact that the empirical values are smaller is accounted for if we assume that the reaction occurs in the surface, where the average potential is reduced to about $\frac{1}{3}$ of its central value.

At 150 MeV, inelastic scattering calculations for nucleons performed with the semiclassical model are almost indistinguishable from those performed with the optical model using the partial wave expansion. This is not true at 40 MeV where focus effects completely change the angular distributions (see Figs. 12.9 and 12.2).

D. CALCULATIONS USING ASYMPTOTIC ELASTIC-SCATTERING INFORMATION

We have seen that the distortion at lower energies makes inelastic scattering by the quasi-three-body mechanism sensitive to information about the effective two-nucleon force off the energy shell. It is interesting to ask how sensitive it is to information about the nucleon-core interaction off the energy shell or, in other words, to the internal details of the elastic scattering wave functions. For collective excitations, only the wave functions at the surface are important, and we might expect inelastic scattering to be quite well described in terms of asymptotic elastic-scattering information.

Intuition gained on the basis of the analytic wave function (11.5) tells us that the most relevant property of the internal wave function is the focus. We know that the focus is caused by the constructive interference of surface partial waves, which is due in large measure to the phase shifts, since the phase shifts are a good approximation to the phases of the partial waves. Thus the use only of the phase shifts to describe inelastic scattering includes a focusing effect. We can, however, compare the focus for two particular potentials that produce the same phase shift at a given energy, the nonlocal potential and its equivalent local potential. The focus is about 15 per cent smaller in magnitude for the nonlocal potential in the case of neutron scattering at low energy. The focus therefore is somewhat sensitive to the details of nucleon-core scattering off the energy shell.

For α-particles the focus is negligible and the use of asymptotic information should provide a good approximation.

[i] THE ADIABATIC METHOD

This method is used to describe collective inelastic scattering by a potential $U = U(h, r)$. U is spherically symmetric and h is a parameter. h will be taken in practice to be the nuclear radius. The theory is described in detail by Austern and Blair (65). In order to make the connection between elastic and inelastic scattering, a slightly new description of elastic scattering is used.

Collective excitation changes h to $h + \alpha$, where α is a scalar. The change in the potential ΔU is defined by

$$U(h + \alpha, r) = U_0 + \Delta U(h, \alpha, r), \qquad (12.84)$$

where $U_0 \equiv U(h, r)$. The increment ΔU may be expanded in a Taylor series in α.

$$\Delta U = \alpha \frac{\partial U}{\partial h} + \frac{1}{2!} \alpha^2 \frac{\partial^2 U}{\partial h^2} + \cdots \qquad (12.85)$$

the derivatives being evaluated at $\alpha = 0$.

The t-matrix for elastic scattering is

$$t(E; \mathbf{k'}, \mathbf{k})$$
$$= \langle \mathbf{k'} | U_0 + \Delta U - (U_0 + \Delta U) \frac{1}{K + U_0 + \Delta U - E - i\epsilon} (U_0 + \Delta U) | \mathbf{k} \rangle.$$
$$(12.86)$$

K is the kinetic energy operator as usual.

Since the Green's function is a nonlocal operator, the initial and final plane waves $|\mathbf{k}\rangle$ and $|\mathbf{k'}\rangle$ have different coordinates $\mathbf{r}_1, \mathbf{r}_2$. The potential is understood to be local, so that there is a factor $\delta(\mathbf{r}_1 - \mathbf{r}_2)$. The scattering amplitude is

$$f(\mathbf{k'}, \mathbf{k}) = -(\mu/2\pi\hbar^2)t(E_k; \mathbf{k'}, \mathbf{k}), \qquad (12.87)$$

where

$$E_k = \frac{\hbar^2 k^2}{2\mu} = \frac{\hbar^2 k'^2}{2\mu}$$

for elastic scattering.

Using the operator algebra introduced in Chapter 2C we may write (12.86) in the form

$$t = t_0 + \Delta t, \qquad (12.88)$$

where

$$t_0 = \langle \mathbf{k}' | U_0 | \chi^{(+)}(\mathbf{k}, \mathbf{r}) \rangle, \tag{12.89a}$$

$$\Delta t = \langle \chi^{(-)}(\mathbf{k}', \mathbf{r}_1) | \omega(1, 2) | \chi^{(+)}(\mathbf{k}, \mathbf{r}_2) \rangle, \tag{12.89b}$$

and the scattering operator for distorted waves is

$$\omega(1, 2) = \Delta U - \Delta U \frac{1}{K + U_0 + \Delta U - E - i\epsilon} \Delta U. \tag{12.90}$$

The iterative solution of (12.90) is

$$\omega(1, 2) = \Delta U - \Delta U G_0 \Delta U + \Delta U G_0 \Delta U G_0 \Delta U - \cdots, \tag{12.91}$$

where G_0 is the free-particle Green's function.

Using the Taylor series expansion (12.85) of ΔU in (12.91), we obtain $\omega(1, 2)$ as a power series in α.

$$\omega(1, 2) = \sum_{n=1}^{\infty} \alpha^n \omega_n(1, 2). \tag{12.92}$$

The first two terms are

$$\omega_1 = \frac{\partial U}{\partial h},$$

$$\omega_2 = \frac{1}{2} \frac{\partial^2 U}{\partial h^2} - \frac{\partial U}{\partial h} G_0 \frac{\partial U}{\partial h}. \tag{12.93}$$

Expanding the distorted waves and the scattering operator in partial wave (12.52) and multipole (12.53) expansions, we have for Δt from (12.89b)

$$\Delta t = (4\pi)^{3/2} k^{-2} \sum_l (2l + 1)^{1/2} e^{2i\sigma_l} Y_l^0(\theta, 0)$$

$$\times \left\{ \sum_n \alpha^n \int dr_1 \int dr_2 u_l(r_1) \omega_{nl}(1, 2) u_l(r_2) \right\}. \tag{12.94}$$

Here ω_{nl} is the lth multipole component of ω_n.

In terms of the S-matrix elements η_l, the t-matrix is

$$t(E_k; \mathbf{k}', \mathbf{k}) = \frac{i}{2k} (4\pi)^{1/2} \left(\frac{4\pi\hbar^2}{2\mu} \right) \sum_l (2l + 1)^{1/2} (\eta_l - 1) Y_l^0(\theta, 0). \tag{12.95}$$

This may be derived from (12.87) and the charged particle analogue of (2.37). We have included the Coulomb phase shift σ_l in η_l.

The increment Δt is

$$\Delta t = \left(\frac{iE}{2k^3} \right) (4\pi)^{3/2} \sum_l (2l + 1)^{1/2} [\eta_l - \eta_l(0)] Y_l^0(\theta, 0), \tag{12.96}$$

where $\eta_l(0)$ is computed in the potential $U(0)$. Comparing (12.94) and (12.96) after expanding the difference in (12.96) in powers of α, we have

$$\int dr_1 \int dr_2 u_l(r_1) \omega(1, 2) u_l(r_2) = \left(\frac{iE}{2k}\right) \frac{1}{n!} \frac{\partial^n \eta_l}{\partial h^n}. \qquad (12.97)$$

The derivatives are evaluated at $\alpha = 0$. For $n = 1$, (12.97) becomes

$$\int dr u_l(r) \frac{\partial U(r)}{\partial h} u_l(r) = \left(\frac{iE}{2k}\right) \frac{\partial \eta_l}{\partial h}. \qquad (12.98)$$

For inelastic scattering we take α to be the nuclear radius and expand it in multipoles.

$$\alpha = \sum_{LM} \xi_L{}^M Y_L{}^{M*}(\Omega_r). \qquad (12.99)$$

We must introduce the nuclear Hamiltonian as a function of α. The nuclear states ψ_i are determined by

$$H(\xi)\psi_i = \epsilon_i \psi_i, \qquad (12.100)$$

where ξ represents all the collective coordinates $\xi_L{}^M$.

The formally exact inelastic-scattering amplitude for excitation of state a from the ground state is

$$f_{a0} = \langle a| \langle \mathbf{k}'| (U_0 + \Delta U) - (U_0 + \Delta U)$$

$$\times \frac{1}{K + U_0 + \Delta U + H(\xi) - E - i\epsilon} (U_0 + \Delta U) |\mathbf{k}\rangle |0\rangle. \quad (12.101)$$

The basic step of the adiabatic method is now introduced. $H(\xi)$ is omitted in the Green's function of (12.101). This is equivalent to freezing the motion of the nucleus during the collision. Thus we have an expression for the inelastic scattering in terms of the elastic-scattering Green's function. The coordinates ξ appear only in ΔU. The initial and final energies are now assumed to be equal and we can use an on-energy-shell approximation for the inelastic amplitude.

$$f_{a0} \cong \langle a| \hat{t}(\mathbf{k}', \mathbf{k}) |0\rangle, \qquad (12.102)$$

where

$$\hat{t}(\mathbf{k}', \mathbf{k}) = \langle \mathbf{k}'| (U_0 + \Delta U) - (U_0 + \Delta U)$$

$$\times \frac{1}{K + U_0 + \Delta U - E - i\epsilon} (U_0 + \Delta U) |\mathbf{k}\rangle. \quad (12.103)$$

In our previous discussion of collective inelastic scattering (Chapter 10D), the term ΔU was given for the elastic scattering optical potential by

$$\Delta U = -U_{0I} \frac{1}{K + U_{II} - E - i\epsilon} U_{I0}. \qquad (12.104)$$

By the same method that the elastic scattering equations (12.89) were derived from (12.86), we may now set

$$\check{t} = t_0 + \Delta\check{t}, \tag{12.105}$$

deriving the following expression for the inelastic-scattering amplitude from $\check{t}$, since t_0 does not contribute to inelastic scattering.

$$\check{f}_{a0} = \langle a| \langle \chi^{(-)}(\mathbf{k}', \mathbf{r}_1)| \, \tau(1, 2) \, |\chi^{(+)}(\mathbf{k}, \mathbf{r}_2)\rangle \, |0\rangle. \tag{12.106}$$

The scattering operator τ is defined formally in the same way as ω, the elastic-scattering operator (12.91).

$$\tau = \Delta U - \Delta U \frac{1}{K + U_0 + \Delta U - E - i\epsilon} \Delta U. \tag{12.107}$$

However, the form (12.99) of α does not commute with the Green's function G_0, so the iteration and Taylor expansion corresponding to (12.92) for ω are written with allowance for this fact.

$$\tau = \sum_n \tau_n, \tag{12.108}$$

where the first two terms are

$$\tau_1 = \alpha \frac{\partial U}{\partial h}, \qquad \tau_2 = \tfrac{1}{2}\alpha^2 \frac{\partial^2 U}{\partial h^2} + \left(\alpha \frac{\partial U}{\partial h}\right) G_0 \left(\alpha \frac{\partial U}{\partial h}\right). \tag{12.109}$$

These terms correspond to the single and two phonon excitations discussed in connection with the DWBA.

We now make a further approximation. We treat α as if it commuted with G_0. Equation (12.108) in this approximation becomes

$$\tau(1, 2) \cong \tfrac{1}{2}\sum_n [\alpha^n(1)\omega_n(1, 2) + \omega_n(1, 2)\alpha^n(2)]. \tag{12.110}$$

Single phonon excitations are exactly treated by (12.110). The physical significance of the approximation for multiple excitations is that all n steps of transferring angular momentum to the nucleus are considered as taking place at the same angular location. This is in the adiabatic spirit, since it means that the scattering occurs fast with respect to motions of the nucleus.

The nuclear matrix elements $\langle a| \, \alpha^n \, |0\rangle$ are defined by

$$\check{f}_{a0} = \langle \chi^{(-)}(\mathbf{k}', \mathbf{r}_1)| \tfrac{1}{2}\sum_n \{\langle a| \, \alpha^n(1) \, |0\rangle \, \omega_n + \omega_n \, \langle a| \, \alpha^n(2) \, |0\rangle\} \, |\chi^{(+)}(\mathbf{k}, \mathbf{r}_2)\rangle. \tag{12.111}$$

They have been discussed in Section A of this chapter. For a $0+$ ground state,

$$\langle a| \, \alpha^n(1) \, |0\rangle = C_{nL} Y_L^{M*}(\Omega_1). \tag{12.112}$$

This equation may be considered as the definition of the coefficients C_{nL}. The adiabatic amplitude for inelastic scattering becomes

$$\tilde{f}_{a0} = \tfrac{1}{2} \sum_n C_{nL} \langle \chi^{(-)}(\mathbf{k}', \mathbf{r}_1)| \, Y_L^{M*}(\Omega_1)\omega_n(1,2)$$
$$+ \, \omega_n(1,2)Y_L^{M*}(\Omega_2) \, |\chi^{(+)}(\mathbf{k}, \mathbf{r}_2)\rangle. \quad (12.113)$$

Note that all final states are regarded as degenerate in energy. In practice, of course, different states can be distinguished by their Q values. The first $2+$ and $3-$ states are single-phonon excitations for which (12.113) is the exact adiabatic amplitude.

The partial wave expansion of (12.113) is

$$\tilde{f}_{a0} = 4\pi k^{-2}(2L+1)^{\tfrac{1}{2}} \sum_{ll'} i^{l-l'}(2l+1)(2l'+1)^{-\tfrac{1}{2}} e^{i(\sigma_l + \sigma_{l'})}$$
$$\times \, C_{lLl'}^{000} C_{lLl'}^{0MM} \, Y_{l'}^M(\theta, 0) R_{ll'}, \quad (12.114)$$

where

$$R_{ll'} = \tfrac{1}{2} \sum_n C_{nL} \int dr_1 \int dr_2 [u_{l'}(k, r_1)\omega_{nl'}(1,2)u_l(k, r_2)$$
$$+ \, u_{l'}(k, r_1)\omega_{nl}(1,2)u_l(k, r_2)]. \quad (12.115)$$

At this stage the use of elastic-scattering phase shifts rather than exact wave functions is introduced. The partial waves u_l and the associated S-matrix elements η_l are continuous, differentiable functions of l, which is just a parameter in the differential equation from which they are derived. They only have physical interpretations for integral values of l. The same is true for the partial Green's functions involved in the ω_{nl}. Therefore the radial integrals in (12.114) are analytic functions of l and l'.

The triangle selection rules for l, l' and L tell us that only a small range of $|l - l'|$ is of physical interest. Over this range we make the approximation

$$R_{ll'} = \tfrac{1}{2} \int dr_1 \int dr_2 [u_{l'}(k, r_1)\omega_{nl'}(1,2)u_l(k, r_2) + u_{l'}(k, r_1)\omega_{nl}(1,2)u_l(k, r_2)]$$

$$\cong \int dr_1 \int dr_2 u_{\bar{l}}(k, r_1)\omega_{n\bar{l}}(1,2)u_{\bar{l}}(k, r_2), \quad (12.116)$$

where

$$\bar{l} = \tfrac{1}{2}(l + l'). \quad (12.117)$$

This approximation is correct up to derivatives of first order in l. We may now use Equation (12.97) for (12.116).

$$R_{ll'} \cong \frac{iE}{2k} \frac{1}{n!} \frac{\partial^n}{\partial h^n} \eta_l. \quad (12.118)$$

The analytic approximations for η_l discussed in Chapter 11A[iii] may be used. The parameters in the analytic forms are found by fitting elastic scattering.

The adiabatic theory with the form (12.118) for $R_{ll'}$ uses only asymptotic elastic-scattering information together with appropriate amplitudes C_{nL} describing the nuclear structure. It is known as the Austern-Blair model. It

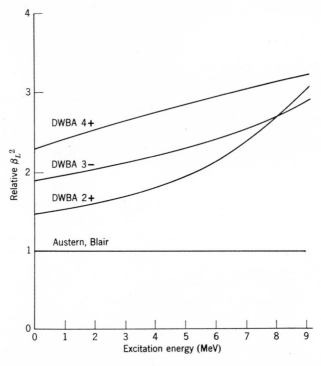

FIG. 12-11 Comparison of $\beta_L{}^2$ for ^{56}Fe (α, α') calculated from the DWBA and the Austern-Blair adiabatic theory. (By permission of D. L. Hendrie.)

is to be compared for single-phonon excitations with the DWBA, which evaluates $R_{ll'}$ by integrating partial waves weighted by a radial form factor, for example dU/dr, derived from an optical-model potential.

If only asymptotic information is to be used, the optical model may be regarded only as a means of parametrizing elastic-scattering phase shifts or S-matrix elements. The optical-model wave function in the interior is irrelevant. The determination of potentials and calculation of wave functions is a cumbersome intermediate step that is circumvented by directly parametrizing η_l.

Comparison of the Austern-Blair model with the corresponding DWBA for single-phonon excitations is shown in Fig. 12.11. Taking the value of $\beta_L{}^2$ obtained by averaging the Austern-Blair cross section over the first four or five maxima as unity, the relative magnitude of $\beta_L{}^2$ obtained in the same way from the DWBA is plotted against excitation energy for $2+$, $3-$ and $4+$ excitations. The reaction used for illustration is ^{56}Fe (α, α'). The curves are independent (within about 1 per cent) of the incident energy (between 23.5 MeV and 50 MeV) and the distorting potential (between 33 MeV and 200 MeV). Because it is an adiabatic approximation, the Austern-Blair model gives worse results for higher excitation energy. Roughly speaking, it over-estimates cross sections by a factor of 2.

In comparison with the highly accurate results of coupled channel calculations for single excitations the Austern-Blair theory is not useful. However, it becomes much more useful as a semiquantitative guide to multiple excitations and very high energy events where more accurate calculations are prohibitive. It is also a useful supplement to our understanding of scattering.

For nucleon scattering the situation is different. The local optical-model potential is at least unique, which lends credibility to the idea that the wave function is a meaningful description of the elastic-scattering process off the energy shell, although the fact that the nonlocal potential gives a slightly different wave function shows that it is not necessarily a physically correct description. The Austern-Blair theory has been found empirically to give a poor description of nucleon inelastic scattering.

[ii] THE FRAUNHOFER APPROXIMATION

This approximation was developed by Drozdov (55), Inopin (56), and Blair (59). The adiabatic approximation for an inelastic transition is just the matrix element of the elastic-scattering amplitude between the initial and final nuclear states, as was described in the previous section [see Equation (12.101)]. For α-particles the smallness of η_l for small l (see Chapter 11 A [iii]) gives rise to the validity of the sharp cutoff model for elastic scattering. The scattering amplitude is obtained by summing the Coulomb amplitudes for partial waves for $l \geq l_0$ and completely omitting amplitudes for $l < l_0$. Since α-particles have short wavelength, it is possible approximately to translate the sharp cutoff in angular momentum into a sharp cutoff in configuration space (in fact a configuration space cutoff results in a less-sharp cutoff in angular momentum space, which is more realistic).

The nucleus may be regarded as a black disc that removes a circular part of the wave front. This is the Fraunhofer approximation for the elastic-scattering amplitude $f(\mathbf{k}', \mathbf{k})$. In mathematical language it consists of integrating a space-dependent phase factor over the projection of the nuclear volume on a plane perpendicular to the beam. For elastic scattering from a spherical nucleus the black area is circular; for inelastic scattering it is the projection of the nonspherical shape given, for example, by (12.13). For single-phonon excitations we use the terms linear in α_{LM}. The elastic-scattering amplitude for the deformed disc is written as $f(\alpha, \theta)$. For small scattering angles it is

$$f(\alpha, \theta) = \frac{ik}{2\pi} \iint dA e^{-i\mathbf{k}'\cdot\mathbf{r}}$$

$$= \frac{ik}{2\pi} \int_0^{2\pi} d\phi \left[\int_0^{R_0} r \, dr \exp\left(-ikr\,\theta \cos \phi\right) \right.$$

$$\left. + \exp\left(-ikR_0\theta \cos \phi\right) R_0^2 \sum_{LM} \alpha_{LM} Y_L{}^M\left(\frac{\pi}{2}, \phi\right) \right]. \quad (12.119)$$

where $\mathbf{k}'$ lies in the x-z plane and makes a small angle θ with the incident direction $\mathbf{k}$. The first term is the contribution from the black circular disc inside R_0. The second term is the contribution from the rim. The ϕ integration produces cylindrical Bessel functions defined by

$$2\pi J_m(z)i^m = \int_0^{2\pi} d\phi e^{iz \cos \phi} \cos (m\phi). \quad (12.120)$$

The integrations in (12.119) can be performed, yielding

$$f(\alpha, \theta) = ikR_0^2 \left\{ \frac{J_1(kR_0\theta)}{kR_0\theta} + \sum_{\substack{LM \\ L+M \text{ even}}} \left(\frac{2L+1}{4\pi}\right)^{1/2} i^L \right.$$

$$\left. \times \frac{[(L-M)! \, (L+M)!]^{1/2}}{(L-M)!! \, (L+M)!!} \alpha_{LM} J_{|M|}(kR_0\theta) \right\}. \quad (12.121)$$

Note the similarity of the selection rules, and the angular-momentum-dependent part of (12.121), to the corresponding part (12.28) of the DWBA. In particular, we notice that only odd M values occur for odd L and only even M values for even L, again resulting in the phase rule for inelastic scattering. The first term of (12.121) gives elastic scattering. Since it depends on J_1, its angular distribution is out of phase with that of inelastic scattering for even L.

The inelastic scattering amplitude is now introduced by taking the matrix element of the elastic-scattering amplitude $f(\alpha, \theta)$ between the nuclear states. This is the adiabatic approximation.

$$f_{a0}(\alpha, 0) = \langle a| f(\alpha, 0) |0\rangle. \quad (12.122)$$

We shall consider the vibrational case for illustration.

The only operators in (12.121) are the α_{LM}; hence the cross sections depend on the squares of the matrix elements.

$$\frac{\beta_L^2}{2L+1} = |\langle a| \alpha_{LM} |0\rangle|^2 = \hbar\omega_L/2B_L. \quad (12.123)$$

This definition of the deformation parameters β_L is equivalent to (12.16). B_L is the surface tension and $\hbar\omega_L$ is the phonon energy in the harmonic vibration approximation.

The cross sections for different states in the Fraunhofer approximation are, for a 0+ ground state,

$$\frac{d\sigma}{d\Omega} \text{(elastic)} = (kR_0^2)^2 \left| \frac{J_1(x)}{x} \right|^2$$

$$\frac{d\sigma}{d\Omega}(0+ \to 0+) = (kR_0^2)^2(\beta_0^2/4\pi)J_0^2(x)$$

$$\frac{d\sigma}{d\Omega}(0+ \to 2+) = (kR_0^2)^2(\beta_2^2/4\pi)[\tfrac{1}{4}J_0^2(x) + \tfrac{3}{4}J_2^2(x)]$$

$$\frac{d\sigma}{d\Omega}(0+ \to 3-) = (kR_0^2)^2(\beta_3^2/4\pi)[\tfrac{3}{8}J_1^2(x) + \tfrac{5}{8}J_3^2(x)], \qquad (12.124)$$

where

$$x = kR\theta.$$

The phase rule for these states is easily understood, since $J_L^2(x)$ quickly assumes its asymptotic form

$$J_L^2(x) \sim \frac{2}{\pi x} \sin^2 x + \frac{\pi}{4} - L\pi. \qquad (12.125)$$

It is interesting to ask how the Fraunhofer approximation compares with the DWBA. A comparison is made in Fig. 12.12 for the inelastic scattering of 43 MeV α-particles from the first 2+ state of ^{24}Mg.

The Fraunhofer approximation predicts the positions of the first five maxima in the experiment just as well as the DWBA, although the more correct treatment of the surface extension in the DWBA predicts fewer large momentum-transfer components. It is interesting that even the DWBA fits the data only up to 70° where the momentum transfer is 3.3 fm^{-1}.

The adiabatic approximation in both its more exact and Fraunhofer forms has been most productive in yielding nuclear structure information from α-particle inelastic scattering. The spins and parities of nuclear states are easily identified and the values of the deformation parameters check qualitatively with those obtained by electromagnetic methods.

It is also very interesting from the point of view of reaction theory, since it is a theory that gives qualitatively correct answers within its range of validity. It is not as relevant as the distorted wave t-matrix approximation to the central problem of describing nuclear phenomena in terms of two-body forces.

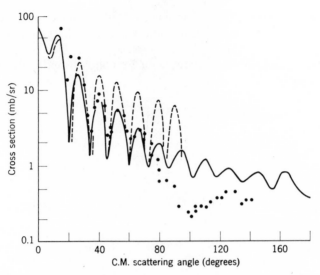

FIG. 12.12 Comparison of Fraunhofer and DWBA fits to the inelastic scattering of 43 MeV α-particles from the first 2+ state of ^{24}Mg. The value of β_2 is about 0.33. (Adapted from Blair, 60.)

[iii] DISPERSION RELATIONS

In Chapter 10*B*[vi] it was shown how dispersion relations derived from analytic properties of scattering amplitudes can be used to relate scattering amplitudes for different processes. The scattering amplitude $R_{ij}(E)$ for a process at energy E is related to the scattering amplitudes for transitions R_{ki} and R_{kj}, between the initial and final states j and i and a complete set of intermediate states k, by

$$R_{ij}(E) = \frac{1}{\pi} \int \frac{dE' \sum_k R_{ki}{}^*(E')R_{kj}(E')}{E' - E}. \tag{10.75}$$

The theory is adapted to the inelastic scattering of a particle x by a nucleus A by first considering the intermediate state to be one in which the outgoing particle is scattered elastically by the nucleus in its final state A^*. The generalization to the realistic case where the elastic scattering is considered also in the initial state will be obvious.

The scattering is represented diagrammatically in Fig. 12.13.

The probability amplitude for the inelastic reaction with interaction only in the final state i is written as a bubble diagram I. It consists of a sum of probability amplitudes represented by a bubble diagram P for inelastic scattering with no intermediate states (plane-wave Born approximation) and bubble diagrams representing inelastic scattering I followed by elastic scattering E

in a complete set of intermediate states k, each with different relative energy. A bubble diagram represents a combination of internal diagrams.

The angular momentum properties of inelastic scattering are of course independent of the mechanism, so we can consider the partial matrix elements $I_{ll'}$, given by (12.30), and sum them with the appropriate spherical harmonics to obtain the total scattering amplitude.

The elastic scattering matrix element is f_l, given by (2.37).

$$f_l = (2ik)^{-1}(\eta_l - 1). \tag{12.126}$$

The matrix element corresponding to the plane-wave term P contains the physical information about the reaction mechanism. The plane-wave amplitude is evaluated for collective or quasi-three-body models yielding the amplitude $I_{ll'}^{(0)}$.

The integral equation relating these amplitudes follows from (10.75)

$$I_{ll'}(E) = I_{ll'}^{(0)} + \frac{1}{\pi} \int_0^\infty \frac{dE' I_{ll'}(E') f_{l'}^*(E')}{E' - E - i\epsilon}. \tag{12.127}$$

The lower limit of integration is zero if there are no thresholds for new reactions. The term $i\epsilon$ is included to give the correct boundary condition.

This integral equation has an analytic solution, which has been discussed by Omnes (58). It is one of a class of singular integral equations whose solution has been given by Muskhelishvili (46). We shall not consider the problems involved in the solution of the equation, but we shall examine the physical information that is used in the theory.

A necessary condition, stated in Section 10B[vi], is that $I_{ll'}(E)$ should vanish fast enough for large real and imaginary E so that the contour integral in Cauchy's integral theorem may be equated to the integral on the real axis. If it does not, we may be able to put in polynomial convergence factors E_n.

$$I_{ll'}(E) - I_{ll'}(E_n) = \frac{1}{\pi} \int dE' \, \mathrm{Im} \, I_{ll'}(E') \left(\frac{1}{E' - E} - \frac{1}{E' - E_n} \right)$$

$$= \frac{E - E_n}{\pi} \int \frac{dE' \, \mathrm{Im} \, I_{ll'}(E')}{(E' - E)(E' - E_n)}. \tag{12.128}$$

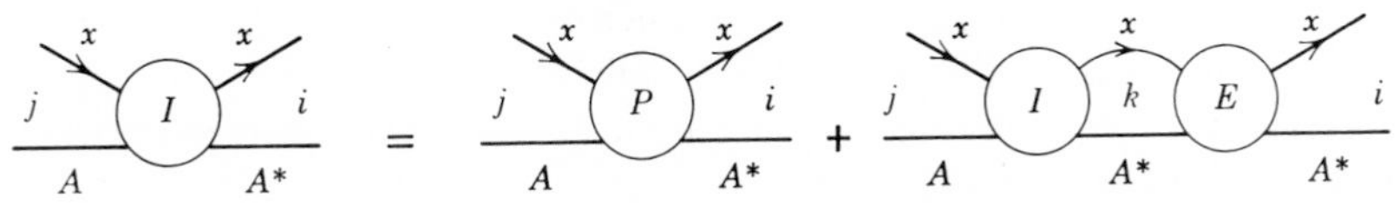

FIG. 12.13 Diagrammatic representation of the integral equation for inelastic scattering of a particle x by a nucleus A with interaction in the final state.

Each subtraction E_n is a new parameter in the theory. Bound states, for example, are taken care of in this way, since they involve poles on the real axis.

The generalization of (12.127) for interaction in both initial and final states is

$$
\begin{aligned}
I_{ll'}(E) &= I_{ll'}^{(0)}(E) + \frac{1}{\pi} \int_0^\infty \frac{dE' I_{ll'}(E') f_{l'}{}^*(E')}{E' - E - i\epsilon} + \frac{1}{\pi} \int_0^\infty \frac{dE' I_{ll'}^*(E') f_l(E')}{E' - E - i\epsilon} \\
&= I_{ll'}^{(0)}(E) + \frac{1}{\pi} \int_0^\infty \frac{dE' [I_{ll'}(E') f_{l'}{}^*(E') + I_{ll'}^*(E') f_l(E')]}{E' - E - i\epsilon}.
\end{aligned}
\tag{12.129}
$$

Equations of this type for direct interactions have been considered by Shapiro (61) and others. Other channels are taken into account by using complex phase shifts, and the lower limit of integration is set equal to zero. Subtractions are not considered. The input information about the nuclear properties is contained in $I_{ll'}^{(0)}$. The distortion enters only through the S-matrix elements η_l for elastic scattering.

The advantage of this method over distorted wave approximations is that the distortion enters to all orders. The first iteration of the integral equation is the distorted wave approximation with the asymptotic form (2.21) used for the distorted waves.

Information about the interior properties of the wave function is not contained in the theory. In principle it could be put in by subtractions, but this would involve an enormous number of parameters.

The usefulness of the theory depends on whether the disadvantage of the omission of off-energy-shell information outweighs the advantage of including distortion to all orders. For quasi-three-body inelastic scattering the cross sections in the distorted wave t-matrix approximation are sensitive to assumptions about the interior. For collective excitations by α-particles the adiabatic theory works fairly well, indicating that the assumptions of the dispersion relation theory are more valid.

E. SUMMARY

Inelastic scattering has been discussed at great length because it is a very simple type of nuclear reaction, which can be used to illustrate most of the points that are relevant to the central theme of understanding nuclei and nuclear reactions in terms of nucleon-nucleon forces. The details of the theories considered in this chapter are similar for other direct reactions, so the discussions of details will serve as an illustration of the principles, which need not be repeated in subsequent chapters.

We shall discuss what information is obtained from inelastic scattering and how it is related, through the models used, to the fundamental questions.

First, in order to have a detailed description of a reaction in terms of a manageable number of coordinates, some collective assumptions must be made, just as for the models of bound states. If the whole nucleus is best described by collective coordinates the connection of inelastic scattering with the basic nuclear forces is rather remote. It must be made through a derivation of the collective model such as the Hartree-Fock calculation of Chapter 6C. To offset this disadvantage, the reaction mechanism is so well understood that angular distributions of the correct shape can be obtained up to several inverse fermis of momentum transfer using, of course, parameters that also describe elastic scattering.

As was the case with Rutherford scattering, information about the target nucleus is not obtained entirely separately from information about the reaction mechanism. The deformation parameter β_L occurs in the coupling factors multiplied by a radius factor R_0. The reaction theory identifies this as one of the collective parameters, the radius of the optical-model potential, which is determined with some ambiguity by elastic scattering, particularly in the case of α-particles. Determination of β_L by electromagnetic methods may be regarded as a physical means of removing the ambiguity in R_0.

The change of spin and parity of the nucleus in a collective excitation is determined uniquely by almost every model for the case of α-particles and by those that include a description of the focusing of the elastic scattering wave functions for the case of nucleons at lower energies. Models that do not include focusing are the Fraunhofer model and models that use eikonal approximations for distorted waves. They result in the phase rule for angular distributions, which is invalid for lower-energy nucleons.

The change of parity is determined by the parity rule for lower energy nucleons. For parity change the cross section invariably falls as the scattering angle becomes less than about 30°. The cross section is not invariably large at forward angles for no parity change because it depends on interference effects involving the focus. The interference effects are of course energy-dependent, and there is an energy in these cases for which the forward cross section is large.

With regard to the reaction mechanism, the adiabatic approximation gives fairly good answers for α-particle scattering. This tends to confirm the physical reality of the collective model description of low-lying states. Internal coordinates of the nucleus are difficult to excite. The adiabatic approximation is tested still further by two-phonon excitations where the approximation that α commutes with G_0 in Equation (12.109) still gives good results.

It is possible to approach one order of approximation closer to a description in terms of nuclear forces by using a description of the nucleus in terms of single-particle wave functions. The collective coordinates then describe the interaction of the particle with the core. It may be that certain low-lying states of odd-A nuclei are well described as collective core excitations. The collective theory of inelastic scattering has had some success in these situations.

The most fundamental situation that is still tractable is where the nuclear wave functions of both states have been described as a linear combination of single-particle wave functions with coefficients determined from an effective two-nucleon interaction for fitting energy levels. Inelastic scattering is then described as a sum of quasi-three-body matrix elements. The coefficients in the sum are given by the effective forces and the nuclear model. The potentials in the three-body problem are the nucleon-core potentials at the appropriate energy, namely the shell-model potential for the bound state and the optical model potential for unbound states, and an effective two-nucleon potential.

The model has had great success at high energy where the distorted wave impulse approximation can be used. The two-nucleon interaction is then described entirely by measurable (on the energy shell) information. Very good answers are obtained by using the free two-nucleon cross sections for the interaction. The nuclear structure information obtained by using this reaction as a probe is very detailed. Models for the coefficients in the bound-state description, which give approximately equally good energy levels, can be distinguished.

The theories mentioned thus far use only direct matrix elements where the projectile is never exchanged with a nuclear particle. Examination of the distorted wave approximation for the quasi-three-body mechanism at lower energy reveals that the antisymmetry effects can be important. Direct and exchange matrix elements are comparable in magnitude. However, they are in phase to quite a close approximation, which gets better at higher energies. This explains why it is unnecessary to antisymmetrize at high energies. The effect of antisymmetry is included, of course, in the two-body cross sections.

The calculations and experiments that would really test the quasi-three-body model at low energies are just being perfected. Examination of the theory shows that it is capable of yielding very useful information about effective nucleon-nucleon forces in nuclear matter at low energies. The possibility that effective forces in the interior may be reduced because of many-body effects is capable of being tested.

It has been seen that detailed information about nuclear structure is not obtainable from angular distribution shapes. Absolute magnitudes are very sensitive to model details. The shape of an angular distribution is characteristic of the energy and the localization of the reaction within the nuclear volume. This is understood on the basis of the uncertainty principle. Momentum-transfer distributions reflect the localization in space of the region in which momentum is transferred. Simple theories which parametrize only the first moments of space distributions are almost as good as detailed distorted wave models for angular shapes. These theories only fail when phase distortions introduced by interferences of contributions from localized space regions are important. This occurs for lower-energy nucleon reactions. The angular momentum properties of the reaction play a large part in the space localization. Hence angular momentum transfer can often be determined merely from angular distribution shapes.

The last thing to be discussed is the information obtainable about strong short-range correlations in nuclei. The effects discussed so far are due to long-range correlations such as those which produce collective excitations.

Short-range correlations are characterized by high momentum-transfer components. Inelastic-scattering models do not in fact reproduce momentum-transfer distributions for momentum transfers greater than a few inverse fermis. It is in the description of high momentum transfer that the models are oversimplified. They all rely on collective potential descriptions of wave functions of nucleons in the nucleus. Such model wave functions describe only the average behavior of nucleons or at best the low-momentum components of the actual nuclear wave functions. Strong nucleon-nucleon forces act when nucleons come within a range of somewhat less than 1 fm. Thus momentum transfers up to a few fm^{-1} are all that can be described by models involving collective potentials.

Another shortcoming of the models discussed here is the omission of certain exchange effects that depend on terms of order $1/A$. One such term is the heavy particle stripping term in which the interaction between the core and the projectile is responsible for inelastic scattering in the quasi-three-body case. Such effects are not necessarily small, although they have never been positively identified.

FURTHER READING

1. R. M. Eisberg and G. Igo, *Phys. Rev.*, **93**, 1039 (1954).
   Experimental verification of the direct interaction mechanism.

2. N. Austern, "Direct Reactions," *Selected Topics in Nuclear Theory*, edited by F. Janouch, International Atomic Energy Agency, Vienna, 1963.
   W. Tobocman, *Theory of Direct Nuclear Reactions*, Oxford University Press, London, 1961.
   Reviews.

3. C. A. Levinson and M. K. Banerjee, *Ann. Phys.* (*N.Y.*,), **2**, 471, 499 (1957); **3**, 67 (1958).
    N. K. Glendenning, *Phys. Rev.*, **114**, 1297 (1959).
    Distorted wave calculations with explanations.

4. I. E. McCarthy and D. L. Pursey, *Phys. Rev.* **122**, 578 (1961).
    A. J. Kromminga and I. E. McCarthy, *Nucl. Phys.* **31**, 678 (1962).
    Qualitative explanations of shapes of distorted wave angular distributions.

5. S. Yoshida, *Proc. Phys. Soc.* (*London*), **A69**, 668 (1956).
    D. M. Chase, L. Wilets, and A. R. Edmonds, *Phys. Rev.*, **110**, 1080 (1958).
    E. Rost and N. Austern, *Phys. Rev.*, **120**, 1375 (1960).
    B. Buck, Phys. Rev., **130**, 712 (1964).
    T. Tamura, *Rev. Mod. Phys.*, **37**, 679 (1965).
    N. Austern and J. S. Blair, *Ann. Phys.* (*N.Y.*), **33**, 15 (1965).
    J. S. Blair, *Phys. Rev.*, **115**, 928 (1959); *Proceedings of the International Conference on Nuclear Structure, Kingston*, edited by D. A. Bromley and E. W. Vogt, University of Toronto Press, Toronto, 1960, p. 824.
    Generalized optical model for collective excitations.

6. R. M. Haybron and H. McManus, *Phys. Rev.*, **140**, B638 (1965).
    A. Agodi and G. P. Schiffrer, *Nucl. Phys.*, **50**, 337 (1964).
    G. R. Satchler, *Nucl. Phys.*, **A95**, 1 (1967).
    K. A. Amos, V. A. Madsen, and I. E. McCarthy, *Nucl. Phys.*, **A94**, 103 (1967).
    The quasi-three-body mechanism.

PROBLEMS

1. Derive the partial wave expansion of the DWBA for $L = 2$ in the rotational excitation model.

2. Use the properties of the angular momentum coefficients to verify the parity rule (12.34) for forward scattering.

3. Plot the first two peaks in the angular distribution for the inelastic scattering of 40 MeV α-particles from a $2+$ state of Mg^{24} using $\beta_2 = 0.33$, $Q = 0$ in the following approximations.

    (i) The Fraunhofer approximation with $R_0 = 6.4$ fm.
    (ii) The plane-wave approximation for a square well, $R_0 = 6.4$ fm.
    (iii) The McCarthy-Pursey approximation for a square well, $R_0 = 6.4$ fm, $\gamma' = 0.9$.

4. For a $0+$ to $2+$ excitation and $l = 3$, write out each of the coupled equations corresponding to (12.5) with the corresponding numerical values of $I, j, l, I', j', l', j'', l''$. Show that there are six equations. How many equations are there for $l > 3, l < 3$?

5. By considering the asymptotic form of $j_l(kr)$ and $h_l^{(1)}(kr)$ for $r \to 0$ verify that the multipole expansion of the Yukawa potential is given by

$$e^{-\mu|\mathbf{r}_1-\mathbf{r}_2|}/|\mathbf{r}_1 - \mathbf{r}_2| = -4\pi \sum_{lm} j_l(i\mu r_<)h_l^{(1)}(i\mu r_>) Y_l^{m*}(\Omega_1) Y_l^m(\Omega_2).$$

6. Write the partial wave expansion of the DWBA for a two-phonon vibrational excitation.

7. In expressions like the one derived in Problem 6 we have two matrix elements that add coherently. What is the evidence indicating that any of the methods of this chapter are capable of reproducing these matrix elements with the correct phase relationships?

13

REARRANGEMENT COLLISIONS

A rearrangement collision occurs when a particle d consisting of a certain number n_d of nucleons enters the reaction region, and a particle p with a different number n_p of nucleons emerges. We use the notation d, p for the particles so that the reader may keep the concrete picture of the deuteron, proton reaction in mind. We shall, in fact, use this reaction as the main illustration of the use of the theory.

If $n_d > n_p$ we have stripping, if $n_d < n_p$ we have pickup. By time-reversal invariance the matrix element for the reaction $C(d, p)F$ is equal to that for the reaction $F(p, d)C$ with corresponding energies, where the nuclei C and F are the core (or target) and the final nucleus in the case of stripping. The equality of the matrix elements has been tested experimentally for several reactions (for example, see Bodansky, Braithwaite, Shreve, Storm, and Weitkamp, 66).

The type of information about nuclear structure yielded by these reactions has been illustrated in Chapter 5C. A stripping reaction occurs with high probability if the structure of the residual nucleus F is such that its wave function has a large component representing the original nucleus coupled to the exchanged particle. Maintaining our analogy with deuteron stripping, the exchanged particle will be denoted by n. We shall be concerned chiefly with the case where n is a single nucleon.

The particle n may enter one of several single-particle states $\phi_i(x_n)$, where x_n represents the coordinates $\mathbf{r}_n, \boldsymbol{\sigma}_n$ of n. The coordinates of the center of mass of n with respect to C are $\mathbf{r}_n$, and the intrinsic coordinates (spin in the case of the neutron) are $\boldsymbol{\sigma}_n$. The same notation with appropriate subscripts is used for the particles d and p. The set i of single-particle quantum numbers is n, l, j, m in the case of the neutron. They are defined by (5.4) and (5.5) except that here we use m to represent the projection of j rather than of l.

The residual nucleus F is formed in an eigenstate $|\rho\rangle$ which may be expanded in the weak-coupling representation (5.30). In the first part of this chapter we shall consider formal theory, so that the set ρ of quantum numbers need not be specified. We use the notation

$$|\rho\rangle \equiv \Phi_{nC}^{(\rho)}(x_n, \xi) = \sum_{i\alpha} t_{i\alpha}^{(\rho)} \phi_i(x_n)\psi_\alpha(\xi), \qquad (13.1)$$

where ξ denotes the coordinates of the core C, $\psi_\alpha(\xi)$ denotes the wave function of the core in a state characterized by the set α of quantum numbers, and $t_{i\alpha}^{(\rho)}$ are expansion coefficients that define the spectroscopic properties of F. In Section B of this chapter the values of these quantities in specific nuclear models will be considered.

The reaction depends on the n-C and p-C potentials $V_n(x_n, \xi)$, $V_p(x_p, \xi)$ and the n-p potential $V_{np}(x_n, x_p)$ According to general scattering theory (10.28), the stripping amplitude for an outgoing particle with wave vector $\mathbf{k}_p$ is

$$T = \langle \phi_p^{(-)}(\mathbf{k}_p, x_p)\Phi_{nC}^{(\rho)} | V_{np} + V_p | \Psi^{(+)}\rangle, \qquad (13.2)$$

where $\Psi^{(+)}$ is the solution with ingoing boundary conditions of the complete many-body problem and $\phi_p^{(-)}(\mathbf{k}_p, x_p)$ is the solution with outgoing boundary conditions of the Schrödinger equation for the motion of p according to the asymptotic potential H_0. If H_0 includes the Coulomb potential, the Coulomb part must be subtracted from the interaction $V_{np} + V_p$. The Dirac brackets in (13.2) imply integrations over all coordinates including sums over spins. It is convenient to introduce the distorted wave formalism, as was first done in Chapter 10D, by redefining H_0 to include an auxiliary potential $\mathscr{V}_p(x_p)$ which will be chosen to cancel $V_p(x_p, \xi)$ as far as possible. In practice $\mathscr{V}_p$ is the appropriate optical-model potential. The residual proton-core potential is $v_p(x_p, \xi)$. The distorted wave is given by

$$(K_p + \mathscr{V}_p - E + i\epsilon)\chi_p^{(-)}(\mathbf{k}_p, x_p) = 0. \qquad (13.3)$$

The Coulomb potential is included in $\mathscr{V}_p$, so that K_p is the kinetic energy operator.

The stripping amplitude in the distorted wave representation is

$$T = \langle \chi_p^{(-)}(\mathbf{k}_p)\Phi_{nC}^{(\rho)} | V_{np} + v_p | \Psi^{(+)}\rangle. \qquad (13.4)$$

It is now necessary to make certain approximations for $\Psi^{(+)}$.

A. THE DISTORTED WAVE BORN APPROXIMATION

The only approximation which thus far has yielded results that are amenable to computation with partial wave expansions of unbound wave functions is the DWBA (Tobocman, 61). The assumption that characterizes the approximation is that scattering of d from the core dominates the reaction, so that $\Psi^{(+)}$ may be approximated by the product of the internal wave function $\phi_d(x_{np})$ of d and a function $\Phi^{(+)}(\mathbf{k}_d, x_d, \xi)$ representing the scattering of d, whose center of mass and internal coordinates are denoted by x_d and whose initial wave vector is $\mathbf{k}_d$, from a core whose internal degrees of freedom may be excited in the scattering.

$$\Psi^{(+)}(\mathbf{k}_d, x_n, x_p, \xi) \cong \phi_d(x_{np})\Phi^{(+)}(\mathbf{k}_d, x_d, \xi), \tag{13.5}$$

where

$$[K_d(x_d) + H_C(\xi) + V_{dC}(x_d, \xi) - E - i\epsilon]\Phi^{(+)}(\mathbf{k}_d, x_d, \xi) = 0. \tag{13.6}$$

The total energy of the system is E. K_d is the complete Hamiltonian of d.

The problem (13.6) of the scattering of a particle from a collective core whose internal Hamiltonian is $H_C(\xi)$ has been discussed formally in Chapter 10D. Equation (13.6) is analogous to (10.103, 10.104). The decomposition into partial waves has been discussed in Chapter 12A, Equations (12.5). We shall not repeat the details of the partial wave decompositions here, but we shall proceed formally so as to make the structure of the theory explicit. The details are given for example by Penny and Satchler (64).

In analogy with Equation (10.102), $\Phi^{(+)}$ is expanded in terms of core wave functions $\psi_\alpha(\xi)$ as follows.

$$\Phi^{(+)}(\mathbf{k}_d, x_d, \xi) = \sum_\alpha \psi_\alpha(\xi) u_\alpha^{(+)}(\mathbf{k}_d, x_d). \tag{13.7}$$

The elastic and inelastic wave functions $u_\alpha^{(+)}$ are obtained by solving a set of coupled differential equations analogous to (10.144), truncated to include only the core states $\psi_\alpha(\xi)$ that are to be included in the bound-state description (13.1).

We shall first consider the term of (13.4) with the interaction V_{np}. The stripping amplitude is written with the substitutions (13.1, 13.5, 13.7) as

$$T_1 = \sum_{i\alpha\alpha'} t_{i\alpha}^{(p)} \langle \chi_p^{(-)}(\mathbf{k}_p)\phi_i\psi_\alpha| V_{np} |\phi_d\psi_{\alpha'}u_{\alpha'}^{(+)}(\mathbf{k}_d)\rangle. \tag{13.8}$$

In considering the term of (13.4) with the interaction v_p we shall keep only the first term of (13.7), since the higher-order terms will produce a result that is of second order in the core excitation. In this approximation the many-body Schrödinger equation is

$$[K_n + K_p + H_C + V_n + V_p - E - i\epsilon]u_0^{(+)}\psi_0\phi_d \cong -V_{np}u_0^{(+)}\psi_0\phi_d,$$

so that

$$u_0^{(+)}\psi_0\phi_d \cong -\frac{1}{K_n + K_p + H_C + V_n + V_p - E} V_{np}u_0^{(+)}\psi_0\phi_d.$$

This is now substituted into (13.4). Using the fact that $\sum_{i\alpha} t_{i\alpha}^{(\rho)} \phi_i \psi_\alpha$ is an eigenstate of $K_n + H_C + V_n$ with eigenvalue E_ρ, we obtain a second term in the stripping amplitude.

$$T_2 = \sum_{i\alpha} t_{i\alpha} \langle \chi_p^{(-)}(\mathbf{k}_p) \phi_i \psi_\alpha | \, v_p \, \frac{1}{K_p + V_p + E_\rho - E} \, V_{np} \, | \phi_d \psi_0 u_0^{(+)}(\mathbf{k}_d) \rangle$$

$$\equiv \sum_{i,\alpha \neq 0} t_{i\alpha}^{(\rho)} \langle w_\alpha^{(-)}(\mathbf{k}_p) \phi_i | \, V_{np} \phi_d \, | u_0^{(+)}(\mathbf{k}_d) \rangle. \tag{13.9}$$

The function $w_\alpha^{(-)}(\mathbf{k}_p)$ is the wave function for the inelastic scattering of the proton from the core in the state α, according to (10.130). We shall use this notation here to replace the optical-model wave function.

$$\chi_p^{(-)}(\mathbf{k}_p) \equiv w_0^{(-)}(\mathbf{k}_p).$$

Using the orthonormality of the core wave functions $\psi_\alpha(\xi)$ in (13.8), we combine (13.8) and (13.9) to obtain the stripping amplitude to first order in the core excitation.

$$T = \sum_{i\alpha} t_{i\alpha}^{(\rho)} \langle w_0^{(-)}(\mathbf{k}_p) \phi_i | \, V_{np} \phi_d \, | u_\alpha^{(+)}(\mathbf{k}_d) \rangle$$

$$+ \sum_{i,\alpha \neq 0} t_{i\alpha}^{(\rho)} \langle w_\alpha^{(-)}(\mathbf{k}_p) \phi_i | \, V_{np} \phi_d \, | u_0^{(+)}(\mathbf{k}_d) \rangle. \tag{13.10}$$

The transformation from the natural coordinates $\mathbf{r}_n$, $\mathbf{r}_p$ to the C.M. and relative coordinates $\mathbf{r}_d$, $\mathbf{r}_{np}$ will be discussed later.

The coefficients $t_{i\alpha}^{(\rho)}$ are the spectroscopic amplitudes for the occurrence of the basis vector $\phi_i(x_n)\psi_\alpha(\xi)$ in the eigenvector $|\rho\rangle$ of the residual nucleus. The distorted waves $u_\alpha^{(+)}$ and $w_\alpha^{(-)}$ are elastic-scattering wave functions with plane ingoing and spherical outgoing waves only for the term in the amplitude (13.10) for which the core C is in its ground state $\alpha = 0$. If the core is in an excited state α, $u_\alpha^{(+)}$ and $w_\alpha^{(-)}$ have only spherical waves in the exterior region, outgoing and ingoing, respectively. We shall base our discussion of rearrangement collisions on Equation (13.10).

The approximation made in deriving (13.10) in the simplest case of deuteron stripping (d, p) on an inert core are already much worse than those made in deriving Equations (10.198, 10.204) for inelastic scattering and breakup in the corresponding static three-body system. In fact we have not justified approximation (13.5) at all in terms of the static three-body problem.

Thus the present theory of stripping must not be taken too seriously as a description of the reaction. It has, however, proved invaluable for the extraction of spectroscopic information, particularly relative spectroscopic factors for different final states in the same experiment. It may be considered as a method of interpolation in data. We shall now consider further approximations that are usually made to reduce the computation of (13.10) to an extremely simple one for a modern computer. These approximations are not incommensurate with the ones already made in deriving (13.10), except in certain cases that will be discussed in Section B[iii].

[i] THE INERT CORE APPROXIMATION

Instead of the approximation (13.5) for $\Psi'^{(+)}$ a further approximation is often used. We factorize $\Psi'^{(+)}$ into three factors, two of which depend only on the coordinates x_n and x_p. The other factor is the wave function of the target, or core in its ground state, which depends only on ξ.

$$\Psi'^{(+)} \cong \phi_d(x_{np})\chi_d^{(+)}(\mathbf{k}_d, x_d)\psi_0(\xi). \tag{13.11}$$

The form of the DWBA is now analogous to the form it takes for the three-body approximation where the particle cannot excite the core. Only the terms $\alpha = 0$ appear in the expansion (13.8) of the stripping amplitude, and the core-excitation term (13.9) vanishes. The deuteron-scattering function is a purely elastic distorted wave $\chi_d^{(+)}(\mathbf{k}_d, x_d)$, and the stripping amplitude is proportional to the single spectroscopic amplitude $t_{i0}^{(\rho)}$.

It is often appropriate, when the approximation (13.11) is used for the stripping process, to consider a more detailed shell model for the final nucleus. In this model the closed-shell core of the shell model is considered inert, but any one of N equivalent particles, labelled by the subscript x, may be concerned in the stripping. The neutron (or proton) n is included in the N particles, so that the target has $(N - 1)$ equivalent particles. The stripping amplitude (13.3) becomes, using (13.4, 13.11) and neglecting v_p,

$$T = A\langle\chi_p^{(-)}(\mathbf{k}_p)\Phi_{xC}^{(\rho)}|\ V_{xp}\ |\phi_d\chi_d^{(+)}(\mathbf{k}_d)\psi_0\rangle. \tag{13.12}$$

The antisymmetrization operator A operates on the N equivalent particles, resulting in a factor N multiplying the amplitude for stripping involving a single neutron. In addition the normalization of the final-state wave function, which is the antisymmetric direct product of a normalized $(N - 1)$-body function with a normalized one-body function, results in a factor $N^{-\frac{1}{2}}$.

The stripping amplitude now reduces to an extremely simple form.

$$T = N^{\frac{1}{2}}\langle\chi_p^{(-)}(\mathbf{k}_p)(\Phi_{nC}^{(\rho)}\ |\ \psi_0)|\ V_{np}\phi_d\ |\chi_d^{(+)}(\mathbf{k}_d)\rangle. \tag{13.13}$$

The notation

$$(\Phi_{nC}^{(\rho)}\ |\ \psi_0) \equiv (n + C\ |\ C) \tag{13.14}$$

denotes an integral over the coordinates ξ only, so that the expression is a function of $\mathbf{r}_n$ and $\boldsymbol{\sigma}_n$. The expression is the nuclear overlap integral. Its spectroscopic properties will be discussed in Section B. At present we shall discuss the radial form for computation. In the three-body approximation $(n + C\ |\ C)$ is the wave function $R_{nlj}(r_n)\ |ljm\rangle$ of the bound particle.

[ii] RADIAL WAVE FUNCTIONS

The shapes of angular distributions for stripping, just as for inelastic scattering, are extremely sensitive to the choice of the bound-state radial wave functions. Since absorption weights the nuclear surface region more strongly than the interior, a different feature of the radial wave function from the feature that determines the energy levels in bound-state calculations is important. In the latter case the interior shape of the wave function, characterized perhaps by the rms radius, is the determining factor. Harmonic oscillator wave functions, which have overlaps of at least 90 per cent with the more realistic wave functions discussed in Chapter 5C are adequate for most nuclear structure calculations. For reactions, the tail of the wave function, which is uniquely determined by the binding energy, is the important feature. This is just the part that is incorrectly reproduced by the harmonic-oscillator wave function.

For states of the final nucleus that are well described by the extreme single-particle model, it is possible to use a radial wave function computed in a finite square well (or a potential with a diffuse surface if desired), whose tail is correct. For many nuclei there is even more precise knowledge of the wave functions, as was discussed in Chapter 5C.

For states that require more sophisticated shell-model descriptions, we usually have the wave functions in terms of linear combinations of harmonic-oscillator functions. A method for computing the overlap integral with accurate boundary conditions has been given by Kawai and Yazaki (67).

The Schrödinger equation for the final nuclear state is, ignoring spins for simplicity,

$$[K_n(\mathbf{r}_n) + H_C(\xi) + V_n(\mathbf{r}_n) - E_\rho]\Phi_{nC}^{(\rho)}(\mathbf{r}_n, \xi) = 0. \qquad (13.15)$$

The overlap integral may be written in the following form (it is easier to discuss the complex conjugate).

$$F^*(\mathbf{r}_n) \equiv (n + C \mid C)^* = (C \mid n + C) = (\psi_0 \mid \Phi_{nC}^{(\rho)}(\mathbf{r}_n))$$

$$= (\psi_0 \mid \frac{1}{E_\rho - K_n - H_C} V_n \mid \Phi_{nC}^{(\rho)}(\mathbf{r}_n))$$

$$= \frac{1}{E_\rho - K_n} (\psi_0 \mid V_n \mid \Phi_{nC}^{(\rho)}(\mathbf{r}_n))$$

$$= \frac{1}{E_\rho - K_n} (C \mid V_n \mid n + C). \qquad (13.16)$$

In commuting $\psi_0(\xi)$ through the operator, we have used the fact that the energy of the core ground state is defined to be zero.

Since V_n is appreciable only in the internal region, only the values of the wave functions in the internal region are important for computing the integral $(C \mid V_n \mid n + C)$. We may therefore use the shell model values of the wave functions to compute this integral. The overlap integral $F^*(\mathbf{r}_n)$ is obtained by solving an inhomogeneous differential equation with the correct boundary conditions.

$$(E_\rho - K_n)F^*(\mathbf{r}_n) = (C|\,V_n\,|n + C). \tag{13.17}$$

In the case where $F^*(\mathbf{r}_n)$ is a single-particle wave function $\phi_i(\mathbf{r}_n)$, the expression (13.17) becomes

$$(E_i - K_n)\phi_i(\mathbf{r}_n) = V_n(\mathbf{r}_n)\phi_i^{(SM)}(\mathbf{r}_n), \tag{13.18}$$

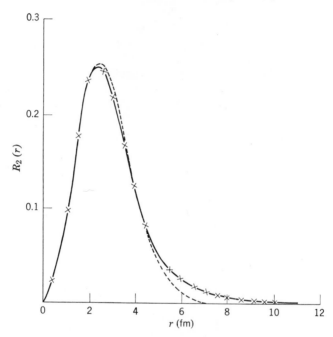

FIG. 13.1 The $1d$ radial wave function for a single particle with a ^{16}O core. The solid line is the exact function. The dotted line is the harmonic oscillator. The crosses indicate the approximation of equation (13.18). The error in the tail region is less than 4 per cent. (Adapted by kind permission of M. Kawai and K. Yazaki.)

where $\phi_i^{(SM)}$ is a harmonic-oscillator wave function. The eigenvalue problem for the well V_n may of course be solved to find an exact value for ϕ_i, which can be used to check the approximation. Such a comparison for a ^{16}O core is shown in Fig. 13.1.

[iii]   THE NEUTRON-PROTON INTERACTION

We shall discuss the n-p interaction explicitly for the case of deuteron stripping. In the basic approximation (13.10) it is represented by

$$V_{np}(x_{np})\phi_d(x_{np}) = (E_d - K_{np})\phi_d(x_{np}), \tag{13.19}$$

where E_d is the deuteron binding energy. Using a specific form for the deuteron wave function, this quantity may be easily evaluated. A common form is the Hulthen wave function for the s-state,

$$\phi_d(r_{np}) = (4\pi)^{-\frac{1}{2}}\Omega\left(\frac{e^{-\gamma r}}{r} - \frac{e^{-\zeta r}}{r}\right), \tag{13.20}$$

where

$$\Omega^2 \int r^2 \, dr \left(\frac{e^{-\gamma r}}{r} - \frac{e^{-\zeta r}}{r}\right)^2 = 1. \tag{13.21}$$

The quantity γ is related to E_d by

$$\gamma^2 = -\frac{ME_d}{\hbar^2}. \tag{13.22}$$

The quantities ζ and Ω have the numerical values

$$\zeta = 7\gamma,$$
$$4\Omega^2 = 2.875 \text{ fm}^{-1}.$$

A form for $V_{np}\phi_d$ which is both very simple and very directly related to the n-p problem may be obtained if we make the approximation

$$V_{np}\phi_d(\mathbf{r}_{np}) = D_0 \, \delta(\mathbf{r}_{np}). \tag{13.23}$$

We have

$$D_0 = \int d^3r V_{np}(r)\phi_d(\mathbf{r})$$

$$= -\frac{\hbar^2}{M}\int d^3r(\nabla^2 - \gamma^2)\phi_d(\mathbf{r}). \tag{13.24}$$

Using any of the well-known forms for $\phi_d(r)$ we find

$$D_0 \cong (1.5)^{\frac{1}{2}} \cdot 10^2 \text{ MeV. fm}^{\frac{3}{2}}.$$

[iv] THE DEUTERON-CORE POTENTIAL

Since analysis of elastic scattering of deuterons does not yield an unambiguous phenomenological potential describing the interaction of a deuteron with the core, this problem requires some discussion. A very simple discussion has been given by Greider and Strobel (66) in the static three-body approximation.

In the case of the (d, p) reaction the stripping amplitude is obtained from (10.189a) as

$$T = \langle \chi_p^{(-)}(\mathbf{k}_p)| \, (V_{np} + V_p - \mathscr{V}_p) - (V_{np} + V_p - \mathscr{V}_p)$$
$$\times \, G^{(+)}(E)(V_n + V_p - V_{dC}) \, |\chi_d^{(+)}(\mathbf{k}_d)\rangle. \quad (13.25)$$

We can now see immediately, at least in the three-body approximation, how to choose the deuteron distorting potential in a way that minimizes the corrections to the DWBA, which are expressed by the second term of (13.25) If we make the approximation that V_n and V_p are functions of $\mathbf{r}_d$ rather than of $\mathbf{r}_n$ and $\mathbf{r}_p$, we may choose V_{dC} so that the corrections vanish.

$$V_{dC}(\mathbf{r}_d) = V_n(\mathbf{r}_d) + V_p(\mathbf{r}_d). \quad (13.26)$$

Actually the deuteron is a very large object with a radius much the same as the nuclear radius, so that the approximation for V_n and V_p is not very good. This fact gives us further insight into the nature of the DWBA for stripping.

The approximation (13.26) at least has the advantage that it is very well defined in terms of elastic-scattering optical models. The deuteron potential is sometimes chosen to be the sum of the proton and neutron optical-model potentials for the appropriate energy. An alternative point of view is the original one that deuteron elastic scattering dominates the reaction, so that an elastic-scattering potential for the deuteron should be used, preferably the one chosen from the equivalent set by the criterion that it should be the nearest to $V_n + V_p$. For many reactions the deuteron-stripping process has been shown experimentally to dominate the nonelastic cross section. The cross section for deuteron breakup (d, np) is much smaller. Thus at least the part of the deuteron elastic-scattering optical-model potential that describes stripping should be omitted. The choice $V_n + V_p$ is preferable on these grounds.

[v] NUMERICAL CALCULATIONS FOR DEUTERON STRIPPING ON AN INERT CORE

In using a reaction theory as a means of extracting nuclear structure information from a reaction, the first step is to calibrate the theory by applying it to a situation where the nuclear structure is well known. In the case of deuteron stripping the simplest case is stripping with a doubly-closed-shell target such as ^{16}O, ^{40}Ca, or ^{208}Pb. In the case of ^{17}O, we are already warned by the quadrupole moment that some core excitation is involved. This is true also for ^{41}Ca and, to a lesser extent, for ^{209}Pb. However, the spectroscopic amplitude $t_{i0}^{(0)}$, for the ground state of the residual nucleus to consist of a particle in the lowest single-particle state i and an unexcited core, may reasonably be expected to dominate the ground-state wave function $|0\rangle$.

In this case (13.10) has only one term. The spectroscopic factor (5.27) for the ground state is given by

$$S^0(\phi_i) = |t_{i0}^{(0)}|^2 = 1.$$

The stripping cross section for unpolarized particles is

$$\frac{d\sigma(\theta)}{d\Omega} = \frac{\mu_d \mu_p}{(2\pi\hbar^2)^2} \frac{k_p}{k_d} \frac{2I_F + 1}{2I_C + 1} \sum_{M_C M_F m_p m_d} |T|^2. \tag{13.27}$$

The notation is explained in Table 13.1.

Particle	d	p	n	C	F
Reduced mass	μ_d	μ_p	—	—	—
Total angular momentum	—	—	$j(l \pm \frac{1}{2})$	I_C	I_F
Projection	—	—	—	M_C	M_F
Orbital angular momentum	—	—	l	—	—
Projection	—	—	m	—	—
Spin	$s_d(1)$	$s_p(\frac{1}{2})$	$s(\frac{1}{2})$	—	—
Projection	m_d	m_p	μ	—	—
Principal quantum number	—	—	n	—	—
Wave number	k_d	k_p	—	—	—
Number of particles equivalent to n	$\nu(1)$	$\nu - 1$	1	$N - 1$	N
Spectroscopic factor	$S_d(1)$	—	—	—	$S_{lsj}^\rho = S^\rho(\phi_i)$
Spectroscopic amplitude	—	—	—	—	$t_{lsj}^\rho = t_{i\alpha}^{(\rho)}$
Reduced width amplitude	—	—	—	—	θ_{lsj}

TABLE 13.1.   Notation used in the description of the reaction $C(d,p)F^{(\rho)}$ (or the time-reversed reaction) in which a general particle d is stripped of a general particle n by a target or core C, leaving an outgoing particle p and the final nucleus F in the eigenstate ρ. Values of relevant quantities for the case where d is a deuteron and p is a proton are given in parentheses. For pickup the nucleus C is left in its αth state.

The expansion of the matrix element in angular momentum eigenstates is obtained from (13.10) by the methods that were given in detail in Chapter 12. We shall consider the case of a target C and final nucleus F with finite masses C, F. This requires some discussion of the coordinates. In order to express the distorted waves as functions of the coordinates $\mathbf{r}_{dC}$ and $\mathbf{r}_{pF}$ of the initial and final particles relative to the initial and final nuclei, we must make a transformation from the more natural coordinate system $\mathbf{r}_{pC}$ and $\mathbf{r}_{nC}$, denoted previously by $\mathbf{r}_p$ and $\mathbf{r}_n$.

The coordinate transformation is understood in terms of the position diagram, Fig. 13.2. The centers of mass of the respective particles are indicated by the points n, p, d, C, F. We may take the natural system to be $\mathbf{r}_{nC}$, $\mathbf{r}_{np}$. The transformation to the system $\mathbf{r}_{dC}$, $\mathbf{r}_{pF}$ is given by

$$-\mathbf{r}_{np} = \alpha(\delta\mathbf{r}_{dC} - \mathbf{r}_{pF})$$
$$\mathbf{r}_{nC} = \alpha(\mathbf{r}_{dC} - \gamma\mathbf{r}_{pF}),$$

(13.28)

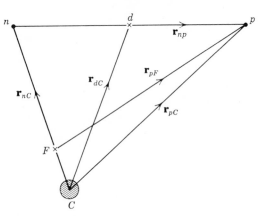

FIG. 13.2 Vector diagram describing the coordinates used in the theory of the (d, p) reaction.

where α, δ, γ are defined, with the masses of the particles denoted by the particle labels, as

$$\alpha = \frac{dF}{n(d+C)} = \frac{2F}{1+F},$$
$$\delta = \frac{C}{F} = \frac{C}{1+C},$$
$$\gamma = \frac{p}{d} = \frac{1}{2}.$$

(13.29)

The more general definitions are useful if the deuteron and proton are to be replaced by heavier ions.

The Jacobian $\mathscr{J}$ of the transformation is given by

$$\mathscr{J} = \alpha^3 = \left[\frac{dF}{n(d+C)}\right]^3.$$

(13.30)

For the three-body approximation with an inert, spin-zero core, the expression for the matrix element T is, neglecting spin-orbit coupling in the optical models and using the orthonormality of the spin functions of n and p,

$$T = \sum_{lsj} T_{lsj}$$

$$= \mathscr{I} \int d^3 r_{dC} \int d^3 r_{pF} \chi^{(-)} {}^*(\mathbf{k}_p, \mathbf{r}_{pF}) \chi^{(+)}(\mathbf{k}_d, \mathbf{r}_{dC})$$

$$\times \sum_{lsj} (-1)^{s_p - m_p} C_{I_C\ j}^{M_C\ M_F - M_C} {}_{I_F}^{M_F} C_{l\ s}^{m\ m_d - m_p} {}_{j}^{M_F - M_C} C_{s_d\ s_p\ s}^{m_d - m_p\ m_d - m_p}$$

$$\times \left[\frac{2s_d + 1}{2s + 1} \right]^{\frac{1}{2}} R_{nlj}(r_{nC}) Y_l^m {}^*(\Omega_{nC}) V_{np}(r_{np}) \phi_d(r_{np}). \tag{13.31}$$

The more general notation has again been retained in case more complicated particles are to be discussed. The Clebsch-Gordan coefficients express the coupling of the angular momenta of the single bound neutron (j) and the core ($I_C = 0$) to that of the final nucleus (I_F), the coupling of the orbital angular momentum of the bound neutron (l) and its spin (s) to its total angular momentum (j) and the coupling of the spins of the deuteron ($s_d = 1$) and the proton ($s_p = \frac{1}{2}$) to the spin of the bound neutron (s). The other spin factors come from rearranging the third Clebsch-Gordan coefficient. The remaining factors have already been discussed. The derivation of the stripping amplitude in a more general case will be given explicitly in Section 13B, Equation (13.42).

For (d, p) stripping on a spin-zero target the angular momentum coupling selection rules ensure that $j = I_F$, so that the fact that parity is a good quantum number allows only one value of l, the angular momentum of the bound neutron, or the angular momentum transfer in the reaction.

It was explained in the case of inelastic scattering, and it is of course true also for stripping, that the localization of the reaction region in space largely determines the shape of the angular distribution. The reaction once again is largely confined to the surface and the space weighting of the surface is very strongly affected by the spherical harmonic in the bound-state wave function. Thus a theory which takes these facts into account will give a qualitative idea of the dependence of the angular distribution on the angular-momentum transfer l and a parameter R characterizing the nuclear surface.

It was discovered by Butler (51) that the plane-wave Born approximation with a radial cutoff R simulating the effects of absorption and possible reduction of the interaction strength in the interior gave a rough qualitative fit to the first peak in the angular distribution and that, in many cases, the peak for the wrong value of l was at such a different angle from the peak for the right value of l that the theory could be used to identify l. Plausible values of R had of course to be used in both cases.

The Butler stripping theory, which has yielded valuable spectroscopic information for many years, is obtained from (13.31) by replacing the distorted waves by the corresponding plane waves. The radial cutoff R is introduced at such a place that $R_{nlj}(r)$ may be considered to be given by the spherical Hankel function for $r > R$.

$$R_{nlj}(r) = \beta r h_l^{(1)}(i\beta r), \qquad r > R, \qquad (13.32)$$

where β is defined by (5.8). The Butler radius R is generally between 2 fm and 3 fm larger than the rms radius of the nucleus. This is partly accounted for by the size of the deuteron and partly by the fact that the phase KR_0 of each scattering-state wave function, where K is the local wave number at the physical surface R_0, is replaced by kR, where k is the exterior wave number. The increase in R compensates the use of a smaller value of K. The differential cross section is given in the three-body approximation by

$$\frac{d\sigma}{d\Omega} = \frac{\mu_d \mu_p}{(2\pi\hbar^2)^2} \frac{k_p}{k_d} \frac{2I_F + 1}{2I_C + 1} [P_d(\kappa)]^2 [W_l(qR, \beta R)]^2 \qquad (13.33)$$

where the relevant momentum-transfer vectors are

$$\boldsymbol{\kappa} = \frac{d-1}{d} \mathbf{k}_d - \mathbf{k}_p,$$

$$\mathbf{q} = \mathbf{k}_d - \frac{C}{F} \mathbf{k}_p. \qquad (13.34)$$

The nuclear wave function needs to be calculated only at the surface, yielding

$$W_l(qR, \beta R) = qR \frac{\partial}{\partial(qR)} j_l(qR) - \frac{\beta R j_l(qR)}{h_l^{(1)}(i\beta R)} \frac{\partial}{\partial(\beta R)} h_l^{(1)}(i\beta R). \quad (13.35)$$

The quantity $P_d(\kappa)$ is the so-called stripping transform, given for a single neutron n by

$$P_d(\kappa) = \int d^3 r_n \, d\boldsymbol{\sigma}_p e^{-i\boldsymbol{\kappa} \cdot \mathbf{r}_n} \phi_{d-n}^*(\boldsymbol{\sigma}_p) \phi_d(\boldsymbol{\sigma}_p, \mathbf{r}_n). \qquad (13.36)$$

This factor allows for the fact that the deuteron (or a larger nucleus d) has internal structure. For deuteron stripping, $P_d(\kappa)$ is simply the Fourier transform of the deuteron wave function, which comes immediately from the analogue of (12.70) for stripping.

We shall not derive the Butler formula here, since it is mainly of historical interest. It is a simple exercise to derive it from (13.31).

The fact that aids in understanding the DWBA is that, in the Butler approximation to the DWBA, the shape of the angular distribution is given by the factor $[W_l(qR, \beta R)]^2$. It is seen from (13.35) to be closely approximated by

$$\frac{d\sigma}{d\Omega} \propto [j_l(qR)]^2. \qquad (13.37)$$

Note the similarity of (13.35, 13.37) to the expression (12.79) derived for inelastic scattering from similar considerations.

In fact, for the reasons discussed in Chapter 12*C*, (13.37) does give a rudimentary idea of the shape of the angular distribution, and is used as a rule of thumb in interpreting angular distributions before performing a DWBA calculation with the intention of fitting the data. For our purpose it provides

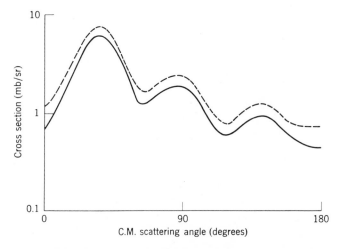

FIG. 13.3.   Differential cross section for the reaction ^{40}Ca(d, p)^{41}Ca (ground state) at 11 MeV calculated in the DWBA with finite range n-p force (solid line) and the zero range approximation (dotted line). (Adapted from Lee, Schiffer, Zeidman, Satchler, Drisko, and Bassel, 64.)

a useful understanding of the shape of the curves, particularly of the first large peak. The shape (13.37) is called a stripping pattern.

As an example of the use of DWBA in a situation where the spectroscopy should be understood, we shall consider the (d, p) reaction on ^{40}Ca, leaving ^{41}Ca in its ground state (Lee, Schiffer, Zeidman, Satchler, Drisko, and Bassel, 64). Several types of approximation have been discussed. First there is the full approximation (13.31) with an n-p force of finite range. One may use the zero range approximation (13.23). The use of these approximations is compared in Fig. 13.3 for 11 MeV (d, p) on ^{40}Ca. Note the difference in absolute magnitude of the curves.

It is interesting to study the differences between the use of two of the ambiguous optical-model potentials for elastic deuteron scattering (see Table 11.2 for the potentials in the scattering of 11.8 MeV deuterons on Cu), the shallowest potential with a depth of about 30 MeV, and the one nearest to $V_p + V_n$ with a depth of about 110 MeV. These potentials will be called x

and z, respectively. The focus for z is much nearer the center of the nucleus than for x, so that one would expect the stripping cross sections, which depend on the wave function rather than just the scattering amplitude, to be different. Figure 13.4 gives striking confirmation of the validity of the approximation

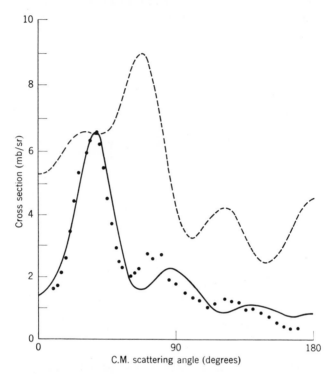

FIG. 13.4   The differential cross section for the reaction ^{40}Ca(d, p)^{41}Ca (ground state) at 11 MeV calculated in the DWBA with the zero range approximation. For the solid curve the deuteron optical-model potential V_{dC} has depth $V = 120.7$ MeV, for the dashed curve $V = 32.5$ MeV. Other parameters are adjusted to give equally good fits to elastic deuteron scattering. Spectroscopic factors for the two curves are 1.00 and 0.90, respectively. Experimental points are shown. (Adapted from Lee, Schiffer, Zeidman, Satchler, Drisko, and Bassel, 64.)

$V_{dC} \cong V_p + V_n$. The dependence of the stripping amplitude on the internal values of the wave functions argues against the use of asymptotic theories such as dispersion relations for a simple description of a reaction involving nucleons.

A refinement which has not been discussed here is the use of spin-orbit coupling in the optical-model potentials. Figure 13.5 shows that the effect on the momentum-transfer distribution in the zero-range approximation is small. Polarization will not be discussed. In fact spin-orbit coupling in the distorted waves always has quite a small effect on the momentum-transfer distribution for nonelastic direct reactions, at least for momentum transfers not too much larger than 1 fm^{-1}. This is the justification for omitting it from calculations.

A further refinement, which again gives small changes, is the use of a non-local potential for calculating the distorted waves.

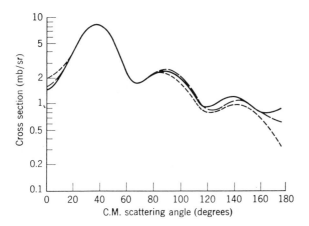

FIG. 13.5   The effect of spin-orbit coupling on the DWBA for the ground-state $l = 3$ transition in ^{40}Ca(d, p)^{41}Ca. In terms of optical-model parameters defined by (11.65), the solid curve is computed with $V_{so} = 0$ for both d and p. The dashed curve has $V_{so} = 8$ for p and 0 for d. The dotted curve has $V_{so} = 8$ for p and 5 for d. (Adapted from Lee, Schiffer, Zeidman, Satchler, Drisko, and Bassel, 64.)

The main questions to which we want the answer from studying stripping on closed-shell nuclei are: How well can the shape of the angular distribution be fitted? How well can the absolute spectroscopic factor be determined?

The curves for ^{40}Ca show that the first peak can generally be fitted very well and that the subsequent peaks can be fitted only qualitatively. The absolute spectroscopic factor is determined by fitting the first peak. Using the most plausible potentials and finite-range interaction, values between about 0.8 and 0.9 are obtained. They must be interpreted in the light of our knowledge that ^{40}Ca is not really inert. The bound-state radial wave function in all these calculations was computed in a Woods-Saxon potential with spin-orbit coupling, chosen to reproduce the correct binding energy. The parameters r_0 and a of the well are generally taken to be those of the proton optical model. In this experiment there is no very direct way to estimate the correct bound-state function. Changes of up to 15 per cent in the spectroscopic factor are produced if the parameters are varied within plausible limits.

The conclusion that may be drawn about the DWBA as a description of the stripping reaction in the quasi-three-body case is that it gives a good semi-quantitative description. It does not describe momentum-transfer distributions as well as the collective theory of inelastic scattering. Stripping is by far the most intensively studied of the quasi-three-body reactions. The success of the relatively crude DWBA gives us hope that a quantitative understanding of such reactions is possible.

B. SPECTROSCOPIC FACTORS

In this section we shall consider the information about the spectroscopic properties of the nuclei F and C, which can be obtained from the form (13.13) of the DWBA. In this approximation the spectroscopic properties are contained in the overlap integral $(n + C \mid C)$. This quantity will be calculated in several specific nuclear models. In order to be sufficiently specific we must display all the relevant quantum numbers, which are defined in Table 13.1 For stripping we have $\alpha = 0$; for pickup we have $\rho = 0$.

$$(\Phi_{nC}^{(\rho)} \mid \psi_\alpha) = (\Phi_{I_F M_F} \mid \psi_{I_C M_C})$$

$$= \int d\xi [\Phi_{nC}^{(\rho)}(\xi, \mathbf{r}_{nC}, \boldsymbol{\sigma}_n)]_{I_F M_F}^* [\psi_\alpha(\xi)]_{I_C M_C}$$

$$= \sum_{ljm} \theta_{lj} C_{I_C\ \ j\ \ I_F}^{M_C\ m\ M_F} \phi_{nljm}^*(\mathbf{r}_{nC}, \boldsymbol{\sigma}_n), \tag{13.38a}$$

$$= \sum_{lsj\mu m} \theta_{lsj} C_{I_C\ \ j\ \ I_F}^{M_C\ M_F-M_C\ M_F} C_{l\ \ s\ \ j}^{m\ \mu\ M_F-M_C}$$

$$\times R_{nlj}(r_{nC}) Y_l^{m*}(\Omega_{nC}) \chi_s^{\mu*}(\boldsymbol{\sigma}_n). \tag{13.38b}$$

The Clebsch-Gordan coefficients express the vector coupling of ϕ_{nljm} and $\psi_{I_C M_C}$ to form $\Phi_{I_F M_F}$ and the vector coupling of $Y_l^m(\Omega_{nC})$ and $\chi_s^\mu(\boldsymbol{\sigma}_n)$ to form $\phi_{nljm}(\mathbf{r}_{nC}, \boldsymbol{\sigma}_n)$.

It is often useful to have a shorthand notation for vector coupling (Macfarlane and French, 60). The two couplings involved here may be represented by

$$\Phi_{I_F M_F} \equiv [\psi_{I_C} \times (nl)_j]_{I_F},$$

$$\phi_{nljm} \equiv [Y_l \times \chi_s]_j. \tag{13.39}$$

The form (13.38a) is appropriate for single-nucleon stripping, where the subscript $s = \frac{1}{2}$ may be dropped. The form (13.38b) is more general. The internal wave function of the particle n (a spin function for a neutron) is $\chi_s^\mu(\boldsymbol{\sigma}_n)$.

The quantities t^p_{lsj} and θ_{lsj} which appear in Table 13.1 are related, dropping unnecessary indices, as follows

$$t_{lj} = N^{\frac{1}{2}}\theta_{lj}C^{Mc}_{Ic}{}^{M_F-Mc}{}_j{}^{M_F}_{I_F}. \tag{13.40a}$$

The spectroscopic factor is, in the general case (13.38b),

$$S_{lsj} = N\theta^2_{lsj}. \tag{13.40b}$$

A similar expansion may be made for the particle d. Assuming that n and p are in an s-state of relative motion in d, we integrate over the internal coordinates $\boldsymbol{\sigma}_n$, $\boldsymbol{\sigma}_p$. In the simple case where n and p are a neutron and a proton, the internal coordinates are the spins and the integral represents a sum over spins.

$$\int d\boldsymbol{\sigma}_n \int d\boldsymbol{\sigma}_p \chi^{m_p}_{s_p}{}^*(\boldsymbol{\sigma}_p)\chi^{\mu}_s{}^*(\boldsymbol{\sigma}_n)[\phi_d(\mathbf{r}_{np}, \boldsymbol{\sigma}_n, \boldsymbol{\sigma}_p)]_{s_d m_d} = a_s\phi_d(r_{np})C^{m_p \mu m_d}_{s_p s s_d}. \tag{13.41}$$

This equation defines the reduced-width amplitude a_s, which is less than unity if d contains less than 100 per cent of the configuration ($n \times p$).

We may now substitute these integrals in (13.13) obtaining

$$T = \sum_{lsj} T_{lsj} = N^{\frac{1}{2}}v^{\frac{1}{2}}\mathscr{I}\int d^3r_{dC}\int d^3r_{pF}\chi^{(-)*}(\mathbf{k}_p, \mathbf{r}_{pF})$$
$$\times \chi^{(+)}(\mathbf{k}_d, \mathbf{r}_{dC})\sum_{lsj} a_s\theta_{lsj}(-1)^{s_p-m_p}C^{Mc}_{Ic}{}^{M_F-Mc}{}_j{}^{M_F}_{I_F}$$
$$\times C^{m}_{l}{}^{m_d-m_p}_{s}{}^{M_F-Mc}_{j}C^{m_d-m_pm_d-m_p}_{s_d}{}_{s_p}{}_{s}\left[\frac{2s_d+1}{2s+1}\right]^{\frac{1}{2}}$$
$$\times R_{nlj}(r_{nC})Y^{m}_{l}{}^*(\Omega_{nC})V_{np}(r_{np})\phi_d(r_{np}). \tag{13.42}$$

To obtain (13.42) we have rearranged the Clebsch-Gordan coefficient in (13.41). We have also included the factor $v^{\frac{1}{2}}$, which is the factor corresponding to $N^{\frac{1}{2}}$ coming from the particle d. There are v particles in d which are treated as identical to n. For the deuteron v is of course unity.

Equation (13.42) is identical to (13.31) except for the reduced-width amplitudes θ_{lsj} and a_s. The corresponding spectroscopic factors are

$$S_{lsj} = N\theta^2_{lsj},$$
$$S_d = va_s^2. \tag{13.43}$$

The factor S_{lsj} is the spectroscopic factor for the final nucleus, which describes the probability of the nucleus F in its final state containing the core in its ground state and the particle n in the single-particle state ϕ_{nlsj}. The factor S_d is the spectroscopic factor for the particle d, which describes the probability of the ground state of the particle d containing the particles n and p. For the deuteron it is unity.

By a straightforward application of angular momentum algebra to the absolute square of (13.42), the differential cross section may be written in the form

$$\frac{d\sigma}{d\Omega} = \frac{\mu_d\mu_p}{(2\pi\hbar^2)^2} \frac{k_p}{k_d} \frac{2I_F + 1}{2I_C + 1} \sum_{M_C M_F m_p m_d l s j} S_{lsj}^\rho \frac{2va_s^2}{2s + 1} |T_{lsj}|^2, \quad (13.44)$$

where T_{lsj} is defined by (13.42). The important fact about (13.44) is that the quantum numbers lsj are summed over incoherently. This is true if spin-orbit coupling is omitted from the distorted waves. Single-particle wave functions with the same l, j but different n contribute coherently.

Note that (13.44) is obtained from the cross section (13.27), in the case of deuteron stripping on an inert core, simply by multiplying (13.27) by the spectroscopic factor S_{lsj}^ρ. Another interpretation of the spectroscopic factor is that it tells how much a particular stripping reaction is like inert-core stripping.

For a spin-zero core the selection rules implied in (13.42) ensure that only one value of l and j occurs in the sum (13.44), so that stripping can be used to find the probability of a particular l, j component occurring in a state of an odd-A nucleus. The angular momentum j of the added single particle is of course equal to I_F in this case.

If the target does not have spin zero, the stripping cross section, neglecting spin-orbit coupling in the optical models, may be an incoherent sum of stripping patterns for more than one value of l. This is harder to interpret, so that the main use of stripping and pickup concerns cases where only one stripping pattern is involved.

We shall now consider applications of stripping theory to different models of nuclear structure.

[i] THE SHELL MODEL

The form (13.42) of the stripping amplitude applies particularly to the shell model, where the final nucleus is described as N equivalent particles outside a closed inert core. Using the notation (13.39) for vector coupling we may write the overlap integral for single-neutron stripping or pickup in the following way.

$$(\Phi_{I_FM_F} | \psi_{I_CM_C}) = (\sum_{J_n} c_{J_n}[(n_pl_pj_p)_{J_p}^P \times (nlj)_{J_n}^N]_{I_F}$$

$$\times |[(n_pl_pj_p)_{J_p}^P \times (nlj)_{J_0}^{N-1}]_{I_C}). \quad (13.45)$$

In this notation all the wave functions are antisymmetrized. The proton configuration is written on the left, the neutron configuration on the right in a particular wave function. There are P protons coupled to J_p. In the final state there are N neutrons coupled to J_n. In the initial state there are $N - 1$

neutrons coupled to J_0. The single-particle quantum numbers are n_p, l_p, j_p for protons and n, l, j for neutrons. As a sufficiently general example we assume that the neutron coupling can be rearranged but the proton coupling is not changed in the reaction. The final state is a linear combination of (target + neutron) wave functions coupled to different neutron angular momenta J_n. The coefficients c_{J_n} in the linear combination are obtained from the n-p and n-n effective matrix elements (see Section 7B[v]).

The wave function of the final nucleus $\Phi_{I_F M_F}$ may be written in the form of the weak coupling expansion (13.1) by recoupling the angular momenta according to Equation (A4.31).

$$
\begin{aligned}
\Phi_{I_F M_F} &= [(n_p l_p j_p)_{J_p}^P \times (nlj)_{J_n}^N]_{I_F} \\
&= [(n_p l_p j_p)_{J_p}^P \times \{(nlj)_{J_0}^{N-1} \times (nlj)_j\}_{J_n}]_{I_F} \\
&= \sum_{I_{C'}} U(J_0 j I_F J_p, J_n I_{C'})[\{(n_p l_p j_p)_{J_p}^P \times (nlj)_{J_0}^{N-1}\}_{I_{C'}} \times (nlj)_j]_{I_F}.
\end{aligned}
$$
(13.46)

We have expressed the wave function of F in the form used in (13.45) as a linear combination of wave functions representing the core C in different angular-momentum states $I_{C'}$, vector coupled to the single neutron. The coefficients in the linear combination are the recoupling coefficients U.

We may now express the wave function (13.46) in our previous notation (13.38) in which the vector coupling of the single-particle wave function ϕ_{nljm} to the core wave function $\psi_{I_{C'} M_{C'}}$ is expressed explicitly by means of a Clebsch-Gordan coefficient

$$
\Phi_{I_F M_F} = \sum_{I_{C'} M_{C'} J_n} c_{J_n} U(J_0 j I_F J_p, J_n I_{C'}) C_{I_{C'} \ \ j \ \ I_F}^{M_{C'} \ m \ M_F} \psi_{I_{C'} M_{C'}} \phi_{nljm}.
$$
(13.47)

The overlap integral is

$$
\begin{aligned}
(\Phi_{I_F M_F} | \psi_{I_C M_C}) \\
&= \sum_{I_{C'} M_{C'} J_n} c_{J_n} U(J_0 j I_F J_p, J_n I_{C'}) C_{I_{C'} \ \ j \ \ I_F}^{M_{C'} m M_F} (\psi_{I_{C'} M_{C'}} \phi_{nljm} | \psi_{I_C M_C}) \\
&= \sum_{J_n} c_{J_n} U(J_0 j I_F J_p, J_n I_C) C_{I_C \ \ j \ \ I_F}^{M_C \ m \ M_F} \phi_{nljm}^*.
\end{aligned}
$$
(13.48)

Using (13.38a, 13.40b) the spectroscopic factor is

$$
S_{lsj}^{I_F I_C} = N |\sum_{J_n} c_{J_n} U(J_0 j I_F J_p, J_n I_C)|^2.
$$
(13.49)

A very good way of normalizing spectroscopic factors for pickup is given by the sum rule

$$
\sum_{I_C} S_{lsj}^{I_F I_C} = N.
$$
(13.50a)

The sum rule is obtained easily from the orthogonality properties (A4.34)

· of the recoupling coefficients U.

$$\sum_{I_C} S_{lsj}^{I_F I_C} = N \sum_{I_C J_n J_{n'}} c_{J_n} c_{J_{n'}} U(J_0 j I_F J_p, J_n I_C) U(J_0 j I_F J_p, J_{n'} I_C)$$
$$= N \sum_{J_n} c_{J_n}^2$$
$$= N.$$

For stripping we have the simple sum rule (5.39), which is independent of the model used for describing the target. In the present case it is

$$\sum_{I_F} S_{lsj}^{I_F I_C} [C_{I_C}^{M_C} {}^{M_F-M_C}_j {}^{M_F}_{I_F}]^2 = 1. \tag{13.50b}$$

It may be applied in conjunction with (13.44) to cross sections for specific cases.

For pickup, (13.50a) applies to all the different states $\psi_{I_C M_C}$ that can be excited in the shell model, that is, without exciting the inner closed-shell core of the nucleus C. For stripping, (13.50b) applies to all the different final states $\Phi_{I_F M_F}$ that are excited by putting the neutron into a particular single-particle state ϕ_{nljm}. The single-particle state is coupled to each of the possible core states $\psi_{I_C M_C}$ to form a set of final states. In this case the single-particle strength is said to be distributed over several final states.

The quantities that depend on the details of the shell-model dynamics, not merely on the angular momentum coupling, are the superposition coefficients c_{J_n} for different couplings of the neutrons in F. Clearly a set of relative spectroscopic factors for the same single-particle orbit ϕ_{nljm} will provide a very sensitive test of the shell-model dynamics.

The extremely useful fact about such a set of relative spectroscopic factors is that they have the same angular momentum transfer l; hence the corresponding stripping patterns are almost the same in shape. Only the energy of the final state distorted wave is changed in the DWBA. In fact, the relative values of the spectroscopic factor do not even depend on whether the DWBA is a good model for the reaction mechanism. All that is necessary is that the reaction mechanism should be such that it changes very little for different rearrangements of the angular momentum coupling of the extra-core particles in the shell model. This should be approximately true for any direct reaction. If it is, the relative spectroscopic factors are given by the relative intensities of the stripping or pickup cross sections for the relevant final states.

The use of rearrangement collisions in the shell model will be illustrated by means of an example. We shall choose the pickup reaction ^{93}Nb(p, d)^{92}Nb. The example will also demonstrate the relative accuracy of different pickup reactions for determining relative spectroscopic factors. If the direct interaction assumption (13.11) is valid, the relative spectroscopic factors will have the same values for the corresponding (d, t) reaction.

The reason for choosing these particular nuclei is that it is possible to determine the n-p and n-n effective matrix elements very easily by the methods of Section 7B[v] from the energy-level spectra of ^{92}Nb and ^{92}Zr, respectively, since these nuclei involve two particles outside a closed core, ^{90}Zr. The internal consistency of the DWBA-shell model can thus be checked.

The overlap integral for this reaction is written in the notation (13.45) as follows.

$$(n + C \mid C) = (\textstyle\sum_{J_n=0,2,4} c_{J_n}[(g_{9\!/\!2}) \times (d_{5\!/\!2})^2{}_{J_n}]_{9\!/\!2} \mid [(g_{9\!/\!2}) \times (d_{5\!/\!2})]I_C).$$
$$(13.51)$$

The ground-state spin of ^{93}Nb is $9\!/\!2$. The final nucleus ^{92}Nb may be left in any of the possible states of spin I_C which can be obtained by coupling the single-particle angular momenta $9\!/\!2$ and $5\!/\!2$.

$$I_C = 2, 3, 4, 5, 6, 7.$$

Thus a single experiment yields six differential cross-section measurements from which relative spectroscopic factors can be extracted and compared with calculations using known effective matrix elements.

Both (p, d) and (d, t) experiments were interpreted, in the way we have outlined, by Sweet, Bhatt, and Ball (64). Rearranging the angular momentum coupling into the form of the weak-coupling expansion, we may substitute the particular angular momentum values for this experiment in (13.49) obtaining

$$S_{d_{5\!/\!2}}^{9\!/\!2 I_C} = 2 \,|\textstyle\sum_{J_n=0,2,4} c_{J_n} U(\tfrac{5}{2} \tfrac{5}{2} \tfrac{9}{2} \tfrac{9}{2}, J_n I_C)|^2. \tag{13.52}$$

The following values of c_{J_n} were obtained from the analysis of the spectra of ^{92}Zr and ^{92}Nb.

$$c_0 = 0.949, \qquad c_2 = 0.297, \qquad c_4 = 0.106.$$

We shall first check the description of the reaction mechanism by comparing the relative intensities for exciting the six states $\psi_{I_C M_C}$ by (p, d) and (d, t) reactions. The comparison is given in Table 13.2. The values in fact differ by about 20 per cent for most of the states. This is the accuracy with which a direct reaction model is capable of predicting the spectroscopic factors for these experiments.

We may now check the combined shell-direct reaction model by comparing the theoretical relative spectroscopic factors (13.52) with the experimental average. The comparison is shown in Table 13.3. It is exact within experimental error.

Note that this comparison tells us that the inert core approximation (13.11) which leads to a stripping amplitude of the form (13.13) is good. The more exact approximation (13.10) could lead to cross sections, each of which depends on all the spectroscopic amplitudes $t_{i\alpha}^{(p)}$ or t_{lsj}^{p}, so that a different

	Relative $d\sigma/d\Omega$		
E_C (MeV)	(p, d)	(d, t)	S^{I_C} (exp)
0	0.36	0.43	0.40
0.135	0.21	0.20	0.21
0.286	0.12	0.10	0.11
0.357	0.13	0.11	0.12
0.479⎱	0.18	0.08	0.08
0.500⎰		0.08	0.08

TABLE 13.2. Relative cross sections for the reactions ^{93}Nb(p, d)^{92}Nb and ^{93}Nb(d, t)^{92}Nb. The last column gives an average experimental value of the relative spectroscopic factor for each state of *C*. (From Macfarlane, 64.)

combination of the c_{J_n} would be involved. This would happen for a vibrational core in which the inelastic-scattering wave functions $u_\alpha^{(+)}$ ($\alpha \neq 0$) are significant. In the present case, inelastic scattering involves single-particle states, so it is considerably weaker. For a vibrational core we would also expect the shell-model calculation of the c_{J_n} to be invalid.

We see that several types of internal consistency are verified. They concern the assumptions of a direct reaction, an inert core mechanism for the DWBA, and an inert closed-shell core in the shell model. All these assumptions are more or less related. None of them depend on the exact form of the DWBA, which was shown in Section *A* to influence the absolute spectroscopic factor strongly and the angular distribution less strongly. Thus the particular form of the optical model or the assumptions for $R_{nlj}(r_n)$ are irrelevant. Also

E_C (MeV)	I_C	S^{I_C} (exp)	S^{I_C} (theory)
0	7	0.40	0.40
0.135	2	0.21	0.22
0.286	5	0.11	0.11
0.357	3	0.12	0.11
0.479	4	0.08	0.09
0.500	6	0.08	0.08

TABLE 13.3. Relative spectroscopic factors for pickup to each of the six states of ^{92}Nb involving rearrangement of the coupling of a single neutron and a single proton. The experimental values are obtained by averaging the relative intensities for (p, d) and (d, t) experiments. (From Macfarlane, 64.)

irrelevant is the shape of the angular distribution except for its slight dependence on the energy of the outgoing deuteron. This is why the Butler theory was used for many years in nuclear spectroscopy.

Another interesting question is that of the sensitivity of the relative spectroscopic factors to the shell-model dynamics. The determination of the effective matrix elements gives a 90 per cent probability of the two neutrons pairing with $J_n = 0$, since $c_0^2 = 0.90$. If we ignore the 10 per cent admixture of states

I_C	$S^{I_C} (c_0 = 1)$	S^{I_C}
2	0.08	0.22
3	0.12	0.11
4	0.15	0.09
5	0.18	0.11
6	0.22	0.08
7	0.25	0.40

TABLE 13.4. Comparison of relative spectroscopic factors for $c_0 = 1$ and for the correctly determined set of c_{J_n}. (From Macfarlane, 64.)

with $J_n \neq 0$, the spectroscopic factor is proportional to the statistical weight of the state C, namely $(2I_C + 1)$. Table 13.4 shows how the correct admixture of states with $J_n \neq 0$ completely upsets this rule.

We have now seen that relative spectroscopic factors for the shell model may be accurately determined under the same conditions as those for the validity of the basic shell-model assumptions and that the accuracy of the determination is meaningful as a verification of the shell-model details.

[ii] DEFORMED NUCLEI

The theory of stripping and pickup involving deformed nuclei is a generalization of the shell-model theory. The wave functions of deformed nuclei have been considered in Sections 7C[iv] and 7C[vii]. The normalized rotational wave function with axial and reflection symmetry was given by (7.85). We shall include the vibrational states V_C and V_F explicitly, since the nuclei C and F may have somewhat different deformations. A simple account of the theory is given by Satchler (58). We shall consider only axially symmetric nuclei for which $K = \Omega$. Representing intrinsic coordinates in the body-fixed frame by x', and intrinsic wave functions by χ_K, we have

$$\Psi_{IMK} = \left(\frac{2I+1}{16\pi^2}\right)^{1/2} [\chi_K(x')D^I_{MK} + (-1)^{I-j}\chi_{(-K)}(x')D^I_{M(-K)}]V.$$

$$(13.53a)$$

For $K = 0$, as it is for the ground state of an even nucleus,

$$\Psi_{IM0} = \left(\frac{2I + 1}{8\pi^2}\right)^{\frac{1}{2}} \chi_0(x') D_{M0}^I V. \tag{13.53b}$$

The rotational eigenfunctions D_{MK}^I are functions of the Euler angles α, β, γ of the body-fixed frame (x') with respect to a space-fixed frame (x). The projections of $\mathbf{I}$ on the z, z' axes are M, K, respectively.

Since stripping is concerned with the details of intrinsic states, we need more explicit notation than that of Section 7C. The intrinsic state $\chi_K(x')$ is a determinant of single-particle intrinsic states (Nilsson wave functions) $\psi_{K\nu}$ for several particles labeled by ν.

$$\chi_K = \det \psi_{K\nu},$$
$$K = \sum_\nu K_\nu. \tag{13.54}$$

The Nilsson single-particle wave function, labeled by K, the parity π, and remaining quantum numbers α, is a linear combination of single-particle wave functions ϕ_{NljK} computed in a spherical harmonic oscillator well. The total number of oscillator quanta is N, in conformity with the notation of Chapter 7C.

$$\psi_{K\pi\alpha}(x') = \sum_{Nlj} c_{Nlj}(K\pi\alpha)\phi_{Nlj}(x'). \tag{13.55}$$

As in the previous section, l and j denote single-particle orbital and total angular momenta. The expansion (13.55) corresponds to the Nilsson expansion (7.106). The coefficients are related by the transformation

$$c_{Nlj}(K\pi\alpha) = \sum_\Lambda a_{Nl\Lambda} C_{l\ \frac{1}{2}\ j}^{\Lambda K - \Lambda K}. \tag{13.56}$$

In (7.106) the quantum number N was suppressed because it was assumed to be approximately good. The expansion (13.55) brings the formalism into line with the shell-model stripping formalism, where we are interested in j rather than Λ, the projection of l. For convenience we shall now drop the quantum numbers N, π, α.

The intrinsic wave functions $\chi_{K_C}^C$ and $\chi_{K_F}^F$ for the nuclei C and F differ by one Nilsson single-particle wave function $\psi_K(x_n')$ for particle n. The overlap of (13.53a,b) will contain separate terms for $K_F \pm K_C$. For each term, respectively, the single particle is stripped into a state whose angular momentum $\mathbf{j}$ has the projection $K = K_F \pm K_C$ on the z-axis. We have for the overlap integral,

$$(\Psi_{I_F M_F K_F} | \Psi_{I_C M_C K_C}) = g\left(\left(\frac{2I_F + 1}{8\pi^2}\right)^{\frac{1}{2}} \chi_{K_F}^F D_{M_F K_F}^{I_F} V_F\right.$$
$$\left.\left|\left(\frac{2I_C + 1}{8\pi^2}\right)^{\frac{1}{2}} \chi_{(\mp K_C)}^C D_{M_C(\mp K_C)}^{I_C} V_C\right). \tag{13.57}$$

The factor g is $\sqrt{2}$ if either of the states C or F has $K = 0$ and 1 otherwise.

We shall be concerned with the rotational properties of (13.57) rather than the intrinsic wave functions. The probability amplitude that $\chi_{K_F}^F$ contains the single-particle orbital ψ_K will be represented by θ_{intr} and not discussed further. We shall consider in detail only the simple case of stripping or pick-up with an even target, inert except for its rotational structure, and a final nucleus described by the extreme Nilsson single-particle model, so that θ_{intr} is unity. The overlap integral is now

$$(\Psi'_{I_F M_F K_F} \mid \Psi_{I_C M_C K_C}) = g\left(\left(\frac{2I_F + 1}{8\pi^2}\right)^{\frac{1}{2}} \psi_{K\pi\alpha}(x') D^{I_F}_{M_F K_F} V_F\right.$$

$$\left. \times \left|\left(\frac{2I_C + 1}{8\pi^2}\right)^{\frac{1}{2}} D^{I_C}_{M_C(\mp K_C)} V_C\right) \theta_{\text{intr}}. \quad (13.58)$$

In order to extract the spectroscopic factor from our definitions (13.38, 13.40), we must express the Nilsson orbital $\psi_K(x')$ in terms of the space-fixed frame

$$\psi_K(x') = \sum_{ljm} c_{lj}(K)\phi_{ljm} D^j_{mK}{}^*. \quad (13.59)$$

The integral (13.57) is now evaluated, using the standard result

$$\langle D^{I_F}_{M_F K_F} \mid D^j_{mK} \mid D^{I_C}_{M_C K_C} \rangle = \frac{8\pi^2}{2I_F + 1} C^{K_C K K_F}_{I_C \, j \, I_F} C^{M_C m M_F}_{I_C \, j \, J_F}. \quad (13.60)$$

We obtain

$$(\Psi'_{I_F M_F K_F} \mid \Psi_{I_C M_C K_C})$$

$$= g\left(\frac{2I_C + 1}{2I_F + 1}\right)^{\frac{1}{2}} \langle V_F \mid V_C \rangle \sum_{ljm} \phi^*_{ljm} c_{lj}(K_F \pm K_C) C^{\mp K_C \, K_F \mp K_C \, K_F}_{I_C \quad j \qquad I_F}$$

$$\times C^{M_C \, m \, M_F}_{I_C \; j \; I_F} \theta_{\text{intr}}. \quad (13.61)$$

Comparing (13.61) and (13.38) we have for the reduced-width amplitude

$$\theta_{lj}(K_F \pm K_C) = g\left(\frac{2I_C + 1}{2I_F + 1}\right)^{\frac{1}{2}} \langle V_F \mid V_C \rangle c_{lj}(K_F \pm K_C) C^{\mp K_C K_F \pm K_C K_F}_{I_C \qquad\qquad\qquad j \qquad I_F} \theta_{\text{intr}}. \quad (13.62)$$

The factor $\langle V_F \mid V_C \rangle$ representing the overlap of the vibrational states will normally be close to unity, since the addition of one particle will not change the nuclear deformation very much. We shall ignore both this factor and θ_{intr} from now on.

There is a sum rule for the spectroscopic factors $\theta_{lj}{}^2 \equiv S_{lj}^{I_F I_C}$. Squaring (13.62) and using the orthogonality of the Clebsch-Gordan coefficients we have, setting $\langle V_F | V_C \rangle \theta_{\text{intr}} = 1$,

$$\sum_{I_F} (2I_F + 1)\theta_{lj}^2 = g^2(2I_C + 1)[c_{lj}(K)]^2. \tag{13.63}$$

We now use the fact that, for a particular Nilsson orbital ψ_K,

$$\sum_{lj} c_{lj}^2(K) = 1. \tag{13.64}$$

The sum rule is

$$\sum_{ljI_F} (2I_F + 1)\theta_{lj}^2 = g^2(2I_C + 1). \tag{13.65}$$

For the case $I_C = 0$, as is always true for stripping on an even nucleus, the selection rules in (13.62) give, as usual,

$$j = I_F. \tag{13.66}$$

The sum rule is now simplified to

$$\sum_{lj} \theta_{lj}^2(2j + 1) = \sum_{lj} S_{lj}^{I_F I_C}(2j + 1) = 2. \tag{13.67}$$

In stripping on an even target with axial symmetry, the neutron enters the Nilsson orbit ψ_{K_F}. This orbit corresponds to a rotational band with different values of I_F.

$$I_F = K_F, K_F + 1, \ldots \tag{13.68}$$

Since $j = K_F$, the stripping patterns for successive states of the band correspond to

$$j = K_F, K_F + 1, \ldots \tag{13.69}$$

with the parity π of the Nilsson orbital. The spectroscopic factor in this case is

$$S_{lj}^{I_F I_C} = \frac{2}{2j + 1} c_{lj}(K_F)\delta_{jI_F}. \tag{13.70}$$

The rotational spectroscopic factors we have discussed thus far assume that a single Nilsson orbital describes the final state. If it is necessary to mix orbitals differing by quantum numbers α other than K, then the model of a single particle in a deformed potential is inadequate, and the intrinsic spectroscopic factor θ_{intr}^2, describing the proportion of the orbital $\psi_{K\pi\alpha}$ in the final state, is necessary. There is little experimental information about this possibility.

However, even with the pure single-particle model, it will be remembered that the rotational states (13.53) are eigenstates of the rotational Hamiltonian T_{rot}^0 of (7.76), but not of the whole rotational Hamiltonian T_{rot} including the coupling term (7.77). The expansion (7.109) showed that the coupling term connects states whose values of K are $\frac{1}{2}$ and $\frac{3}{2}$.

In order to test the DWBA stripping theory and the single-particle Nilsson model simultaneously, we must allow for the mixing of bands with these two values of K, both in the eigenvalue calculations and in the expression (13.62) for the reduced width amplitude. With band mixing the reduced-width amplitude becomes

$$\theta_{lj}^{I_F I \sigma}(K_F) = \sum_{K=\frac{1}{2},\frac{3}{2}} a_K \theta_{lj}(K), \qquad K_F = \frac{1}{2}, \frac{3}{2}. \qquad (13.71)$$

The band-mixing coefficients a_K are obtained by diagonalizing a Hamiltonian that includes the coupling term, so that the energy level spectrum is fitted.

| | | | E_F (KeV) | | | | | $d\sigma(60°)/d\Omega(mb/sr)$ | |
| | | | Experiment | Theory | | | | Experiment | Theory |
I_F	K_F	l	Experiment	Theory	$a_{\frac{1}{2}}$	$a_{\frac{3}{2}}$	$a_{\frac{7}{2}}$	Experiment	Theory
$\frac{1}{2}$	$\frac{1}{2}$	—	—	149.0	1	0	0	—	0.005
$\frac{3}{2}$	$\frac{1}{2}$	1	205	205.4	0.994	−0.110	0	0.47	0.72
$\frac{3}{2}$	$\frac{3}{2}$	1	0	0	0.110	0.994	0	0.078	0.09
$\frac{5}{2}$	$\frac{1}{2}$	3	304	303.4	0.986	−0.165	0	0.021	0.08
$\frac{5}{2}$	$\frac{3}{2}$	3	79	77.9	0.166	0.986	0	0.25	0.36
$\frac{7}{2}$	$\frac{1}{2}$	3	434	433.8	0.978	−0.209	0	0.092	0.08
$\frac{7}{2}$	$\frac{3}{2}$	—	—	187.5	0.209	0.978	0	—	0.02
$\frac{7}{2}$	$\frac{7}{2}$	3	351	351.0	0	0	1	0.25	0.41

TABLE 13.5.   Comparison of the theory described in the text with the experiments ^{186}W(d, p)^{187}W at 11.96 MeV. The states shown are all the states predicted by the Nilsson orbitals $\frac{1}{2}$−[510], $\frac{3}{2}$−[512] and $\frac{7}{2}$−[503]. The two with the smallest cross sections were not observed. (From Erskine, 65.)

Experiments and calculations by Erskine (65) on ^{182}W, ^{184}W, and ^{186}W tested both the single-particle rotational model and the DWBA for 12 MeV deuteron stripping. In Table 13.5 we compare the measured differential cross sections at 60° with those calculated using the DWBA with band mixing for several low-lying states of ^{177}W. In the same table we compare the experimental and calculated eigenvalues and show the band-mixing coefficients a_K. Both energy levels and cross sections were taken into account in choosing the values of the a_K coefficients.

The Nilsson orbitals $\frac{1}{2}$−[510], $\frac{3}{2}$−[512] and $\frac{7}{2}$−[503] for a deformation parameter $\eta = 4$ were used in the calculation. The optical-model parameters were of the type $V_{dC} \cong V_n + V_p$. The absolute spectroscopic factors were not taken seriously. The cross section was in fact multiplied by 1.5 for all states. Typical angular distribution fits for ^{182}W(d, p)^{183}W are shown in Fig. 13.6.

Comparison of the theoretical and experimental numbers of Table 13.5 again tests the nuclear structure model and the direct interaction assumption. This time even the relative spectroscopic factors for the same l compare only semiquantitatively. Comparison of the theoretical and experimental angular distribution shapes, for example those of Fig. 13.6, tests the DWBA more

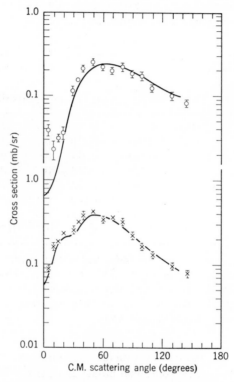

FIG. 13.6   Angular distributions of the reaction ^{182}W(d, p)^{183}W at 11.96 MeV for two different final states: $l = 3, j = \frac{5}{2}, Q = 3.868$ MeV (top) and $l = 1, j = \frac{3}{2}, Q = 3.921$ MeV (bottom). (Adapted from Erskine, 65.)

stringently, but no attempt was made to predict absolute spectroscopic factors and then to test the DWBA as a complete description of the reaction. Again we see that the DWBA is an extremely useful means of extracting spectroscopic information irrespective of whether it is a good description of the reaction mechanism. However, the precision of the model is not up to the standard set by the DWBA-shell model.

A possible source of error in the model is the fact the inelastic scattering from a deformed nucleus is much more probable than from a nucleus for which the shell model is a good description. The more general stripping amplitude (13.10) would be a better approximation than (13.13). No successful improvements of this type have yet been made. A discussion is given by Iano and Austern (66). This calculation includes inelastic scattering in the exit channel, whose effect is found to be negligible.

[iii] VIBRATIONAL NUCLEI

Stripping on a vibrational nucleus provides the simplest example of a case where core excitation by inelastic scattering is likely to be important. We shall first consider the spectroscopic factor for the simple stripping theory (13.13) which assumes that core excitation is negligible.

The target nucleus is assumed to consist primarily of a vibrational core whose wave function is

$$\psi_\alpha(\xi) = \psi_{N_C\lambda_C\mu_C}(\xi), \tag{13.72}$$

where N_C is the number of phonons of type $\lambda_C\mu_C$. In addition we may treat some nucleons in an unfilled subshell separately. Their wave function is $\chi_{J_C m_C}$. The wave function of the target nucleus $\psi_{I_C M_C}$ is given by coupling the angular momenta of the core and the extra-core nucleons.

$$\psi_{I_C M_C} = \sum_{m_C} \psi_{N_C\lambda_C(M_C - m_C)}\chi_{J_C m_C} C_{J_C}^{m_C\ M_C - m_C\ M_C}{}_{\lambda_C}^{}{}_{I_C}. \tag{13.73}$$

For the final nucleus the wave function of the nucleons that originally constituted the nucleus C is denoted by (13.73) with primed subscripts. The exchanged single particle, whose wave function is ϕ_{nljm}, is coupled to the extra-core nucleons in the rearranged nucleus C to produce the extra-core quantum numbers J_F, m_F. The wave function of the final nucleus is

$$\Phi_{I_F M_F} = \sum_{m_F} \psi_{N_C'\lambda_C'(M_F - m_F)}\chi_{J_F m_F} C_{J_F}^{m_F\ M_F - m_F\ M_F}{}_{\lambda_C'}^{}{}_{I_F}. \tag{13.74}$$

The overlap integral is simplified by the assumption that the state of the vibrational core of the shell model is not changed in the reaction. This gives the relations

$$N_C = N_C', \qquad \lambda_C = \lambda_C', \qquad M_C - m_C = M_F - m_F. \tag{13.75}$$

The overlap integral is

$$(\Phi_{I_F M_F} \mid \psi_{I_C M_C}) = \delta_{N_C N_C'}\delta_{\lambda_C\lambda_C'} \sum_{m_C m_F} C_{J_C}^{m_C\ M_C - m_C\ M_C}{}_{\lambda_C}^{}{}_{I_C}$$
$$\times C_{J_F}^{m_F\ M_F - m_F\ M_F}{}_{\lambda_C}^{}{}_{I_F}(\chi_{J_F m_F} \mid \chi_{J_C m_C}). \tag{13.76}$$

We now make use of (13.38a) to expand the shell-model overlap as

$$(\chi_{J_F m_F} \mid \chi_{J_C m_C}) = \sum_{lj} \theta_{lj}^{J_F J_C} C_{J_C}^{m_C\ m_F - m_C\ m_F}{}_{j}^{}{}_{J_F}\phi_{nlj(m_F - m_C)}^*, \tag{13.77}$$

where $\theta_{lj}^{J_F J_C}$ is the shell-model reduced-width amplitude.

The total overlap integral is now obtained by combining (13.75, 13.76, 13.77), and is reduced to a simpler form. The reduction constitutes a good exercise in the use of angular momentum algebra. In this case the sum of products of three Clebsch-Gordan coefficients is reduced to the product of a Clebsch-Gordan coefficient and a recoupling coefficient U by (A4.38). To obtain the right ordering of the quantum numbers in (13.76, 13.77), we must rearrange them according to (A4.26). We obtain

$$
(\Phi_{I_F M_F} \mid \psi_{I_C M_C}) = \delta_{N_C N_C'} \delta_{\lambda_C \lambda_C'} \left[\frac{(2I_C + 1)(2J_F + 1)}{(2\lambda_C + 1)(2j + 1)} \right]^{\frac{1}{2}} (-1)^{\lambda_C - I_F + J_C + j}
$$

$$
\times \sum_{l j m_C} C_{I_C \ J_C \ \lambda_C}^{M_C \ -m_C \ M_C - m_C} C_{\lambda_C \ J_F \ I_F}^{M_C - m_C \ M_F - M_C + m_C \ M_F}
$$

$$
\times C_{J_C \ J_F \ j}^{-m_C \ M_F - M_C + m_C \ M_F - M_C} \theta_{lj}^{J_F J_C} \phi^*_{nlj(M_F - M_C)}
$$

$$
= \delta_{N_C N_C'} \delta_{\lambda_C \lambda_C'} \sum_{lj} \left[\frac{(2I_C + 1)(2J_F + 1)}{(2\lambda_C + 1)(2j + 1)} \right]^{\frac{1}{2}} (-1)^{\lambda_C - I_F + J_C + j}
$$

$$
\times U(I_C J_C I_F J_F, \lambda_C j) \theta_{lj}^{J_F J_C} C_{I_C \ j \ I_F}^{M_C \ M_F - M_C \ M_F} \phi^*_{nlj(M_F - M_C)}. \quad (13.78)
$$

Comparing (13.26) and (13.78) we obtain for the reduced-width amplitude

$$
\theta_{lj}^{I_F I_C} = \delta_{N_C N_C'} \delta_{\lambda_C \lambda_C'} \left[\frac{(2I_C + 1)(2J_F + 1)}{(2\lambda_C + 1)(2j + 1)} \right]^{\frac{1}{2}} (-1)^{\lambda_C - I_F + J_C + j}
$$

$$
\times U(I_C J_C I_F J_F, \lambda_C j) \theta_{lj}^{J_F J_C}. \quad (13.79)
$$

The spectroscopic factor is expressed as

$$
S_{lj}^{I_F I_C} = \delta_{N_C N_C'} \delta_{\lambda_C \lambda_C'} (2I_C + 1)(2J_F + 1)[W(I_C J_C I_F J_F, \lambda_C j)]^2 S_{lj}^{J_F J_C}. \quad (13.80)
$$

The use of the Racah coefficient W, according to (A4.32), provides a slight further simplification. The number of equivalent particles N is included in the shell-model spectroscopic factor $S_{lj}^{J_F J_C}$. The sum rule (5.39) is easily verified.

While the differences between the vibrational case and the shell-model and rotational cases are not sufficient to introduce any really new principles into the theory of stripping according to (13.13), the enhanced probability of core excitation due to inelastic scattering makes it a particularly useful illustration of a case where Equation (13.10) must be used.

Comparisons of this theory with experiment are still in their early stages, so a detailed account of the angular momentum coupling will not be given. It is interesting, however, to note the possibility of stripping to states that cannot be excited in the inert-core approximation.

An example is deuteron stripping on an even target in the $1f_{7/2}$ shell, for example ^{42}Ca, ^{44}Ca, ^{46}Ti, in which the final state is $\frac{5}{2}-$. Since the spin-orbit splitting for Ca is about 5.5 MeV, it is unlikely that low-lying $\frac{5}{2}-$ states contain significant admixtures from the $1f_{5/2}$ single-neutron wave function. The $\frac{5}{2}-$ states of ^{43}Ca, ^{45}Ca, and ^{47}Ti have excitation energies of 374 KeV, 176 KeV and 0, respectively. The target nuclei have 2+ first excited states for which inelastic-scattering cross sections and $B(E2)$ values are enhanced over their values for the single-particle excitation model, although they are not excited as strongly as rotational states. For our purpose these states may be regarded as vibrational, although the higher levels of these nuclei are not predicted well by a simple vibrational model. The $1f_{7/2}$ neutron may couple to the 2+ state of the core to produce a $\frac{5}{2}-$ state in the final nucleus.

The stripping amplitude for this state is, from (13.10),

$$T = t_{i\alpha}^{(\rho)} \langle w_0^{(-)}(\mathbf{k}_p)\phi_i| \, V_{np}\phi_d \, |u_\alpha^{(+)}(\mathbf{k}_d)\rangle$$
$$+ t_{i\alpha}^{(\rho)} \langle w_\alpha^{(-)}(\mathbf{k}_p)\phi_i| \, V_{np}\phi_d \, |u_0^{(+)}(\mathbf{k}_d)\rangle, \qquad (13.81)$$

where the single-particle state i is $1f_{7/2}$, the core state α is 2+, and the final state ρ is $\frac{5}{2}-$.

The inelastic distorted wave $u_\alpha^{(+)}$ has no plane-wave part, so the familiar stripping pattern, which is approximated by the plane-wave theory, is expected to be absent. Experimental data for 7.0 MeV (d, p) reactions on these nuclei are shown in Fig. 13.7. The angular distributions are all similar, as expected. They do not have the familiar shape of a large peak followed by smaller ones as do the angular distributions for stripping to the $\frac{7}{2}-$ levels of the same nuclei. Their absolute magnitudes are lower than those for the $\frac{7}{2}-$ levels by an order of magnitude, as is expected if the mechanism is inelastic scattering. No significant anomalies are seen in the $\frac{7}{2}-$ angular distributions, so the theory leading to (13.80) is adequate for the case where elastic scattering wave functions $u_0^{(+)}$ are not forbidden by a selection rule.

The addition of core excitation terms can of course have an effect on the shape of the stripping angular distribution for two final states with the same value of l but different j. Strongly j-dependent shapes have been observed (Lee and Schiffer, 64). They can be explained by optical-model spin-orbit effects, which are the only serious j-dependent effects in the inert core approximation for the angular distribution shape.

C. SUMMARY AND DISCUSSION

Stripping and pickup are the nuclear reactions about which we have the most experimental information. The information that they yield about nuclei is of several types. Much of it can be obtained directly from the experiment without theoretical analysis.

The Q-value for a stripping experiment yields direct information about the binding energy of the particle n in the nucleus $n + C$. Thus we can, for example, determine single-particle energy levels. It is possible to pick up a particle from a level which is lower in energy than the upper shell-model levels, and thus to examine the lower single-particle levels. This type of information is better obtained by breakup reactions, which will be discussed in the next chapter. Here we shall just note that the Q-value in this case includes rearrangement energy, since a nucleus with a hole in a lower state can spontaneously rearrange itself to fill the hole.

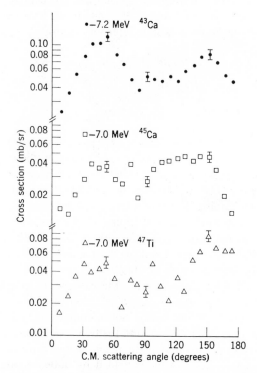

FIG. 13.7   Angular distributions for (d, p) stripping to the $\frac{5}{2}-$ states of ^{43}Ca, ^{45}Ca, and ^{47}Ti. (Adapted from Belote, Dorenbusch, Hansen, and Rapaport, 65.)

Stripping and pickup are suited for examining the single-particle levels of nuclei near the top of the Fermi sea, including levels that are unoccupied in the ground state. If the reaction theory is well enough understood, they can be used to predict the orbital angular momentum transfer l, which for single-nucleon stripping on a spin-zero target is the orbital angular momentum of the single-particle state into which the particle n is stripped. This prediction is made from the shape of the angular distribution, which usually shows a stripping pattern with a large forward peak followed by smaller oscillations. This pattern often bears some resemblance to the spherical Bessel function shape predicted by the Butler theory.

Angular distribution shapes are often different for reactions with the same orbital angular momentum transfer *l*, but different *j*. In principle the *j*-dependence can be used to determine *j*, but there is no theory that will consistently predict it.

For angular distributions that have the stripping pattern, the DWBA without core excitation predicts shapes well enough to be a reliable means of determining *l*. The first peak can generally be fitted very well. Some angular distributions do not have the stripping pattern. It is necessary to include core excitation in their description. The theory of this has not progressed very far.

A test of the simple DWBA is stripping on a closed-shell target where the reaction mechanism is well understood. The theory predicts absolute cross sections within 20 per cent in such situations. The shape of the first peak is well fitted and the subsequent oscillations are described qualitatively. This test gives us confidence in using the DWBA to predict *l*. Furthermore, it suggests that the direct interaction assumption is correct.

Relative cross sections for excitations of states with the same *l* give very significant information about the amplitudes with which the different independent particle configurations contribute to the eigenstates of the final nucleus. It is just these amplitudes that nuclear structure theory tries to predict. Therefore relative spectroscopic factors test nuclear structure theories. The test is very sensitive. The condition for relative cross sections to be proportional to spectroscopic factors is that the reaction should be direct and inelastic scattering of the initial or final particles should be small compared with elastic scattering. The question of whether the DWBA is a good reaction model is irrelevant, although of course the fact that it is a fairly good reaction model helps to confirm the direct interaction assumption. Further confirmation is obtained by correct prediction of relative spectroscopic factors in cases where they can be calculated by fairly reliable external means.

In our illustrations of these principles, we have considered only single-nucleon stripping. There is much experimental information about stripping of two and even three nucleons, for which the theory of spectroscopic factors is similar in principle but more complicated. In shell-model nuclei, two-nucleon stripping tests the amplitude for an eigenstate to consist of the core plus two particles with certain angular momentum coupling. These amplitudes are the coefficients of fractional parentage for adding two particles. Relative spectroscopic factors for two-nucleon stripping in such nuclei yield the same information as those for single-nucleon stripping with equal sensitivity. In addition two-nucleon stripping can yield information about nuclei whose excited states are more complicated, such as closed-shell nuclei. Descriptions of the excited states of closed-shell nuclei involve particle-hole coupling as was shown in a brief example, Section 7*B*[vii].

In studies of two-nucleon stripping no effects have yet been found that cannot be described by conventional nuclear structure theories that describe only long-range weak correlations. Again we are frustrated if we expect to use this reaction as a probe for strong short-range correlations between two nucleons. The reason is that two-nucleon stripping can occur without the two nucleons coming any closer together on the average than their most probable position correlation in the shell model and without relative momentum components any larger on the average than the expectation value for shell-model wave functions.

One more aspect of stripping has not been discussed. This is so-called heavy particle stripping in which a core of finite mass is exchanged between the two nuclei. Plane-wave models of the process predict that the proton in, for example, (d, p) heavy particle stripping should come out in the backward direction. Backward peaks may also occur in conventional stripping because for the backward direction the foci of the optical-model wave functions coincide, thereby enhancing the magnitude of the contribution to the matrix element from the focal region. No really satisfactory theory for backward directions is available.

FURTHER READING

1. S. T. Butler, *Proc. Roy. Soc. (London)*, **A208**, 559 (1951).

   A. B. Bhatia, K. Huang, R. Huby, and H. C. Newns, *Phil. Mag.*, **43**, 485 (1952).

   Early plane-wave stripping theories with applications to *l* determination.

2. S. T. Butler and O. Hittmaier, *Nuclear Stripping Reactions*, John Wiley and Sons, Inc., New York, 1957.

   W. Tobocman, *Theory of Direct Nuclear Reactions*, Oxford University Press, London, 1961.

   Reviews of earlier work.

3. M. H. Macfarlane and J. B. French, *Rev. Mod. Phys.*, **32**, 567 (1960).

   Review of particle-transfer reactions in spectroscopy.

4. *Nuclear Spectroscopy with Direct Reactions*, Vol. II, Proceedings, edited by F. E. Throw, Argonne National Laboratory Report No. ANL-6878, 1964.

   Conference proceedings containing many examples.

5. R. H. Bassel, "Some applications of the distorted Wave approximation for Direct Nuclear Reactions," *Few Nucleon Problems*, Vol. II, edited by M. Cerineo, Federal Nuclear Energy Commission of Yugoslavia, Zagreb, 1964.

L. L. Lee, Jr., J. P. Schiffer, B. Zeidman, G. R. Satchler, R. M. Drisko, and R. H. Bassel, *Phys. Rev.*, **136**, B971 (1964).

R. H. Bassel, R. M. Drisko, and G. R. Satchler, *The Distorted-wave Theory of Direct Nuclear Reactions*, Oak Ridge National Laboratory Report No. ORNL-3240, 1962.

N. Austern, "Direct Reactions," *Selected Topics in Nuclear Theory*, edited by F. Janouch, International Atomic Energy Agency, Vienna, 1963.

Details and reviews of work involving the distorted wave Born approximation.

6. N. K. Glendenning, *Nucl. Phys.*, **29**, 109 (1962).

S. Yoshida, *Nucl. Phys.*, **33**, 685 (1962).

J. R. Rook and D. Mitra, *Nucl. Phys.*, **51**, 96 (1964).

Two-nucleon stripping.

7. E. Rost, *Phys. Rev.*, **154**, 994 (1967).

M. Kawai and K. Yazaki, *Prog. Theor. Phys.*, **37**, 638 (1967).

The form factor for the bound state in stripping and pickup.

8. S. K. Penny and G. R. Satchler, *Nucl. Phys.*, **53**, 145 (1964).

P. J. Iano and N. Austern, *Phys. Rev.*, **151**, 853 (1966).

A. J. Kromminga, K. L. Lim, and I. E. McCarthy, *Phys. Rev.*, **157**, 770 (1967).

Core excitation in stripping.

PROBLEMS

1. Write a formal matrix element corresponding to (13.10) for stripping on a rotational target with possible inelastic scattering in entrance and exit channels.

2. Write all the terms of the matrix element (13.10) with specific numerical values for the quantum numbers for excitation of each of the states of Table 7.8 in the reaction ^{62}Ni(d, n)^{63}Cu.

3. In the theory of stripping on a vibrational target according to (13.10), it is possible to have j-forbidden stripping, that is, stripping to a state that is absolutely forbidden in the jj-coupling model, so that the term in $u_0^{(+)}(\mathbf{k}_d, x_d)$ is zero. Give an example of such a reaction. Would you expect the angular distribution to resemble a stripping pattern? Is it possible to have corresponding j-forbidden reactions with the theory of Problem 1 for stripping on a rotational target?

4. Draw the angular distribution for the reaction ^{40}Ca(d, p)^{41}Ca to the ground state of ^{41}Ca at 11 MeV deuteron energy in the Butler theory, assuming that the interaction takes place on a surface shell of radius 6 fm. (Look up the spins

and energies in Appendix 2.) Compare the result with the DWBA curves of Fig. 13.3.

5. Using the same theory as for Problem 4 in the jj-coupling model, draw the angular distribution for the reaction $^{37}Cl(p, d)^{36}Cl$ to the ground state of ^{36}Cl at 10 MeV proton energy. What values of l contribute to this reaction?

6. Calculate the relative spectroscopic factors in the two cases of $l = 5$ stripping for a residual nucleus described by the Nilsson wave function of Table 7.9 with $\eta = 4$.

7. What are the relative intensities of all the possible stripping reactions that add a $1f_{7/2}$ neutron to ^{41}Ca? Assume the jj-coupling model.

8. For the (d, p) reaction on a nucleus that may be regarded as a single proton bound to an inert core, draw diagrams showing the mechanisms that may compete with stripping of the deuteron. Under what conditions would you expect these mechanisms to be important?

14

BREAKUP REACTIONS

Breakup reactions are ones in which a particle P collides with a target T, and the final state consists of three or more bodies, A, B, C, ... These reactions were specifically excluded in our general treatment of reaction theory in Chapter 8 because they are too complicated for a general description. For example, in a reaction with a three-body final state there are four possible compound nuclei relevant to the problem, the PT, AB, BC, and CA systems.

The principles involved in the study of breakup reactions will be sufficiently illustrated if we consider the ones with a three-body final state. There are two general ways of obtaining physical information from such a reaction.

In the first way, only the three particles in the final state are considered. The initial state is merely a convenient way of producing the required final state. Study of the momenta of the final-state particles is an excellent method of obtaining information about resonant interactions in any of the three two-body systems involved. If there is a resonance in the AB system, and the CA and BC systems occur in the experiment at relative energies far from resonance, then the AB system will have a longer lifetime than the other two. Such a reaction is sometimes called a sequential reaction with particle C separating before particles A and B.

The second way of considering the reaction is as a quasi-three-body process. This only applies to reactions of the form $P + T \rightarrow P + A + B$, where T consists of a bound state of A and B. It is then possible to describe the whole reaction as a potential scattering problem. For the pairs with positive relative energy, the potential is complex if the particular three-body partition is only one of many possible reaction channels, most of which involve different partitions. In calculations the complex two-body potentials are usually equated with the complex potentials for each two-body system in the absence of the third at the same relative energy. Any additional potential is called a three-body force. Where all the two-body systems occur at relative energies well below thresholds for excitation of any of the individual particles, the two-body potentials may be considered as real. Examples are three-nucleon reactions or low-energy reactions involving nucleons and α-particles whose first excited state is at about 20 MeV.

Three-nucleon reactions must be studied with the full Faddeev theory of Chapter 10E. The main difficulty of the problem is the multiplicity of co-ordinates. In all studies up to the present, the number of coordinates needed to specify intermediate states in the integral equations is reduced to one. The reduction is accomplished by assuming that the two-body potentials are separable, that is, in momentum space, $V(\mathbf{p}_1, \mathbf{p}_2) = V_1(\mathbf{p}_1)V_2(\mathbf{p}_2)$. This assumption is probably not very realistic. Potentials obtained from field theories are local. Separable potentials may always be chosen to fit two-body data, but they are different in different orbital angular momentum states and, in general, more than one is required in each state. Thus the use of a single separable potential is confined to very low energies where relative s-states dominate. Even with these disadvantages the use of separable potentials has produced remarkably good results for three-nucleon reactions (Aaron, Amado and Yam, 65).

We shall discuss the principles of the three-nucleon calculation without giving the details. The Faddeev equations (10.170) may be solved if the two-body t-matrix is known. If the interaction of two particles is described by a single bound state or resonance, it is clear from Equation (10.100) that the Green's function, and hence the t-matrix, is separable. A separable t-matrix arises from a separable potential. Thus the use of a separable potential in the s-state is equivalent to the assumption that the scattering is a sequential process involving first the scattering of the third particle from the single bound state or resonance from which the separable potential is calculated and then the decay of this state. For the n-n-p system there is a bound state for triplet n-p scattering (the deuteron) and a resonance near zero energy for singlet n-p scattering and for n-n scattering. The reduction in the multiplicity of co-ordinates is due to the fact that only the coordinates of the bound state or resonance, which acts like a particle, are involved in intermediate states.

In Fig. 14.1 we show the results of the calculation by Aaron, Amado, and Yam (65) of the total cross sections for scattering of a neutron by a deuteron and for breakup of the deuteron by the neutron at different energies.

A reaction which has been most fruitful for the study of nuclear structure is the (p, 2p) reaction. The proton is assumed to be knocked out of a single-particle state. With a sufficiently reliable theory of the reaction mechanism, the reaction can be analysed to yield information about the nuclear structure of the target and about the force involved in the internal p-p collision. In this chapter we shall consider the reaction mechanism and the conditions under which nuclear structure information can be extracted.

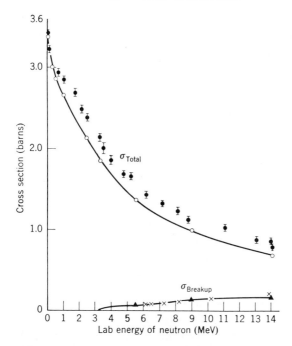

FIG. 14.1   Total and breakup cross sections for neutron-deuteron scattering. The open circles and crosses are theoretical points. (Adapted from Aaron, Amado, and Yam, 65.)

A.   SEQUENTIAL REACTIONS

The information obtained from a study of the kinematics of the final state is almost directly factual. It is possible to deduce, from the kinematics, where the resonances in the two-body systems are located in energy and their widths. The resonances in the AB system appear as sharp intensity maxima in the three-body cross section at values of the relative energy in the AB system where there is a resonance in the isolated AB system. Thus the determination of resonance positions and widths is almost purely an experimental problem, although a difficult one, because there are five independent variables involved. It has been discussed in Chapter 9A[vi] with reference to the Dalitz plot.

One or two modifications of the direct translation of information about the three-body system to corresponding information about one of the two-body subsystems in isolation are understood by considering the calculation of the three-body cross section in the extreme sequential model.

This model treats a three-body scattering process by the methods of two body scattering problems. The resonant system AB is assumed to be formed by a two-body direct interaction process involving, for example, the inelastic scattering of C or a rearrangement collision $CA + B \rightarrow AB + C$. The differential cross section for this process, ignoring the subsequent breakup of AB, is $d\sigma_0$.

If the lifetime of AB is long, it is sometimes said to forget how it was formed and therefore to decay independently according to the Breit-Wigner single-level theory. Again one must be careful in the use of time-dependent arguments in the absence of time measurement. The time dependence of the decay of an isolated resonance is $\exp\left[(t_0 - t)\Gamma/\hbar\right]$ where t_0 is the time at which the system is formed, so that most of the decays occur soon after formation.

A more correct statement about the independence of formation and decay of the AB system uses the analogy with the formation of the AB system in an inelastic two-body reaction. In such a reaction the formation and decay of the compound nucleus are independent if the resonances do not overlap. This means that the contribution to the scattering amplitude from a particular partial wave at a certain value of the energy is not added coherently to contributions from other partial waves. Although the three-body system is much more complicated, the condition may be stated as follows. The decay of the AB system is independent of its formation if the three-body scattering amplitude, in the region of phase space where one partial wave in the AB system is resonant, does not depend on other partial waves in the AB system or vary rapidly with the kinematic variables involving C. This condition is of course fulfilled more exactly if the width Γ is very small, which means that the lifetime of AB is very long.

The dependence of the three-body cross section on the relative energy E_{AB} of A and B is revealed, for example, by the energy spectrum of C. Assuming that Γ is very small,

$$d^2\sigma_C = \frac{\Gamma_{fx}}{\Gamma} \frac{\Gamma}{2\pi} \frac{dE_{AB}}{(E_{AB} - \Delta E)^2 + \Gamma^2/4} \, d\sigma_0. \qquad (14.1)$$

Here the AB system decays from the state x to the final state f. ΔE is the energy difference between the center of the excited state x and the final state f. Γ_{fx}/Γ is the relative probability for the decay of the excited state x to the final state f.

We have tacitly assumed the validity of (14.1) in our discussion of inelastic scattering, where the residual nucleus usually decays by emitting a γ-ray. The width of the excited state for γ emission is extremely small.

Particle widths are generally not as small as γ-ray widths and, in fact, are energy dependent. The partial width amplitudes (8.68) contain the penetration factor v_λ, which may increase rapidly with energy. Thus a given AB resonance may produce a peak in the three-particle cross section at a value of E_{AB} that is somewhat lower than the corresponding peak energy of the isolated AB cross section.

Of course, for AB elastic scattering, the resonant term is added coherently to a potential scattering term, so that the shape of the two-body cross section often looks nothing like the Breit-Wigner form. There is no interference term in the three-particle cross section (14.1), which depends on E_{AB} more like an inelastic cross section.

A classic example of the use of this theory is the deduction by Werntz (62) of the existence, energy, and spin of the first excited state of the α-particle from the t(d, pn)t experiment of Lefevre, Borchers, and Poppe (62). In this case the resonance in the t-p system was deduced from the neutron energy spectrum. The initial direct process is a (d, n) rearrangement collision leaving the proton and triton in a resonant state. The wave function of the resonant t-p system differs from a bound-state wave function in that it has different boundary conditions. Asymptotically it is the direct product of a triton wave function with a proton wave function, which has plane waves superimposed on ingoing spherical waves. One of the partial waves in this wave function is assumed to be resonant, and the resonance parameters are found by curve fitting.

The virtual state has spin and parity 0+, it occurs 0.40 MeV above the t-p threshold, and its reduced width γ_p^2/a is 4.2 MeV where $a = 3.0$ fm.

B. THE (p, 2p) REACTION

The (p, 2p) reaction is interesting from the point of view of nuclear structure when it occurs in a region of phase space where it may be considered as a quasi-three-body potential scattering problem, namely the direct removal of a proton from a nucleus caused by a collision with the incident proton. It can be considered in this way when the relative energies of all the two-body systems are high enough for isolated resonances to be unimportant. The proton-core interaction may then be represented by an optical-model potential.

In a (p, 2p) experiment the momentum of each of the particles in the final state is completely determined. The momentum transfer $\mathbf{K}$ to the residual nucleus is therefore measured, and the differential cross section may be obtained as a function of $\mathbf{K}$. In general, it depends of course on other kinematic variables too. For convenience, the values of $\mathbf{K}$ measured in a particular experiment are usually restricted to a subset of phase space that depends on one parameter. For example, many experiments have been performed in coplanar symmetric geometry where $\theta_L = \theta_R = \theta$, $\phi_L = 0$, $\phi_R = \pi$, $E_L = E_R$. The differential cross section for a particular value of $E_L + E_R$ is expressed as a function of θ. The definition of the kinematic quantities is shown in Fig. 14.2.

Much of the information obtainable from the reaction is again almost directly experimental. Maxima are observed in the curves of the differential cross section plotted against the separation energy Q, which is the energy difference between the final and initial states. The maxima are interpreted as corresponding directly to energy levels of single particles in the initial nucleus. This interpretation must be confirmed by using it successfully in a theory of the angular correlation, which is the differential cross section for the two protons to emerge at particular angles. Each single-particle maximum has a substructure corresponding to different final states of the residual nucleus.

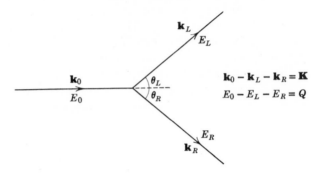

FIG. 14.2   Definition of the kinematical quantities used in the description of the (p, 2p) reaction.

Figure 14.3 shows the Q distribution in two different experiments on the reaction ^{12}C(p, 2p)^{11}B: (1) at 155 MeV where the substructure is not resolved and (2) at 50 MeV where the substructure of the peak at $Q = -16$ MeV is resolved.

The peaks in the 155 MeV curve are considered as due to knocking out protons from a p-state at 16 MeV and an s-state at about 36 MeV. The resolution of the p-state peak shown in the 50 MeV curve indicates that most of the peak is due to reactions which leave the ^{11}B nucleus in its ground state.

[i]   THE DISTRIBUTION OF SEPARATION ENERGIES

There are two features of the peaks in the spectrum of separation energies which must be explained, namely their positions and their widths. The peaks themselves are divided into two types: those for which the residual nucleus is in its ground state and those for which it is excited.

For the study of nuclear spectroscopy, the (p, 2p) reaction may be considered as equivalent to an (n, d) pickup reaction in which the proton is removed from a shell-model state. The peak at the lowest separation energy corresponds to the removal of a proton from the uppermost single-particle state, leaving the final nucleus in its ground state. If the final nucleus or core

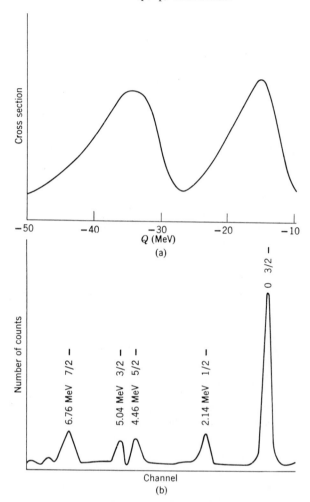

FIG. 14.3   The distribution of energy transfer Q in the reaction ^{12}C(p, 2p)^{11}B. (*a*) 155 MeV, $\theta = 44°$. The ordinate is the cross section plotted on an arbitrary linear scale. (Adapted from Garron, Jacmart, Riou, Ruhla, Teillac, and Strauch, 62.) (*b*) 50 MeV, $\theta = 35°$. The abscissa is the channel number in an experimental recording device, which is roughly proportional to Q. (Adapted from Pugh, Hendrie, Chabre, Boschitz, and McCarthy, 67.)

cannot be regarded as inert, there is a finite probability that it will be left in excited states. One therefore expects subsequent peaks corresponding to this possibility (Fig. 14.3*b*). The reaction may be considered as a probe for exciting different states of the final nucleus. The (p, 2p) reaction will be described in the next subsection by a direct interaction theory in which there is an overlap integral for the nuclear structure. The overlap integral is the same as for pickup. The same sum rules for excited final states apply, and the spectroscopic information obtained is the same. Only the reaction mechanism is different. The spectroscopic aspects were discussed in detail in Chapter 13*B*.

There is very different information available from the (p, 2p) reaction owing to the fact that strongly bound nucleons can be removed. We shall consider the peak corresponding to the removal of a 1*s*-state proton. In ^{12}C this peak has a width of about 11 MeV (Figure 14.3*a*), whereas the widths of the *p*-state peaks are zero within experimental error.

The explanation of the *s*-state peaks is that the residual nucleus has a hole in an *s*-state. The hole can be absorbed, which is equivalent to the nucleus rearranging itself so that all the lower single-particle states are occupied. Thus the shell-model potential for the hole is complex. The energy eigenvalue is complex, and the imaginary part gives rise to the width of the peak.

Remarkably accurate predictions of the widths of *s*-state peaks in (p, 2p) reactions have been made by Köhler (66), who calculated the energy eigenvalues for finite nuclei with a single hole by the local nuclear matter model (see Chapter 6*B*). The expectation value of the energy is given by Equation (6.41).

$$E = \sum_i \langle \chi_i | \, \mathscr{H} \, | \chi_i \rangle + \tfrac{1}{2} \sum_{ijkl} \int d^3 r_1' \int d^3 r_2' \int d^3 r_1 \int d^3 r_2 \chi_i^*(\mathbf{r}_1) \chi_j^*(\mathbf{r}_2)$$

$$\times \, \langle \mathbf{r}_{12} | \, K_\alpha \, | \mathbf{r}_{12}' \rangle [\chi_k(\mathbf{r}_1') \chi_l(\mathbf{r}_2') - \chi_k(\mathbf{r}_2') \chi_l(\mathbf{r}_1')]. \quad (6.41)$$

In order to discuss the imaginary part, we consider the spectral representation of the Green's function G_α in the Brueckner-Bethe-Goldstone equation (6.38), this time with boundary conditions appropriate to a particle-hole pair α in nuclear matter. The method is analogous to the optical-model derivations (9.90) and (10.122). The Green's function is

$$G_\alpha = [\mathscr{H}_\alpha + V_\alpha - E]^{-1}, \quad (14.2)$$

where $V_\alpha(\equiv V_{ij})$ is the nonlocal Brueckner-Bethe-Goldstone potential operator defined by (6.21) and $\mathscr{H}_\alpha$ is the kinetic energy operator. V_α is nonlocal because it includes the effect of the Pauli exclusion principle.

We define the eigenstate $\psi_\alpha(E_\alpha)$ of the problem of the interaction of the pair α with relative energy and wave number E_α, k_α by

$$(\mathscr{H}_\alpha + V_\alpha - E_\alpha)\psi_\alpha(E_\alpha) = 0. \quad (14.3)$$

The essential part of the energy expectation value (6.41) is the matrix element $\langle r_{12} | \, K_\alpha \, | r_{12}' \rangle$ of the *K*-matrix which is defined by (6.37) or, alternatively, dropping the prime from V_α which indicated the subtraction of a single-particle potential,

$$K_\alpha = V_\alpha - V_\alpha G_\alpha V_\alpha. \tag{14.4}$$

The contribution of the second term in (14.4) to the matrix element of K_α is, using the spectral representation of G_α and taking only the term corresponding to unbound states,

$$\langle \mathbf{r}_{12}| V_\alpha G_\alpha V_\alpha |\mathbf{r}_{12}'\rangle = \int dE' \frac{\langle \mathbf{r}_{12}| V_\alpha |\psi_\alpha(E')\rangle\langle\psi_\alpha(E')| V_\alpha |\mathbf{r}_{12}'\rangle}{E' - E_\alpha}. \tag{14.5}$$

The imaginary part of (14.5) is

$$\mathrm{Im}\,\langle \mathbf{r}_{12}| K_\alpha |\mathbf{r}_{12}'\rangle = -\pi\,\langle \mathbf{r}_{12}| V_\alpha |\psi_\alpha(E_\alpha)\rangle\langle\psi_\alpha(E_\alpha)| V_\alpha |\mathbf{r}_{12}'\rangle \text{ for physically acces-}$$
$$\text{sible values of } E_\alpha,$$
$$= 0 \text{ otherwise.} \tag{14.6}$$

This term is proportional to the square of the scattering amplitude on the energy shell of the particle-hole pair α.

In the normal nuclear matter calculation of Chapter 6B, there are no physically accessible relative energies E_α to which a pair of particles can scatter. However, if one member of the pair is a hole and the other a particle, scattering is no longer forbidden by the Pauli principle and the conservation of energy. The nucleus can spontaneously rearrange itself. The process is described in the present language as the scattering of the hole to a higher occupied state. Hence the imaginary part of the energy (6.41) is finite.

In the calculation of Köhler, the width Γ of the single-hole state was found to depend on the Fermi momentum k_F, since K_α depends on k_F. It also depends strongly on the momentum k_α of the hole. This is clear from the fact that a deeper hole will have more particles whose momentum is higher so that the scattering can take place to more states $|k_\alpha\rangle$. There are more imaginary terms in the sum (6.41).

The dependence of the width Γ on the hole momentum for $k_F = 1.4$ fm^{-1} is shown in Fig. 14.4. If the momentum of the hole is k_F, we expect the width of the hole state to be zero, since there are no particles with which scattering is energetically possible. In other words, if we knock a particle out of the topmost single-particle state, we leave a core nucleus that cannot rearrange itself. This accounts for the negligible widths of the $1p$ states in $1p$-shell nuclei. As the size of the nucleus increases, the kinetic energy of the $1s$ hole, which is the difference between the $1s$ eigenvalue and the depth of the single particle well, decreases. The width of the $1s$ state Γ_{1s} is larger for larger nuclei. However, the increase is expected to be small after the light nuclei, since the radius is proportional to $A^{1/3}$.

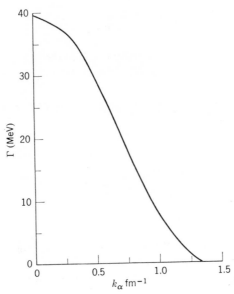

FIG. 14.4 The dependence of the width Γ of the single-hole state in the local nuclear matter model as a function of the hole momentum k_α at the Fermi momentum $k_F = 1.4$ fm^{-1}. (Adapted from Köhler, 66.)

These expectations are expressed quantitatively by the results of Köhler for the widths of $1s$ states in different nuclei shown in Table 14.1.

In fact, the $1s$ hole state in ^{40}Ca has not been observed because of its large width. The widths of the lower states in heavier nuclei can be as high as 30 MeV according to the calculation. The use of (p, 2p) reactions to describe their properties is limited by this fact. Figure 14.4 may be used as a rough guide to determine which single-hole states are amenable to investigation by the (p, 2p) reaction.

We saw in Chapter 6B that the real part of the hole energy is given quite well by the local nuclear matter model. The calculation of the particle-hole scattering correction shows that the correction may be about 10 MeV for $1s$

Nucleus	^{8}Be	^{12}C	^{16}O	^{27}Al	^{40}Ca	^{208}Pb
Γ_{1s} (theory)	8.1	11.5	13.7	19.6	21.6	29.8
Γ_{1s} (p, 2p)	10	11	14	20	—	—

TABLE 14.1. Widths Γ_{1s} in MeV of the $1s$ hole state in various nuclei calculated by the local nuclear matter model and compared with the values found by (p, 2p) experiments. (From Köhler, 66.)

states and 2 MeV for $1p$ states in light nuclei. This is of the order of 25 per cent, which would account for the discrepancies between theory and experiment for ^{16}O shown in Table 6.3. The correction is often called the rearrangement energy.

[ii] ANGULAR CORRELATION IN THE QUASI-THREE-BODY MODEL

The quasi-three-body model assumes that a proton is removed from the nucleus leaving a core which is inert. The fact that the particular channel under consideration is not the only possible one is described by complex proton-core potentials V_p. The formal theory for nonidentical particles was given in Chapter 10E, leading to the following equation for the breakup amplitude, which is analogous to Equation (13.13) for pickup in the case of a single particle outside an inert core.

$$T = A\langle \chi_L^{(-)}(\mathbf{k}_L)\chi_R^{(-)}(\mathbf{k}_R)| \, T_{pp} \, |\psi_0\chi_0^{(+)}(\mathbf{k}_0)\rangle. \tag{14.7}$$

We have identified the particles scattered to the left and right by subscripts L and R, respectively. The wave function of the bound proton is ψ_0. The theory must be antisymmetrized.

We shall assume that there is no spin-orbit coupling in any of the potentials. In this case we can use the type of antisymmetry analysis that has previously been used to derive Equations (3.101) for p-p scattering and (12.44) for quasi-three-body inelastic scattering to obtain

$$\frac{d^3\sigma}{d\Omega_L \, d\Omega_R \, dE_L} = \sum_{MM'\mu} Z_{MM'\mu} \{ \tfrac{3}{4} A_{11}^2 |M_T|^2 + \tfrac{1}{4} A_{10}^2 |M_S|^2 \}. \tag{14.8}$$

The triplet and singlet matrix elements M_T, M_S are given by

$$M_{\substack{S\\T}} = \int d^3r_1 \int d^3r_2 [\chi_L^{(-)*}(\mathbf{k}_L, \mathbf{r}_1)\chi_R^{(-)*}(\mathbf{k}_R, \mathbf{r}_2) \pm \chi_L^{(-)*}(\mathbf{k}_L, \mathbf{r}_2)\chi_R^{(-)*}(\mathbf{k}_R, \mathbf{r}_1)]$$

$$\times t(|\mathbf{r}_1 - \mathbf{r}_2|)\psi_L^\mu(\mathbf{r}_2)\chi_0^{(+)}(\mathbf{k}_0, \mathbf{r}_1). \tag{14.9}$$

The partial wave decomposition of (14.9) is analogous to that of Equation (12.55) for inelastic scattering. Defining the partial wave expansion of the factors in (14.9) by

$$\chi_0^{(+)}(\mathbf{k}_0, \mathbf{r}_1) = (k_0 r_1)^{-1} \sum_l [4\pi(2l+1)]^{1/2} i^l e^{i\sigma_l} u_l(k_0, r_1) Y_l^0(\Omega_1),$$

$$\chi_L^{(-)*}(\mathbf{k}_L, \mathbf{r}_1) = (k_L r_1)^{-1} \sum_{l'm'} 4\pi i^{-l'} e^{i\sigma_{l'}} u_{l'}(k_L, r_1) Y_{l'}^{m'*}(\Omega_1) Y_{l'}^{m'}(\Omega_L),$$

$$\chi_R^{(-)*}(\mathbf{k}_R, \mathbf{r}_2) = (k_R r_2)^{-1} \sum_{l''m''} 4\pi i^{-l''} e^{i\sigma_{l''}} u_{l''}(k_R, r_2) Y_{l''}^{m''}(\Omega_2) Y_{l''}^{m''*}(\Omega_R),$$

$$t(|\mathbf{r}_1 - \mathbf{r}_2|) = \sum_n 4\pi t_n(r_1, r_2) \sum_p Y_n^p(\Omega_1) Y_n^{p*}(\Omega_2),$$

we may write the direct and exchange matrix elements as

$$M^{D/E} = \sum_{ll'l''n} F_{ll'l''n} R_{ll'l''n}^{D/E} \sum_p \mathcal{Y}_{ll'l''n,L}^{D/E p,\mu}, \tag{14.10}$$

where

$$F_{ll'l''n} = (4\pi)^2 (2n+1)(2l+1)i^{l-l'-l''}$$

$$\times\, e^{i(\sigma_l+\sigma_{l'}+\sigma_{l''})}\left[\frac{4\pi(2L+1)}{(2l'+1)(2l''+1)}\right]^{1/2}(-1)^p,$$

$$\mathscr{Y}_{ll'l''n,L}^{Dp,\mu} = C_{nll'}^{p0p}C_{nll''}^{000}C_{n\ L\ l''}^{-p\mu\mu-p}C_{nLl'}^{000}Y_{l'}^{p}(\Omega_L)Y_{l''}^{\mu-p}(\Omega_R),$$

$$\mathscr{Y}_{ll'l''n,L}^{Ep,\mu} = C_{nll''}^{p0p}C_{nll'}^{000}C_{n\ L\ l'}^{-p\mu\mu-p}C_{nLl''}^{000}Y_{l'}^{\mu-p}(\Omega_L)Y_{l''}^{p}(\Omega_R),$$

$$R_{ll'l''n}^{D} = (k_0 k_L k_R)^{-1}\int dr_1\int dr_2 u_{l'}(k_L,r_1)u_{l''}(k_R,r_2)t_n(r_1,r_2)u_l(k_0,r_1)R_{Lj}(r_2),$$

$$R_{ll'l''n}^{E} = (k_0 k_L k_R)^{-1}\int dr_1\int dr_2 u_{l'}(k_L,r_2)u_{l''}(k_R,r_1)t_n(r_1,r_2)u_l(k_0,r_1)R_{Lj}(r_2).$$

$$(14.11)$$

The normalization constant $Z_{MM'\mu}$ is given in the case of a closed shell initial nucleus by

$$Z_{MM'\mu} = \frac{2\pi}{\hbar}\frac{M_0}{\hbar k_0}\frac{2M_0^3}{(2\pi\hbar)^6}(E_L E_R)^{1/2}N[\theta_{Lj}^{J'J}]^2\frac{1}{2J+1}$$

$$\times\, [C_{J'\ \ j}^{M'\ M-M'\ M}C_{J\ L\ s}^{\mu\ -\mu+M-M'\ M-M'}]^2. \quad (14.12)$$

J', j, and J are the angular momenta of the residual nucleus, the struck proton and the initial nucleus. M', m, and M are the corresponding projection quantum numbers. L and s are the orbital angular momentum and spin of the struck proton. μ is the projection of L. N is the number of protons in the relevant shell-model state. M_0 is the nucleon mass. By analogy with the theory of pickup, we have defined a reduced-width amplitude $\theta_{Lj}^{J'J}$ which describes the probability amplitude that the initial state contains the (core + proton) configuration.

The case where a proton is removed from a closed shell in the initial nucleus is particularly simple because there is only one possible spin transition. The probability of this transition is given by the factor in (14.12) involving the Clebsch-Gordan coefficients. The factor $1/(2J+1)$ averages over initial spin states. The physical reason for the factor N is that there are N possible spin projections which could, in principle, be distinguished experimentally but, in fact, are not if polarizations are not measured. N is 4 in the $^{12}C(p, 2p)^{11}B$ case. The remaining factors in (14.12) come from phase-space considerations described in the discussion of Equation (10.63).

The quasi-three-body model strictly applies only to the reaction which leaves the final nucleus in its ground state. It includes no degrees of freedom for excitation of the core. Calculations of momentum-transfer distributions for excited states of the final nucleus would strictly require a multichannel treatment like that outlined in Chapter 13 for stripping and pickup.

The bound-state factor $\theta_{Lj}^{J'J} \psi_L^\mu(\mathbf{r})$ really represents an overlap integral of the form (13.38). The reader is again referred to Chapter 13 for the discussion of the spectroscopic properties of this factor. Its radial dependence, however, is much more critically investigated by means of the (p, 2p) reaction.

Before the (p, 2p) reaction can be used as a sensitive probe for nuclear structure, its mechanism must be understood. The detailed study of angular correlations has thus far concentrated entirely on this aspect, rather than spectroscopy. We shall therefore concentrate on the mechanism of the quasi-three-body situation. We shall assume the validity of the quasi-three-body model. This assumption may be justified by the fact that it gives correct answers for the (p, p′) problem at high energies (Chapter 12B[iii]).

It is a good idea to concentrate first on high energies where distorted waves are not far from plane waves and, in fact, are given very accurately in the reaction region by eikonal approximations (Chapter 12C[ii]), which are approximately plane waves with complex wave numbers. We shall consider coplanar symmetric geometry.

For plane waves the triplet matrix element M_T vanishes. The singlet-matrix element M_S factorizes with the use of the transformation

$$\mathbf{r} = \mathbf{r}_1 - \mathbf{r}_2$$

$$\mathbf{r}' = \mathbf{r}_2.$$

$$M_S = \int d^3 r\, e^{i(\mathbf{k}_0 - \mathbf{k}_L)\cdot\mathbf{r}} t(r) \int d^3 r'\, e^{i\mathbf{K}\cdot\mathbf{r}'} \psi_L^\mu(\mathbf{r}').   \tag{14.13}$$

The second factor, just as in the case of plane wave inelastic scattering, is the Fourier transform of the nuclear structure factor with respect to the momentum transfer $\mathbf{K}$. For a reaction concentrated near the surface R, it gives a momentum-transfer distribution proportional to $[j_L(KR)]^2$. For $L > 0$ there is a minimum at minimum momentum transfer and for $L = 0$ there is a maximum. In the coplanar symmetric case, K is minimum near $\theta = 45°$. If the struck particle were not even bound to the core we would have a free p-p collision in which $K = 0$ at 45°. For $L > 0$ there are two major peaks in the curve of differential cross section plotted against K or θ. For $L = 0$ there is one peak situated at about 45°. For large separation energies this peak is shifted considerably. The spread of the two peaks for $L > 0$ is larger for smaller R and larger L. R may be considered as a measure of the average collision radius. For the purpose of discussion we shall characterize it by the rms radius of $\psi_L^\mu(\mathbf{r})$.

The first factor in (14.13) is the p-p scattering amplitude. It is on the energy shell if $Q = 0$. At high incident energies it is close to the energy shell and the impulse approximation is made. The square of the first factor is replaced by the p-p cross section (at 90° in the coplanar symmetric geometry) calculated at an energy given by assuming a collision with a proton whose momentum is exactly equal and opposite to the momentum transfer, since the original nucleus was stationary. Thus the p-p collision occurs at low center of mass energies for $\theta < 45°$ and higher center of mass energies for $\theta > 45°$. The factor therefore weights the side of the angular distribution curve for small θ. The left peak is higher than the right. The plane wave impulse approximation for the $1s$ and $1p$ states of ^{12}C at 155 MeV is illustrated in Fig. 14.5.

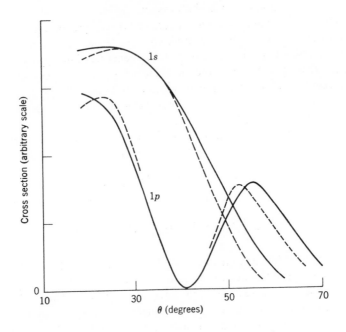

FIG. 14.5   The plane wave impulse approximation (on an arbitrary linear scale) for the $^{12}C(p, 2p)^{11}B$ reaction at 155 MeV. For the $1s$ and $1p$ states, respectively, the full line is calculated with $R = 1.5$ fm and 2.2 fm, the dotted line is for $R = 1.9$ fm and 2.8 fm.

If the second factor of (14.13) is replaced by the zero range distorted wave approximation, we again have the distorted wave impulse approximation (DWIA), which is a high-energy limit of the distorted wave t-matrix approximation.

Early calculations of (p, 2p) angular distributions at high energy were done in the DWIA, using the semiclassical approximation of Chapter 12C[ii] for the distorted waves. Such calculations are reviewed by Jacob and Maris

(66). Angular correlations for isolated shell-model states were obtained experimentally by considering only (p, 2p) events in particular peaks in the Q distribution. In this way the s-states and states for $L > 0$ were distinguished. Sometimes the minima for minimum K in the experiments were much shallower than the theoretical minima and in one case, Li^6, where R is rather large so that the two peaks are in any case close, no minimum was observed at 155 MeV in spite of improved angular resolution and resolution of Q. A minimum for Li^6 was later observed at higher energy, and a calculation by Lim and McCarthy (64b) showed that poor resolution of the individual energies E_L and E_R, which was present in the 155 MeV experiment, can fill in the minimum. Further filling in was shown by Jackson (67) to be given by poor definition of the coplanarity of the reaction. States for $L > 0$ are in fact always characterized at high energy by a minimum in the angular correlation curve for minimum K.

The results of the semiclassical approximation for 155 MeV (p, 2p) experiments on p-shell nuclei were confirmed by a distorted wave impulse approximation calculation by Lim and McCarthy (64b) using partial wave expansions of the optical-model wave functions. A calculation by Jackson and Berggren (65) for ^{6}Li at 180 MeV showed that the semiclassical approximation at that energy is practically indistinguishable from the more exact optical-model treatment. The semiclassical model however does not describe changes in the direction of the proton trajectories.

The uniqueness of the determination of nuclear structure information from the (p, 2p) angular correlation was illustrated in the 155 MeV calculation of Lim and McCarthy. The nuclear structure information consists of a determination of L and the rms radius of the wave function of a particular single-particle state. The overall width of the angular correlation curve, which depends only on R for given L in the plane-wave theory, was shown to depend again only on R in the distorted wave impulse approximation. Optical-model potentials affected aspects of the curve other than the overall width. The curves were fairly insensitive to the initial state parameters, but an increase of Vr_0^2 in the final state led to a shift of the whole curve to larger angles because of increased refraction of the protons as they leave the nucleus. Increasing W damped the whole cross section. In this way the values of the square well parameters for shell-model wave functions given in Chapter 5C were obtained. The binding energies are of course obtained from the Q distribution, so R is the only free square well parameter. The sensitivity of the angular correlation to changes in R is illustrated for ^{12}C in Fig. 14.5. The determination of the rms radii of single-particle radial wave functions constitutes the chief contribution of the angular correlation analysis so far.

One disturbing feature of this calculation was that, in order to locate the angular correlation curve properly along the θ axis, unrealistically large values of Vr_0^2 for the final state had to be used. The effect was only a few degrees and was ignored at high energy. We shall see later that it is a significant effect.

The other aspect of nuclear physics that can be examined at high energies, is the radial dependence of the effective local two-nucleon pseudo-potential. In Fig. 14.6 we compare calculations for the p-state (p, 2p)

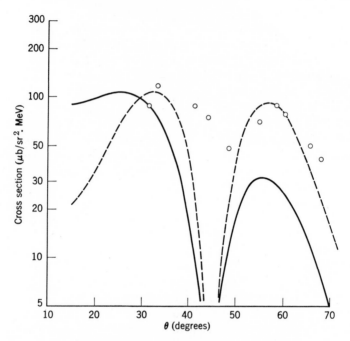

FIG. 14.6   The DWTA for the reaction $^{12}C(p, 2p)^{11}B$ at 155 MeV ($1p$ state). The solid line is calculated with the free p-p pseudopotential (3.102). The dashed line is calculated with the core terms in the pseudopotential multiplied by 1.8, and normalized to p-p scattering.

reaction on ^{12}C at 155 MeV for different pseudopotentials with experiment. There is a large difference between the curves for the free p-p pseudopotential of (3.102) and one modified by increasing the last two terms by a factor of 1.8 and normalizing the new pseudopotential to low energy p-p scattering. The latter pseudopotential in fact fits the (p, 2p) data better. This is thus far not understood.

The quality of fits to the angular correlation obtainable for light nuclei at 155 MeV is indicated for the $1s$ and $1p$ states in Fig. 14.7. The $1s$ curve is normalized relative to the $1p$ curve by giving them spectroscopic factors of 2 and N, respectively, where N is the number of $1p$ protons. Only the overall

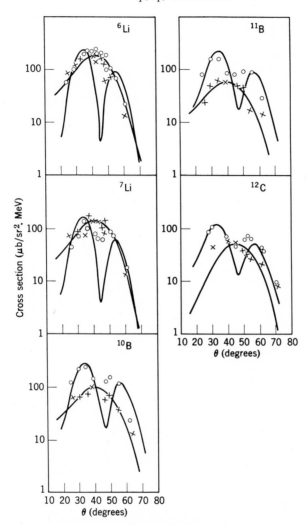

FIG. 14.7 Comparison of the DWIA with experiments at 155 MeV. $1s$ states are indicated by crosses, $1p$ states by circles. (Adapted from Lim and McCarthy, 64b.)

widths and relative normalizations of the $1s$ and $1p$ curves are regarded as significant. The independence of the effects of optical-model and nuclear parameters was used in adjusting the optical-model parameters for best fit without regard to elastic scattering. The values of the square well parameters quoted in Table 5.5 were derived from this analysis.

A much more critical test of the (p, 2p) theory occurs for reactions at lower energy. In 1965 the angular correlation for coplanar symmetric geometry was measured at 50 MeV for ^{12}C(p, 2p)^{11}B by Pugh, Hendrie, Chabre, and Boschitz (65). It became possible to consider only events that left the residual nucleus in its ground state and really to test the distorted wave *t*-matrix approximation.

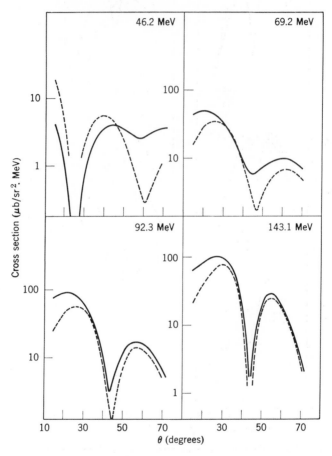

FIG. 14.8   Comparison of the DWIA (dashed line) with the DWTA (solid line) at various energies for singlet (p, 2p) events in the reaction ^{12}C(p, 2p)^{11}B($1p$ state).

The calculation was carried out by Lim and McCarthy (66). It was first shown that the high-energy limit, the distorted wave impulse approximation, is inapplicable at 50 MeV. Comparison of the two approximations for different energies is shown in Fig. 14.8.

This figure is of great general interest in the theory of quasi-three-body reactions because it shows what energy range can be considered as "high."

We define high energies for nuclear reactions to be those for which the impulse approximation is good. This means that we can use experimental information about the nucleon-nucleon force to describe that subsystem. This is a great simplification in principle and for calculations. Reactions at high energy probe nuclear structure without the complication of requiring a good nucleon-nucleon model.

The energy of the final state is critical for the validity of the impulse approximation because there is more distortion in the two final state waves than in the single entrance channel wave. It appears that a minimum requirement for the validity of the impulse approximation for light nuclei is that no distorted wave should have an energy less than 65 MeV.

The fact that the distorted wave impulse approximation is invalid at 50 MeV means that off-energy-shell matrix elements of the *t*-matrix are important. Also the fact that the triplet cross section is not negligible for the coplanar symmetric case as it is at 155 MeV means that symmetric collisions do not dominate the matrix element. Effects that are not given by the distorted wave impulse approximation are called three-body effects.

That the distortion is responsible for the introduction of off-shell *t*-matrix elements is shown by writing the optical-model wave functions $\chi^{(\pm)}(\mathbf{k}_i, \mathbf{r})$ in, for example, the first term of (14.9) as Fourier transforms of momentum-distortion amplitudes $\phi^{(\pm)}(\mathbf{k}_i, \mathbf{k})$ and $\psi_L{}^\mu(\mathbf{r})$ as the Fourier transform of $\phi_L{}^\mu(\mathbf{k})$. The term becomes

$$M_1 = \int d^3k \int d^3k' \int d^3k'' \int d^3k''' \phi^{(-)*}(\mathbf{k}_L, \mathbf{k}) \phi^{(-)*}(\mathbf{k}_R, \mathbf{k}') \phi^{(+)}(\mathbf{k}_0, \mathbf{k}'')$$

$$\times \phi_L{}^\mu(\mathbf{k}''') t(\mathbf{k}, \mathbf{k}', \mathbf{k}'', \mathbf{k}'''). \quad (14.14)$$

The (p-p) *t*-matrix element is given by

$$t(\mathbf{k}, \mathbf{k}', \mathbf{k}'', \mathbf{k}''') = \int d^3r_1 \int d^3r_2 e^{-i\mathbf{k}\cdot\mathbf{r}_1} e^{-i\mathbf{k}'\cdot\mathbf{r}_2} t(|\mathbf{r}_1 - \mathbf{r}_2|) e^{i\mathbf{k}''\cdot\mathbf{r}_1} e^{i\mathbf{k}'''\cdot\mathbf{r}_2}. \quad (14.15)$$

For plane waves $\phi^{(\pm)}(\mathbf{k}_i, \mathbf{k}) = \delta(\mathbf{k}_i - \mathbf{k})$. Otherwise the *t*-matrix element (14.15) occurs in (14.2) for all values of the four arguments including those which do not conserve momentum. Off-shell matrix elements are weighted by the product of the momentum distortion amplitudes ϕ.

Figure 14.8 shows another phenomenon in the angular correlation, which was previously encountered for inelastic scattering to a 2+ state. The minimum for minimum K is filled in by distortion. This was again shown to be a focal effect by using the simple wave function (11.5) in the (p, 2p) matrix element (Lim and McCarthy, 63).

Using optical-model parameters obtained by fitting p-^{11}B elastic scattering at 17 MeV (which gives the appropriate relative energy) and p-^{12}C scattering at 50 MeV, the dashed curve in Fig. 14.9 was obtained.

Clearly the distorted wave approximation fails for this very simple reaction

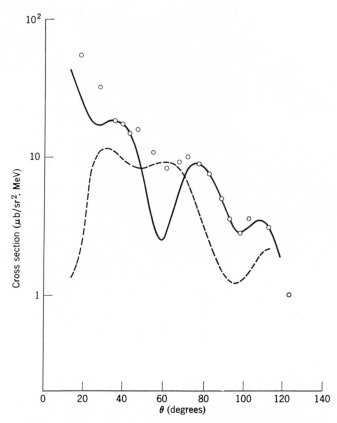

FIG. 14.9   The DWTA for the reaction ^{12}C(p, 2p)^{11}B at 50 MeV ($1p$ state). The dashed curve is calculated using the free potentials for each two-body subsystem. The solid curve is calculated with enhanced final-state potentials. The exchange parameter is $(A_{11}/A_{10})^2 = \frac{1}{3}$.

which really tests it. The approximation is corrected by a simple ad hoc procedure. If the optical-model parameter $Vr_0{}^2$ for the final state is increased by 20 per cent, the full line in Fig. 14.9 is obtained.

Unfortunately the insensitivity of the changes in shape of the angular correlation curve produced by varying a certain parameter to variations of another parameter does not persist at 50 MeV. Changes of rms radius produce effects similar to changes in potentials. The curve-fitting situation will be in a state of uncertainty until more experiments are analyzed. For the curves of Fig. 14.9 the value of R determined at 155 MeV was used. Any departure from the free two-body pseudopotential (3.102) worsened the fit.

The peaks in the angular correlation can be understood as follows. The original two peaks are the first rise of the curve at small angles and the peak at 70°. The filling-in of the minimum at about 40° is a distortion effect.

The peak at $110°$ is due to triplet scattering. It is fitted by using $(A_{11}/A_{10})^2 = \frac{1}{3}$, which is consistent with the values for p-p potentials given in Table 3.3.

That the shift of the angular correlation curve by $10°$ at 50 MeV is a three-body effect rather than a failure of the quasi-three-body model is indicated by the fact that a similar increase of Vr_0^2 was necessary to locate the 155 MeV curves for several different nuclear structure situations. Subsequent $^{12}C(p, 2p)^{11}B$ experiments at 50 MeV and 45 MeV with asymmetric geometry have confirmed that approximately a 20 per cent increase in Vr_0^2 will produce the required shift.

As was the case with stripping, absolute spectroscopic factors provide a better test of the reaction mechanism than mere fits to the angular correlation shape. From this point of view, ^{12}C is an unfortunate target since knowledge of its spectroscopic factor depends sensitively on the details of an intermediate coupling shell-model calculation. Calculations by Cohen and Kurath (65) indicate that $N[\theta_{Lj}^{JJ}]^2$ is about 2.8. In all the calculations shown, this number is set equal to 4. The study of (p, 2p) angular correlations has not yet reached the stage where the reaction rivals stripping as a means of analysing spectroscopic factors. Analyses of high-energy data in the DWIA by Jain and Jackson (67) provide more hope in this respect. These calculations use shell-model spectroscopic factors. In particular, the left-hand peak is well fitted for $^{12}C(p, 2p)^{11}B$ at 160 MeV, although the right-hand peak is too low as it was in the calculation of Fig. 14.6 for the realistic pseudo-potential.

We may summarize our discussion of (p, 2p) angular correlations by saying that at high energies they are capable of yielding a unique determination of the rms radius of the nuclear structure factor $\psi_L^\mu(\mathbf{r})$ for any state from which a proton can be knocked out of the nucleus, provided the width of the state is not too large. This provides us with a tremendously powerful tool for the investigation of nuclear structure. At low energies they present us with a situation which is sensitive to a three-body description beyond that afforded by the distorted wave t-matrix approximation. There is an indication that the three-body effect can be understood as an effective increase in the final state proton-core potential.

FURTHER READING

1. Conference on Correlations of Particles Emitted in Nuclear Reactions, *Rev. Mod. Phys.*, **37**, No. 3.

    Conference proceedings containing many examples of sequential reactions.

2. O. Chamberlain and E. Segrè, *Phys. Rev.*, **87**, 81 (1952).
H. Tyrén, P. Hillman, and Th. A. J. Maris, *Nucl. Phys.*, **7**, 10 (1958).
R. J. Griffiths and R. M. Eisberg, *Nucl. Phys.*, **12**, 225 (1959).
T. J. Gooding and H. G. Pugh, *Nucl. Phys.*, **18**, 46 (1960).
H. G. Pugh, D. L. Hendrie, M. Chabre, and E. Boschitz, *Phys. Rev. Letters* **14**, 434 (1965).
Original experimental papers.

3. G. Jacob and Th. A. J. Maris, *Rev. Mod. Phys.*, **38**, 121 (1966).
Review of early work.

4. M. Riou, *Rev. Mod. Phys.*, **37**, 375 (1965).
Review of single-particle separation energies.

5. K. Dietrich, *Phys. Letters*, **2**, 139 (1962).
V. V. Balashov, A. N. Boyarkina, and I. Rotter, *Nucl. Phys.*, **59**, 417 (1965).
Models for states of the residual nucleus.

6. B. K. Jain and D. F. Jackson, *Nucl. Phys.*, A99, 113 (1967).
Spectroscopy with the (p, 2p) reaction.

7. K. L. Lim and I. E. McCarthy, *Nucl. Phys.*, **88**, 433 (1966).
Review of distorted wave theory.

8. H. G. Pugh, D. L. Hendrie, M. Chabre, E. Boschitz, and I. E. McCarthy, *Phys. Rev.*, **155**, 1054 (1967).
The (p, 2p) reaction at 50 MeV.

PROBLEMS

1. In an experiment in which neutrons are elastically scattered from ^{4}He there is a resonance at 1.1 MeV of width $\Gamma = 1.7$ MeV, corresponding to a $1p_{3/2}$ state of ^{5}He. Energies are neutron energies in the laboratory system. Draw the unnormalized energy spectrum of protons at $20°$ in the experiment ^{4}He(d, pn)^{4}He in the region where the ^{5}He resonance is important. Useful information is that the rms radius of ^{4}He is about 1.6 fm.

2. What is the angle of minimum momentum transfer in the experiment ^{12}C(p, 2p)^{11}B at 50 MeV, and 150 MeV where $Q = 16$ MeV and coplanar symmetric geometry is used? Use (a) relativistic, (b) nonrelativistic kinematics.

3. Draw the angular correlation for s- and p-states in the plane-wave theory for the reaction ^{12}C(p, 2p)^{11}B for incident energies of 50 MeV and 150 MeV.

Use coplanar symmetric geometry and assume that the reaction region is concentrated at a radius of 1.7 fm for the s-state and 2.8 fm for the p-state. Compare the results with the distorted wave curves of Fig. 14.8.

4. Using the plane-wave approximation, draw the angular correlation for the reaction $^{14}N(p, pd)^{12}C$ at 150 MeV, where the deuteron is counted in a fixed counter at 30° and the other counter is moved. Assume equal energies E_L, E_R. Consider only the reaction with the smallest separation energy.

5. Using the plane-wave approximation, plot the ratio E_L/E_R for the reaction $^{12}C(p, 2p)^{11}B$ at 150 MeV in which both counters are fixed at 30°. How would the curve be modified by distortion? Consider only the removal of the $1p$ proton.

6. The reaction $^{12}C(p, pd)^{10}B$ at 1000 MeV has an appreciable cross section. Can you explain this?

7. Use information available in Chapter 11 to put distortion into the 150 MeV calculation of Problem 3 using the simple wave functions (11.5). Compare the results with the distorted wave curves of Fig. 14.8.

8. In the 150 MeV $(p, 2p)$ reaction on ^{11}B, peaks are observed at 11 MeV, 15 MeV, 21 MeV, 37 MeV. The experiments do not resolve states of the residual nucleus. Explain the peaks.

9. Which single-particle states would you hope to investigate with the reaction $^{89}Y(p, 2p)^{88}Sr$?

10. Derive Equation (14.12).

APPENDIX 1
Units and Constants

The basic system of units of nuclear physics is the MeV-fermi system. One million electron volts (1 MeV) is the energy given to a particle with the charge e of a single electron when it is accelerated over a potential of one million volts. One fermi (1 fm) is 10^{-13} cm. The abbreviation fm coincides with that of the name for this unit which is recommended by the International Union of Pure and Applied Physics, the femtometer meaning 10^{-15} m.

Quantity	Formula	Value
Mass of the electron	mc^2	0.511 MeV
Mass of the proton	Mc^2	938.7 MeV
Classical radius of the electron	e^2/mc^2	2.82 fm
Fine structure constant	$e^2/\hbar c$	1/137
$\{$ de Broglie wave number k of a 1 MeV proton		0.2195 fm^{-1}
$\{$ Kinetic energy of a proton with $k = 1$ fm^{-1}		20.75 MeV

TABLE A1.1. Quantities useful in nuclear physics in MeV-fermi units.

All the quantities used in nuclear physics can be expressed in terms of these units together with c, the velocity of light and $\hbar$, Planck's constant divided by 2π. We give in Table A1.1 some particularly useful quantities in terms of these units. Quantities are very easily expressed in terms of the quantities of Table A1.1. Examples are given in the text.

An exception to the general use of the MeV-fermi system is the commonly used unit of cross section, the barn. 1 barn = 10^2 fm^2. Differential cross sections are usually expressed in millibarns (mb) per sterradian (sr). 1 mb = 10^{-1} fm^2.

APPENDIX 2
Mass Defects and Spins of Nuclei

The following table gives the mass defects and spins of nuclei up to the beginning of the $1g$ shell. The mass defect of a nucleus in MeV is $\mathcal{M} - A$ where $\mathcal{M}$ is the mass of the nucleus and A is the mass number expressed in mass units so that the mass defect of ^{12}C is zero. One mass unit is 931.4 MeV.

The ground-state spin J of each nucleus in units of $\hbar$ is shown with its mass defect. The proton and neutron numbers are Z and N. A star (*) indicates an unstable nucleus.

Quantities whose value is not certain are bracketed.

A	Z	N	Name	$\mathcal{M} - A$	J
1	0	1	n*	8.07	½
	1	0	p	7.29	½
2	1	1	d	13.13	1
3	1	2	t*	14.95	½
	2	1	He	14.93	½
4	2	2	He	2.42	0
5	2	3	He*	11.45	—
	3	2	Li*	11.67	—
6	2	4	He*	17.59	(0)
	3	3	Li	14.09	1
7	3	4	Li	14.91	3/2
	4	3	Be*	15.77	—
8	3	5	Li*	20.94	(2, 3)
	4	4	Be*	4.94	(0)
	5	3	B*	22.92	(2, 3)
9	3	6	Li*	23.10	—
	4	5	Be	11.35	3/2
	5	4	B*	12.42	—
10	4	6	Be*	12.60	(0)
	5	5	B	12.05	3
	6	4	C*	15.66	(0)

A	Z	N	Name	$\mathcal{M} - A$	J
11	5	6	B	8.67	$\frac{3}{2}$
	6	5	C*	10.65	$\frac{3}{2}$
12	5	7	B*	13.37	(1)
	6	6	C	0	0
	7	5	N*	17.36	(1)
13	5	8	B*	16.56	$\frac{3}{2}$
	6	7	C	3.12	$\frac{1}{2}$
	7	6	N*	5.34	$\frac{1}{2}$
14	6	8	C*	3.02	0
	7	7	N	2.86	1
	8	6	O*	8.01	(0)
15	6	9	C*	9.87	$\frac{5}{2}$
	7	8	N	0.10	$\frac{1}{2}$
	8	7	O*	2.86	$\frac{1}{2}$
16	7	9	N*	5.68	2
	8	8	O	−4.74	0
	9	7	F*	10.90	(0)
17	7	10	N*	7.87	$\frac{1}{2}$
	8	9	O	−0.81	$\frac{5}{2}$
	9	8	F*	1.95	$(\frac{5}{2})$
18	8	10	O	−0.78	0
	9	9	F*	0.87	(1)
	10	8	Ne*	5.32	(0)
19	8	11	O*	3.33	$(\frac{5}{2})$
	9	10	F	−1.48	$\frac{1}{2}$
	10	9	Ne*	1.75	$\frac{1}{2}$
20	9	11	F*	−0.01	(2, 3)
	10	10	Ne	−7.04	(0)
	11	9	Na*	8.(31)	—
21	9	12	F*	−0.0(3)	—
	10	11	Ne	−5.73	$\frac{3}{2}$
	11	10	Na*	−2.2(0)	$(\frac{3}{2})$
22	10	12	Ne	−8.02	0
	11	11	Na*	−5.18	3
	12	10	Mg*	−0.1(4)	—
23	10	13	Ne*	−5.15	$(\frac{5}{2})$
	11	12	Na	−9.53	$\frac{3}{2}$
	12	11	Mg*	−5.4(5)	$(\frac{3}{2})$
24	10	14	Ne*	−5.9(6)	(0)
	11	13	Na*	−8.41	4
	12	12	Mg	−13.193	0
	13	11	Al*	0.0(9)	(4)
25	11	14	Na*	−9.3(6)	$(\frac{5}{2})$
	12	13	Mg	−13.19	$\frac{5}{2}$
	13	12	Al*	−8.93	$(\frac{5}{2})$

A	Z	N	Name	$\mathcal{M} - A$	J
26	12	14	Mg	−16.21	0
	13	13	Al*	−12.20	—
	14	12	Si*	−7.1(5)	—
27	12	15	Mg*	−15.58	$(\frac{1}{2})$
	13	14	Al	−17.20	$\frac{5}{2}$
	14	13	Si*	−12.38	$(\frac{5}{2})$
28	12	16	Mg*	−15.01	(0)
	13	15	Al*	−16.85	(3)
	14	14	Si	−21.49	0
	15	13	P*	−7.(7)	(2, 3)
29	13	16	Al*	−18.22	$(\frac{5}{2})$
	14	15	Si	−21.90	$\frac{1}{2}$
	15	14	P*	−16.95	$(\frac{1}{2})$
30	13	17	Al*	−17.(1)	—
	14	16	Si	−24.44	0
	15	15	P*	−20.19	(1)
	16	14	S*	−14.22	—
31	14	17	Si*	−22.96	$(\frac{1}{2})$
	15	16	P	−24.44	$\frac{1}{2}$
	16	15	S*	−18.99	$(\frac{1}{2})$
32	14	18	Si*	−24.0(8)	0
	15	17	P*	−24.30	(1)
	16	16	S	−26.01	0
	17	15	Cl*	−13.01	(1)
33	15	18	P*	−26.33	$(\frac{1}{2})$
	16	17	S	−26.58	$\frac{3}{2}$
	17	16	Cl*	−21.0(0)	$(\frac{3}{2})$
34	15	19	P*	−24.(8)	(1)
	16	18	S	−29.93	0
	17	17	Cl*	−24.41	3
35	16	19	S*	−28.84	$\frac{3}{2}$
	17	18	Cl	−29.01	$\frac{3}{2}$
	18	17	Ar*	−23.0(4)	$(\frac{3}{2})$
36	16	20	S	−30.65	0
	17	19	Cl*	−29.52	2
	18	18	Ar	−30.22	(0)
37	16	21	S*	−26.9(8)	$(\frac{7}{2})$
	17	20	Cl	−31.77	$\frac{3}{2}$
	18	19	Ar*	−30.95	$\frac{3}{2}$
	19	18	K*	−24.8(0)	$(\frac{3}{2})$
38	17	21	Cl*	−29.80	2
	18	20	Ar	−34.72	(0)
	19	19	K*	−28.79	3

A	Z	N	Name	$\mathcal{M} - A$	J
39	17	22	Cl*	−29.8(0)	(3/2)
	18	21	Ar*	−33.23	7/2
	19	20	K	−33.80	3/2
	20	19	Ca*	−27.3(0)	(3/2)
40	17	23	Cl*	−27.(5)	(2)
	18	22	Ar	−35.04	0
	19	21	K*	−33.52	4
	20	20	Ca	−34.85	0
	21	19	Sc*	−20.(9)	(4)
41	18	23	Ar*	−33.0(6)	(7/2)
	19	22	K	−35.55	3/2
	20	21	Ca*	−35.14	(7/2)
	21	20	Sc*	−28.64	(7/2)
42	18	24	Ar*	−34.4(2)	0
	19	23	K*	−35.0(1)	2
	20	22	Ca	−38.54	0
	21	21	Sc*	−32.2(8)	0
43	19	24	K*	−36.5(7)	3/2
	20	23	Ca	−38.39	7/2
	21	22	Sc*	−36.17	7/2
44	19	25	K*	−35.(3)	—
	20	24	Ca	−41.46	0
	21	23	Sc*	−37.81	(2, 3)
	22	22	Ti*	−37.6(5)	0
45	19	26	K*	−36.6	(3/2)
	20	25	Ca*	−40.81	(5/2)
	21	24	Sc	−41.06	7/2
	22	23	Ti*	−39.00	7/2
46	20	26	Ca	−43.14	0
	21	25	Sc*	−41.75	4
	22	24	Ti	−44.12	0
	23	23	V*	−37.06	(0)
47	20	27	Ca*	−42.3(3)	(7/2)
	21	26	Sc*	−44.33	(7/2)
	22	25	Ti	−44.94	5/2
	23	24	V*	−42.01	(7/2)
48	20	28	Ca	−44.37	0
	21	27	Sc*	−44.4(9)	(6, 7)
	22	26	Ti	−44.48	0
	23	25	V*	−44.47	(4)
	24	24	Cr*	−43.0	0
49	20	29	Ca*	−41.4(4)	(3/2)
	21	28	Sc*	−46.5(2)	(7/2)
	22	27	Ti	−48.56	7/2
	23	26	V*	−47.95	7/2
	24	25	Cr*	−45.39	5/2

A	Z	N	Name	$\mathcal{M} - A$	J
50	21	29	Sc*	$-45.(1)$	$(5, 4)$
	22	28	Ti	-51.42	0
	23	27	V*	-49.21	6
	24	26	Cr	-50.24	0
	25	25	Mn*	-42.64	(0)
51	22	29	Ti*	$-49.7(1)$	$(\frac{3}{2})$
	23	28	V	-52.19	$\frac{7}{2}$
	24	27	Cr*	-51.44	$\frac{7}{2}$
	25	26	Mn*	-48.26	$(\frac{5}{2}, \frac{7}{2})$
52	23	29	V*	-51.43	(2)
	24	28	Cr	-55.41	0
	25	27	Mn*	-50.70	(6)
	26	26	Fe*	-48.32	0
53	23	30	V*	-52	$(\frac{5}{2})$
	24	29	Cr	-55.28	$\frac{3}{2}$
	25	28	Mn*	-54.68	$\frac{7}{2}$
	26	27	Fe*	-50.70	$(\frac{7}{2})$
54	23	31	V*	-49	—
	24	30	Cr	-56.93	0
	25	29	Mn*	-55.55	3
	26	28	Fe	-56.24	0
	27	27	Co*	-47.99	(0)
55	24	31	Cr*	-55.11	$(\frac{3}{2})$
	25	30	Mn	-57.70	$\frac{5}{2}$
	26	29	Fe*	-57.47	$(\frac{3}{2})$
	27	28	Co*	-54.01	$(\frac{7}{2})$
56	25	31	Mn*	-56.90	3
	26	30	Fe	-60.60	0
	27	29	Co*	-56.03	4
	28	28	Ni*	-53.91	0
57	25	32	Mn*	-57.5	$(\frac{5}{2}, \frac{7}{2})$
	26	31	Fe	-60.17	$\frac{1}{2}$
	27	30	Co*	-59.33	$\frac{7}{2}$
	28	29	Ni*	-56.10	$(\frac{3}{2})$
58	26	32	Fe	-62.14	0
	27	31	Co*	-59.83	2
	28	30	Ni	-60.22	0
	29	29	Cu*	-51.65	—
59	26	33	Fe*	-60.65	$\frac{3}{2}$
	27	32	Co	-62.23	$\frac{7}{2}$
	28	31	Ni*	-61.15	$(\frac{3}{2})$
	29	30	Cu*	-56.35	$(\frac{3}{2})$
60	27	33	Co*	-61.65	5
	28	32	Ni	-64.46	0
	29	31	Cu*	-58.34	2

A	Z	N	Name	$\mathcal{M} - A$	J
61	26	35	Fe*	−59	$(\tfrac{3}{2}, \tfrac{5}{2})$
	27	34	Co*	−62.93	$\tfrac{7}{2}$
	28	33	Ni	−64.21	$\tfrac{3}{2}$
	29	32	Cu*	−61.89	$\tfrac{3}{2}$
	30	31	Zn*	−56.5	$(\tfrac{3}{2})$
62	27	35	Co*	−61.52	—
	28	34	Ni	−66.74	0
	29	33	Cu*	−62.81	1
	30	32	Zn*	−61.12	0
63	28	35	Ni*	−65.51	$(\tfrac{5}{2})$
	29	34	Cu	−65.58	$\tfrac{3}{2}$
	30	33	Zn*	−62.21	$(\tfrac{3}{2}, \tfrac{5}{2})$
64	28	36	Ni	−67.10	0
	29	35	Cu*	−65.42	1
	30	34	Zn	−65.99	0
	31	33	Ga	−58.92	(1)
65	28	37	Ni*	−65.13	$(\tfrac{5}{2})$
	29	36	Cu	−67.26	$\tfrac{3}{2}$
	30	35	Zn*	−65.91	$\tfrac{5}{2}$
	31	34	Ga*	−62.66	$(\tfrac{3}{2})$
66	28	38	Ni*	−66.04	0
	29	37	Cu*	−66.25	(1)
	30	36	Zn	−68.88	0
	31	35	Ga*	−63.70	(0)
	32	34	Ge*	−60.7	0
67	29	38	Cu*	−67.28	$(\tfrac{3}{2})$
	30	37	Zn	−67.85	$\tfrac{5}{2}$
	31	36	Ga*	−66.86	$\tfrac{3}{2}$
	32	35	Ge*	−62.4	$(\tfrac{3}{2}, \tfrac{5}{2})$
68	29	39	Cu*	−65.41	(1)
	30	38	Zn	−69.99	0
	31	37	Ga*	−67.068	1
	32	36	Ge*	−66	0
69	30	39	Zn*	−68.42	$(\tfrac{1}{2})$
	31	38	Ga	−69.32	$\tfrac{3}{2}$
	32	37	Ge*	−67.10	$(\tfrac{3}{2}, \tfrac{5}{2})$
70	30	40	Zn	−69.54	0
	31	39	Ga*	−68.89	1
	32	38	Ge	−70.55	0
71	30	41	Zn*	−67.52	$(\tfrac{1}{2})$
	31	40	Ga	−70.13	$\tfrac{3}{2}$
	32	39	Ge*	−69.90	$(\tfrac{1}{2})$
	33	38	As*	−67.89	$(\tfrac{5}{2})$
72	30	42	Zn*	−68.14	0
	31	41	Ga*	−68.58	3

A	Z	N	Name	$\mathcal{M} - A$	J
72	32	40	Ge	−72.57	0
	33	39	As*	−68.21	2
	34	38	Se*	−67	0
73	31	42	Ga*	−69.73	$(3/2)$
	32	41	Ge	−71.29	$9/2$
	33	40	As*	−70.90	$(3/2)$
	34	39	Se*	−68.16	$(9/2)$
74	32	42	Ge	−73.41	0
	33	41	As*	−70.85	2
	34	40	Se	−72.21	0
75	32	43	Ge*	−71.83	$(1/2)$
	33	42	As	−73.03	$3/2$
	34	41	Se*	−72.16	$5/2$
	35	40	Br*	−69.44	$(3/2, \, 5/2)$
76	32	44	Ge	−73.20	0
	33	43	As*	−72.28	2
	34	42	Se	−75.25	0
	35	41	Br*	−70.62	1
77	32	45	Ge*	−71.16	$(7/2)$
	33	44	As*	−73.91	$(3/2)$
	34	43	Se	−74.59	$1/2$
	35	42	Br*	−73.23	$(3/2)$
	36	41	Kr*	−70.34	$(1/2)$
78	33	45	As*	−72.7	(2)
	34	44	Se	−77.01	0
	35	43	Br*	−73.44	(1)
	36	42	Kr	−74.14	0
79	33	46	As*	−73.68	$(3/2)$
	34	45	Se*	−75.91	$7/2$
	35	44	Br	−76.07	$3/2$
	36	43	Kr*	−74.45	$(1/2)$
80	34	46	Se	−77.75	0
	35	45	Br*	−75.88	1
	36	44	Kr	−77.88	(0)
81	34	47	Se*	−76.39	$(1/2)$
	35	46	Br	−77.97	$3/2$
	36	45	Kr*	−77.7	$(7/2)$
	37	44	Rb*	−75.4	$3/2$
82	34	48	Se	−77.58	0
	35	47	Br*	−77.49	5
	36	46	Kr	−80.58	0
	37	45	Rb*	−76.41	—
82	38	44	Sr*	−76	(0)
83	35	48	Br*	−79.01	$(3/2)$
	36	47	Kr	−79.98	$9/2$

A	Z	N	Name	$\mathcal{M} - A$	J
83	37	46	Rb*	−79	$5/2$
	38	45	Sr*	−77	—
84	35	49	Br*	−77.73	(2, 1)
	36	48	Kr	−82.43	0
	37	47	Rb*	−79.75	2
	38	46	Sr	−80.63	(0)
	39	45	Y*	−74.3	—
85	35	50	Br*	−78.7	$(3/2)$
	36	49	Kr*	−81.48	$9/2$
	37	48	Rb	−82.15	$5/2$
	38	47	Sr*	−81.04	$(9/2)$
86	36	50	Kr	−83.25	0
	37	49	Rb*	−82.71	2
	38	48	Sr	−84.49	0
	39	47	Y*	−79.22	—
	40	46	Zr*	−78	0
87	35	52	Br*	−73	$(3/2, 5/2)$
	36	51	Kr*	−80.69	$(7/2)$
	37	50	Rb*	−84.58	$3/2$
	38	49	Sr	−84.86	$9/2$
	39	48	Y*	−83.2	$(1/2)$
	40	47	Zr*	−79.6	$(7/2, 9/2)$
88	36	52	Kr*	−79.8	(0)
	37	51	Rb*	−82.6	2
	38	50	Sr	−87.89	0
	39	49	Y*	−84.27	(4)
	40	48	Zr*	−83.7	0
89	36	53	Kr*	−77.7	$(5/2, 7/2)$
	37	52	Rb*	−82.29	$(3/2)$
	38	51	Sr*	−86.21	$(5/2)$
	39	50	Y	−87.67	$1/2$
	40	49	Zr*	−84.84	$(9/2)$
	41	48	Nb*	−80.9	$(9/2)$
90	36	54	Kr*	−74.8	(0)
	38	52	Sr*	−85.92	(0)
	39	51	Y*	−86.47	2
	40	50	Zr	−88.8	0
	41	49	Nb*	−82.65	—
	42	48	Mo*	−80.1	(0)
91	37	54	Rb*	−78	$(3/2, 5/2)$
	38	53	Sr*	−83.68	$(5/2)$
	39	52	Y*	−86.35	$1/2$
	40	51	Zr	−87.89	$5/2$
	41	50	Nb*	−86.75	$9/2$
	42	49	Mo*	−82.29	$(9/2)$

A	Z	N	Name	$\mathcal{M} - A$	J
92	37	55	Rb*	−75	—
	38	54	Sr*	−82.91	(0)
92	39	53	Y*	−84.82	(2)
	40	52	Zr	−88.45	(0)
	41	51	Nb*	−86.42	(2, 3)
	42	50	Mo	−86.80	0
	43	49	Tc*	−78.7	—
93	38	55	Sr*	−79.4	—
	39	54	Y*	−84.25	$(\tfrac{1}{2})$
	40	53	Zr*	−87.13	$(\tfrac{5}{2})$
	41	52	Nb	−87.20	$\tfrac{9}{2}$
	42	51	Mo*	−86.78	$(\tfrac{5}{2})$
	43	50	Tc*	−83.59	$(\tfrac{9}{2})$

APPENDIX 3
Functions Used in Potential Scattering

The theory of scattering by a spherically symmetric potential is basic to most nuclear reaction calculations. Although integration of the Schrödinger equation must be performed numerically for most potentials, there are some functions that are common to all such calculations. These are the solutions of the Schrödinger equation in the region outside the nuclear potential $V(r)$, which is assumed to fall off with increasing r in such a way that

$$\lim_{r \to \infty} rV(r) = 0. \tag{A3.1}$$

The Coulomb potential acts in the exterior region. The Schrödinger equation for this potential is

$$\left(\nabla^2 + k^2 - \frac{2\eta k}{r}\right)\Psi(\mathbf{r}) = 0, \tag{A3.2}$$

where the Coulomb parameter η is given by

$$\eta = \mu Z Z' e^2 / \hbar^2 k, \tag{A3.3}$$

and the wave number k is given for incident energy E by

$$k^2 = 2\mu E / \hbar^2. \tag{A3.4}$$

The reduced mass of the incident particle is μ and the incident energy is E. The charge numbers of the target and projectile are Z and Z', respectively.

A. THE PARTIAL WAVE EXPANSION

The Coulomb equation (A3.2) is familiar from the theory of the hydrogen atom. It may be separated in spherical polar coordinates. If we choose the z-axis (the quantization axis) to be parallel to the incident direction, the symmetry of the problem is such that $\Psi(\mathbf{r})$ cannot depend on the azimuthal angle ϕ. We may expand it in the complete orthogonal set of Legendre polynomials $P_l(\cos \theta)$.

$$\Psi(\mathbf{r}) = \sum_l R_l(r)P_l(\cos \theta). \tag{A3.5}$$

The complete angular equation is discussed in Appendix 4. We shall concentrate at present on the radial equation.

$$\frac{1}{r^2}\frac{d}{dr}\left(r^2\frac{d}{dr}\right)R_l(r) + \left[k^2 - \frac{2\eta k}{r} - \frac{l(l+1)}{r^2}\right]R_l(r) = 0. \tag{A3.6}$$

The substitution

$$R_l(r) = r^l e^{ikr} f_l(r) \tag{A3.7}$$

transforms (A3.6) into the confluent hypergeometric equation whose solutions are standard. We shall describe the solutions but not derive them. The equation is studied in detail for example by Morse and Feshbach (53).

$$r\frac{d^2 f_l}{dr^2} + [2ikr + 2(l+1)]\frac{df_l}{dr} + [2ik(l+1) - 2\eta k]f_l = 0. \tag{A3.8}$$

There are two independent solutions of this equation. They depend on three parameters η, l, and k. The solution that is regular at the origin is written

$$f_l(r) = a_l Q(l + 1 + i\eta, 2l + 2, -2ikr). \tag{A3.9}$$

The function Q is the confluent hypergeometric function. Its variables are defined in a conventional way to correspond with the coefficients of (A3.8). The constant a_l remains to be determined. The asymptotic form of the radial wave function for large r comes from a standard result in the theory of the confluent hypergeometric equation. It is

$$R_l(r) \sim a_l \frac{e^{\eta\pi/2+i\sigma_l}\Gamma(2l+2)}{(2k)^l\Gamma(l+1+i\eta)kr} \sin(kr - l\pi/2 - \eta \ln 2kr + \sigma_l), \tag{A3.10}$$

where the Coulomb phase shift is

$$\sigma_l = \arg \Gamma(l + 1 + i\eta). \tag{A3.11}$$

An alternative separation of the Coulomb problem (A3.2) is in parabolic coordinates,

$$\xi = r - z = r(1 - \cos \theta)$$
$$\eta = r + z = r(1 + \cos \theta) \tag{A3.12}$$
$$\phi = \phi.$$

If we again define the z-axis to be the symmetry axis, it is clear that the solution is independent of ϕ. We define the function q by

$$\Psi = e^{ikz}q. \tag{A3.13}$$

The asymptotic form of Ψ for large r is

$$\Psi \sim v^{-\frac{1}{2}}\left[e^{ikz} + f_C(\theta)\frac{e^{ikr}}{r}\right], \tag{A3.14}$$

where $v^{-\frac{1}{2}}e^{ikz}$ is a plane wave normalized to unit incident flux. The probability flux for a plane wave is v, the velocity of the particle.

An expression $e^{ikz}q(r - z)$ can be of the form (A3.14), but an expression $e^{ikz}q(r + z)$ cannot. Hence the function q of (A3.13) is expected to depend only on the coordinate $\xi = r - z$.

Substituting (A3.13) into the original Schrödinger equation (A3.2), we find that q also satisfies the confluent hypergeometric equation.

$$\xi\frac{d^2q}{d\xi^2} + (1 - ik\xi)\frac{dq}{d\xi} - \eta kq = 0. \tag{A3.8a}$$

The solution is, transforming back to spherical polar coordinates by means of (A3.12) and using (A3.13),

$$\Psi(\mathbf{r}) = v^{-\frac{1}{2}}\Gamma(1 + i\eta)e^{-\eta\pi/2}e^{ikr\cos\theta}Q\left(-i\eta, 1, 2ikr\sin^2\frac{\theta}{2}\right). \tag{A3.15}$$

The asymptotic form of $\Psi(\mathbf{r})$ for large r is

$$\Psi(\mathbf{r}) \sim v^{-\frac{1}{2}}\left\{ e^{i[kz - \eta\ln k(r-z)]}\left(1 - \frac{\eta^2}{ik(r - z)}\right) + \frac{1}{r}f_C(\theta)e^{i(kr - \eta\ln 2kr)}\right\}, \tag{A3.16}$$

where the Coulomb scattering amplitude $f_C(\theta)$ is given by

$$f_C(\theta) = -\frac{\eta}{2k\sin^2\theta/2}e^{-i\eta\ln(\sin^2\theta/2)+2i\sigma_0}. \tag{A3.17}$$

The quantity σ_0 is defined by (A3.11).

We are now able to find the constant a_l of (A3.9). We multiply (A3.5) by $P_{l'}(\cos\theta)$ and integrate over $\cos\theta$. The orthogonality of the Legendre polynomials (A4.14, A4.15) gives

$$R_l(r) = \frac{2l + 1}{2}\int_0^\pi \sin\theta\, d\theta P_l(\cos\theta)\Psi(r, \theta). \tag{A3.18}$$

The integral in (A3.18) need not be performed because we know $R_l(r)$ from (A3.7, 9), apart from a_l, and we know $\Psi(r, \theta)$ from (A3.15). Substituting for R_l and Ψ in (A3.18) gives for a_l

$$a_l = v^{-\frac{1}{2}}(2ik)^l e^{-\eta\pi/2}\Gamma(l + 1 + i\eta)/(2l)!. \tag{A3.19}$$

We thus have the partial wave expansion of $\Psi(\mathbf{r})$ from (A3.5, A3.7, A3.9, A3.19).

$$\Psi(\mathbf{r}) = v^{-\frac{1}{2}}e^{-\eta\pi/2} \sum_l \frac{\Gamma(l+1+i\eta)}{(2l)!} (2ikr)^l e^{ikr}$$

$$\times \; Q(l+1+i\eta, 2l+2, -2ikr)P_l(\cos\theta). \quad \text{(A3.20)}$$

It is more usual to write (A3.20) as

$$\Psi(\mathbf{r}) = v^{-\frac{1}{2}}(kr)^{-1} \sum_l (2l+1)i^l e^{i\sigma_l} F_l(\eta, kr) P_l(\cos\theta)$$

$$= v^{-\frac{1}{2}}(kr)^{-1}4\pi \sum_{lm} i^l e^{i\sigma_l} F_l(\eta, kr) Y_l^{m*}(\Omega_r) Y_l^m(\Omega_k), \quad \text{(A3.21)}$$

where Ω_r and Ω_k are the polar angles of $\mathbf{r}$ and $\mathbf{k}$, respectively. The function $F_l(\eta, kr)$ is the regular Coulomb function.

$$F_l(\eta, kr) = \tfrac{1}{2}e^{-\eta\pi/2} \frac{|\Gamma(l+1+i\eta)|}{(2l+1)!} (2kr)^{l+1} Q(l+1+i\eta, 2l+2, -2ikr).$$

$$\text{(A3.22)}$$

The asymptotic form of $F_l(\eta, kr)$ for large r is

$$F_l(\eta, kr) \sim \sin\left(kr - \frac{l\pi}{2} - \eta \ln 2kr + \sigma_l\right). \quad \text{(A3.23)}$$

Besides defining the quantities associated with Coulomb scattering we have derived the partial wave expansion (A3.21) of a Coulomb wave. The extension of this to the solution of a scattering problem including a short-range potential is obvious. The same equation holds with $F_l(\eta, kr)$ replaced by the solution $u_l(k, r)$ of the more general radial equation. The asymptotic form of $u_l(k, r)$ includes the irregular solution $G_l(\eta, kr)$ of (A3.6) because the short-range potential alters the conditions near the origin. The asymptotic form of $G_l(\eta, kr)$ for large kr is

$$G_l(\eta, kr) \sim \cos\left(kr - \frac{l\pi}{2} - \eta \ln 2kr + \sigma_l\right). \quad \text{(A3.24)}$$

Denoting the non-Coulomb phase shift by δ_l, we have

$$u_l(k, r) \sim e^{i(\delta_l+\sigma_l)} \sin\left(kr - \frac{l\pi}{2} - \eta \ln 2kr + \delta_l + \sigma_l\right). \quad \text{(A3.25)}$$

B. THE COULOMB FUNCTIONS

The Coulomb functions $F_l(\eta, kr)$ and $G_l(\eta, kr)$ are plotted for $l = 1$ in Figs. A3.1 and A3.2 for different values of η. It is interesting to compare them with the values for $\eta = 0$. For $\eta = 0$ they are the regular and irregular Riccatti-Bessel functions $U_1(kr)$ and $V_1(kr)$ which are defined in terms of the

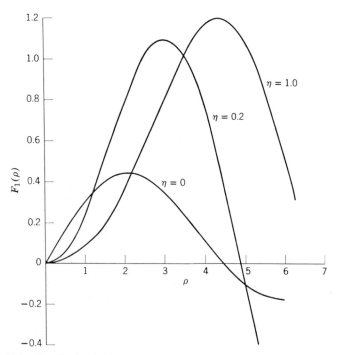

FIG. A3.1 The Coulomb function $F_1(\eta, \rho)$ plotted against ρ for the indicated values of η.

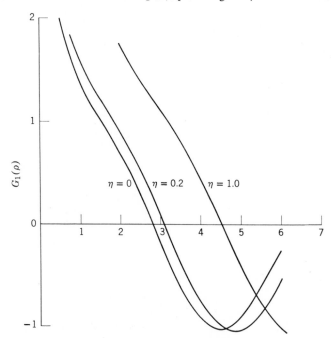

FIG. A3.2 The Coulomb function $G_1(\eta, \rho)$ plotted against ρ for the indicated values of η.

η	σ_0	η	σ_0
0	0	2.0	0.130
0.2	−0.112	2.2	0.281
0.4	−0.207	2.4	0.452
0.6	−0.272	2.6	0.638
0.8	−0.304	2.8	0.838
1.0	−0.301	3.0	1.053
1.2	−0.267	3.2	1.281
1.4	−0.204	3.4	1.521
1.6	−0.115	3.6	1.773
1.8	−0.003	3.8	2.036

TABLE A3.1.   Values of the s-wave Coulomb phase shift σ_0 for different values of η.

spherical Bessel and Neumann functions by (2.19, 2.20). The values of the Coulomb functions for different values of l are related to those for $l = 1$ in the same way that $j_l(kr)$ is related to $j_1(kr)$. (See Fig. 2.1).

The Coulomb phase shifts are plotted for different values of η in Table A3.1. For orientation we have given in Table A3.2 the values of the Coulomb parameter η for protons of various energies scattered by targets of various charges.

The Coulomb functions are computed by means of recurrence relations. The irregular function G_l is found most easily using forward recurrence on l.

$$G_{l+1} = \frac{(2l + 1)[\eta + l(l + 1)/\rho]G_l - (l + 1)[l^2 + \eta^2]^{\frac{1}{2}}G_{l-1}}{l[(l + 1)^2 + \eta^2]^{\frac{1}{2}}}. \quad (A3.26)$$

Forward recurrence does not work for F_l. Round-off errors in computation accumulate so rapidly that the computation becomes meaningless after a few

$E_{C.M.}$ (MeV)	$Z' = 5$	$Z' = 25$	$Z' = 50$
5	0.35	1.7	3.5
10	0.25	1.2	2.5
20	0.17	0.87	1.7
50	0.11	0.55	1.11
100	0.08	0.39	0.79
150	0.06	0.32	0.64

TABLE A3.2.   Values of the Coulomb parameter η for protons of different incident energies E in the C.M. system on different targets with charges Z'. The approximation $\mu = M$ has been made.

values of l. Instead it is sufficient to recur backwards (Stegun and Abramowitz, 55). The following method has proved successful in practice.

To compute F_l for $l = l_0 + 1, \ldots, 0$, let $l^{(1)} = l_0 + 10$. Let $F_{l^{(1)}+1}^{(1)} = 0$ and $F_{l^{(1)}}^{(1)} = 0.1$. Values of $F_l^{(1)}$ from $l = 0$ to $l^{(1)} - 1$ are computed by means of

$$F_{l-1}^{(1)} = \frac{(2l + 1)[\eta + l(l + 1)/\rho]F_l^{(1)} - l[(l + 1)^2 + \eta^2]^{\frac{1}{2}}F_{l+1}^{(1)}}{(l + 1)[l^2 + \eta^2]^{\frac{1}{2}}}. \qquad \text{(A3.27)}$$

We find F_l by

$$F_l = F_l^{(1)}\alpha^{-1}, \qquad l = l_0 + 1, \ldots, 0, \qquad \text{(A3.28)}$$

where

$$\alpha = (F_0^{(1)}G_1 - F_1^{(1)}G_0)(1 + \eta^2)^{\frac{1}{2}}. \qquad \text{(A3.29)}$$

In order to start the recurrence for G_l, we need the values of the functions for $l = 0$ and 1. For the case of the Riccatti-Bessel functions ($\eta = 0$) we have exact formulas. They will be discussed below. For the more general Coulomb functions it is necessary to use asymptotic formulas valid for $kr \gg l$.

$$\begin{aligned}
F_0 &\sim \sin(\operatorname{Re}\phi_0)e^{-\operatorname{Im}\phi_0} \\
F_1 &\sim \sin(\operatorname{Re}\phi_1)e^{-\operatorname{Im}\phi_1} \\
G_0 &\sim \cos(\operatorname{Re}\phi_0)e^{-\operatorname{Im}\phi_0} \\
G_1 &\sim \cos(\operatorname{Re}\phi_1)e^{-\operatorname{Im}\phi_1}
\end{aligned} \qquad \text{(A3.30)}$$

where

$$\begin{aligned}
\phi_0 &= \rho - \ln 2\rho + \sigma_0 + \sum_{k=2}^{\infty} \frac{a_k}{\rho^{k-1}}\left(\frac{1}{1 - k}\right), \\
\phi_1 &= \rho - \ln 2\rho + \sigma_1 - \frac{\pi}{2} + \sum_{k=2}^{\infty} \frac{b_k}{\rho^{k-1}}\left(\frac{1}{1 - k}\right), \\
\rho &= kr.
\end{aligned} \qquad \text{(A3.31)}$$

There are recurrence relations for the coefficients a_k and b_k.

$$a_1 = -\eta, \qquad a_2 = -\frac{\eta^2}{2} + i\eta,$$

$$b_1 = -\eta, \qquad b_2 = -\frac{2 + \eta^2}{2} + \frac{i\eta}{2}. \qquad \text{(A3.32)}$$

Both a_k and b_k satisfy the formula

$$a_k = -(\tfrac{1}{2}\sum_{m=1}^{k-1} a_m a_{k-m}) - i\frac{k - 1}{2}a_{k-1}. \qquad \text{(A3.33)}$$

The Coulomb phase shifts are found by means of the recurrence relations

$$\mathrm{Re}\,(e^{2i\sigma_{l+1}}) = \cos 2\sigma_{l+1} = \left[\frac{(l+1)^2 - \eta^2}{(l+1)^2 + \eta^2}\cos 2\sigma_l\right] - \left[\frac{2\eta(l+1)}{(l+1)^2 + \eta^2}\sin 2\sigma_l\right],$$

$$\mathrm{Im}\,(e^{2i\sigma_{l+1}}) = \sin 2\sigma_{l+1} = \left[\frac{(l+1)^2 - \eta^2}{(l+1)^2 + \eta^2}\sin 2\sigma_l\right] - \left[\frac{2\eta(l+1)}{(l+1)^2 + \eta^2}\cos 2\sigma_l\right],$$

$$\text{(A3.34a)}$$

or

$$\sigma_l - \sigma_0 = \sum_{s=1}^{l}\tan^{-1}\frac{\eta}{s}. \tag{A3.34b}$$

The starting values are

$$\sigma_0 = \arg\Gamma(1 + i\eta),$$
$$\sigma_1 = \sigma_0 + \tan^{-1}\eta, \tag{A3.35}$$

where σ_0 may be approximated for all η by

$$\sigma_0 = -\eta + \left(\frac{\eta}{2}\right)\ln(\eta^2 + 16) + \tfrac{1}{2}\tan^{-1}\left(\frac{\eta}{4}\right)$$

$$- \left[\tan^{-1}\eta + \tan^{-1}\left(\frac{\eta}{2}\right) + \tan^{-1}\left(\frac{\eta}{3}\right)\right]$$

$$- \frac{\eta}{12(\eta^2 + 16)}\left[1 + \frac{1}{30}\frac{\eta^2 - 48}{(\eta^2 + 16)^2} + \frac{1}{105}\frac{\eta^4 - 160\eta^2 + 1280}{(\eta^2 + 16)^4}\right]. \tag{A3.36}$$

For matching the internal scattering solution to the external solution in the Coulomb field we need the derivatives F_l', G_l' of F_l, G_l. They are obtained from the formula

$$Y_l' = \frac{[(l+1)^2/\rho + \eta]Y_l - [(l+1)^2 + \eta^2]^{1/2}Y_{l+1}}{l+1}, \tag{A3.37}$$

where Y_l is either F_l or G_l.

C. THE RICCATTI-BESSEL FUNCTIONS

For the case $\eta = 0$, that is, for the Schrödinger equation in free space, the Coulomb functions reduce to the Riccati-Bessel functions.

$$F_l(0, \rho) = U_l(\rho) = \rho j_l(\rho),$$
$$G_l(0, \rho) = V_l(\rho) = -\rho n_l(\rho). \tag{A3.38}$$

These functions are computed by means of the recurrence relations (A3.26,

A3.27). The starting values are easily evaluated for all ρ.

$$U_0(\rho) = \sin \rho, \qquad\qquad V_0(\rho) = \cos \rho,$$

$$U_1(\rho) = \frac{\sin \rho}{\rho} - \cos \rho, \qquad V_1(\rho) = \frac{\cos \rho}{\rho} + \sin \rho. \tag{A3.39}$$

For a potential $V(r)$ whose derivative is zero at $\rho = 0$, the solution of the Schrödinger equation for very small ρ is the same as that in free space with the wave number K given by

$$K^2 = \frac{2\mu[E - V(0)]}{\hbar^2}. \tag{A3.40}$$

K is complex if $V(r)$ is complex. For very small ρ we have

$$U_l(\rho) \rightarrow \frac{\rho^{l+1}}{(2l + 1)!!},$$

$$V_l(\rho) \rightarrow \frac{(2l - 1)!!}{\rho^l}, \qquad \rho \rightarrow 0. \tag{A3.41}$$

The derivatives of the Riccatti-Bessel functions are formed by (A3.37).

D. THE LEGENDRE POLYNOMIALS

The Legendre polynomials $P_l(\cos \theta)$ are useful for axially symmetric problems. For problems with more general angular properties we need the spherical harmonics, which are described in Appendix 4. The generating function for the $P_l(\cos \theta)$ is

$$T(\cos \theta, s) = (1 - 2s \cos \theta + s^2)^{-\frac{1}{2}}$$
$$= \sum_l P_l(\cos \theta)s^l, \qquad s < 1. \tag{A3.42}$$

They are computed by means of the recurrence relation

$$(l + 1)P_{l+1}(\cos \theta) = (2l + 1) \cos \theta \, P_l(\cos \theta) - lP_{l-1}(\cos \theta). \tag{A3.43}$$

The starting values are

$$P_0(\cos \theta) = 1, \qquad P_1(\cos \theta) = \cos \theta. \tag{A3.44}$$

APPENDIX 4
Angular Momentum

In nuclear physics we are concerned with a system which is, to a first approximation, spherical. The angular properties of wave functions are therefore standard for all of nuclear physics. We shall describe some of the standard functions and the coefficients which relate them for different situations involving several particles. Their most useful properties will be stated without proof. Complete discussions are to be found in the books by Edmonds (57) and Rose (57). The reader is warned that different authors use different phase conventions for many of the quantities. Wave functions for many particles may be expanded in terms of independent particle wave functions, which are *antisymmetrized products of single-particle wave functions computed in a spherical potential.

A. ANGULAR MOMENTUM OPERATORS

Let the solution of the single-particle Schrödinger equation be $\phi(x, y, z)$ in cartesian coordinates.

$$(H - E)\phi(x, y, z) = 0. \tag{A4.1}$$

For a rotation by an angle α about the z-axis, denoted by the rotation operator $R_z(\alpha)$, the linearity of solutions of the Schrödinger equation gives for an infinitesimal rotation α

$$R_z(\alpha)\phi(x, y, z) = \phi(x + \alpha y, y - \alpha x, z)$$

$$= \left[1 + \alpha\left(y\frac{\partial}{\partial x} - x\frac{\partial}{\partial y}\right)\right]\phi(x, y, z). \tag{A4.2}$$

Using the fact that

$$\mathbf{p} = -i\hbar\mathbf{\nabla}, \tag{A4.3}$$

we can write $R_z(\alpha)$, defined by (A4.2), as

$$R_z(\alpha) = 1 + \frac{\alpha}{i\hbar}M_z, \tag{A4.4}$$

520

where

$$\mathbf{M} = \mathbf{r} \times \mathbf{p}. \tag{A4.5}$$

The vector operator $\mathbf{M}$ is the angular momentum operator. If ϕ is invariant under rotations about the z-axis, then $M_z\phi$ is also a solution of (A4.1) so that M_z commutes with H. M_z is therefore a constant of the motion. For a spherical problem, $\mathbf{M}$ is a constant of the motion.

The corresponding operators for the x and y axes are M_x and M_y. The three components of $\mathbf{M}$ satisfy the commutation rules

$$M_x M_y - M_y M_x = i\hbar M_z, \tag{A4.6}$$

and the two other equations obtained by cyclic permutations of x, y, z.

Any operator $\mathbf{J}/\hbar$ which satisfies (A4.6) is defined as an angular momentum operator. It is convenient to express angular momenta in units of $\hbar$.

$$\hbar\mathbf{M} = \mathbf{J}. \tag{A4.7}$$

Properties of $\mathbf{J}$ which follow algebraically from the commutation rules (A4.6) are as follows.

(1) J^2 commutes with J_z.

(2) Eigenvalues of J^2 are of the form $j(j + 1)$ where j is either an integer or a half-integer.

(3) Eigenvalues of J_z are m, where

$$m = j, j - 1, \ldots, -j. \tag{A4.8}$$

(4) If we denote a simultaneous eigenfunction of J^2 and J_z with eigenvalues $j(j + 1)$ and m by $|jm\rangle$, then

$$(J_x + iJ_y)|jm\rangle = [(j - m)(j + m + 1)]^{1/2}|j(m + 1)\rangle, \tag{A4.9a}$$

$$(J_x - iJ_y)|jm\rangle = [(j + m)(j - m + 1)]^{1/2}|j(m - 1)\rangle. \tag{A4.9b}$$

The operators on the left-hand sides of (A4.9a, b) are angular momentum raising and lowering operators.

A common notation, which is used throughout this book, is to denote the angular momentum operator by the same symbol $\mathbf{j}$ that expresses the eigenvalue $j(j + 1)$ of j^2.

B. SPHERICAL HARMONICS

The Schrödinger equation (A4.1) separates in spherical polar coordinates if the potential is spherical. The angular equation is

$$\frac{1}{\sin\theta}\frac{\partial}{\partial\theta}\left(\sin\theta\frac{\partial}{\partial\theta}\right)Y + \frac{1}{\sin^2\theta}\frac{\partial^2}{\partial\phi^2}Y + l(l + 1)Y = 0, \tag{A4.10}$$

where l is an integer.

Specializing $\mathbf{J}$ to be the differential operator $\mathbf{l}$ for orbital angular momentum, we have

$$l_z = -i \frac{\partial}{\partial \phi},$$

$$l_x \pm i l_y = e^{\pm i\phi} \left[\pm \frac{\partial}{\partial \theta} + i \cot \theta \frac{\partial}{\partial \phi} \right].$$

(A4.11)

The eigenfunctions Y_l^m of l^2 and l_z are the spherical harmonics. The corresponding eigenvalues are $l(l+1)$ and $m = -l, \ldots, l$. Normalized spherical harmonics are given by

$$Y_l^m(\theta, \phi) = \frac{(-1)^{l+m}}{(2l)!!} \left[\frac{(2l+1)(l-m)!}{4\pi(l+m)!} \right]^{1/2} (\sin \theta)^m$$

$$\times \frac{d^{l+m}}{(d \cos \theta)^{l+m}} [(\sin \theta)^{2l}] e^{im\phi}. \quad \text{(A4.12)}$$

Some important properties of the spherical harmonics are as follows.

(1) $\qquad\qquad Y_l^{m*}(\theta, \phi) = (-1)^m Y_l^{-m}(\theta, \phi),$ (A4.13)

(2) $\qquad\qquad Y_l^0(\theta, 0) = \left[\frac{2l+1}{4\pi} \right]^{1/2} P_l(\cos \theta),$ (A4.14)

where $P_l(\cos \theta)$ is a Legendre polynomial.

(3) The $Y_l^m(\Omega)$, where Ω denotes the pair of coordinates θ, ϕ, form a complete orthonormal set.

$$\int d\Omega\, Y_l^{m*}(\Omega) Y_{l'}^{m'}(\Omega) = \delta_{ll'} \delta_{mm'},$$

(A4.15)

where

$$d\Omega = d(\cos \theta)\, d\phi.$$

(4) The addition theorem. Let Ω, Ω' be two points on the unit sphere subtending an angle α at the center.

$$Y_l^0(\alpha, 0) Y_l^0(0, 0) = \left[\frac{2l+1}{4\pi} \right]^{1/2} Y_l^0(\alpha, 0) = \sum_m Y_l^{m*}(\Omega) Y_l^m(\Omega')$$

$$= \sum_m Y_l^{-m}(\Omega) Y_l^{-m*}(\Omega')$$

$$= \sum_m Y_l^m(\Omega) Y_l^{m*}(\Omega'). \quad \text{(A4.16)}$$

(5) The parity of $Y_l^m(\Omega)$ is $(-1)^l$.

$$Y_l^m(\pi - \theta, \pi + \phi) = (-1)^l Y_l^m(\theta, \phi).$$

(A4.17)

C. SPIN

In addition to the space coordinates, nucleons have spin coordinates $\boldsymbol{\sigma}$. Properties of the components of $\boldsymbol{\sigma}$ are given in (3.25). They are

$$\sigma_1^2 = \sigma_2^2 = \sigma_3^2 = 1,$$
$$\sigma_1\sigma_2 = i\sigma_3, \qquad \sigma_2\sigma_3 = i\sigma_1, \qquad \sigma_3\sigma_1 = i\sigma_2.$$

(A4.18a)

The simplest matrix representation with these properties is

$$\sigma_1 = \begin{pmatrix} 0 & 1 \\ 1 & 0 \end{pmatrix}, \qquad \sigma_2 = \begin{pmatrix} 0 & -i \\ i & 0 \end{pmatrix}, \qquad \sigma_3 = \begin{pmatrix} 1 & 0 \\ 0 & -1 \end{pmatrix}. \quad \text{(A4.18b)}$$

The angular momentum operator for spin $\frac{1}{2}$ is

$$\mathbf{J} \equiv \mathbf{s},$$

where $s = \frac{1}{2}$ and the corresponding projection quantum number μ takes the values $\pm\frac{1}{2}$.

The spin functions corresponding to $|jm\rangle$ are denoted $\chi_{\frac{1}{2}}^\mu(\boldsymbol{\sigma})$ or α, β, where

$$\chi_{\frac{1}{2}}^{\frac{1}{2}}(\boldsymbol{\sigma}) = \alpha, \qquad \chi_{\frac{1}{2}}^{-\frac{1}{2}}(\boldsymbol{\sigma}) = \beta.$$

Their most important property is that they are orthonormal. The symbolic integral over the spin coordinate $\boldsymbol{\sigma}$ of a single particle gives

$$\int d\boldsymbol{\sigma} \chi_{\frac{1}{2}}^\mu(\boldsymbol{\sigma}) \chi_{\frac{1}{2}}^{\mu'}(\boldsymbol{\sigma}) = \delta_{\mu\mu'}. \tag{A4.19}$$

D. VECTOR ADDITION OF ANGULAR MOMENTA

Consider the operators $\mathbf{j}_1$ and $\mathbf{j}_2$ representing different angular momenta, either the angular momenta of different particles or the spin and orbital angular momenta of the same particle. Each separately satisfies the commutation rules (A4.6). It is required to find the simultaneous eigenvectors of $\mathbf{j}_1$ and $\mathbf{j}_2$. The simultaneous eigenvectors are vectors in the direct product space of $|j_1m_1\rangle$ and $|j_2m_2\rangle$, the eigenvectors of j_1^2, j_{1z} and j_2^2, j_{2z}, respectively. Thus they are linear combinations of the products $|j_1m_1\rangle|j_2m_2\rangle$ corresponding to the eigenvalues

$$j_{12}(j_{12} + 1) = j(j + 1), \qquad j_{12z} = m, \tag{A4.20}$$

for the total angular momentum operator $\mathbf{j}_{12}$, with eigenvector $|j_1j_2jm\rangle$.

$$|j_1j_2jm\rangle = \sum_{m_1m_2} C_{j_1\,j_2\,j}^{m_1m_2m} |j_1m_1\rangle|j_2m_2\rangle. \tag{A4.21}$$

The coefficient in the linear combination is the Clebsch-Gordan coefficient. From the definition, it is clear that for $C^{m_1 m_2 m_3}_{j_1 j_2 j_3}$ we have the triangle rule

$$|j_\alpha + j_\beta| \geq |j_\gamma| \text{ for } \alpha, \beta, \gamma = 1, 2, 3 \text{ and } \alpha \neq \beta \neq \gamma. \qquad (A4.22)$$

The projection quantum numbers must satisfy

$$m_1 + m_2 = m_3. \qquad (A4.23)$$

Thus one of the sums in (A4.21) is redundant.

A useful function related to the Clebsch-Gordan coefficient is the Wigner $3j$ symbol, which has simple symmetry properties.

$$\begin{pmatrix} a & b & c \\ \alpha & \beta & \gamma \end{pmatrix} = \frac{(-1)^{b-a+\gamma}}{(2c+1)^{1/2}} C^{\alpha\beta-\gamma}_{abc}. \qquad (A4.24)$$

The symmetry properties of the Clebsch-Gordan coefficients are summed up by the statement that an even permutation of the columns of the $3j$ symbol causes no change in value while an odd permutation introduces a factor $(-1)^{a+b+c}$. The following relation also exits

$$\begin{pmatrix} a & b & c \\ \alpha & \beta & \gamma \end{pmatrix} = (-1)^{a+b+c} \begin{pmatrix} a & b & c \\ -\alpha & -\beta & -\gamma \end{pmatrix}. \qquad (A4.25)$$

The symmetry properties of the Clebsch-Gordan coefficients may be written more explicitly.

$$\begin{aligned}
C^{\alpha\beta\gamma}_{abc} &= (-1)^{a+b-c} C^{-\alpha-\beta-\gamma}_{a\ b\ c} \\
&= C^{-\beta-\alpha-\gamma}_{b\ a\ c} \\
&= (-1)^{a+b-c} C^{\beta\alpha\gamma}_{bac} \\
&= \left[\frac{2c+1}{2a+1}\right]^{1/2} (-1)^{b+\beta} C^{-\gamma\beta-\alpha}_{c\ b\ a} \\
&= \left[\frac{2c+1}{2a+1}\right]^{1/2} (-1)^{a-\alpha+c-\gamma} C^{\gamma-\beta\alpha}_{c\ b\ a} \\
&= \left[\frac{2c+1}{2a+1}\right]^{1/2} (-1)^{a-\alpha+c-\gamma} C^{\beta-\gamma-\alpha}_{b\ c\ a} \\
&= \left[\frac{2c+1}{2b+1}\right]^{1/2} (-1)^{a-\alpha} C^{\alpha-\gamma-\beta}_{a\ c\ b} \\
&= \left[\frac{2c+1}{2b+1}\right]^{1/2} (-1)^{a-\alpha} C^{\gamma-\alpha\beta}_{c\ a\ b}. \qquad (A4.26)
\end{aligned}$$

The Clebsch-Gordan coefficients are computed by a formula due to Wigner (31).

$$C^{m_1 m_2 m}_{j_1 \, j_2 \, j} = \delta_{m(m_1+m_2)} \left[\frac{(j_1 + j_2 - j)! \, (j + j_1 - j_2)! \, (j + j_2 - j_1)! \, (2j + 1)!}{(j + j_1 + j_2 + 1)!} \right]^{\frac{1}{2}}$$

$$\times \sum_k \left[\frac{(-1)^k \{(j_1 + m_1)! \, (j_1 - m_1)! \, (j_2 + m_2)!\}^{\frac{1}{2}}}{k! \, (j_1 + j_2 - j - k)! \, (j_1 - m_1 - k)! \, (j_2 + m_2 - k)!} \right.$$

$$\left. \times \frac{(j_2 - m_2)! \, (j + m)! \, (j - m)!\}^{\frac{1}{2}}}{(j - j_2 + m_1 - k)! \, (j - j_1 - m_2 + k)!} \right] \tag{A4.27}$$

Special values are

$$C^{\alpha 0 \gamma}_{a 0 c} = \delta_{ac} \delta_{\alpha \gamma},$$

$$C^{000}_{abc} = 0 \quad \text{if} \quad a + b + c \text{ is an odd integer}, \tag{A4.28}$$

$$C^{\alpha \alpha \gamma}_{a a c} = 0 \quad \text{if} \quad 2a + c \text{ is an odd integer}.$$

Clebsch-Gordan coefficients of particular interest are those for $j_2 = \frac{1}{2}$, 1, $\frac{3}{2}$, and 2. Their values are given in Table A4.1.

TABLE A4.1. Clebsch-Gordan coefficients $C^{m_1 m_2 m}_{j_1 \, j_2 \, j}$ for positive values of m_2 and for (a) $j_2 = \frac{1}{2}$, (b) $j_2 = 1$, (c) $j_2 = \frac{3}{2}$, (d) $j_2 = 2$. Values for negative values of m_2 are obtained by using the symmetry relations (A4.26). The sign of m is reversed and the coefficient is multiplied by $(-1)^{j_1 + j_2 - j}$.

(a)

$j_2 = \frac{1}{2}$	$m_2 = \frac{1}{2}$
$j = j_1 + \frac{1}{2}$	$\left[\dfrac{j_1 + m + \frac{1}{2}}{2j + 1} \right]^{\frac{1}{2}}$
$j = j_1 - \frac{1}{2}$	$\left[\dfrac{j_1 - m + \frac{1}{2}}{2j + 1} \right]^{\frac{1}{2}}$

(b)

$j_2 = 1$	$m_2 = 1$	$m_2 = 0$
$j = j_1 + 1$	$\left[\dfrac{(j_1 + m)(j_1 + m + 1)}{(2j_1 + 1)(2j_1 + 2)} \right]^{\frac{1}{2}}$	$\left[\dfrac{(j_1 - m + 1)(j_1 + m + 1)}{(2j_1 + 1)(j_1 + 1)} \right]^{\frac{1}{2}}$
$j = j_1$	$-\left[\dfrac{(j_1 + m)(j_1 - m + 1)}{2j_1(j_1 + 1)} \right]^{\frac{1}{2}}$	$\left[\dfrac{m^2}{j_1(j_1 + 1)} \right]^{\frac{1}{2}}$
$j = j_1 - 1$	$\left[\dfrac{(j_1 - m)(j_1 - m + 1)}{2j_1(2j_1 + 1)} \right]^{\frac{1}{2}}$	$-\left[\dfrac{(j_1 - m)(j_1 + m)}{j_1(2j_1 + 1)} \right]^{\frac{1}{2}}$

TABLE A4.1. (continued)

(c)

$j_2=\frac{3}{2}$	$m_2=\frac{3}{2}$	$m_2=\frac{1}{2}$
$j=j_1+\frac{3}{2}$	$\left[\dfrac{(j_1+m-\frac{1}{2})(j_1+m+\frac{1}{2})(j_1+m+\frac{3}{2})}{(2j_1+1)(2j_1+2)(2j_1+3)}\right]^{\frac{1}{2}}$	$\left[\dfrac{3(j_1+m+\frac{1}{2})(j_1+m+\frac{3}{2})(j_1-m+\frac{3}{2})}{(2j_1+1)(2j_1+2)(2j_1+3)}\right]^{\frac{1}{2}}$
$j=j_1+\frac{1}{2}$	$-\left[\dfrac{3(j_1+m-\frac{1}{2})(j_1+m+\frac{1}{2})(j_1-m+\frac{3}{2})}{2j_1(2j_1+1)(2j_1+3)}\right]^{\frac{1}{2}}$	$-\left[\dfrac{(j_1-3m+\frac{3}{2})^2(j_1+m+\frac{1}{2})}{2j_1(2j_1+1)(2j_1+3)}\right]^{\frac{1}{2}}$
$j=j_1-\frac{1}{2}$	$\left[\dfrac{3(j_1+m-\frac{1}{2})(j_1-m+\frac{1}{2})(j_1-m+\frac{3}{2})}{(2j_1-1)(2j_1+1)(2j_1+2)}\right]^{\frac{1}{2}}$	$-\left[\dfrac{(j_1+3m-\frac{1}{2})^2(j_1-m+\frac{1}{2})}{(2j_1-1)(2j_1+1)(2j_1+2)}\right]^{\frac{1}{2}}$
$j=j_1-\frac{3}{2}$	$-\left[\dfrac{(j_1-m-\frac{1}{2})(j_1-m+\frac{1}{2})(j_1-m+\frac{3}{2})}{2j_1(2j_1-1)(2j_1+1)}\right]^{\frac{1}{2}}$	$\left[\dfrac{3(j_1+m-\frac{1}{2})(j_1-m-\frac{1}{2})(j_1-m+\frac{1}{2})}{2j_1(2j_1-1)(2j_1+1)}\right]^{\frac{1}{2}}$

(d)

$j_2=2$	$m_2=2$	$m_2=1$	$m_2=0$
$j=j_1+2$	$\left[\dfrac{(j_1+m-1)(j_1+m)(j_1+m+1)(j_1+m+2)}{(2j_1+1)(2j_1+2)(2j_1+3)(2j_1+4)}\right]^{\frac{1}{2}}$	$\left[\dfrac{(j_1-m+2)(j_1+m)(j_1+m+1)(j_1+m+2)}{(2j_1+1)(j_1+1)(2j_1+3)(j_1+2)}\right]^{\frac{1}{2}}$	$\left[\dfrac{3(j_1-m+1)(j_1-m+2)(j_1+m+1)(j_1+m+2)}{(2j_1+1)(2j_1+2)(2j_1+3)(j_1+2)}\right]^{\frac{1}{2}}$
$j=j_1+1$	$-\left[\dfrac{(j_1+m-1)(j_1+m)(j_1+m+1)(j_1-m+2)}{2j_1(2j_1+1)(j_1+1)(2j_1+3)}\right]^{\frac{1}{2}}$	$-\left[\dfrac{(j_1-2m+2)^2(j_1+m)(j_1+m+1)}{2j_1(2j_1+1)(j_1+1)(2j_1+3)}\right]^{\frac{1}{2}}$	$-\left[\dfrac{3m^2(j_1-m+1)(j_1+m+1)}{j_1(2j_1+1)(j_1+1)(j_1+2)}\right]^{\frac{1}{2}}$
$j=j_1$	$\left[\dfrac{3(j_1+m-1)(j_1+m)(j_1-m+1)(j_1-m+2)}{(2j_1-1)2j_1(j_1+1)(2j_1+3)}\right]^{\frac{1}{2}}$	$-\left[\dfrac{3(1-2m)^2(j_1+m)(j_1-m+1)}{(2j_1-1)j_1(j_1+1)(2j_1+3)}\right]^{\frac{1}{2}}$	$\left[\dfrac{\{3m^2-j_1(j_1+1)\}^2}{(2j_1-1)j_1(j_1+1)(2j_1+3)}\right]^{\frac{1}{2}}$
$j=j_1-1$	$-\left[\dfrac{(j_1+m)(j_1-m-1)(j_1-m)(j_1-m+1)}{(2j_1-1)2j_1(2j_1+1)(j_1+1)}\right]^{\frac{1}{2}}$	$-\left[\dfrac{(j_1+2m+1)^2(j_1-m)(j_1-m+1)}{(2j_1-1)2j_1(2j_1+1)(j_1+1)}\right]^{\frac{1}{2}}$	$-\left[\dfrac{3m^2(j_1-m)(j_1+m)}{(j_1-1)2j_1(2j_1+1)(j_1+1)}\right]^{\frac{1}{2}}$
$j=j_1-2$	$\left[\dfrac{(j_1-m-1)(j_1-m)(j_1-m+1)(j_1-m+2)}{(2j_1-2)(2j_1-1)2j_1(2j_1+1)}\right]^{\frac{1}{2}}$	$-\left[\dfrac{(j_1+m)(j_1-m-1)(j_1-m)(j_1-m+1)}{(j_1-1)(2j_1-1)2j_1(2j_1+1)}\right]^{\frac{1}{2}}$	$\left[\dfrac{3(j_1-m-1)(j_1-m)(j_1+m-1)(j_1+m)}{(2j_1-2)(2j_1-1)2j_1(2j_1+1)}\right]^{\frac{1}{2}}$

The orthogonality properties are as follows

$$\sum_{m_1 m_2} C^{m_1 m_2 m}_{j_1 \ j_2 \ j} C^{m_1 m_2 m'}_{j_1 \ j_2 \ j'} = \delta_{jj'} \delta_{mm'},$$

$$\sum_{jm} C^{m_1 m_2 m}_{j_1 \ j_2 \ j} C^{m_1' m_2' m}_{j_1 \ j_2 \ j} = \delta_{m_1 m_1'} \delta_{m_2 m_2'}.$$

(A4.29)

E. REARRANGEMENT OF THE COUPLING OF ANGULAR MOMENTA

The coupling of more than two angular momentum vectors can be achieved by coupling them two at a time by means of Equation (A4.21). The order of coupling, however, is important. For two angular momenta we have, from the symmetry relations (A4.26),

$$|j_2 j_1 jm\rangle = (-1)^{j_1 + j_2 - j} |j_1 j_2 jm\rangle.$$

(A4.30)

Wave functions for a set of more than two angular momenta coupled in a certain order are linear combinations of wave functions for the same angular momenta coupled in a different order. The coefficients in the linear combinations increase rapidly in complexity as the number of angular momenta increases.

For three angular momenta where j_1 and j_2 are first coupled to j_{12} which is in turn coupled to j_3 to produce a total angular momentum j, we write the wave function as

$$|(j_1 j_2) j_{12} j_3 jm\rangle = \sum_{j_{23}} U(j_1 j_2 j j_3, j_{12} j_{23}) |j_1 (j_2 j_3) j_{23} jm\rangle, \quad \text{(A4.31)}$$

where the notation is self-explanatory. The coefficients U are recoupling coefficients. Note that they do not depend on the projection quantum numbers. This is expected physically, since the relationship of the wave functions for differently coupled angular momenta cannot depend on the direction of an arbitrarily defined z-axis.

There are alternative notations for U.

$$U(j_1 j_2 j j_3, \ j_{12} j_{23}) = [(2j_{12} + 1)(2j_{23} + 1)]^{1/2} W(j_1 j_2 j j_3, j_{12} j_{23}), \quad \text{(A4.32)}$$

where W is the Racah coefficient.

$$U(j_1 j_2 j j_3, j_{12} j_{23}) = (-1)^{j_1 + j_2 + j + j_3} [(2j_{12} + 1)(2j_{23} + 1)]^{1/2} \begin{Bmatrix} j_1 & j_2 & j_{12} \\ j_3 & j & j_{23} \end{Bmatrix},$$

(A4.33)

where the symbol in braces is the $6j$ symbol of Wigner.

The symmetry properties are best illustrated by the $6j$ symbol for which the value is invariant under any permutation of the columns and under the exchange of any two elements of the top row with those directly beneath them.

The orthogonality relations are as follows.

$$\sum_{j_{12}} U(j_1 j_2 jj_3, j_{12}j_{23})U(j_1 j_2 jj_3, j_{12}j_{23}') = \delta_{j_{23}j_{23}'},$$

$$\sum_{j_{23}} U(j_1 j_2 jj_3, j_{12}j_{23})U(j_1 j_2 jj_3, j_{12}'j_{23}) = \delta_{j_{12}j_{12}'}. \qquad (A4.34)$$

By coupling the particles two at a time using Clebsch-Gordan coefficients we have

$$U(j_1 j_2 jj_3, j_{12}j_{23}) = \sum_{m_1 m_2} C^{m_1\ m_2\ m_1+m_2}_{j_1\ j_2\ j_{12}} C^{m_1+m_2\ m-m_1-m_2\ m}_{j_{12}\ j_3\ j}$$

$$\times\ C^{m_2\ m-m_1-m_2\ m-m_1}_{j_2\ j_3\ j_{23}} C^{m_1\ m-m_1\ m}_{j_1\ j_{23}\ j}. \qquad (A4.35)$$

From (A4.35) we see the reason for defining the recoupling coefficients. Many expressions obtained from nuclear matrix elements contain sums over projection quantum numbers because of the way the angular momenta are coupled. The final expression does not depend on these projection quantum numbers. The sums can often be performed by using the recoupling coefficients, whose computation is much shorter than that of the original expression. Other useful relationships between the recoupling and Clebsch-Gordan coefficients are as follows.

$$C^{m_1\ m_2\ m_1+m_2}_{j_1\ j_2\ j_{12}} C^{m_1+m_2\ m-m_1-m_2\ m}_{j_{12}\ j_3\ j}$$

$$= \sum_{j_{23}} C^{m_2\ m-m_1-m_2\ m-m_1}_{j_2\ j_3\ j_{23}} C^{m_1\ m-m_1\ m}_{j_1\ j_{23}\ j} U(j_1 j_2 jj_3, j_{12}j_{23}), \qquad (A4.36)$$

$$C^{m_2\ m-m_1-m_2\ m-m_1}_{j_2\ j_3\ j_{23}} C^{m_1\ m-m_1\ m}_{j_1\ j_{23}\ j}$$

$$= \sum_{j_{12}} C^{m_1\ m_2\ m_1+m_2}_{j_1\ j_2\ j_{12}} C^{m_1+m_2\ m-m_1-m_2\ m}_{j_{12}\ j_3\ j} U(j_1 j_2 jj_3, j_{12}j_{23}), \qquad (A4.37)$$

$$\sum_{m_2} C^{m_1\ m_2\ m_1+m_2}_{j_1\ j_2\ j_{12}} C^{m_1+m_2\ m-m_1-m_2\ m}_{j_{12}\ j_3\ j} C^{m_2\ m-m_1-m_2\ m-m_1}_{j_2\ j_3\ j_{23}}$$

$$= C^{m_1\ m-m_1\ m}_{j_1\ j_{23}\ j} U(j_1 j_2 jj_3, j_{12}j_{23}). \qquad (A4.38)$$

F. COUPLING OF FOUR ANGULAR MOMENTA

Wave functions of four angular momenta coupled in a certain order are linear combinations of wave functions of the same four angular momenta coupled in a different order. The coefficients in the linear combination are the $9j$ symbols.

$$|(j_1 j_2)j_{12}(j_3 j_4)j_{34}jm\rangle = \sum_{j_{13}j_{24}} [(2j_{12}+1)(2j_{34}+1)(2j_{13}+1)(2j_{24}+1)]^{1/2}$$

$$\times \begin{Bmatrix} j_1 & j_2 & j_{12} \\ j_3 & j_4 & j_{34} \\ j_{13} & j_{24} & j \end{Bmatrix} |(j_1 j_3)j_{13}(j_2 j_4)j_{24}jm\rangle. \qquad (A4.39)$$

The symmetry properties of the $9j$ symbol are as follows. The exchange of any two rows or columns results in a phase factor $(-1)^{\Sigma}$, where Σ is the sum of the nine values of j.

The orthogonality relations are as follows.

$$\sum_{j_{12}j_{34}} \begin{Bmatrix} j_1 & j_2 & j_{12} \\ j_3 & j_4 & j_{34} \\ j_{13} & j_{24} & j \end{Bmatrix} \begin{Bmatrix} j_1 & j_2 & j_{12} \\ j_3 & j_4 & j_{34} \\ j_{13}' & j_{24}' & j \end{Bmatrix}$$

$$= [(2j_{12} + 1)(2j_{34} + 1)(2j_{13} + 1)(2j_{24} + 1)]^{-1}\delta_{j_{13}j_{13}'}\delta_{j_{24}j_{24}'},$$

$$\sum_{j_{13}j_{24}} \begin{Bmatrix} j_1 & j_2 & j_{12} \\ j_3 & j_4 & j_{34} \\ j_{13} & j_{24} & j \end{Bmatrix} \begin{Bmatrix} j_1 & j_2 & j_{12}' \\ j_3 & j_4 & j_{34}' \\ j_{13} & j_{24} & j \end{Bmatrix}$$

$$= [(2j_{12} + 1)(2j_{34} + 1)(2j_{13} + 1)(2j_{24} + 1)]^{-1}\delta_{j_{12}j_{12}'}\delta_{j_{34}j_{34}'}. \quad (A4.40)$$

The $9j$ symbol may be expanded in terms of $6j$ symbols.

$$\begin{Bmatrix} j_1 & j_2 & j_{12} \\ j_3 & j_4 & j_{34} \\ j_{13} & j_{24} & j \end{Bmatrix} = (-1)^{j_1 - j_{12} - j_{13}}[(2j_{12} + 1)(2j_{34} + 1)(2j_{13} + 1)(2j_{24} + 1)]^{-\frac{1}{2}}$$

$$\times \sum_r (-1)^r U(j_{12}j_3jj_4, rj_{34})U(j_{13}j_2jj_4, rj_{24})U(j_3j_1rj_2, j_{13}j_{12}). \quad (A4.41)$$

G. MULTIPOLE EXPANSION OF A CENTRAL POTENTIAL

The central potential $V(|r_1 - r_2|)$ may be expanded in the complete set of Legendre polynomials $P_n(\cos \omega_{12})$, where ω_{12} is the angle between $\hat{\mathbf{r}}_1$ and $\hat{\mathbf{r}}_2$.

$$V(r) \equiv V(|\mathbf{r}_1 - \mathbf{r}_2|) = \sum_n (2n + 1)v_n(r_1, r_2)P_n(\cos \omega_{12}). \quad (A4.42)$$

Using the addition theorem (A4.16) and the relation (A4.14) between Legendre polynomials and spherical harmonics, we have

$$V(|\mathbf{r}_1 - \mathbf{r}_2|) = 4\pi \sum_{n\nu} v_n(r_1, r_2)Y_n^{\nu*}(\Omega_1)Y_n^{\nu}(\Omega_2)$$

$$= 4\pi \sum_{n\nu} v_n(r_1, r_2)Y_n^{\nu}(\Omega_1)Y_n^{\nu*}(\Omega_2). \quad (A4.43)$$

Using the orthonormality of the spherical harmonics, again with (A4.14), we find the following general expression for v_n.

$$v_n(r_1, r_2) = \frac{1}{2} \int d(\cos \omega_{12})V(|\mathbf{r}_1 - \mathbf{r}_2|)P_n(\cos \omega_{12}). \quad (A4.44)$$

Special cases of interest are the Gaussian and Yukawa potentials. For the Gaussian potential $V^G(r) = e^{-(r/\alpha)^2}$,

$$v_n^G(r_1, r_2) = (-i)^n j_n\left(\frac{2ir_1r_2}{\alpha^2}\right)e^{-(r_1^2+r_2^2)/\alpha^2}. \quad (A4.45)$$

For the Yukawa form, $V^Y(r) = e^{-\mu r}/\mu r$,

$$v_n{}^Y(r_1, r_2) = -j_n(i\mu r_<)h_n^{(1)}(i\mu r_>). \tag{A4.46}$$

H. MATRIX ELEMENTS

The computation of probability amplitudes in nuclear physics always reduces to the computation of one or more matrix elements of the form

$$\mathscr{M}_L{}^M = \langle \phi_f| \, V_L{}^M \, |\phi_i\rangle, \tag{A4.47}$$

where ϕ_f, ϕ_i and $V_L{}^M$ are functions of the same coordinates r, θ, ϕ, $\boldsymbol{\sigma}$. $V_L{}^M$ is obtained by expanding a nonspherical potential in spherical harmonics. Angular and spin integrations can always be done explicitly.

The simplest case is where ϕ_f and ϕ_i do not depend on spin so that the matrix element reduces to a linear combination of matrix elements of the following form

$$\mathscr{M} = \int d\Omega Y_{l_1}^{m_1*}(\Omega)Y_L{}^M(\Omega)Y_{l_2}{}^{m_2}(\Omega). \tag{A4.48}$$

To compute this matrix element we use the expansion of the product of two spherical harmonics of the same coordinates, as a linear combination of single spherical harmonics.

$$Y_L{}^M(\Omega)Y_{l_2}{}^{m_2}(\Omega) = \sum_{\lambda\mu}\left[\frac{(2L+1)(2l_2+1)}{4\pi(2\lambda+1)}\right]^{\frac{1}{2}} C_{l_2\,L\,\lambda}^{m_2 M\mu}C_{l_2 L\lambda}^{0\,0\,0}Y_\lambda{}^\mu(\Omega). \tag{A4.49}$$

Multiplying by $Y_{l_1}^{m_1*}(\Omega)$ and using the orthogonality of the spherical harmonics (A4.15), we have

$$\begin{aligned}\mathscr{M} &= \left[\frac{(2L+1)(2l_2+1)}{4\pi(2l_1+1)}\right]^{\frac{1}{2}} C_{l_2\,L\,l_1}^{m_2 M m_1}C_{l_2 L l_1}^{0\,0\,0}, \qquad l_1 + l_2 + L \text{ even},\tag{A4.50}\\ &= 0, \, l_1 + l_2 + L \text{ odd}.\end{aligned}$$

This is a special case of the Wigner-Eckart theorem which states that a matrix element of the form (A4.47) can always be reduced to the product of a Clebsch-Gordan coefficient depending on the projection quantum numbers and a reduced matrix element that is independent of the projection quantum numbers. The theorem is in fact true whether L is an integer or a half-integer. In the case of (A4.50) it is written

$$\langle l_1 m_1| \, Y_L{}^M \, |l_2 m_2\rangle = C_{l_2\,L\,l_1}^{m_2 M m_1}\langle l_1\| \, Y_L \, \|l_2\rangle, \tag{A4.51}$$

where the reduced matrix element is given by

$$\langle l_1\| \, Y_L \, \|l_2\rangle = \left[\frac{(2L+1)(2l_2+1)}{4\pi(2l_1+1)}\right]^{\frac{1}{2}} C_{l_2 L l_1}^{0\,0\,0}. \tag{A4.52}$$

In cases where the wave functions ϕ_f and ϕ_i of (A4.47) involve the coupling of several angular momenta, they are first reduced to direct products of eigenfunctions $|jm\rangle$ of a single $\mathbf{j}$ by repeated use of (A4.21). For example, it is a good exercise in the algebra of this appendix to show that

$$\langle j_1 j_2 jm| \ Y_L{}^M(2) \ |j_1'j_2'j'm'\rangle = C_{j'}^{m'}{}_L^M{}_j^m \langle j_1 j_2 j\| \ Y_L(2) \ \|j_1' j_2' j'\rangle, \quad (A4.53)$$

where the operator $Y_L{}^M(2)$ acts in the space of $\mathbf{j}_2$ and the reduced matrix element is

$$\langle j_1 j_2 j\| \ Y_L(2) \ \|j_1'j_2'j'\rangle = U(j_1'j_2'jL, j'j_2)\delta_{j_1 j_1'} \ \langle j_2\| \ Y_L(2) \ \|j_2'\rangle. \quad (A4.54)$$

The matrix element of the spin-orbit coupling potential $\mathbf{l} \cdot \mathbf{s}$ between jj-coupling wave functions is used frequently. The wave function

$$|ljm\rangle = \mathscr{Y}_{jls}^m = \sum_\mu C_l^{m-\mu}{}_s^\mu{}_j^m Y_l^{m-\mu}(\Omega_r)\chi_s^\mu(\boldsymbol{\sigma}) \quad (A4.55)$$

is a simultaneous eigenfunction of $j^2 = l^2 + s^2 + 2\mathbf{l} \cdot \mathbf{s}$, l^2 and s^2, with eigenvalues $j(j+1)$, $l(l+1)$, and $s(s+1)$.

$$\langle l_1 j_1 m_1| \ \mathbf{l} \cdot \mathbf{s} \ |l_2 j_2 m_2\rangle = \delta_{l_1 l_2}\delta_{j_1 j_2}\delta_{m_1 m_2}\tfrac{1}{2}[j(j+1) - l(l+1) - s(s+1)].$$

$$(A4.56)$$

The Wigner-Eckart theorem for jj-coupling wave functions is

$$\langle l_1 j_1 m_1| \ Y_L{}^M \ |l_2 j_2 m_2\rangle = C_{j_2}^{m_2}{}_L^M{}_{j_1}^{m_1}\langle l_1 j_1\| \ Y_L \ \|l_2 j_2\rangle, \quad (A4.57)$$

where we can see by changing the order of coupling in (A4.54) applied to (A4.56) that

$$\langle l_1 j_1\| \ Y_L \ \|l_2 j_2\rangle = \left[\frac{(2L+1)(2j_2+1)}{4\pi(2j_1+1)}\right]^{\frac{1}{2}} C_{j_2 L j_1}^{-\frac{1}{2} 0 -\frac{1}{2}} C_{l_2 L l_1}^{0 0 0}.$$

$$\equiv \langle j_1\| \ Y_L \ \|j_2\rangle. \quad (A4.58)$$

I. ROTATION FUNCTIONS

Consider the jj-coupling wave function

$$\mathscr{Y}_{jls}^m(\mathbf{r}, \boldsymbol{\sigma})$$

for a single particle whose space coordinates are denoted by $\mathbf{r}$. If we perform a rotation of the coordinate frame with Euler angles α, β, γ so that $\mathbf{r}$ becomes $\mathbf{r}'$, we do not essentially change the system. In particular, eigenvalues are preserved, so the wave function

$$\mathscr{Y}_{jls}^m(\mathbf{r}', \boldsymbol{\sigma})$$

in the rotated space is obtained from that in the original space by a unitary transformation.

$$\mathscr{Y}_{jls}^m(\mathbf{r}', \boldsymbol{\sigma}) = \sum_{m'} D_{m'm}^j(\alpha, \beta, \gamma)\mathscr{Y}_{jls}^{m'}(\mathbf{r}, \boldsymbol{\sigma}). \quad (A4.59)$$

The coefficients $D^j_{m'm}(\alpha, \beta, \gamma)$ of the transformation are the rotation functions. The simple case of an eigenstate of l (a spherical harmonic) was considered in Chapter 7, Equation (7.69).

Spherical harmonics may be expressed as rotation functions.

$$Y_l^m(\beta, \alpha) = \left[\frac{2l+1}{4\pi}\right]^{1/2} D^{l*}_{m0}(\alpha, \beta, \gamma), \tag{A4.60a}$$

$$Y_l^m(\beta, \gamma) = \left[\frac{2l+1}{4\pi}\right]^{1/2} (-1)^m D^{l*}_{0m}(\alpha, \beta, \gamma). \tag{A4.60b}$$

It is usually unnecessary to evaluate rotation functions, since they appear in matrix elements for which the angular integral is an extension of the Wigner-Eckart theorem.

$$\int \sin \beta \, d\beta \, d\alpha \, d\gamma \, D^{j_1}_{m_1 m_1'} D^{j_2}_{m_2 m_2'} D^{J*}_{MM'} = \frac{8\pi^2}{2J+1} C^{m_1 m_2 M}_{j_1 j_2 J} C^{m_1' m_2' M'}_{j_1 j_2 J}. \tag{A4.61}$$

The orthogonality relation for the rotation functions is

$$\int \sin \beta \, d\beta \, d\alpha \, d\gamma \, D^{j_1*}_{m_1 m_1'} D^{j_2}_{m_2 m_2'} = \frac{8\pi^2}{2j_1+1} \delta_{j_1 j_2} \delta_{m_1 m_2} \delta_{m_1' m_2'}. \tag{A4.62}$$

Wave functions with axial symmetry are invariant under a rotation by an angle ϕ about the z-axis, which is represented by

$$D^l_{mm'}(z_\phi) = e^{-im\phi} \delta_{mm'}. \tag{A4.63}$$

Some wave functions are invariant under a rotation by π about the x-axis, given by

$$D^j_{mm'}(x_\pi) = (-1)^j \delta_{m(-m')}. \tag{A4.64}$$

J. TIME REVERSAL

We shall discuss the behavior of angular momentum eigenstates under time reversal. Let $\psi(t)$ be a wave function satisfying the Schrödinger equation

$$H\psi(t) = i\hbar \frac{\partial}{\partial t} \psi(t). \tag{A4.65}$$

If H is real, the complex conjugate of (A4.65) is

$$H^*\psi^* = H\psi^* = -i\hbar \frac{\partial}{\partial t} \psi^* = i\hbar \frac{\partial}{\partial(-t)} \psi^*. \tag{A4.66}$$

The original Schrödinger equation with time reversed is satisfied by $\psi^*(t)$ if H is real. The time reversed state is $\psi^*(t)$. We say that in this case the time-reversal operator T is equal to the complex conjugation operator u.

$$T = u, \qquad H \text{ real.} \tag{A4.67}$$

Time reversal is easily understood for a plane wave. The operation T reverses the direction of momentum.

$$Te^{i\mathbf{k}\cdot\mathbf{r}} = e^{i(-\mathbf{k})\cdot\mathbf{r}}. \tag{A4.68}$$

The time-reversal operator transforms a spherical harmonic as follows.

$$TY_l^m(\Omega) = (-1)^m Y_l^{-m}(\Omega). \tag{A4.69}$$

The spin-orbit coupling operator is

$$\boldsymbol{\sigma} \cdot \mathbf{l} = -i\hbar\boldsymbol{\sigma} \cdot (\mathbf{r} \times \boldsymbol{\nabla}). \tag{A4.70}$$

Thus if H contains $\boldsymbol{\sigma} \cdot \mathbf{l}$ it is not real and T is not equivalent to u. In addition to u, we must have a unitary transformation U, so that

$$H = UH^*U^{-1}. \tag{A4.71}$$

We prove that the time-reversed state is $U\psi^*$ as follows. Operating on (A4.66) with U we have

$$(UH^*U^{-1})U\psi^* = i\hbar\frac{\partial}{\partial(-t)}\, U\psi^*. \tag{A4.72}$$

For spin-orbit coupling the appropriate unitary transformation operator is σ_2, given by (A4.18). From (A4.18, A4.70) we have

$$\mathbf{l}^* = -\mathbf{l},$$

$$\sigma_1^* = \sigma_1,$$

$$\sigma_2^* = -\sigma_2,$$

$$\sigma_3^* = \sigma_3.$$

We may show that (A4.71) is satisfied for $\boldsymbol{\sigma} \cdot \mathbf{l}$ if $U = \sigma_2$, by using the commutation rules (A4.18a).

$$\sigma_2(\sigma_1^*l_1^* + \sigma_2^*l_2^* + \sigma_3^*l_3^*)\sigma_2^{-1} = \sigma_2(-\sigma_1l_1 + \sigma_2l_2 - \sigma_3l_3)\sigma_2$$
$$= \sigma_1l_1 + \sigma_2l_2 + \sigma_3l_3.$$

The time-reversal operator T for particles with spin $\tfrac{1}{2}$ is thus given by

$$T = \sigma_2 u. \tag{A4.73}$$

Operating on the spin functions $\chi_{\frac{1}{2}}^\mu$, T gives

$$T\chi_{\frac{1}{2}}^{\mu} = (-1)^\mu \chi_{\frac{1}{2}}^{-\mu}. \tag{A4.74}$$

This is proved as follows

$$\sigma_2 u \chi_{\frac{1}{2}}^{\frac{1}{2}} = \sigma_2 u \begin{pmatrix} 1 \\ 0 \end{pmatrix} = \begin{pmatrix} 0 & -i \\ i & 0 \end{pmatrix} \begin{pmatrix} 1 \\ 0 \end{pmatrix} = i \begin{pmatrix} 0 \\ 1 \end{pmatrix},$$

$$\sigma_2 u \chi_{\frac{1}{2}}^{-\frac{1}{2}} = \sigma_2 u \begin{pmatrix} 0 \\ 1 \end{pmatrix} = \begin{pmatrix} 0 & -i \\ i & 0 \end{pmatrix} \begin{pmatrix} 0 \\ 1 \end{pmatrix} = -i \begin{pmatrix} 1 \\ 0 \end{pmatrix}.$$

Thus the time-reversal operator for both integer and half-integer spins reverses the angular momentum projections M and multiplies by $(-1)^M$.

The time-reversal operation on the *jj*-coupling wave functions (A4.55) is understood by means of the first of the properties (A4.26) of the Clebsch-Gordan coefficients.

$$\begin{aligned} T|ljm\rangle &= \sum_\mu C_l^{m-\mu}{}_s^{\mu}{}_j^{m} T[Y_l^{m-\mu}(\Omega)\chi_s^{\mu}(\sigma)] \\ &= (-1)^{l+\frac{1}{2}-j} \sum_\mu C_l^{\mu-m}{}_s^{-\mu}{}_j^{-m} (-1)^m Y_l^{\mu-m}(\Omega)\chi_s^{-\mu}(\sigma) \\ &= (-1)^{l+\frac{1}{2}-j+m} |lj-m\rangle. \end{aligned} \qquad (A4.75)$$

Notice that by a slight change of the definition of the phase of the angular momentum eigenfunctions we can have a uniform definition of the time-reversal operator for any eigenstate $|jm\rangle$. If we redefine the eigenfunction of l^2, l_3 to be $i^l Y_l^m(\Omega)$ and the spin eigenfunction to be $i^s \chi_s^\mu(\sigma)$, then

$$T|jm\rangle = (-1)^{j-m}|j-m\rangle. \qquad (A4.76)$$

This phase convention has been used, for example, in the definition (8.103) of the angular part of the channel wave function $|\lambda\rangle$. The factor i^l appears explicitly in our usual definition of elastic scattering wave functions (see, for example, (2.17)).

REFERENCES

Aaron, R., Amado, R. D., and Yam, Y. Y. (64). *Phys. Rev.*, **136**, B650 (1964). **[10*E*,14]**

Aaron, R., Amado, R. D., and Yam, Y. Y. (65). *Phys. Rev.*, **140**, B1291 (1965); *Rev. Mod. Phys.*, **37**, 516 (1965). **[10*E*,14]**

Agodi, A. and Schiffrer, G. P. (64). *Nucl. Phys.*, **50**, 337 (1964). **[12*B*]**

Almquist, E., Kuehner, J., McPherson, D., and Vogt, E. W. (64). *Phys. Rev.*, **136**, B84 (1964). **[9*C*]**

Amos, K. A. (64). Ph.D. thesis, University of Adelaide, unpublished. **[2*B*]**

Amos, K. A. (66). *Nucl. Phys.*, **77**, 225 (1966). **[2*B*,11*A*]**

Amos, K. A. (67), unpublished. **[12*B*]**

Amos, K. A., Madsen, V. A., and McCarthy, I. E. (67). *Nucl. Phys.*, **A94**, 103 (1967). **[12*B*]**

Amos, K. A. and McCarthy, I. E. (63). *Phys. Rev.*, **132**, 2261 (1963). **[12*B*]**

Aston, F. W. (27). *Proc. Roy. Soc.* (*London*), **A115**, 487 (1927). **[1]**

Austern, N. (61). *Ann. Phys.* (*N.Y.*), **15**, 299 (1961). **[11*A*]**

Austern, N. (63). "Direct Reactions," *Selected Topics in Nuclear Theory*, edited by F. Janouch, International Atomic Energy Agency, Vienna, 1963, p. 17. **[12*A*]**

Austern, N. and Blair, J. S. (65). *Ann. Phys.* (*N.Y.*), **33**, 15 (1965). **[11*A*,12*D*]**

Bayman, B. F. and Lande, A. (66). *Nucl. Phys.*, **77**, 1 (1966). **[7*B*]**

Becker, R. A. (54). *Introduction to Theoretical Mechanics*, McGraw-Hill Book Company, Inc., New York, 1954, p. 230. **[1*A*]**

Belote, T. A., Dorenbusch, W. A., Hansen, O., and Rapaport, J. (65). *Nucl. Phys.*, **73**, 321 (1965). **[13*A*]**

Bethe, H. A. (56). *Phys. Rev.*, **103**, 1353 (1956). **[4]**

Bethe, H. A. (65). *Phys. Rev.*, **138**, B804 (1965). **[4*C*]**

Bethe, H. A. (67). *Proceedings of the International Conference on Nuclear Structure, Tokyo*, The Physical Society of Japan, Tokyo, 1967. **[4*C*]**

Bethe, H. A. and Goldstone, J. (56). *Proc. Roy. Soc.* (*London*), **A238**, 551 (1956). **[4*A*]**

Bjorklund, F. and Fernbach, S. (58). *Phys. Rev.*, **109**, 1295 (1958). **[11*C*]**

Blair, J. S. (59). *Phys. Rev.*, **115**, 928 (1959). **[12*D*]**

Blair, J. S. (60). *Proceedings of the International Conference on Nuclear Structure, Kingston*, edited by D. A. Bromley and E. W. Vogt, University of Toronto Press, Toronto, 1960, p. 824. **[12*A*,12*D*]**

Blatt, J. M. and Weisskopf, V. F. (52). *Theoretical Nuclear Physics*, John Wiley and Sons, New York, 1952, p. 584. **[7*B*,7*C*]**

535

Bloch, C. (57). *Nucl. Phys.*, **4**, 503 (1957). **[8B]**

Bodansky, D., Braithwaite, W. T., Shreve, D. C., Storm, D. W., and Weitkamp, W. G. (66). *Phys. Rev. Letters*, **17**, 589 (1966). **[13]**

Bohr, A. and Mottelson, B. R. (57). *Kgl. Danske Videnskab. Selskab, Mat-fys. Medd.*, **27**, No. 16 (1953) (second edition, 1957). **[7C]**

Bohr, N. (36). *Nature*, **137**, 344 (1936). **[7C,9B]**

Bohr, N. and Kalckar, F. (37). *Kgl. Danske Videnskab. Selskab. Mat-fys. Medd.*, **14**, No. 10 (1937). **[7C]**

Breit, G., Hull, M. H., Lassila, K. E., and Pyatt, K. D. (60). *Phys. Rev.*, **120**, 2227 (1960). **[3E]**

Breit, G. and Wigner, E. P. (36). *Phys. Rev.* **49**, 519, 642 (1936). **[8B]**

Brink, D. M. and Stephen, R. O. (63). *Phys. Letters*, **5**, 77 (1963). **[9C]**

Brody, T. A., Jacob, G. and Moshinsky, M. (60). *Nucl. Phys.*, **17**, 16 (1960). **[7B]**

Brody, T. A. and Moshinsky, M. (60). *Tables of Transformation Brackets*, Universidad National Autonoma de Mexico, 1960. **[7B]**

Brown, G. E. (58). *Rev. Mod. Phys.*, **31**, 893 (1959). **[9B]**

Brown, G. E., de Dominicis, C., and Langer, R. E. (58). *Ann. Phys. (N.Y.)*, **6**, 209 (1959). **[9B]**

Brueckner, K. A. (59). *Proceedings of the International Conference on the Nuclear Optical Model*, Florida State University Press, Tallahassee, 1959, p. 145. **[6B]**

Brueckner, K. A. and Gammel, J. L. (58). *Phys. Rev.*, **109**, 1023 (1958). **[4,4C]**

Brueckner, K. A., Gammel, J. L., and Weitzner, H. (58). *Phys. Rev.* **110**, 431 (1958). **[6B]**

Brueckner, K. A., Lockett, A. M., and Rotenberg, M. (61). *Phys. Rev.*, **121**, 255 (1961). **[5C,6B]**

Brueckner, K. A. and Masterson, K. S. (62). *Phys. Rev.*, **128**, 2267 (1962). **[3E]**

Bryan, R. A. and Scott, B. L. (64). *Phys. Rev.*, **135**, B434 (1964). **[3A]**

Buck, B. (63). *Phys. Rev.*, **130**, 712 (1963). **[12A]**

Butler, S. T. (51). *Proc. Roy. Soc.*, **A208**, 559 (1951). **[5B,12C,13A]**

Chadwick, J. (32a). *Proc. Roy. Soc. (London)*, **A136**, 692 (1932). **[1]**

Chadwick, J. (32b). *Proc. Roy. Soc. (London)*, **A136**, 735 (1932). **[1]**

Chase, D. M., Wilets, L., and Edmonds, A. R. (58). *Phys. Rev.*, **110**, 1080 (1958). **[9B,12A]**

Clegg, A. B. (61). *Phil. Mag.*, **6**, 1207 (1961). **[7C]**

Cockcroft, J. D. and Walton, E. T. S. (32). *Proc. Roy. Soc. (London)*, **A136**, 610, 619 (1932). **[1]**

Curie-Joliot, I. and Joliot, F. (32). *Compt. Rend.*, **194**, 273 (1932). **[1]**

Davidson, J. P. (65). *Rev. Mod. Phys.*, **37**, 105 (1965). **[7C]**

Davydov, A. S. and Filippov, G. F. (58). *Nucl. Phys.*, **8**, 257 (1958). **[7C]**

Dawson, J. F., Talmi, I., and Walecka, J. D. (62). *Ann. Phys. (N.Y.)*, **18**, 330 (1962). **[7B]**

de Shalit, A. and Talmi, I. (63). *Nuclear Shell Theory*, Academic Press, New York and London, 1963. **[7B]**

Dirac, P. A. M. (58). *The Principles of Quantum Mechanics* (fourth edition), Oxford University Press, London, 1958, p. 136. **[7C]**

Dodd, L. R. and Greider, K. R. (66). *Phys. Rev.*, **146**, 675 (1966). **[10E]**

Dodd, L. R. and McCarthy, I. E. (64). *Phys. Rev.*, **134**, A1136 (1964). [9*A*]

Donovan, P. F. (65). *Rev. Mod. Phys.*, **37**, 501 (1965). [9*A*]

Drozdov, S. I. (55). *Zh. Eksperim. i Teor. Fiz.*, **28**, 734, 736 (1955) [English translation; *Soviet Physics JETP*, **1**, 591, 588 (1955)]. [12*D*]

Edmonds, A. R. (57). *Angular Momentum in Quantum Mechanics*, Princeton University Press, Princeton, 1957. [*A*4]

Elliott, J. P. and Lane, A. M. (57). "The Nuclear Shell Model," *Encyclopedia of Physics*, Vol. XXXIX, Berlin: Springer-Verlag, 1957. [7*B*]

Elliott, J. P. and Skyrme, T. H. R. (55). *Proc. Roy. Soc. (London)*, **A232**, 561 (1955). [7*B*]

Elsasser, W. M. (34). *J. Phys. et Radium*, **5**, 389, 635 (1934). [5]

Elton, L. R. B. and Swift, A. (67). *Nucl. Phys.*, **A94**, 52 (1967). [5*C*]

Ericson, T. (63). *Ann. Phys. (N.Y.)*, **23**, 390 (1963). [9*C*]

Erskine, J. R. (65). *Phys. Rev.*, **138**, B66 (1965). [13*B*]

Faddeev, L. D. (60). *Zh. Eksperim. i Teor. Fiz.*, **39**, 1459 (1960) [English translation; *Soviet Phys. JETP*, **12**, 1014 (1961)]. [4*C*,10*E*,14]

Feenberg, E. (47). *Rev. Mod. Phys.*, **19**, 239 (1947). [7*C*]

Fermi, E. (50). *Nuclear Physics*, University of Chicago Press, Chicago, 1950. [7*C*]

Fernbach, S., Serber, R., and Taylor, T. B. (49). *Phys. Rev.*, **75**, 1352 (1949). [11]

Feshbach, H. (58). *Ann. Phys. (N.Y.)*, **5**, 357 (1958). [10*E*]

Feshbach, H., Porter, C. E., and Weisskopf, V. F. (54). *Phys. Rev.*, **96**, 448 (1954). [9*B*,11]

Feynman, R. P. (49). *Phys. Rev.*, **76**, 749 (1949). [2*C*]

Fox, J. D., Moore, C. F., and Robson, D. (64). *Phys. Rev. Letters*, **12**, 198 (1964). [8*B*]

Gammel, J. L. and Thaler, R. M. (57). *Phys. Rev.*, **107**, 291 (1957). [3*E*,4*C*]

Garron, J. P., Jacmart, J. C. Riou, M., Ruhla, C., Teillac, J., and Strauch, K., *Nucl. Phys.*, **37**, 126 (1962). [14*B*]

Geiger, H. (10). *Proc. Roy. Soc. (London)*, **83**, 492 (1910). [1*A*]

Geiger, H. and Marsden, E. (09). *Proc. Roy. Soc. (London)*, **82**, 495 (1909). [1*A*]

Gell-Mann, M. and Goldberger, M. L. (53). *Phys. Rev.*, **91**, 398 (1953). [10*A*]

Gillet, V. and Vinh Mau, N. (64). *Nucl. Phys.*, **54**, 321 (1964). [7*B*,12,12*B*]

Glassgold, A. E. and Kellogg, P. J. (58). *Phys. Rev.*, **109**, 1291 (1958). [11]

Glauber, R. (59). "High Energy Collision Theory," *Lectures in Theoretical Physics*, Vol. 1., edited by W. E. Brittin and L. G. Dunham, Interscience Publishers, New York, 1959. [12*C*]

Glendenning, N. K. (59). *Phys. Rev.*, **114**, 1297 (1959). [12*A*]

Goldberg, M. D., Mughabghab, S. F., Magurno, B. A., and May, V. M. (67). Brookhaven National Laboratory Report No. BNL325, second edition, Supplement No. 2, Vol. III, unpublished. [9]

Goldhammer, P. (63). *Rev. Mod. Phys.*, **35**, 40 (1963). [7*D*]

Gomes, L. C., Walecka, J. D., and Weisskopf, V. F. (58). *Ann. Phys. (N.Y.)*, **3**, 241 (1958). [4*B*]

Gray, W. S., Kenefick, R. A., Kraushaar, J. J., and Satchler, G. R. (66). *Phys. Rev.*, **142**, 735 (1966).

Green, A. M. (63). *Nucl. Phys.*, **33**, 218 (1963). [3*E*]

Green, T. S. and Middleton, R. (56). *Proc. Phys. Soc. (London)*, **A69**, 28 (1956). **[5C]**

Greider, K. R. (65), unpublished. **[6A]**

Greider, K. R. and Dodd, L. R. (66). *Phys. Rev.*, **146**, 671 (1966). **[10E]**

Greider, K. R. and Strobel, G. L. (66), unpublished. **[13A]**

Hamada, T. and Johnston, I. D. (62). *Nucl. Phys.*, **34**, 38a (1962). **[3E]**

Hauser, W. and Feshbach, H. (52). *Phys. Rev.*, **87**, 366 (1952). **[9,9C,11B]**

Haxel, O., Jensen, J. H. D., and Suess, H. E. (49). *Phys. Rev.*, **75**, 1766 (1949). **[5]**

Haxel, O., Jensen, J. H. D., and Suess, H. E. (50). *Z. Phys.*, **128**, 298 (1950). **[5A]**

Haybron, R. M. and McManus, H. (65). *Phys. Rev.*, **140**, B638 (1965). **[12,12B]**

Heisenberg, W. (32). *Z. Phys.*, **77**, 1 (1932). **[1]**

Hendrie, D. L. (67), unpublished. **[12D]**

Herman, R. and Hofstadter, R. (60). *High Energy Eledtron Scattering Tables*, Stanford University Press, Stanford, 1960. **[1A]**

Hofstadter, R. (56). *Rev. Mod. Phys.*, **28**, 214 (1956). **[1]**

Holland, R. E., Lynch, F. J., Perlow, G. J., and Hanna, S. S. (60). *Phys. Rev. Letters*, **4**, 181 (1960). **[9A]**

Hull, M. H., Lassila, K. E., Ruppel, H. M., McDonald, F. A., and Breit, G. (61). *Phys. Rev.*, **122**, 1606 (1961). **[3E]**

Humblet, J. and Rosenfeld, L. (61). *Nucl. Phys.*, **26**, 529 (1961). **[8C]**

Iano, P. J. and Austern, N. (66). *Phys. Rev.*, **151**, 853 (1966). **[13B]**

Inglis, D. R. (53). *Rev. Mod. Phys.*, **25**, 390 (1953). **[7B]**

Inopin, E. V. (56). *Zh. Eksperim. i Teor. Fiz.*, **31**, 901 (1956) [English translation; Soviet Phys. JETP, **4**, 764 (1957)]. **[12D]**

Jackson, D. F. (67). *Phys. Rev.*, **155**, 1065 (1967). **[14B]**

Jackson, D. F. and Berggren, T. (65). *Nucl. Phys.*, **62**, 353 (1965). **[14B]**

Jacob, G. and Maris, Th. A. J. (66). *Rev. Mod. Phys.*, **38**, 121 (1966). **[14B]**

Jain, B. K. and Jackson, D. F. (67). *Nucl. Phys.*, **A99**, 113 (1967). **[14B]**

Jastrow, R. (51). *Phys. Rev.*, **81**, 165 (1951). **[3E]**

Johnson, R. R. and Hintz, N. M. (67). *Phys. Rev.*, **153**, 1169 (1967). **[9C]**

Kapur, P. L. and Peierls, R. E. (39). *Proc. Roy. Soc. (London)*, **A166**, 277 (1938). **[8B,9A,9B]**

Kawai, M. and Yazaki, K. (67). *Prog. Theor. Phys.*, **37**, 638 (1967). **[13A]**

Kerman, A. K., McManus, H., and Thaler, R. M. (59). *Ann. Phys. (N.Y.)*, **8**, 551 (1959). **[9B]**

Köhler, H. S. (66) *Nucl. Phys.*, **88**, 529 (1966). **[14A]**

Krieger, T. J. and Pearlstein, S. (65). Brookhaven National Laboratory Report No. BNL904(N-8), unpublished. **[9]**

Kromminga, A. J. and McCarthy, I. E. (61). *Phys. Rev. Letters*, **6**, 62 (1961). **[12A]**

Kromminga, A. J. and McCarthy, I. E. (62). *Nucl. Phys.*, **31**, 678 (1962). **[12C]**

Kurath, D. (56). *Phys. Rev.*, **101**, 216 (1956). **[7B,9C]**

Lane, A. M. and Robson, D. (66). *Phys. Rev.*, **151**, 774 (1966). **[8C]**

Lane, A. M. and Thomas, R. G. (58). *Rev. Mod. Phys.*, **30**, 257 (1958). **[8C]**

Lane, A. M., Thomas, R. G., and Wigner, E. P. (55). *Phys. Rev.*, **98**, 693 (1955). **[9B]**

Lassila, K. E., Hull, M. H., Ruppel, H. M., McDonald, F. A., and Breit, G. (62). *Phys. Rev.*, **126**, 881 (1962) **[3E]**

Lee, L. L., Jr. and Schiffer, J. P. (64). *Phys. Rev. Letters*, **12**, 108 (1964). **[13B]**

Lee, L. L., Jr., Schiffer, J. P., Zeidman, B., Satchler, G. R., Drisko, R. M. and Bassel, R. H. (64). *Phys. Rev.*, **136**, B971 (1964). **[13A]**

Lefevre, H. W., Borchers, R. R., and Poppe, C. H. (62). *Phys. Rev.*, **128**, 1328 (1962). **[14A]**

Lim, K. L. and McCarthy, I. E. (63). *Proceedings of the International Conference on Direct Interactions and Nuclear Reaction Mechanisms, Padua 1962*, Gordon and Breach, New York, 1963, p. 180. **[14B]**

Lim, K. L. and McCarthy, I. E. (64a). *Phys. Rev. Letters*, **13**, 446 (1964). **[3E,14B]**

Lim, K. L. and McCarthy, I. E. (64b). *Phys. Rev.*, **133**, B1006 (1964). **[5C,14B]**

Lim, K. L. and McCarthy, I. E. (66). *Nucl. Phys.*, **88**, 433 (1966). **[14B]**

Lippmann, B. and Schwinger, J. (50). *Phys. Rev.*, **79**, 469 (1950). **[10A]**

Lovelace, C. A. (64). *Phys. Rev.*, **135**, 1225 (1964). **[10E]**

Lynch, F. J., Holland, R. E. and Hamermesh, M. (60). *Phys. Rev.*, **120**, 513 (1960). **[9A]**

McCarthy, I. E. and Pursey, D. L. (61). *Phys. Rev.*, **122**, 578 (1961). **[11A,12C]**

Macfarlane, M. H., Argonne National Laboratory Report No. ANL-6878, unpublished. **[13B]**

Macfarlane, M. H. and French, J. B. (60). *Rev. Mod. Phys.*, **32**, 567 (1960). **[5C,13A]**

McGruer, J. N., Warburton, E. K., and Bender, R. S. (56). *Phys. Rev.*, **100**, 235 (1956). **[5C]**

Mayer, M. G. (48). *Phys. Rev.*, **74**, 235 (1948). **[5]**

Mayer, M. G. (49). *Phys. Rev.*, **75**, 1969 (1949). **[5]**

Mehta, M. L. (60). *Nucl. Phys.*, **18**, 395 (1960). **[9C]**

Melkanoff, M. A., Nodvik, J. S., Saxon, D. S., and Cantor, D. G. (61). *A FORTRAN Program for Elastic Scattering Analyses with the Nuclear Optical Model*, University of California Press, Berkeley and Los Angeles, 1961. **[11B]**

Morse, P. M. and Feshbach, H. (53). *Methods of Theoretical Physics*, McGraw-Hill Book Company, Inc., New York, 1953. **[A3]**

Moshinsky, M. (59). *Nucl. Phys.*, **13**, 104 (1959). **[7B]**

Mössbauer, R. L. (58). *Z. Phys.*, **151**, 124 (1958); *Naturwissenschaften*, **45**, 538 (1958); *Z. Naturforsch.*, **14A**, 211 (1959). **[9A]**

Moszkowski, S. A. (57). "Models of Nuclear Structure," *Encyclopedia of Physics*, Vol. XXXIX, Berlin: Springer-Verlag, 1957. **[7C]**

Moszkowski, S. A. (65). *Phys. Rev.*, **140**, B283 (1965). **[4C,10E]**

Mottelson, B. R. and Nilsson, S. G. (59). *Kgl. Danske Videnskab. Selskab, Mat-fys. Skr.*, **1**, No. 8 (1959). **[7C]**

Muskhelishvili, N. I. (46). *Singular Integral Equations*, Gostekhizdat, Moscow, 1946. **[12D]**

Nathan, O. and Nilsson, S. G. (65). "Collective Nuclear Motion and the Unified Model," *α, β, γ Ray Spectroscopy*, Edited by K. Siegbahn, North-Holland Publishing Company, Amsterdam, 1965, p. 601. **[7C]**

Newton, R. G. (60). *J. Math. Phys.*, **1**, 319 (1960). **[10C]**

Nilsson, S. G. (55). *Kgl. Danske Videnskab. Selskab, Mat-fys. Medd.*, **29**, No. 16 (1955). [7C]

Omnes, R. (58). *Nuovo Cimento*, **8**, 316 (1958). [12D]

Omnes, R. (64). *Phys. Rev.* **134**, B1358 (1964). [10E]

Pal, M. K. and Kerman, A. K. (67), unpublished. [6D]

Pal, M. K. and Stamp, A. P. (67). *Phys. Rev.*, **158**, 924 (1967). [6C,7E]

Pandya, S. P. (63). *Nucl. Phys.*, **43**, 636 (1963). [7B]

Pauling, L. and Wilson, E. B. (35). *Introduction to Quantum Mechanics*, McGraw-Hill Book Company, Inc., New York and London, 1935, p. 275. [7C]

Penny, S. K. and Satchler, G. R. (64). *Nucl. Phys.*, **53**, 145 (1964). [13]

Perey, F. G. (63). *Phys. Rev.*, **131**, 745 (1963). [11C]

Perey, F. G. and Buck, B. (62). *Nucl. Phys.*, **32**, 353 (1962). [9B,11D]

Perey, F. G. and Perey, C. (63). *Phys. Rev.*, **132**, 755 (1963). [11C]

Porter, C. E. and Thomas, R. G. (56). *Phys. Rev.*, **104**, 483 (1956). [9C]

Porter, C. E. and Rosenzweig, N. (60). *Suomalaisen Tiedeakatemian Toimituksia AVI*, No. 44 (1960). [9C]

Preston, M. A. (62). *Physics of the Nucleus*, Addison-Wesley Publishing Company, Reading, 1962, p. 265. [7C]

Pugh, H. G., Hendrie, D. L., Chabre, M., and Boschitz, E. (65). *Phys. Rev. Letters*, **14**, 434 (1965). [14B]

Pugh, H. G., Hendrie, D. L., Chabre, M., Boschitz, E., and McCarthy, I. E. (67). *Phys. Rev.*, **155**, 1054 (1967). [14B]

Riou, M. (65). *Rev. Mod. Phys.*, **37**, 375 (1965). [5C]

Rodberg, L. S. (63). unpublished. [11C]

Rose, M. E. (57). *Elementary Theory of Angular Momentum*, John Wiley and Sons, New York, 1957. [A4]

Rosenfeld, L. (48). *Nuclear Forces*, North-Holland Publishing Company, Amsterdam, 1948, p. 233. [7B]

Rosenfeld, L. (65). *Nucl. Phys.*, **70**, 1 (1965). [9A]

Ross, A., Mark, H., and Lawson, R. D. (56). *Phys. Rev.*, **104**, 401 (1956). [5B,5C]

Rost, E. (62). *Phys. Rev.*, **128**, 2708 (1962). [11A]

Rost, E. and Austern, N. (60). *Phys. Rev.*, **120**, 1375 (1960). [12A]

Rutherford, E. (11). *Phil. Mag.*, **21**, 669 (1911). [1]

Satchler, G. R. (58). *Ann. Phys. (N.Y.)*, **3**, 275 (1958). [13B]

Satchler, G. R. (65). *Nucl. Phys.*, **70**, 177 (1965). [11C,12C]

Sasakawa, T. (59). *Prog. Theor. Phys. Suppl.*, **11**, 69 (1959). [9A]

Sasakawa, T. (67), unpublished. [8B]

Schmidt, T. (37). *Z. Phys.*, **106**, 358 (1937). [5B]

Selove, W. (65). *Rev. Mod. Phys.*, **37**, 460 (1965). [9A]

Serber, R. (47). *Phys. Rev.*, **72**, 1114 (1947). [3E]

Shapiro, I. S. (61). *Nucl. Phys.*, **28**, 244 (1961). [12D]

Sheline, R. K. (60). *Rev. Mod. Phys.*, **32**, 1 (1960). [7C]

Stegun, I. A. and Abramowitz, M. (55). *Phys. Rev.*, **98**, 1851 (1955). [A3]

Tabakin, F. (64). *Ann. Phys.* (*N.Y.*), **30,** 51 (1964). [**3***E***,4***C***,6***D*]

Talmi, I. (52). *Helv. Phys. Acta*, **15,** 185 (1952). [**7***B*]

Tamura, T. (65). *Rev. Mod. Phys.*, **37,** 679 (1965). [**12***A*]

Thankappan, V. K. and True, W. W. (65). *Phys. Rev.*, **137,** B793 (1965). [**7***C*]

Thomas, L. H. (35). *Phys. Rev.*, **47,** 903 (1935). [**5***A*]

Tobocman, W. (61). *Theory of Direct Nuclear Reactions*, Oxford University Press, London, 1961. [**5***B*]

True, W. W. (63). *Phys. Rev.*, **130,** 1530 (1963). [**7***B*]

Vogt, E. W., McPherson, D., Kuehner, J., and Almquist, E. (64). *Phys. Rev.*, **136,** B99 (1964). [**9***C*]

Walecka, J. D. and Gomes, L. C. (67). *Anais da Academia Brasileira Ciêncas*, 1967. [**4***B*]

Watson, K. M. (58). *Rev. Mod. Phys.*, **30,** 565 (1958). [**9***B*]

Weizsäcker, C. F. von (35). *Z. Phys.*, **96,** 431 (1935). [**7***C*]

Werntz, C. (62). *Phys. Rev.*, **128,** 1336 (1962). [**14***A*]

Wigner, E. P. (31). *Gruppentheorie*, F. Vieweg and Son, Braunschweig, 1931; reprint: Edward Brothers, Ann Arbor, Michigan, 1944. [**9***C*]

Wigner, E. P. (51). *Ann. Math.*, **53,** 36 (1951). [**9***B*]

Wigner, E. P. (57). *Gatlinburg Conference on Neutron Physics by Time of Flight*, Oak Ridge National Laboratory Report No. ORNL-2309, 1957, unpublished, p. 59. [**9***C*]

Wigner, E. P. (58). "Isotopic Spin—A Quantum Number for Nuclei," *Proceedings of the Robert A. Welch Foundation Conferences on Chemical Research*, Vol. I, edited by W. O. Milligan, Rice University, Houston, 1958, p. 67. [**7***A*]

Wigner, E. P. and Eisenbud, L. (41). *Proc. Nat. Acad. Sci. U.S.*, **27,** 281 (1941). [**3***C*]

Wigner, E. P. and Eisenbud, L. (47). *Phys. Rev.*, **29** (1947). [**8***B*]

Wilkinson, D. H. (58). "The Structure of Light Nuclei," *Proceedings of the Robert A. Welch Foundation Conferences on Chemical Research*, Vol. I, edited by W. O. Milligan, Rice University, Houston, 1958, p. 13. [**7***B*]

Wolfenstein, L. (51). *Phys. Rev.*, **82,** 690 (1951). [**9***C*]

Woods, R. D. and Saxon, D. S. (54). *Phys. Rev.*, **5,** 577 (1954). [**11**]

Yoshizawa, Y. (62). *Phys. Letters*, **2,** 261 (1962). [**7***C*]

Yukawa, H. (35). *Proc. Math. Soc. Japan*, **17,** 48 (1935). [**3***A*]

INDEX*

*The pages where a concept is defined or treated in detail are indicated by italics.

543